Sustainability: A Comprehensive Foundation

Collection Editor:

Tom Theis and Jonathan Tomkin, Editors

Sustainability: A Comprehensive Foundation

Collection Editor:

Tom Theis and Jonathan Tomkin, Editors

Authors:

Said Al-Hallaj

Steve Altaner

Amy Ando

Jeffrey Brawn

Julie Cidell

George Crabtree

John Cuttica

Serap Erdal

Eugene Goldfarb

David Grimley

U of I Open Source Textbook
Initiative

Martin Jaffe

Rob Kanter

Angela Kent

Amid Khodadoust

Riza Kizilel

Cindy Klein-Banai

Andrew Leakey

Sohail Murad

Krishna Reddy

John Regalbuto

Dennis Ruez

Eric Snodgrass

Tom Theis

Jonathan Tomkin

Michael Ward

Gillen Wood

Online:

< http://legacy.cnx.org/content/col11325/1.43/ >

OpenStax-CNX

Table of Contents

Foreword[1]

Sustainability is derived from two Latin words: *sus* which means up and *tenere* which means to hold. In its modern form it is a concept born out of the desire of humanity to continue to exist on planet Earth for a very long time, perhaps the indefinite future. Sustainability is, hence, essentially and almost literally about holding up human existence. Possibly, the most succinct articulation of the issue can be found in the Report of the World Commission on Environment and Development. The report entitled "Our Common Future[2]" primarily addressed the closely related issue of Sustainable Development. The report, commonly know as the Brundtland Report after the Commission Chair Gro Harlem Brundtland, stated that "Humanity has the ability to make development sustainable to ensure that it meets the needs of the present without compromising the ability of future generations to meet their own needs." Following the concept of Sustainable Development, the commission went on to add " Yet in the end, sustainable development is not a fixed state of harmony, but rather a process of change in which the exploitation of resources, the direction of investments, the orientation of technological development, and institutional change are made consistent with future as well as present needs. We do not pretend that the process is easy or straightforward. Painful choices have to be made. Thus, in the final analysis, sustainable development must rest on political will." Sustainability and the closely related concept of Sustainable Development are, therefore, very human constructs whose objective is to insure the very survival of humanity in a reasonably civilized mode of existence. Here, however, I will focus primarily on Sustainability.

The seriousness of the issue of Sustainability has become increasingly important and obvious over the last fifty years driven by an increasing human population with increasing per capita resource consumption on a planet which is after all finite. Note that the World population[3] increased from approximately 2.5 billion in 1950 to about 7.0 billion in 2012. Furthermore, total World consumption expenditures[4] rose from about 171 Billion in 1960 to approximately 44,000 billions in 2010 expressed in 2012 U.S. dollars. This is not to say that consumption is necessarily bad, but rather that there are so many people consuming so many resources that both the World environment and human consumption will have to be managed with far more care and delicacy than has been necessary in all of the historical past.

A text such as the one being presented here is of paramount importance because it will help to educate the next generation of students on the very important subject of sustainability. Now sustainability is not exactly a discipline such as, for example, physics. Rather it is truly a metadiscipline drawing on nearly all of existing human knowledge in approximately equal parts and with more or less equal importance. This is not to say that different disciplines have not in the past drawn ideas from each other, creating hybrid disciplines such as, for instance, biophysics - a fusion of physics and biology. Rather, in Sustainability the range of ideas and issues reach from the depth of biological sciences to the physical sciences and to the social sciences, including politics. Additionally, the relative importance of each of these aspects seems to be about the same. The reasons for this inherent, perhaps unprecedented complexity, is that sustainability is about sustaining human existence which requires many things to be sustained including functioning economic, social, and political systems along with a supportive physical and biological environment and more.

Hence, the effort to produce a text covering the breadth of sustainability must by necessity come from a comprehensive group of specialists as is the case here. This allows each field of study to bring its own unique perspective and shed its own light on a very complex and important subject which could otherwise

---

[1]This content is available online at <http://legacy.cnx.org/content/m43491/1.2/>.

be intractable. The authors very interestingly point out in the preface that the text does not necessarily present a self-consistent set of ideas. Rather, a degree of diversity is accepted within the overall rubric of Sustainability and Science itself. This may be unusual for an academic text, but it is necessary here. The reason is that environmental problems of our time are both time-sensitive and evolving, and a complete understanding does not exist and may never exist. But the issues still have to be addressed in good faith, in a timely manner, with the best science on hand. With the reader's indulgence, I would like to draw an analogy to a physician who has the responsibility of healing or attempting to heal patients using the best available medical science in a timely manner, knowing that a complete understanding of medical science does not exist and, in fact, may never exist.

It is my sincerest hope this work shared freely and widely will be an educational milestone as humanity struggles to understand and solve the enormous environmental challenges of our time. Further, the text "Sustainability: A comprehensive Foundation," helps to provide the intellectual foundation that will allow students to become the engines that move and maintain society on the path of Sustainability and Sustainable Development through the difficult process of change alluded to in "Our Common Future."

Heriberto Cabezas
Cincinnati, Ohio
March 2012

Preface[5]

This text is designed to introduce the reader to the essential concepts of sustainability. This subject is of vital importance – seeking as it does to uncover the principles of the long-term welfare of all the peoples of the planet – but is only peripherally served by existing college textbooks.

The content is intended to be useful for both a broad-based introductory class on sustainability and as a useful supplement to specialist courses which wish to review the sustainability dimensions of their areas of study. By covering a wide range of topics with a uniformity of style, and by including glossaries, review questions, case studies, and links to further resources, the text has sufficient range to perform as the core resource for a semester course. Students who cover the material in the book will be conversant in the language and concepts of sustainability, and will be equipped for further study in sustainable planning, policy, economics, climate, ecology, infrastructure, and more.

Furthermore, the modular design allows individual chapters and sections to be easily appropriated – without the purchase of a whole new text. This allows educators to easily bring sustainability concepts, references, and case studies into their area of study.

This appropriation works particularly well as the text is free – downloadable to anyone who wishes to use it. Furthermore, readers are encouraged to work with the text. Provided there is attribution to the source, users can adapt, add to, revise and republish the text to meet their own needs.

Because sustainability is a cross-disciplinary field of study, producing this text has required the bringing together over twenty experts from a variety of fields. This enables us to cover all of the foundational components of sustainability: understanding our motivations requires the humanities, measuring the challenges of sustainability requires knowledge of the sciences (both natural and social), and building solutions requires technical insight into systems (such as provided by engineering, planning, and management).

Readers accustomed to textbooks that present material in a unitary voice might be surprised to find in this one statements that do not always agree. Here, for example, cautious claims about climate change stand beside sweeping pronouncements predicting future social upheaval engendered by a warming world. And a chapter that includes market-based solutions to environmental problems coexists with others that call for increased government control. Such diversity of thought characterizes many of the fields of inquiry represented in the book; by including it, we invite users to engage in the sort of critical thinking a serious study of sustainability requires.

It is our sincerest hope that this work is shared freely and widely, as we all struggle to understand and solve the enormous environmental challenges of our time.

---

[5]This content is available online at <http://legacy.cnx.org/content/m41663/1.3/>.

Available for free at Connexions <http://legacy.cnx.org/content/col11325/1.43>

4

Chapter 1

Introduction to Sustainability: Humanity and the Environment

1.1 An Introduction to Sustainability: Humanity and the Environment[1]

1.1.1 Learning Objectives

After reading this chapter, students should be able to

- learn the meaning of sustainability in its modern context
- acquire a basic facility for using the IPAT equation
- learn about patterns of human consumption
- understand the major factors that contribute to unsustainable impacts

1.2 What is Sustainability?[2]

In 1983 the United Nations General Assembly passed resolution 38/161 entitled "Process of Preparation of the Environmental Perspective to the Year 2000 and Beyond[3] ," establishing a special commission whose charge was:

(a) To propose long-term environmental strategies for achieving sustainable development to the year 2000 and beyond;

(b) To recommend ways in which concern for the environment may be translated into greater co-operation among developing countries and between countries at different stages of economic and social development and lead to the achievement of common and mutually supportive objectives which take account of the interrelationships between people, resources, environment and development;

(c) To consider ways and means by which the international community can deal more effectively with environmental concerns, in the light of the other recommendations in its report;

(d) To help to define shared perceptions of long-term environmental issues and of the appropriate efforts needed to deal successfully with the problems of protecting and enhancing the environment, a long-term agenda for action during the coming decades, and aspirational goals for the world community, taking into account the relevant resolutions of the session of a special character of the Governing Council in 1982.

---

[1]This content is available online at <http://legacy.cnx.org/content/m41187/1.5/>.
[2]This content is available online at <http://legacy.cnx.org/content/m41188/1.7/>.
[3]http://www.un.org/documents/ga/res/38/a38r161.htm

The commission later adopted the formal name "World Commission on Environment and Development" (WCED) but became widely known by the name of its chair Gro Harlem Brundtland[4] , a medical doctor and public health advocate who had served as Norway's Minister for Environmental Affairs and subsequently held the post of Prime Minister during three periods. The commission had twenty-one members[5] drawn from across the globe, half representing developing nations. In addition to its fact-finding activities on the state of the global environment, the commission held fifteen meetings in various cities around the world seeking firsthand experiences on the how humans interact with the environment. The Brundtland Commission issued its final report "Our Common Future[6] " in 1987.

Although the Brundtland Report did not technically invent the term "sustainability," it was the first credible and widely-disseminated study that probed its meaning in the context of the global impacts of humans on the environment. Its main and often quoted definition refers to **sustainable development** as "...development that meets the needs of the present without compromising the ability of future generations to meet their own needs." The report uses the terms "sustainable development," "sustainable," and "sustainability" interchangeably, emphasizing the connections among social equity, economic productivity, and environmental quality. The pathways for integration of these may differ nation by nation; still these pathways must share certain common traits: "the essential needs of the world's poor, to which overriding priority should be given, and the idea of limitations imposed by the state of technology and social organization on the environment's ability to meet present and future needs."

Thus there are three dimensions that sustainability seeks to integrate: economic, environmental, and social (including sociopolitical). Economic interests define the framework for making decisions, the flow of financial capital, and the facilitation of commerce, including the knowledge, skills, competences and other attributes embodied in individuals that are relevant to economic activity. Environmental aspects recognize the diversity and interdependence within living systems, the goods and services produced by the world's ecosystems, and the impacts of human wastes. Socio-political refers to interactions between institutions/firms and people, functions expressive of human values, aspirations and well-being, ethical issues, and decision-making that depends upon collective action. The report sees these three elements as part of a highly integrated and cohesively interacting, if perhaps poorly understood, system.

The Brundtland Report makes it clear that while sustainable development is enabled by technological advances and economic viability, it is first and foremost a social construct that seeks to improve the quality of life for the world's peoples: physically, through the equitable supply of human and ecological goods and services; aspirationally, through making available the widespread means for advancement through access to education, systems of justice, and healthcare; and strategically, through safeguarding the interests of generations to come. In this sense sustainability sits among a series of human social movements that have occurred throughout history: human rights, racial equality, gender equity, labor relations, and conservation, to name a few.

---

[4]http://www.un.org/News/dh/hlpanel/brundtland-bio.htm
[5]http://en.wikisource.org/wiki/Brundtland_Report
[6]http://www.un-documents.net/wced-ocf.htm

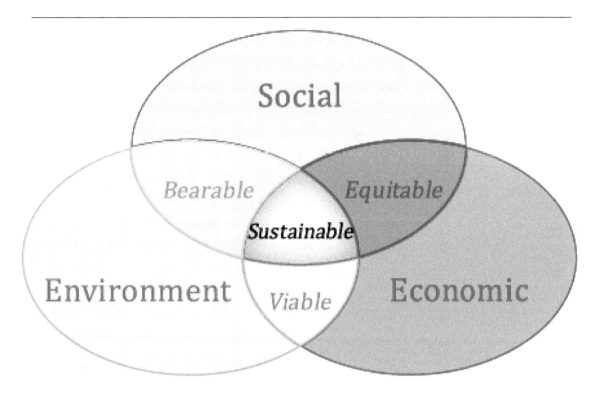

Figure 1.1: Overlapping Themes of the Sustainability Paradigm A depiction of the sustainability paradigm in terms of its three main components, showing various intersections among them. *Source: International Union for the Conservation of Nature*[7]

The intersection of social and economic elements can form the basis of social equity. In the sense of enlightened management, "viability" is formed through consideration of economic and environmental interests. Between environment and social elements lies "bearability," the recognition that the functioning of societies is dependent on environmental resources and services. At the intersection of all three of these lies sustainability.

The US Environmental Protection Agency[8] (US EPA) takes the extra step of drawing a distinction between sustainability and sustainable development, the former encompassing ideas, aspirations and values that inspire public and private organizations to become better stewards of the environment and that promote positive economic growth and social objectives, the latter implying that environmental protection does not preclude economic development and that economic development must be ecologically viable now and in the long run.

The Chapter **The Evolution of Environmental Policy in the United States** (Section 2.1) presents information on how the three components that comprise sustainability have influenced the evolution of environmental public policy. The Chapter **Sustainability: Ethics, Culture, and History** (Section 10.1) explores in greater detail the ethical basis for sustainability and its cultural and historical significance.

---

[7]http://cmsdata.iucn.org/downloads/iucn_future_of_sustainability.pdf
[8]http://www.epa.gov/sustainability/basicinfo.htm#sustainability

1.3 The IPAT Equation[9]

As attractive as the concept of sustainability may be as a means of framing our thoughts and goals, its definition is rather broad and difficult to work with when confronted with choices among specific courses of action. The Chapter **Problem-Solving, Metrics, and Tools for Sustainability** (Section 9.1) is devoted to various ways of measuring progress toward achieving sustainable goals, but here we introduce one general way to begin to apply sustainability concepts: the IPAT equation.

As is the case for any equation, IPAT expresses a balance among interacting factors. It can be stated as

$$I = P \times A \times T \tag{1.1}$$

where I represents the impacts of a given course of action on the environment, P is the relevant human population for the problem at hand, A is the level of consumption per person, and T is impact per unit of consumption. Impact per unit of consumption is a general term for technology, interpreted in its broadest sense as any human-created invention, system, or organization that serves to either worsen or uncouple consumption from impact. The equation is not meant to be mathematically rigorous; rather it provides a way of organizing information for a "first-order" analysis.

Suppose we wish to project future needs for maintaining global environmental quality at present day levels for the mid-twenty-first century. For this we need to have some projection of human population (P) and an idea of rates of growth in consumption (A).

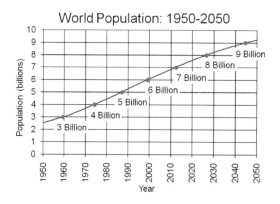

Figure 1.2: World Population Growth *Source: U.S. Census Bureau, International Data Base, December 2010 Update*[10]

Figure **World Population Growth** (Figure 1.2) suggests that global population in 2050 will grow from the current 6.8 billion to about 9.2 billion, an increase of 35%. Global GDP (Gross Domestic Product, one measure of consumption) varies from year to year but, using Figure **Worldwide Growth of Gross Domestic Product** (Figure 1.3) as a guide, an annual growth rate of about 3.5% seems historically accurate (growth at 3.5%, when compounded for forty years, means that the global economy will be four times as large at mid-century as today).

---

[9]This content is available online at <http://legacy.cnx.org/content/m41190/1.5/>.
[10]http://www.census.gov/population/international/data/idb/worldpopgraph.php

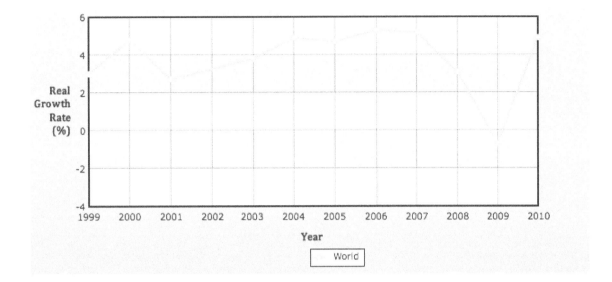

Figure 1.3: Worldwide Growth of Gross Domestic Product *Source: CIA World Factbook, Graph from IndexMundi*[11]

Thus if we wish to maintain environmental impacts (I) at their current levels (i.e. $I_{2050} = I_{2010}$), then

$$P_{2010} \times A_{2010} \times T_{2010} = P_{2050} \times A_{2050} \times T_{2050} \qquad (1.2)$$

or

$$\frac{T_{2050}}{T_{2010}} = \left[\frac{P_{2010}}{P_{2050}}\right] \times \left[\frac{A_{2010}}{A_{2050}}\right] = \left[\frac{1}{1.35}\right] \times \left[\frac{1}{4}\right] = \left[\frac{1}{5.4}\right] \qquad (1.3)$$

This means that just to maintain current environmental quality in the face of growing population and levels of affluence, our technological decoupling will need to reduce impacts by about a factor of five. So, for instance, many recently adopted "climate action plans" for local regions and municipalities, such as the Chicago Climate Action Plan[12] , typically call for a reduction in greenhouse gas emissions (admittedly just one impact measure) of eighty percent by mid-century. The means to achieve such reductions, or even whether or not they are necessary, are matters of intense debate; where one group sees expensive remedies with little demonstrable return, another sees opportunities for investment in new technologies, businesses, and employment sectors, with collateral improvements in global and national well-being.

1.4 Human Consumption Patterns and the "Rebound" Effect[13]

In 1865 William Jevons[14] (1835-1882), a British economist, wrote a book entitled "The Coal Question[15] ," in which he presented data on the depletion of coal reserves yet, seemingly paradoxically, an increase in the consumption of coal in England throughout most of the 19th century. He theorized that significant improvements in the efficiency of the steam engine had increased the utility of energy from coal and, in effect, lowered the price of energy, thereby increasing consumption. This is known as the **Jevons paradox**,

---

[11]http://www.indexmundi.com/g/g.aspx?c=xx&v=66
[12]http://www.chicagoclimateaction.org/pages/introduction/10.php
[13]This content is available online at <http://legacy.cnx.org/content/m41191/1.6/>.
[14]http://en.wikipedia.org/wiki/William_Stanley_Jevons
[15]http://www.econlib.org/library/YPDBooks/Jevons/jvnCQ.html

the principle that as technological progress increases the efficiency of resource utilization, consumption of that resource will increase. Increased consumption that negates part of the efficiency gains is referred to as "rebound," while **overconsumption** is called "backfire." Such a counter-intuitive theory has not been met with universal acceptance, even among economists (see, for example, "The Efficiency Dilemma[16] "). Many environmentalists, who see improvements in efficiency as a cornerstone of sustainability, openly question the validity of this theory. After all, is it sensible to suggest that we *not* improve technological efficiency?

Whether or not the paradox is correct, the fact that it has been postulated gives us pause to examine in somewhat greater depth consumption patterns of society. If we let Q be the quantity of goods and services delivered (within a given time period) to people, and R be the quantity of resources consumed in order to deliver those goods and services, then the IPAT equation can be rewritten in a slightly different way as:

$$I = P \times \left[\frac{\text{GDP}}{P}\right] \times \left[\frac{Q}{\text{GDP}}\right] \times \left[\frac{R}{Q}\right] \times \left[\frac{I}{R}\right] \tag{1.4}$$

where $\left[\frac{R}{Q}\right]$ represents the "resource intensity," and $\left[\frac{I}{R}\right]$ is the impact created per unit of resources consumed. Rearranging this version of the equation gives:

$$R = Q \times \left[\frac{R}{Q}\right] \tag{1.5}$$

which says simply that resources consumed are equal to the quantity of goods and services delivered times the resource intensity. The inverse of resource intensity $\left[\frac{Q}{R}\right]$ is called the resource use efficiency, also known as "resource productivity" or "**eco-efficiency**," an approach that seeks to minimize environmental impacts by maximizing material and energy efficiencies of production. Thus we can say:

$$R = Q \times \left[\frac{1}{\text{Eco} - \text{efficiency}}\right] \tag{1.6}$$

that is, resources consumed are equal to goods and services delivered divided by eco-efficiency. Whether or not gains in eco-efficiency yield genuine savings in resources and lower environmental impacts depends on how much, over time, society consumes of a given product or service (i.e. the relative efficiency gain, $\frac{\Delta e}{e}$) must outpace the quantity of goods and services delivered $\frac{\Delta Q}{Q}$. In the terms of Jevons paradox, if $\frac{\Delta Q}{Q} \geq \frac{\Delta e}{e}$ then the system is experiencing "backfire."

Part of the problem in analyzing data pertaining to whether or not such "overconsumption" is happening depends on the specific good or service in question, the degree to which the data truly represent that good or service, and the level of detail that the data measure. Table **Historical Efficiency and Consumption Trends in the United States** (Table 1.1) summarizes some recent findings from the literature on the comparative efficiency and consumption for several activities over extended periods of observation. Taken collectively these activities capture several basic enabling aspects of modern society: major materials, transportation, energy generation, and food production. In all cases the data show that over the long term, consumption outpaces gains in efficiency by wide margins, (i.e., $\frac{\Delta Q}{Q} \geq \frac{\Delta e}{e}$). It should also be noted that in all cases, the increases in consumption are significantly greater than increases in population. The data of Table **Historical Efficiency and Consumption Trends in the United States** (Table 1.1) do not verify Jevons paradox; we would need to know something about the prices of these goods and services over time, and examine the degree to which substitution might have occurred (for instance aluminum for iron, air travel for automobile travel). To see if such large increases in consumption have translated into comparable decreases in environmental quality, or declines in social equity, other information must be examined. Despite this, the information presented does show a series of patterns that broadly reflect human consumption of goods and services that we consider essential for modern living and for which efficiency gains have not kept pace; in a world of finite resources such consumption patterns cannot continue indefinitely.

---

[16]http://www.newyorker.com/reporting/2010/12/20/101220fa_fact_owen

Activity	Time Period	Avg Annual Efficiency Improvement (%)	Avg Annual Increase in Consumption (%)	Ratio: Consumption/Efficiency
Pig Iron	1800-1990	1.4	4.1	3.0
Aluminum	1900-2005	1.2	9.8	7.9
Fertilizer	1920-2000	1.0	8.8	8.9
Electricity-Coal	1920-2007	1.3	5.7	4.5
Electricity-Oil	1920-2007	1.5	6.2	4.2
Electricity-Nat Gas	1920-2007	1.8	9.6	5.5
Freight Rail Travel	1960-2006	2.0	2.5	1.2
Air Passenger Travel	1960-2007	1.3	6.3	4.9
Motor Vehicle Travel	1940-2006	0.3	3.8	11.0

Table 1.1: Historical Efficiency and Consumption Trends in the United States *Source: Dahmus and Gutowski, 2011 (p. 11)*

Our consumption of goods and services creates a viable economy, and also reflects our social needs. For example, most of us consider it a social good that we can travel large distances rather quickly, safely, and more or less whenever we feel the need. Similarly, we realize social value in having aluminum (lightweight, strong, and ductile) available, in spite of its energy costs, because it makes so many conveniences, from air travel to beverage cans, possible. This is at the center of the sustainability paradigm: human behavior is a social and ethical phenomenon, not a technological one. Whether or not we must "overconsume" to realize social benefits is at the core of sustainable solutions to problems.

1.4.1 Resources

For more information about eco-efficiency, see the World Business Council for Sustainable Development report titled "Eco-Efficiency: Creating more value with less impact[17] "

1.4.2 References

Dahmus, J. B., and T. G. Gutowski (2011) "Can Efficiency Improvements Reduce Resource Consumption? A Historical Analysis of Ten Activities" Journal of Industrial Ecology (accepted for publication).

1.5 Challenges for Sustainability[18]

The concept of sustainability has engendered broad support from almost all quarters. In a relatively succinct way it expresses the basis upon which human existence and the quality of human life depend: responsible behavior directed toward the wise and efficient use of natural and human resources. Such a broad concept invites a complex set of meanings that can be used to support divergent courses of action. Even within the Brundtland Report a dichotomy exists: alarm over environmental degradation that typically results from economic growth, yet seeing economic growth as the main pathway for alleviating wealth disparities.

---

[17]http://www.wbcsd.org/plugins/docsearch/details.asp?txtDocTitle=efficiency&DocTypeId=25&CharValList=25;&ObjectId=Mjc5&URLBack
[18]This content is available online at <http://legacy.cnx.org/content/m41192/1.5/>.

The three main elements of the sustainability paradigm are usually thought of as equally important, and within which tradeoffs are possible as courses of action are charted. For example, in some instances it may be deemed necessary to degrade a particular ecosystem in order to facilitate commerce, or food production, or housing. In reality, however, the extent to which tradeoffs can be made before irreversible damage results is not always known, and in any case there are definite limits on how much substitution among the three elements is wise (to date, humans have treated economic development as the dominant one of the three). This has led to the notion of **strong sustainability**, where tradeoffs among natural, human, and social capital are not allowed or are very restricted, and **weak sustainability**, where tradeoffs are unrestricted or have few limits. Whether or not one follows the strong or weak form of sustainability, it is important to understand that while economic and social systems are human creations, the environment is not. Rather, a functioning environment underpins both society and the economy.

This inevitably leads to the problem of metrics: what should be measured and how should the values obtained be interpreted, in light of the broad goals of the sustainability paradigm? The Chapter **Problem-Solving, Metrics, and Tools for Sustainability** (Section 9.1) addresses this in detail, but presented here is a brief summary of the findings of the Millennium Ecosystem Assessment[19] (MEA), a project undertaken by over a thousand internationally recognized experts, from 2001-2005, who assessed the state of the world's major ecosystems and the consequences for humans as a result of human-induced changes. In its simplest form, a system[20] is a collection of parts that function together. The MEA presents findings as assessments of **ecosystems** and **ecosystem services**: provisioning services such as food and water; regulating services such as flood control, drought, and disease; supporting services such as soil formation and nutrient cycling; and cultural services such as recreational, spiritual, religious and other nonmaterial benefits. MEA presents three overarching conclusions:

Approximately 60% (15 out of 24) of the ecosystem services examined are being degraded or used unsustainably, including fresh water, capture fisheries, air and water purification, and the regulation of regional and local climate, natural hazards, and pests. The full costs of the loss and degradation of these ecosystem services are difficult to measure, but the available evidence demonstrates that they are substantial and growing. Many ecosystem services have been degraded as a consequence of actions taken to increase the supply of other services, such as food. These trade-offs often shift the costs of degradation from one group of people to another or defer costs to future generations.

There is established but incomplete evidence that changes being made are increasing the likelihood of nonlinear changes in ecosystems (including accelerating, abrupt, and potentially irreversible changes) that have important consequences for human well-being. Examples of such changes include disease emergence, abrupt alterations in water quality, the creation of "dead zones" in coastal waters, the collapse of fisheries, and shifts in regional climate.

The harmful effects of the degradation of ecosystem services are being borne disproportionately by the poor, are contributing to growing inequities and disparities across groups of people, and are sometimes the principal factor causing poverty and social conflict. This is not to say that ecosystem changes such as increased food production have not also helped to lift many people out of poverty or hunger, but these changes have harmed other individuals and communities, and their plight has been largely overlooked. In all regions, and particularly in sub-Saharan Africa, the condition and management of ecosystem services is a dominant factor influencing prospects for reducing poverty.

---

[19]http://www.maweb.org/en/index.aspx
[20]http://en.wikipedia.org/wiki/System

Organizations such as the World Commission on Environment and Development, the Millennium Ecosystem Assessment, and several others including the Intergovernmental Panel on Climate Change[21] , the Organization for Economic Cooperation and Development,[22] and the National Academy Report to Congress[23] have all issued reports on various aspects of the state of society and the environment. The members of these groups are among the best experts available to assess the complex problems facing human society in the 21st century, and all have reached a similar conclusion: absent the enactment of new policies and practices that confront the global issues of economic disparities, environmental degradation, and social inequality, the future needs of humanity and the attainment of our aspirations and goals are not assured.

---

[21] http://www.ipcc.ch/

[22] http://www.oecd.org/home/

[23] http://www.nationalacademies.org/annualreport/

1.6 Chapter Review Questions[24]

Question 1.6.1

What are the essential aspects of "sustainability" as defined in the Brundtland Report?

Question 1.6.2

Define "strong" and "weak" sustainability and give examples of each.

Question 1.6.3

State, in your own words, the meaning of the "IPAT" equation?

Question 1.6.4

What is the "rebound" effect and how is it related to human patterns of consumption?

---

[24]This content is available online at <http://legacy.cnx.org/content/m41193/1.5/>.

Chapter 2

The Evolution of Environmental Policy in the United States

2.1 The Evolution of Environmental Policy in the United States – Chapter Introduction[1]

2.1.1 Introduction

It is not uncommon to think of the sustainability paradigm as being a recent interpretation of environmental policy, one that was given credence by the United Nations report "Our Common Future" (the Brundtland Report[2]) when it was first presented in 1987. Certainly the period during the final decade of the twentieth century was witness to significant growth in our understanding of the complexity and global reach of many environmental problems and issues, and as discussed in Chapter **An Introduction to Sustainability: Humanity and the Environment** (Section 1.1), the Brundtland report gave a clear voice to these concerns through its analysis of human dependency and quality of life on ecological systems, social networks, and economic viability—systems that are closely intertwined and that require more integrated approaches to solving the many problems that confront humanity at this time. It is also true that it was among the first widely disseminated writings to define and use the modern meaning of the term "sustainable" through the often-quoted concept of "sustainable development." However, it would be a mistake to conclude that sustainability as a mental construct and policy framework for envisioning the relationship of humans and nature came into being suddenly and at a single moment in time. Most environmental historians who have studied U.S. policy have discerned at least three distinct periods during which new concepts and ideas, scientific understandings, technological advances, political institutions, and laws and regulations came or were brought into being in order to understand and manage human impacts on the environment. These were (1) the American conservation movement, (2) the rise of environmental risk management as a basis for policy, and (3) the integration of social and economic factors to create what we now refer to as the sustainability paradigm. In this chapter we will explore the roots of modern sustainability (Module **The American Conservation Movement** (Section 2.2)), see how our thinking about the environment has shifted (Module **Environmental Risk Management** (Section 2.3)), and examine the ways that our environmental public policies have changed through time (Module **Sustainability and Public Policy** (Section 2.4)). Along the way it is important to understand that this has been an evolutionary process and that these environmental "eras," while reflecting the norms, attitudes, and needs of the day, are still very much embodied within the modern concept of sustainability.

---

[1]This content is available online at <http://legacy.cnx.org/content/m42118/1.4/>.

[2]http://www.un-documents.net/wced-ocf.htm

2.2 The American Conservation Movement[3]

2.2.1 Learning Objectives

After reading this module, students should be able to

- understand the history of environmental policy in the United States and the role of different groups in shaping environmental policy

2.2.2 Introduction

To most early colonists who immigrated to North America, for whom the concept of "wastage" had no specific meaning, the continent was a land of unimaginably vast resources in which little effort was made to treat, minimize, or otherwise manage. This is not surprising, when one stand of trees was consumed for housing or fuel, another was nearby; when one field was eroded to the point of limited fertility, expansion further inland was relatively simple; when rivers became silted so that fisheries were impaired, one moved further upstream; and when confronted with endless herds of wild animals, it was inconceivable that one might over-consume to the point of extinction. European-settled America was a largely agrarian society and, apart from the need to keep spaces productive and clear of debris, there was little incentive to spend time and energy managing discharges to the "commons[4]" (see Module **The Tragedy of the Commons** (Section 6.2)). These attitudes persisted well into the 19th century and aspects of them are still active in the present day. While such practices could hardly be said to constitute an "environmental policy," they did serve the purpose of constellating a number of groups into rethinking the way we went about managing various aspects of our lives, in particular our relationship to the land and the resources it contained or provided. As early as the mid-18th century, Jared Eliot[5] (1685-1763) of Connecticut, a minister, doctor, and farmer, wrote a series of treatises on the need for better farming methods. He summarized:

> When our fore-Fathers settled here, they entered a Land which probably never had been Ploughed since the Creation, the Land being new they depended upon the natural Fertility of the Ground, which served their purpose very well, and when they had worn out one piece they cleared another, without any concern to amend their Land...(Carman, Tugwell, & True, 1934, p. 29 (p. 26)).

Although Eliot avidly instructed his fellow farmers on better methods of "field husbandry," there is little evidence that his writings had a lasting effect (he is most known for advances in the design of the "drill plough," an early planter that produced even rows of crops, increasing yields).

By 1850, the population of the United States was approaching 25 million and increasing at the rate of three to four percent per year (for comparison the population of England was about 26 million, of France 36 million, and Germany about 40 million). Although the westward migration across North America was well underway, most people still lived within a relatively narrow strip of land along the east coast. By modern measures the United States was not densely populated, and yet the perception of the country as "big" and on the international stage was in contrast to the mentality just a few decades before of a new world that had broken with the old, one of endless open spaces and inexhaustible resources. The country was also becoming more urbanized (about 15 percent of the population lived in cities, three times the proportion of just fifty years before), and increasingly literate.

Thus by the mid-19th century the American public was prepared to listen to the messages of various groups who had become concerned about the impacts of growth on society. Three groups in particular, of considerably different sympathies and character, came to have profound influences on the way we thought of ourselves in relation to the environment, on our land use policies, and on providing environmental goods and services to the growing population: the "resource efficiency" group, the transcendentalist movement, and organized industrial interests.

---

[3]This content is available online at <http://legacy.cnx.org/content/m42117/1.4/>.

[4]http://en.wikipedia.org/wiki/The_commons

[5]http://en.wikipedia.org/wiki/Jared_Eliot

2.2.3 Resource Efficiency

As typified by the concerns of Jared Eliot nearly a century before, there were always some who were alarmed at widespread agricultural practices that were wasteful, inefficient and, using the modern terminology, unsustainable. By the early 1800s the cumulative impacts of soil erosion and infertility, decreasing crop yields, and natural barriers to expansion such as terrain and poor transportation to markets led to an organized effort to understand the causes of these problems, invent and experiment with new, more soil-conserving and less wasteful practices, communicate what was being learned to the public, and begin to build government institutions to promote better stewardship of the land and its resources. Although initial conservation concerns were associated with farming, the same approach soon found its way into the management of forests and timbering, wastes from mining and smelting, and by the end of the century the control of human disease outbreaks (most commonly associated with cholera and typhoid) and the impact of chemical exposure on workers. There were many individuals who contributed to understanding the scientific underpinnings of the environment and educating practitioners: Eugene Hilgard[6] (agricultural science), John Wesley Powell[7] (water rights), George Perkins Marsh[8] (ecological science), Franklin Hough[9] and Gifford Pinchot[10] (sustainable forestry), J. Sterling Morton[11] (forestry and environmental education; co-founder of Arbor Day[12]), Frederick Law Olmsted[13] (landscape architecture), and Alice Hamilton[14] (industrial hygiene), to name a few. These resource conservationists were instrumental in applying scientific methods to solving the problems of the day, problems that were rooted in our behavior toward the environment, and that had serious consequences for the well-being of people. It was as a result of these efforts that the basis for the fields of environmental science and engineering, agronomy and agricultural engineering, and public health was established. Over time these fields have grown in depth and breadth, and have led to the establishment of new areas of inquiry.

Just as importantly, several federal institutions were created to oversee the implementation of reforms and manage the government's large land holdings. Legislation forming the Departments of the Interior[15] (1849), and Agriculture[16] (1862), the U.S. Forest Service[17] (1881), the Geological Survey[18] (1879), and the National Park Service[19] (1916) were all enacted during this period. It was also the time when several major conservation societies, still active today, came into being: the Audubon Society[20] (1886), the Sierra Club[21] (1892), and the National Wildlife Federation[22] (1935). Arbor Day was first celebrated in 1872, and Bird Day[23] in 1894.

2.2.4 The Transcendental Movement

It is beyond the scope of this text to analyze in great depth the basis of the transcendental movement[24] in America. It arose in the 1830s in reaction to the general state of culture and society, increasing urbanism, and the rigidity of organized religions of the time. It professed a way of thinking in which the individual's unique relationship to their surroundings was valued over conformity and unreflective habits of living. But however

---

[6] http://en.wikipedia.org/wiki/Eugene_W._Hilgard

[7] http://en.wikipedia.org/wiki/John_Wesley_Powell

[8] http://www.clarku.edu/departments/marsh/about/index.cfm

[9] http://www.fs.fed.us/aboutus/history/chiefs/hough.shtml

[10] http://www.foresthistory.org/ASPNET/people/Pinchot/Pinchot.aspx

[11] http://en.wikipedia.org/wiki/Julius_Sterling_Morton

[12] http://www.arborday.org/arborday/history.cfm

[13] http://en.wikipedia.org/wiki/Frederick_Law_Olmsted

[14] http://www.nlm.nih.gov/changingthefaceofmedicine/physicians/biography_137.html

[15] http://www.doi.gov/archive/history.html

[16] http://www.usrecallnews.com/2008/06/history-of-the-u-s-department-of-agriculture-usda.html

[17] http://www.fs.fed.us/aboutus/history/

[18] http://pubs.usgs.gov/circ/c1050/

[19] http://www.nps.gov/history/history/hisnps/

[20] http://www.audubon.org/

[21] http://www.sierraclub.org/history/

[22] http://www.nwf.org/About/History-and-Heritage.aspx

[23] http://en.wikipedia.org/wiki/Bird_Day

[24] http://plato.stanford.edu/entries/transcendentalism/

philosophical its aims and ethereal its goals, transcendentalism had a profound connection to the natural environment; indeed, it is difficult to understand without reference to human-environmental interactions and a re-envisioning of the social contract of humanity with nature. Such were conditions at the time that transcendentalism resonated with an increasingly literate society, and became a major force in the further development of conservation as an accepted part of the American experience.

The acknowledged leader of the transcendental movement was Ralph Waldo Emerson[25] (1803-1882). In his seminal essay *Nature*[26] (1836), Emerson sets the tone for a new way of envisioning our relation to the natural world:

To speak truly, few adult persons can see nature. Most persons do not see the sun. At least they have a very superficial seeing. The sun illuminates only the eye of the man, but shines into the eye and the heart of the child. The lover of nature is he whose inward and outward senses are still truly adjusted to each other; who has retained the spirit of infancy even into the era of manhood. His intercourse with heaven and earth, becomes part of his daily food. In the presence of nature, a wild delight runs through the man, in spite of real sorrows. Nature says, – he is my creature, and maugre all his impertinent griefs, he shall be glad with me. Not the sun or the summer alone, but every hour and season yields its tribute of delight; for every hour and change corresponds to and authorizes a different state of the mind, from breathless noon to grimmest midnight. Nature is a setting that fits equally well a comic or a mourning piece. In good health, the air is a cordial of incredible virtue. Crossing a bare common, in snow puddles, at twilight, under a clouded sky, without having in my thoughts any occurrence of special good fortune, I have enjoyed a perfect exhilaration. I am glad to the brink of fear. In the woods too, a man casts off his years, as the snake his slough, and at what period so ever of life, is always a child. In the woods, is perpetual youth. Within these plantations of God, a decorum and sanctity reign, a perennial festival is dressed, and the guest sees not how he should tire of them in a thousand years. In the woods, we return to reason and faith. There I feel that nothing can befall me in life, – no disgrace, no calamity, (leaving me my eyes,) which nature cannot repair. Standing on the bare ground, – my head bathed by the blithe air, and uplifted into infinite space, – all mean egotism vanishes. I become a transparent eye-ball; I am nothing; I see all; the currents of the Universal Being circulate through me; I am part or particle of God. The name of the nearest friend sounds then foreign and accidental: to be brothers, to be acquaintances, – master or servant, is then a trifle and a disturbance. I am the lover of uncontained and immortal beauty. In the wilderness, I find something more dear and connate than in streets or villages. In the tranquil landscape, and especially in the distant line of the horizon, man beholds somewhat as beautiful as his own nature. (Emerson, 1836 (p. 26)).

Here Emerson makes clear that his connection to the "Universal Being" is made possible through communion with Nature, a creation so much greater than he that he sees his physical reality as "nothing," but his true nature (i.e. his soul) becomes visible in the "tranquil landscape," and the "distant line of the horizon." Such metaphorical language was and remains a powerful reminder that our existence is dependent on the natural world, and that we mismanage the environment at our peril.

---

[25]http://plato.stanford.edu/entries/emerson/
[26]http://oregonstate.edu/instruct/phl302/texts/emerson/nature-emerson-a.html

Figure 2.1: Kindred Spirits. The painting, dated 1849, depicts the artist, Thomas Cole, and poet, William Cullen Bryant. *Source: Asher Brown Durand via Wikimedia Commons*[27]

Yet, it is difficult to fully appreciate Emerson's vision of humans and nature through language alone. As

---

[27]http://commons.wikimedia.org/wiki/File:Asher_Durand_Kindred_Spirits.jpg

might be expected, the counter-reaction to the state of society and its attitudes toward the environment found expression in other media as well, in particular the rise of a cadre of American landscape artists. The camera had not yet been perfected, and of course there was no electronic media to compete for people's attention, thus artists' renditions of various scenes, especially landscapes, were quite popular. Figure **Kindred Spirits** (Figure 2.1), a rendering by A.B. Durand (1796-1886) of an artist and a poet out for a hike amid a lush forest scene captures much of the essence of transcendental thought, which had strongly influenced Durand's style. The offset of the human subjects, to left-of-center, is purposeful: the main subject is nature, with humans merely a component. This theme carried through many of the landscapes of the period, and helped to define what became known, among others, as the "Hudson River School[28]," whose artists depicted nature as an otherwise inexpressible manifestation of God. This is further expressed in the painting, *In the Heart of the Andes*, by Frederic Church (Figure **In the Heart of the Andes** (Figure 2.2)). Here, the seemingly sole theme is the landscape itself, but closer inspection (see detail in red square) reveals a small party of people, perhaps engaged in worship, again offset and virtually invisible amid the majesty of the mountains.

---

[28]http://www.metmuseum.org/toah/hd/hurs/hd_hurs.htm

Figure 2.2: In the Heart of the Andes. The painting, dated 1859, depicts a majestic landscape and closer inspection reveals a small party of people near the bottom left. *Source: Frederic Edwin Church via Wikimedia Commons*[29].

Other notable contributors to the transcendental movement were Henry David Thoreau[30] (1817-1862), abolitionist and author of Walden and Civil Disobedience, Margaret Fuller[31] (1810-1850), who edited the transcendental journal "The Dial" and wrote Woman in the Nineteenth Century, widely considered the first American feminist work, and Walt Whitman[32] (1819-1892) whose volume of poetry Leaves of Grass celebrates both the human form and the human mind as worthy of praise.

It is important to recognize that the transcendental redefinition of our social contract with the environment was holistic. Within it can be found not only a new appreciation of nature, but also the liberation of the human mind from convention and formalism, attacks on slavery, the need for racial equality, concern

---

[29]http://commons.wikimedia.org/wiki/File:Church_Heart_of_the_Andes.jpg
[30]http://plato.stanford.edu/entries/thoreau/
[31]http://www.distinguishedwomen.com/biographies/fuller-m.html
[32]http://www.whitmanarchive.org/

for universal suffrage and women's rights, and gender equity. In many ways it was a repositioning of the ideals of the enlightenment[33] that had figured so prominently in the founding documents of the republic. These social concerns are represented today within the sustainability paradigm in the form of such issues as environmental justice[34] , consumer behavior, and labor relations.

Transcendentalism as a formal movement diminished during the latter half of the 19th century, but it had a far-reaching influence on the way society perceived itself relative to the environment. Perhaps no one is more responsible for translating its aspirations into environmental public policy than John Muir[35] (1838-1914), a Scottish-born immigrant who was heavily influenced by Emerson's writings (it is said that the young Muir carried with him a copy of *Nature* from Scotland). The two first met in 1871 during a camping trip to the Sierra Mountains of California. Upon learning of Emerson's planned departure, Muir wrote to him on May 8, 1871 hoping to convince him to stay longer, "I invite you join me in a months worship with Nature in the high temples of the great Sierra Crown beyond our holy Yosemite. It will cost you nothing save the time & very little of that for you will be mostly in Eternity" (Chou, 2003 (p. 26)).

Muir was a naturalist, author, organizer (founder of the Sierra Club), and as it turns out a remarkably effective political activist and lobbyist. His association with Theodore Roosevelt[36] (1858-1919, 26th president of the United States), began with a 1903 campaign visit by Roosevelt to California, where he specifically sought out Muir, whose reputation was by then well known, as a guide to the Yosemite area (see Figure **Roosevelt and Muir** (Figure 2.3)).

---

[33]http://www.newworldencyclopedia.org/entry/Age_of_Enlightenment
[34]http://www.epa.gov/environmentaljustice/
[35]http://www.sierraclub.org/john_muir_exhibit/life/muir_biography.aspx
[36]http://www.theodoreroosevelt.org/life/conservation.htm

Figure 2.3: Roosevelt and Muir Theodore Roosevelt and John Muir at Yosemite National Park in 1903.

It was one of Muir's special talents that he could bridge across their rather different views on the environment (he a strict preservationist, Roosevelt a practical outdoorsman). By all accounts they had frank but cordial exchanges; for example, upon viewing the giant Sequoias, Muir remarked[37] to Roosevelt, "God has cared for these trees...but he cannot save them from fools – only Uncle Sam can do that." Roosevelt was so taken with his companion that he insisted they avoid political crowds and camp together overnight in the mountains.

The subsequent legacy of the Roosevelt administration in the name of conservation, even by today's standards, was significant. Known as the "conservation president," Roosevelt was responsible for 225 million acres of land added to the U.S. Forest Service, and the creation of 50 wildlife refuges and 150 national forests representing, in total, 11 percent of the total land area of the 48 contiguous states.

2.2.5 The Role of Industry

Today the behavior of industry toward the environment is often portrayed as either indifferent or hostile, whether true or not, and it was no different during the formative period of American conservation. The industries of the day – agriculture, timber, and mining – enabled by the major transportation sector – railroads and steamboats – had little incentive to manage their emissions to the environment responsibly, or to use natural resources wisely. Regulations were few, the science underpinning environmental impacts was nascent, the commons itself was viewed as essentially infinite, and however misguided, exploitation of resources and the generation of a certain amount of waste was seen as a necessary byproduct of expansion, job creation, and social well-being. And yet, as human-created organizations go, industries are extraordinarily sensitive to economic conditions. If the sustainability paradigm is to be believed, then economic viability is of paramount concern and the engagement of industrial forces must of necessity be part of its enactment. These are the engines that provide employment, and that control large quantities of capital for investment. Further, viewed from the life cycle perspective of the flow of materials (refer to Module **Life Cycle Assessment** (Section 9.2)), products that turn raw materials into mostly waste (defined here as a quantity of material that no one values, as opposed to salable products) are simply inefficient and reduce profitability.

---

[37]http://www.sierraclub.org/john_muir_exhibit/writings/favorite_quotations.aspx

Figure 2.4: The Oregon Trail. The painting, dated 1869, depicts the westward migration of settlers via wagon trains, on horseback, and by foot. *Source: Albert Bierstadt via Wikimedia Commons*[38].

As noted in Resource Efficiency (Section 2.2.3: Resource Efficiency) above, industrial activities during this time were responsible for significant environmental degradation. Policy reformers of the day, such as Carl Schurz[39] (as secretary of the Interior) turned their attention in particular to land reforms, which impacted the expansion of railroads, and forest preservation. And yet, industry played an unquestionable role as enablers of societal shifts occurring in America by making goods and services available, increasing the wealth of the emerging middle class, and in particular providing relatively rapid access to previously inaccessible locations – in many cases the same locations that preservationists were trying to set aside. Reading, hearing stories about, and looking at pictures of landscapes of remote beauty and open spaces was alluring and stirred the imagination, but being able to actually visit these places firsthand was an educational experience that had transformative powers. Alfred Bierstadt's *The Oregon Trail* (Figure **The Oregon Trail** (Figure 2.4)), painted in 1868, depicts the westward migration of settlers via wagon trains, on horseback, and simply walking – a journey, not without peril, that took about six months. The next year saw the completion of the transcontinental railroad[40] , and within a few years it became possible to complete the same journey in as little as six days in comparative comfort and safety.

The movement to designate certain areas as national parks is an illustrative example of the role of industry in promoting land conservation, thereby setting in motion subsequent large conservation set-asides that reached their zenith during the Roosevelt administration. It began, in 1864, with the efforts of several California citizens to have the U.S. Congress accept most of Yosemite[41] , which had been under the "protection" of the State of California as a national preserve. The petition cited its value "for public use, resort,

---

[38] http://commons.wikimedia.org/wiki/File:Albert_Bierstadt_Oregon_Trail_.jpg
[39] http://books.google.com/books?id=Xh88sn29RVwC&pg=PA241&lpg=PA241&dq=Carl+Schurz+timber+reform&source=bl&ots=yaqq7EQn
[40] http://www.sfmuseum.org/hist1/rail.html
[41] http://en.wikipedia.org/wiki/History_of_the_Yosemite_area

and recreation," reasoning that already reflected the combined interests of the resource efficiency group, preservationists, and business opportunists. Frederick Law Olmsted (1822-1903), the landscape architect most well known for the design of New York's Central Park, and an ardent believer in the ability of open spaces to improve human productivity, oversaw the initial efforts to manage the Yosemite area. Although the effort was infused with renewed vigor after John Muir's arrival in the late 1860s, it wasn't until 1906 that the park was officially designated.

In the meantime, similar interests had grown to name Yellowstone[42] as a national park, with the same basic justification as for Yosemite. Since there were no states as yet formed in the region the pathway was more straightforward, and was made considerably easier by the lack of interest by timber and mining companies to exploit (the area was thought to have limited resource value), and the railroads who, seeing potential for significant passenger traffic, lobbied on its behalf. Thus the first national park was officially designated in 1872, only three years after the completion of the transcontinental railroad. Indeed, in relatively rapid succession the Union Pacific Railroad got behind the Yosemite efforts, and the Northern Pacific Railroad lobbied heavily for the creation of parks at Mount Rainier[43] (1899) and Glacier[44] (1910). By 1916, when the National Park Service was formed, sixteen national parks had been created. States too began to see value in creating and, to a degree, preserving open spaces, as evidenced by New York's Adirondack Park[45] (1894), still the largest single section of land in the forty-eight contiguous states dedicated to be "forever wild."

2.2.6 Results of the American Conservation Movement

With the advent of the First World War, and subsequent political, social, and economic unrest that lasted for another thirty years, actions motivated by the conservation movement declined. The coalition between the resource efficiency group and those wishing to preserve nature, always uncomfortable, was further eroded when it became clear that the main reason Congress was "setting aside" various areas was mainly to better manage commercial exploitation. And yet, the period from 1850 to 1920 left a remarkable legacy of environmental reform, and laid the foundation for future advances in environmental policy. In summary, the conservation movement accomplished the following:

- Redefined the social contract between humans and the environment, establishing a legacy of conservation as part of the American character, and a national model for the preservation of natural beauty.
- Invented the concept of national parks and forests, wildlife refuges, and other sites for commercial and recreational uses by society.
- Developed the first scientific understanding of how the environment functioned, integrating the scientific approach to resource management into government policy.
- Pioneered technological practices to improve resource management.
- Established the major federal institutions with responsibility for land and resource conservation.
- Communicated the impact of pollution on human health and welfare.
- Through publications and travel, exposed many to the beauty of the natural environment and the consequences of human activities.
- Finally, although sustainability as a way of envisioning ourselves in relation to the environment was still many years away, already its three principal elements, imperfectly integrated at the time, are seen clearly to be at work.

2.2.7 References

Carman, H.J., Tugwell, R.G., & True, R.H. (Eds.). (1934). *Essays upon field husbandry in New England, and other papers, 1748-1762, by Jared Eliot*. New York: Columbia University Press.

---

[42]http://en.wikipedia.org/wiki/Yellowstone_National_Park
[43]http://www.nps.gov/history/history/online_books/mora/adhi/adhi2.htm
[44]http://www.nps.gov/archive/glac/history/overview.htm
[45]http://www.apa.state.ny.us/about_park/history.htm

Chou, P.Y. (Ed.). (2003). Emerson & John Muir. *WisdomPortal*. Retrieved December 11, 2011 from http://www.wisdomportal.com/Emerson/Emerson-JohnMuir.html[46] .

2.3 Environmental Risk Management[47]

2.3.1 Learning Objectives

After reading this module, students should be able to

- trace the basic elements of the sustainability paradigm through the evolution of U.S. environmental policy, including the National Environmental Policy Act of 1970
- understand the role of risk management as modern environmental policy has been implemented

2.3.2 General Definitions

For most people, the concept of risk is intuitive and, often, experiential; for instance most people are aware of the considerably greater likelihood of suffering an injury in an automobile accident (116/100 million vehicle miles) versus suffering an injury in a commercial airplane accident (0.304/100 million airplane miles). Environmental risk can be defined as the chance of harmful effects to human health or to ecological systems resulting from exposure to any physical, chemical, or biological entity in the environment that can induce an adverse response (see Module **Risk Assessment Methodology for Conventional and Alternative Sustainability Options** (Section 7.5) for more detail on the science of risk assessment). Environmental risk assessment[48] is a quantitative way of arriving at a statistical probability of an adverse action occurring. It has four main steps:

1. Identification of the nature and end point of the risk (e.g. death or disability from hazardous chemicals, loss of ecological diversity from habitat encroachment, impairment of ecosystem services, etc.)
2. Development of quantitative methods of analysis (perturbation-effect, dose-response)
3. Determination of the extent of exposure (i.e. fate, transport, and transformation of contaminants to an exposed population), and
4. Calculation of the risk, usually expressed as a statistical likelihood.

Risk management[49] is distinct from risk assessment, and involves the integration of risk assessment with other considerations, such as economic, social, or legal concerns, to reach decisions regarding the need for and practicability of implementing various risk reduction activities. Finally, risk communication[50] consists of the formal and informal processes of communication among various parties who are potentially at risk from or are otherwise interested in the threatening agent/action. It matters a great deal how a given risk is communicated and perceived: do we have a measure of control, or are we subject to powerful unengaged or arbitrary forces?

2.3.3 The Beginnings of Modern Risk Management

The beginnings of environmental risk management can be traced to the fields of public health[51] , industrial hygiene[52] , and sanitary engineering[53] , which came into prominence in the latter decades of the 19th

---

[46]http://www.wisdomportal.com/Emerson/Emerson-JohnMuir.html
[47]This content is available online at <http://legacy.cnx.org/content/m42115/1.4/>.
[48]http://www.epa.gov/ebtpages/enviriskassessment.html
[49]http://www.epa.gov/nrmrl/basicinfo.html
[50]http://odphp.osophs.dhhs.gov/pubs/prevrpt/archives/95fm1.htm
[51]http://www.whatispublichealth.org/what/index.html
[52]http://www.aiha.org/aboutaiha/Pages/WhatIsanIH.aspx
[53]http://en.wikipedia.org/wiki/Sanitary_engineering

century and beginning of the 20th. The spread of disease was a particularly troublesome problem as the country continued to urbanize. For instance if you lived your life in, say, Chicago during the period 1850-1900[54] (a typical lifespan of the day), you had about a 1 in 100 chance of dying of cholera[55] (and a 1 in 2000 chance of dying of typhoid), of which there were periodic epidemics spread by contaminated drinking water. Chicago's solution was to cease polluting its drinking water source (Lake Michigan) by reversing the flow of its watercourses so that they drained into the adjacent basin (the Mississippi). The widespread chlorination[56] of municipal water after 1908 essentially eliminated waterborne outbreaks of disease in all major cities (with some notable exceptions—the outbreak of chlorine-resistant Cryptosporidium parvum in Milwaukee's drinking water[57] in 1993 resulted in the infection of 403,000 people with 104 deaths).

Parallel work on the effects of chemical exposure on workers (and poor working conditions in general) were pioneered by Alice Hamilton (1869-1970), who published the first treatise on toxic chemical exposure "Industrial Poisons in the United States" in 1925. Hamilton is considered the founder of the field of occupational health[58] . In 1897 she was appointed professor of pathology at the Women's Medical School of Northwestern University, and in 1902 she accepted the position of bacteriologist at the Memorial Institute for Infectious Diseases in Chicago. Dr. Hamilton joined Jane Addams's Hull House[59] , in Chicago, where she interacted with progressive thinkers who often gravitated there, and to the needs of the poor for whom Hull House provided services.

2.3.4 Environmental Contamination and Risk

Events during the period 1920-1950 took an unfortunate turn. Global conflicts and economic uncertainty diverted attention from environmental issues, and much of what had been learned during the previous hundred years, for example about soil conservation and sustainable forestry, ceased to influence policy, with resultant mismanagement on a wide scale (see Figures **Texas Dust Storm** (Figure 2.5) and **Clear Cutting, Louisiana, 1930** (Figure 2.6)).

Figure 2.5: Texas Dust Storm. Photograph shows a dust storm approaching Stratford, TX in 1935. *Source: NOAA via Wikimedia Commons*[60]

---

[54] http://www.encyclopedia.chicagohistory.org/pages/432.html

[55] http://en.wikipedia.org/wiki/Cholera

[56] http://www.doh.wa.gov/ehp/dw/publications/331-253.pdf

[57] http://www.cdc.gov/ncidod/eid/vol9no4/02-0417.htm

[58] http://www.niehs.nih.gov/health/topics/population/occupational/index.cfm

[59] http://www.hullhouse.org/aboutus/history.html

[60] http://commons.wikimedia.org/wiki/File:Dust-storm-Texas-1935.png

Figure 2.6: Clear Cutting, Louisiana, 1930. Typical cut-over longleaf pine area, on Kisatchie National Forest. Areas of this type were the first to be planted on this forest. Circa 1930s. *Source: Wait, J.M. for U.S. Forest Service. U.S. Forest Service photo courtesy of the Forest History Society*[61]*, Durham, N.C.*

In the aftermath of the World War II, economic and industrial activity in the United States accelerated, and a consumer-starved populace sought and demanded large quantities of diverse goods and services. Major industrial sectors, primary metals, automotive, chemical, timber, and energy expanded considerably; however there were still few laws or regulations on waste management, and the ones that could and often were invoked (e.g. the Rivers and Harbors Act of 1899[62]) were devised in earlier times for problems of a different nature. The Module **Systems of Waste Management** (Section 7.2) provides a more detailed accounting of the current framework for managing waste. Here we recount the circumstances that eventually resulted in the promulgation of environmental risk as a basis for public policy, with subsequent passage of major environmental legislation.

---

[61]http://foresthistory.org/dbtw-wpd/exec/dbtwpub.dll?AC=GET_RECORD&XC=/dbtw-wpd/exec/dbtwpub.dll&BU=http%3A%2F%2Ffores wpd%2Ftextbase%2FWebQuery.htm&TN=FHSphoto&SN=AUTO14191&SE=308&RN=6&MR=10&TR=0&TX=1000&ES=0&CS=1&XP=&RI 8859-1&OEH=ISO-8859-1

[62]http://en.wikipedia.org/wiki/Rivers_and_Harbors_Act_of_1899

Figure 2.7: Zinc Smelter. Photograph shows a local smelter in a small valley town in Pennsylvania with, essentially, uncontrolled emissions. *Source: The Wire Mill, Donora, PA, taken by Bruce Dresbach in 1910. Retrieved from the Library of Congress*[63]

If there were any doubts among American society that the capacity of the natural environment to absorb human-caused contamination with acceptably low risk was indeed infinite, these were dispelled by a series of well-publicized incidents that occurred during the period 1948-1978. Figure **Zinc Smelter** (Figure 2.7) shows a local smelter in a small valley town in Pennsylvania with, essentially, uncontrolled emissions. During periods of atmospheric stability (an inversion), contaminants became trapped, accumulated, and caused respiratory distress so extraordinary that fifty deaths were recorded. Figure **Noon in Donora** (Figure 2.8) illustrates the dramatically poor air quality, in the form of reduced visibility, during this episode. Such incidents were not uncommon, nor were they limited to small American towns. A well-documented similar episode occurred in London, England in 1952[64] with at least 4000 deaths, and 100,000 illnesses resulting.

---

[63]http://www.loc.gov/pictures/item/2002713075/
[64]http://en.wikipedia.org/wiki/Great_Smog

Figure 2.8: Noon in Donora. Photograph, dated October 29, 1948, illustrates the extremely poor air quality in the Pennsylvania town at the time. *Source: NOAA*[65]

The generally poor state of air quality in the United States was initially tolerated as a necessary condition of an industrialized society. Although the risks of occupational exposure to chemicals was becoming more well known, the science of risk assessment as applied to the natural environment was in its infancy, and the notion that a polluted environment could actually cause harm was slow to be recognized, and even if true it was not clear what might be done about it. Nevertheless, people in the most contaminated areas could sense the effects of poor air quality: increased incidence of respiratory disease, watery eyes, odors, inability to enjoy being outside for more than a few minutes, and diminished visibility.

---

[65]http://oceanservice.noaa.gov/education/kits/pollution/media/supp_pol02c.html

Figure 2.9: Cuyahoga River Fire, 1969. Photograph illustrates a 1969 fire on the Cuyahoga River, one of many fires during the time period. *Source: NOAA*[66].

Environmental degradation of the era was not limited to air quality. Emissions of contaminants to waterways and burial underground were simple and common ways to dispose of wastes. Among the most infamous episodes in pollution history were the periodic fires that floated through downtown Cleveland, Ohio on the Cuyahoga River[67], causing considerable damage (Figure **Cuyahoga River Fire 1969** (Figure 2.9)), and the discovery of buried hazardous solvent drums in a neighborhood of Niagara Falls, NY in 1978, a former waste disposal location for a chemical company (Figure **Love Canal** (Figure 2.10)).

---

[66]http://oceanservice.noaa.gov/education/kits/pollution/media/supp_pol02d.html
[67]http://www.ohiohistorycentral.org/entry.php?rec=1642

Infrared aerial photo of Love Canal area (taken in spring 1978) showing 99th Street elementary school in center, two rings of homes bordering the landfill and LaSalle Housing Development in upper right. White patchy areas indicate barren sections where vegetation will not grow, presumably due to leaching chemical contamination.

Figure 2.10: Love Canal. The Love Canal region of Niagara Falls, NY, 1978 showing the local grade school and neighboring houses. *Source: New York State Department of Health (1981, April). Love Canal: A special report to the Governor and Legislature, p. 5.*

2.3.5 Risk Management as a Basis for Environmental Policy

Environmental scientists of the day were also alarmed by the extent and degree of damage that they were documenting. The publication of *Silent Spring*[68] in 1962 by Rachel Carson[69] (1907-1964), about the impact of the widespread and indiscriminate use of pesticides, was a watershed moment, bringing environmental concerns before a large portion of the American, and global, public. Carson, a marine biologist and conservationist who initially worked for the U.S. Bureau of Fisheries, became a full time nature writer in the 1950s. She collected scientifically documented evidence on the effects of pesticides, particularly DDT[70], heptachlor[71], and dieldrin[72], on humans and mammals, and the systemic disruption they caused to ecosystems. *Silent Spring* is credited with bringing about a ban on the use of DDT[73] in the United States, and setting in motion a chain of events that would ultimately result in the transformation of environmental public policy from one based on the problems and attitudes that brought about nineteenth century conservation, to one based on the management of risks from chemical toxins. The U.S. Environmental Protection Agency[74] was established in 1970, just eight years after the publication of *Silent Spring*. The same year Earth Day[75] was created.

As noted, the modules in the Chapter **Modern Environmental Management** (Section 7.1) contain a comprehensive treatment of the major laws and regulations that underpin the risk management approach to environmental policy. However it is worth considering one law in particular at this point, the National Environmental Policy Act[76] of 1970 (NEPA), because it provides a legal basis for U.S. environmental policy, and lays out its terms clearly and unambiguously. NEPA established a national goal to create and maintain "conditions under which [humans] and nature can exist in productive harmony, *and fulfill the social, economic and other requirements of present and future generations of Americans*[emphasis added]" (NEPA, 1970 (p. 35)). Further, NEPA saw the need for long term planning, to "fulfill the responsibilities of each generation as trustee of the environment for succeeding generations," for equity "to assure for all Americans safe, healthful, productive, and esthetically and culturally pleasing surroundings," and for economic prosperity as we "achieve a balance between population and resource use that will permit high standards of living and a wide sharing of life's amenities" (NEPA, 1970 (p. 35)). Although the exact word "sustainable" does not appear, NEPA is in all major respects congruent with the goals of the Brundtland Report (written 17 years later, see Chapter **Introduction to Sustainability: Humanity and the Environment** (Section 1.1)), retains the character of American conservation, and anticipates the need to integrate environmental quality with social and economic needs.

Every four to six years the U.S. EPA releases its Report on the Environment[77], a collection of data and analysis of trends on environmental quality. It is quite comprehensive; reporting on an array of measures that chart progress, or lack thereof, on human impacts on the environment and, in turn, the effects of our actions on human health. It is difficult to summarize all the information available in a concise way, however most measures of human exposure to toxic chemicals, dating in many cases back to the late 1980s, show clear downward trends, in some cases dramatically so (for example DDT in human tissues, lead in blood serum, exposure to hazardous wastes from improper disposal, exposure to toxic compounds emitted to the air). In addition, many of other indicators of environmental quality such as visibility, drinking water quality, and the biodiversity of streams, show improvement. These are success stories of the risk management approach to environmental quality. On the other hand, other measures, such as hypoxia in coastal waters, quantities of hazardous wastes generated, and greenhouse gases released are either not improving or are getting worse.

---

[68]http://www.nrdc.org/health/pesticides/hcarson.asp
[69]http://www.rachelcarson.org/
[70]http://www.pan-uk.org/pestnews/Actives/ddt.htm
[71]http://www.atsdr.cdc.gov/toxfaqs/tf.asp?id=744&tid=135
[72]http://www.atsdr.cdc.gov/toxfaqs/tf.asp?id=316&tid=56
[73]http://www.epa.gov/aboutepa/history/topics/ddt/
[74]http://www.epa.gov/aboutepa/history/
[75]http://www.epa.gov/earthday/history.htm
[76]http://www.epa.gov/compliance/basics/nepa.html
[77]http://www.epa.gov/roe/

2.3.6 References

National Environmental Policy Act of 1970, 42 U.S.C., 4321, et seq. (1970). http://www.epa.gov/compliance/basics/nepa.html[78]

2.4 Sustainability and Public Policy[79]

2.4.1 Learning Objectives

After reading this module, students should be able to

- understand the problem-driven nature of policy development, from relatively local agricultural problems to regional problems often driven by industrial development to global problems associated with population-driven human consumption

2.4.2 Complex Environmental Problems

NEPA, both in tone and purpose, was in sharp contrast to the many environmental laws that followed in the 1970s and 1980s that defined increasingly proscriptive methods for controlling risks from chemical exposure (this is sometimes termed the "command-and-control[80] " approach to environmental management). In many ways these laws and regulations are ill-suited to the types of environmental problems that have emerged in the past twenty years. Whereas the focus of our environmental policy has been on mitigating risk from local problems that are chemical – and media – (land, water, or air) specific, the need has arisen to address problems that are far more complex, multi-media, and are of large geographic, sometimes global, extent.

An early example of this type of shift in the complexity of environmental problems is illustrated by the phenomenon of acidic rainfall[81] , a regional problem that occurs in many areas across the globe. Although the chemical cause of acid rain is acidic gases (such as sulfur dioxide[82] and nitrogen oxides[83]) released into the atmosphere from combustion processes (such as coal burning), the problem was made considerably worse because of the approach to problem solving typical of the day for episodes such as the Donora disaster (see Figures **Zinc Smelter** (Figure 2.7) and **Noon in Donora** (Figure 2.8)).

---

[78]http://www.epa.gov/compliance/basics/nepa.html
[79]This content is available online at <http://legacy.cnx.org/content/m42116/1.4/>.
[80]http://www.enviroliteracy.org/article.php/1329.html
[81]http://www.epa.gov/ne/eco/acidrain/history.html
[82]http://www.epa.gov/oaqps001/sulfurdioxide/
[83]http://www.epa.gov/oaqps001/nitrogenoxides/

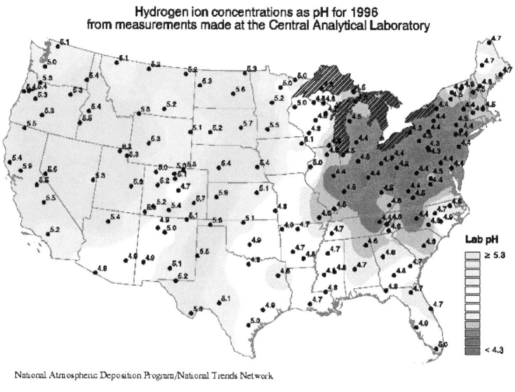

Figure 2.11: Hydrogen Ion Concentrations as pH for 1996. Figure shows the distribution in rainfall pH in the United States for the year 1996. *Source: National Atmospheric Deposition Program/National Trends Network via National Park Service*[84].

In order to prevent the local accumulation of contaminants, emission stacks were made much taller, effectively relying on the diluting power of the atmosphere to disperse offending pollutants. The result was a significant increase in the acidity of rainfall downwind of major sources, with associated impacts on aquatic and forest resources. Figure **Hydrogen Ion Concentrations as pH for 1996** (Figure 2.11) shows this pattern for the eastern United States in 1996. A more comprehensive solution to this problem (short of replacing coal as a fuel source), has involved integrated activity on many fronts: science to understand the impacts of acid rain, technology to control the release of acidic gases, politics in the form of amendments to the Clean Air Act[85] , social equity that defined the role of regional responsibilities in the face of such large geographic disparities, and economics to understand the total costs of acid rain and design markets[86] to spread the costs of control. Although acidic rainfall is still an issue of concern, its impacts have been mitigated to a significant degree.

---

[84]http://www.nature.nps.gov/air/edu/lessons/figure3.cfm

[85]http://www.epa.gov/air/caa/

[86]http://www.edf.org/page.cfm?tagID=1085

2.4.3 Sustainability as a Driver of Environmental Policy

The level of complexity illustrated by the acid rain problem can be found in a great many other environmental problems today, among them:

- Hypoxic[87] conditions in coastal regions of the world caused by excessive release of nutrients, principally dissolved nitrogen and phosphorous from artificial fertilizer applied to crops (in addition to the Gulf of Mexico[88] and Chesapeake Bay[89] in the United States, there are over 400 such areas worldwide[90]),
- Stratospheric ozone depletion[91] caused by the release of certain classes of chlorofluorocarbon[92] compounds used as propellants and refrigerants (with increases in the incident of skin cancers and cataracts),
- Urbanization[93] and sprawl[94] , whereby the population density in urban areas, with its attendant problems (degradation of air and water quality, stormwater management[95] , habitat destruction, infrastructure renewal, health care needs, traffic congestion, loss of leisure time, issues of social equality), continues to grow (for example eighty percent of the population of the United States, about fifty percent of global, now lives in urban regions),
- Global climate change[96] , and its resultant impacts (increases in temperature and storm and flooding frequency, ocean acidification[97] , displacement of human populations, loss of biodiversity, sea-level rise), caused by the human-induced emission of greenhouse gases[98] .

Problems such as these, which require highly integrated solutions that include input from many disciplines and stakeholders, have been termed "wicked" (Batie, 2008 (p. 38); Kreuter, DeRosa, Howze, & Baldwin, 2004 (p. 38)). Wicked problems have certain key characteristics:

- There is not universal agreement on what the problem is – different stakeholders define it differently.
- There is no defined end solution, the end will be assessed as "better" or "worse."
- The problem may change over time.
- There is no clear stopping rule – stakeholders, political forces and resource availability will make that determination on the basis of "judgments."
- The problem is associated with high uncertainty of both components and outcomes.
- Values and societal goals are not necessarily shared by those defining the problem or those attempting to make the problem better.

Wicked problems are not confined to environmental issues, for example the same characteristics arise for problems such as food safety, health care disparities, and terrorism, but in the context of environmental policy they create the need to reassess policy approaches and goals, laws and regulations, as well as methods and models for integrated research.

Table **The Evolution of U.S. Environmental Policy** (Table 2.1) summarizes the major attributes of U.S. environmental policy as it has evolved over the past two centuries. To most observers it would seem to be true that advances in public policy, in any realm, are driven by problems, real and perceived, that require systemic solutions. Environmental policy is no exception. Early conservationists were alarmed at the inefficiencies of human resource management and the encroachment of humans on unspoiled lands. During the 20th century many groups: scientists, economists, politicians, and ordinary citizens, became

---

[87]http://oceanservice.noaa.gov/outreach/pdfs/coastalhypoxia.pdf
[88]http://toxics.usgs.gov/hypoxia/hypoxic_zone.html
[89]http://www.pewclimate.org/docUploads/Regional-Impacts-Chesapeake.pdf
[90]http://www.wri.org/map/world-hypoxic-and-eutrophic-coastal-areas
[91]http://www.nas.nasa.gov/About/Education/Ozone/
[92]http://www.epa.gov/ozone/science/ods/classone.html
[93]http://www.wri.org/publication/content/8840
[94]http://en.wikipedia.org/wiki/Urban_sprawl
[95]http://extension.usu.edu/waterquality/htm/urbanstormwater/
[96]http://www.epa.gov/climatechange/index.html
[97]http://www.nrdc.org/oceans/acidification/
[98]http://www.epa.gov/climatechange/emissions/index.html

alarmed and fearful of the consequences of toxic pollutant loads to the environment that included localized effects on human health and well-being. And now, as we proceed into the 21st century, an array of complex problems that have the potential to alter substantially the structure and well-being of large segments of human societies, calls for a renewal and reassessment of our approach to environmental policy. This has, thus far, proven to be a difficult transition. Many of these complex problems have multiple causes and impacts, affect some groups of people more than others, are economically demanding, and are often not as visibly apparent to casual observers as previous impacts, nor are the benefits perceived to be commensurate with costs. Devising a regulatory strategy for such problems requires an adaptive and flexible approach that current laws do not foster.

	1850-1920	1960-1990	1990-present
Focus	Conservation/sanitation	Media/site/problem specific	Complex regional/global problems
Outcome	Land preservation/efficiency/control of disease	Manage anthropocentricand ecological risk	Global sustainable development
Principal Activity	Resource management reform/simple contaminant controls	Compliance/remediation/technological emphasis on problem solving	Integration of social, economic, and technological information for holistic problem solving
Economic Focus	Profit maximization/public health	Cost minimization	Strategic investments/long-term societal well-being
Regulatory Activity	Low	Heavy	Adaptive and Flexible
Conceptual Model	Expansion vs. preservation	Command-and-control	Systems/life cycle approach
Disciplinary Approach	Disciplinary and insular	Multidisciplinary	Interdisciplinary/Integrative

Table 2.1: **The Evolution of U.S. Environmental Policy** Table summarizes the major attributes of U.S. environmental policy as it has evolved over the past two centuries. *Source: T. Theis adapted from Fiksel, Graedel, Hecht, Rejeski, Saylor, Senge, et al. (2009) (p. 38).*

2.4.4 References

Batie, S. S. (2008, December). Wicked problems and applied economics. *American Journal of Agricultural Economics, 90*, 1176-1191 doi: 10.1111/j.1467-8276.2008.01202.x

Fiksel, J., Graedel, T., Hecht, A. D., Rejeski, D., Saylor, G. S., Senge, P. M., Swackhamer, D. L., & Theis, T. L. (2009). EPA at 40: Bringing environmental protection into the 21st century. *Environmental Science and Technology, 43*, 8716-8720. doi: 10.1021/es901653f

Kreuter, M. W., DeRosa, C., Howze, E. H., & Baldwin, G. T. (2004, August). Understanding wicked problems: A key to advancing environmental health promotion. *Health, Education and Behavior, 31*, 441-54. doi: 10.1177/1090198104265597

2.5 Public Health and Sustainability[99]

2.5.1 Learning Objectives

After reading this module, students should be able to

- understand what public health is
- recognize public health impacts of non-sustainable development
- identify key public health impacts of climate change

2.5.2 Introduction

"Much discussion about sustainability treats the economy, livelihoods, environmental conditions, our cities and infrastructure, and social relations as if they were ends in themselves; as if they are the reason we seek sustainability. Yet their prime value is as the foundations upon which our longer-term health and survival depend." (McMichael, 2006 (p. 47))

Ecological sustainability is more than just continuing the resource flows of the natural world to sustain the economic machine, while maintaining diversity of species and ecosystems. It is also about sustaining the vast support systems for health and life which could be considered the real bottom line of sustainability. Before examining the public health effects of non-sustainable development, we should define public health.

- The website for UIC's School of Public Health[100] says "we are passionate about improving the health and well-being of the people of Chicago, the state of Illinois, the nation and the world."
- The Illinois Department of Public Health[101] is responsible for protecting the state's 12.4 million residents, as well as countless visitors, through the prevention and control of disease and injury."
- The New Zealand Ministry of Health[102] defines it as "the science and art of promoting health, preventing disease and prolonging life through organized efforts of society."
- The National Resources Defense Council[103] an NGO devoted to environmental action, states that public health is "the health or physical well-being of a whole community."

2.5.3 Impacts of Non-Sustainable Development

We have built our communities in ways that are unsustainable from many aspects. Not only does development create urban sprawl, impact land use, and fuel consumption, we can identify negative health consequences related to these development trends.

2.5.3.1 Obesity

If our communities are not walkable or bikeable, we need to drive to schools, shops, parks, entertainment, play dates, etc. Thus we become more sedentary. A sedentary lifestyle increases the risk of overall mortality (2 to 3-fold), cardiovascular disease (3 to 5-fold), and some types of cancer, including colon and breast cancer. The effect of low physical fitness is comparable to that of hypertension, high cholesterol, diabetes, and even smoking (Wei et al., 1999 (p. 48); Blair et al., 1996 (p. 47)).

---

[99]This content is available online at <http://legacy.cnx.org/content/m43321/1.2/>.
[100]http://www.uic.edu/sph/
[101]http://www.idph.state.il.us/about/abouthome.htm
[102]http://www.health.govt.nz/
[103]http://www.nrdc.org/reference/glossary/p.asp&usg=AFrqEzcXBXgcIzAeeOmfGermViDFW6tePw

2.5.3.2 Economic Segregation

Walkable and safe communities provide sidewalks, bike paths, proximity, and connections to community services such as grocery stores, schools, health care, parks, and entertainment. Community design that creates a segregated housing environment with only expensive housing and no affordable housing segregates people by socio-economic level (i.e. poor from non-poor) and this generally leads to segregation by race. Lack of physical activity will occur in neighborhoods with no good green and safe recreational sites. If we have poor public transit systems partly due to lack of density (only more expensive, low-density housing) and our love of the automobile, then we have increased emissions that contribute to global warming.

2.5.3.3 The Olympics as an Example

A natural experiment during the 1996 Summer Olympic Games in Atlanta shows the impact of car use on health. During the games, peak morning traffic decreased 23% and peak ozone levels decreased 28%. Asthma-related emergency room visits by children decreased 42% while children's emergency visits for non-asthma causes did not change during same period (Friedman, Powell, Hutwagner, Graham, & Teague, 2001 (p. 47)). We also saw that with the Beijing Olympics in 2008 where driving days were rationed, more than 300,000 heavy-emitting vehicles (about 10% of total) were barred from the city's administrative area in order to decrease pollution for athletes and visitors This reduced the number of vehicles by about 1.9 million or 60% of the total fleet during the Olympic Games. Emissions of black carbon, carbon monoxide and ultrafine particles were reduced by 33%, 47%, and 78% respectively compared to the year before the Olympics. Frequency of respiratory illnesses during the 2008 games were found to be significantly less in certain populations compared to previous years and this was hypothesized to be related to the reduction of vehicles on the road (Wang et al., 2009 (p. 47); Jentes et al., 2010 (p. 47)).

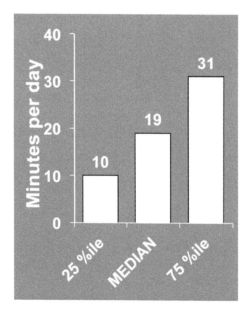

Figure 2.12: Minutes Americans Walk per Day *Source: National Household Travel Survey, 2001, USDOT*[104]

Figure **Minutes Americans Walk per Day** (Figure 2.12) shows the average time Americans spend walking a day. People who walk to and from public transit get an fair amount of physical activity related

---

[104]http://nhts.ornl.gov/index.shtml

to using transit, thus the name given to modes of transit that do not involve driving: active transit. Those people who did not own a car or were not a primary driver had higher walking times (Besser & Dannenberg, 2005 (p. 47)).

2.5.3.4 Water Quality

Increasing numbers of roads and parking lots are needed to support an automobile transportation system, which lead to increased non-point source water pollution and contamination of water supplies (road runoff of oil/gas, metals, nutrients, organic waste, to name a few) with possible impacts on human health. Increased erosion and stream siltation causes environmental damage and may affect water treatment plants and thus affect water quality.

2.5.3.5 Social Capital

On the social sustainability side, we can look at social capital otherwise defined as the "connectedness" of a group built through behaviors such as social networking and civic engagement, along with attitudes such as trust and reciprocity. Greater social capital has been associated with healthier behaviors, better self-rated health, and less negative results such as heart disease. However, social capital has been diminishing over time. Proposed causes include long commute times, observed in sprawling metropolitan areas. Past research suggests that long commute times are associated with less civic participation; Robert Putnam suggests that every ten additional minutes of commuting predicts a 10% decline in social capital (Besser, Marcus, & Frumkin, 2008 (p. 47)). **Urban sprawl** is considered the reason for most long commutes.

As of 2011, according to an article in the Chicago Tribune[105] , Chicago commuting times are some of the worst – with Chicagoans spending 70 hours per year more on the road than they would if there was no congestion – up from 18 hours in 1982. They have an average commute time of 34 minutes each way. These drivers also use 52 more gallons per year per commuter, increasing their costs and pollution.

Residents of sprawling counties were likely to walk less during leisure time, weigh more, and have greater prevalence of hypertension than residents of compact counties (Ewing, Schmid, Killingsworth, Zlot, & Raudenbush (p. 47), 2003 (p. 47)).

While more compact development is found to have a negative impact on weight, we also find that individuals with low BMI are more likely to select locations with dense development. This suggests that efforts to curb sprawl, and thereby make communities more exercise-friendly, may simply attract those individuals who are predisposed to physical activity (Plantinga & (p. 47)Bernell, 2007 (p. 47)).

2.5.4 Impacts of Climate Change

Public health studies have been conducted with regard to many of the predicted environmental effects of climate change. Thus, it is somewhat easier to examine the public health implications of this outcome of unsustainable behavior. Figure **How Climate Change Affects Population** (Figure 2.13) describes the pathways by which climate change affects public health. To the left we see the natural and anthropogenic, or human-caused activities that affect climate change, which result in climatic conditions and variability; if we can mitigate those events we can reduce climate change. These activities first result in environmental impacts such as severe weather events, disturbed ecosystems, sea-level rise, and overall environmental degradation. Those impacts can then result in a broad range of health effects that we can adapt to, to a certain extent. These impacts are generally categorized into three areas: heat induced morbidity and mortality, infectious diseases, and impacts due to the effect of extreme weather such as flooding and drought on the social welfare of the population.

---

[105]http://articles.chicagotribune.com/2011-01-20/news/ct-met-traffic-congestion-0120-20110119_1_congestion-david-schrank-urban-mobility-report

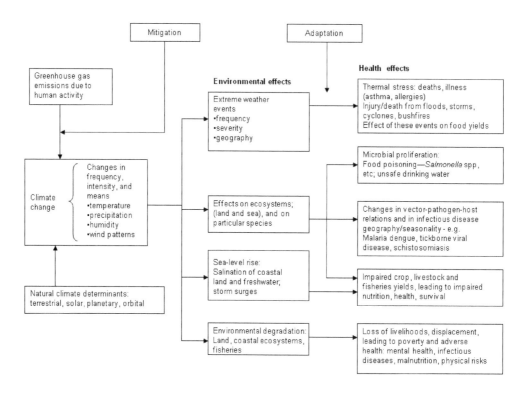

Figure 2.13: How Climate Change Affects Population Diagram summarizing the main pathways by which climate change affects population health. *Source:Created by Cindy Klein-Banai, based on McMichael et al., 2006* (p. 47)

Measurement of health effects from climate change can only be very approximate. One major study, by the World Health Organization (WHO), was a quantitative assessment of some of the possible health impacts that looked at the effects of the climate changes since the mid-1970s and determined that this may have resulted in over 150,000 deaths in 2000. The study concluded that the effects will probably grow in the future (World Health Organization, 2009 (p. 48)).

2.5.4.1 Extreme Weather

Climate change can influence heat-related **morbidity** and **mortality**, generally a result of the difference between temperature extremes and mean climate in a given area. Higher temperatures in the summer increase mortality. Studies on the effects of heat waves in Europe indicate that half of the excess heat during the European heat wave of 2003 was due to global warming and, by inference, about half of the excess deaths during that heat wave could be attributed to human-generated greenhouse gas emissions (see Haines, Kovats, Campbell-Lendrum, & Corvalan, 2006 (p. 47); Hellmann, Lesht, & Nadelhoffer, 2007 (p. 47); McMichael, 2006 (p. 47)). Urban centers are more susceptible due to the urban heat island effect that produces higher temperatures in urban areas as compared to the near-by suburbs and rural areas. Lack of vegetation or evaporation, and large areas of pavement, in cities result in an "Urban Heat Island," where urban areas are warmer than the neighboring suburban and rural areas (See Figure **Sketch of an Urban Heat-Island Profile** (Figure 2.14)). Adaptation can help reduce mortality through greater prevention awareness and by providing more air-conditioning and cooling centers.

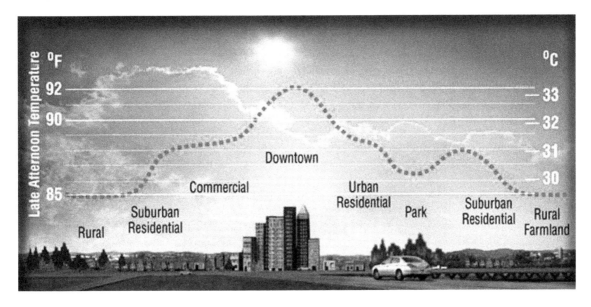

Figure 2.14: **Sketch of an Urban Heat-Island Profile.** *Source: Heat Island Group*[106].

The reduction of extreme cold due to global warming, could reduce the number of deaths due to low temperatures. Unlike for heat, those deaths are usually not directly related to the cold temperature itself but rather to influenza. Also, deaths related to cold spells would increase to a lesser extent by (1.6%), while heat waves increase them by 5.7%.

Since **volatile organic compounds** are precursors of ozone, and VOC emissions increase with temperature, this could lead to an increase in ozone concentrations. For fifteen cities in the eastern United States, the average number of days exceeding the health-based eight-hour ozone standard is projected to increase by 60 percent (from twelve to almost twenty days each summer) by the 2050s because of warmer temperatures (Lashof, & Patz, 2004 (p. 47)). Pollen levels may increase with increased CO_2 levels since that promotes growth and reproduction in plants. This will increase the incidence of allergic reactions. Similarly, poison ivy will grow more and be more toxic.

Infectious diseases are influenced by climate as pathogen survival rates are strongly affected by temperature change. Diseases carried by birds, animals, and insects (vector-born) – such as malaria, dengue fever, and dengue hemorrhagic fever – may be influenced by temperature as mosquitoes are sensitive to climate conditions such as temperature humidity, solar radiation, and rainfall. For example, there has been a strengthening of the relationship between the El Nino global weather cycle and cholera outbreaks in Bangladesh. Increases in malaria in the highlands of eastern Africa may be associated with local warming trends. Temperature also affects the rate of food-born infectious disease. In general, however, it is hard to isolate the effects of climate change that affect the transmission rate and geographic boundaries of infectious disease from other social, economic, behavioral, and environmental factors (see McMichael et al., 2006 (p. 47)). Increased precipitation from extreme rainfall events can cause flooding which, especially in cities with combined sewer and stormwater systems can be contaminated by sewage lines. This can happen when the deep tunnels that carry stormwater in Chicago reach capacity and untreated sewage then must be released

[106]http://heatisland.lbl.gov/

into Lake Michigan. E. Coli levels in the lake then increase, forcing beaches to close to prevent the spread of infection.

Diseases are re-emerging and emerging infectious due to intensified food production in "factory" farms. Examples include mad cow disease (1980s in Britain); the encroachment on rain forest by pig farmers exposed pigs and farmers to the "Nipah" virus carried by rainforest bats that were seeking food from orchards around the pig farms – driven by deforestation and the drought of El Nino. This caused infection of pigs which lead to human illness and more than one hundred deaths. Poultry farming (avian influenza viruses) - crowded 'factory farming' may increase the likelihood of viral virulence when there is no selective advantage in keeping the host bird alive. Other food related issues are discussed in the next section.

2.5.4.2 Food Production

Climate change can influence regional famines because droughts and other extreme climate conditions have a direct influence on food crops and also by changing the ecology of plant pathogens (Patz et al., 2005 (p. 47)).

There are likely to be major effects of climate change on agricultural production and fisheries. This can be both positive and negative depending on the direct effects of temperature, precipitation, CO_2, extreme climate variations, and sea-level rise. Indirect effects would have to do with changes in soil quality, incidence of plant diseases and weed and insect populations. Food spoilage will increase with more heat and humidity. Persistent drought has already reduced food production in Africa. There could be reduction in nutritional quality due to a reduction in the amount of nitrogen crops incorporate when CO_2 levels increase.

Malnutrition will be increased due to drought, particularly poorer countries. Increasing fuel costs also increase the cost of food, as we are already seeing in 2011. Again, this incremental cost rise affects those who already spend a large portion of their income on food and can contribute to malnutrition. About one-third, or 1.7 billion, of all people live in water-stressed countries and this is anticipated to increase to five billion by 2025. Frequency of diarrhea and other diseases like conjunctivitis that are associated with poor hygiene and a breakdown in sanitation may increase.

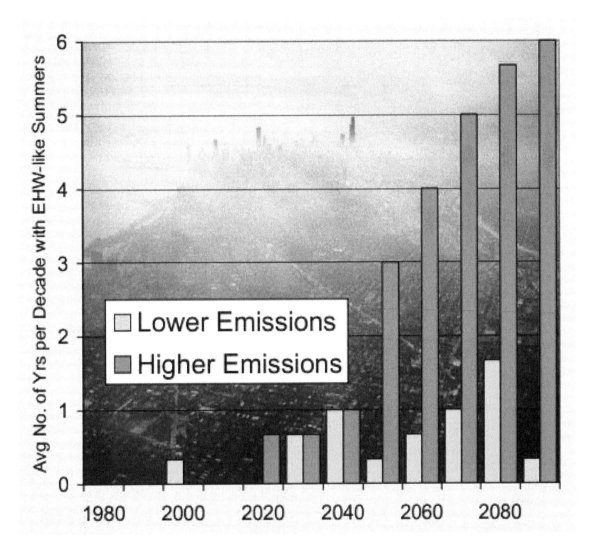

Figure 2.15: Projection for Future EHW-like Summers in Chicago. The average number of summers per decade with mortality rates projected to equal those of the Chicago analog to the European Heat Wave of 2003. Values shown are the average of three climate models for higher (orange) and lower (yellow) emission scenarios for each decade from 1980 to 2090 *Source: Hellmann et al., 2007* (p. 47).

Various studies suggest that increases in population at risk from malnutrition will increase from 40-300 million people over the current 640 million by 2060 (Rosenzweig, Parry, Fischer & Frohberg, 1993 (p. 47)). A more recent study said that today 34% of the population is at risk and by 2050 this value would grow to 64-72%. Climate change is associated with decreased pH (acidification) of oceans due to higher CO_2 levels. Over the past 200 years ocean pH has been reduced by 0.1 units and the IPCC predicts a drop of 0.14 to 0.35 units by 2100. This may affect shell-forming organisms and the species that depend on them. There could be a reduction in plankton due to the North Atlantic Gulf Stream (Pauly & Alder, 2005 (p. 47)). With already overexploited fish populations, it will be harder for them to recover.

Natural disasters like floods, droughts, wildfires, tsunamis, and extreme storms have resulted in millions of deaths over the past 25 years and negatively affected the lives of many more. Survivors may experience increased rates of mental health disorders such as **post-traumatic stress disorder**. Wildfires reduce air quality, increasing particulate matter that provokes cardiac and respiratory problems. Sea level rise will increase flooding and coastal erosion. Indirect effects of rising sea levels include the infiltration of salt water and could interfere with stormwater drainage and sewage disposal. This could force coastal communities to migrate and create refugees with health burdens such as overcrowding, homelessness, and competition for resources. Air pollution is likely to be worse with climate change. It can also lead to mobilization of dangerous chemicals from storage or remobilize chemicals that are already in the environment.

Specific regional effects have may be more severe. Vulnerable regions include temperate zones predicted to experience disproportionate warming, areas around the Pacific and Indian Oceans that are currently subject to variability in rainfall, and large cities where they experience the urban heat island effect (Patz et al., 2005 (p. 47)). The Chicago area is one urban area where analysis has been performed to determine the specific health effects that are projected due to climate change (see Figure **Projection for Future EHW-like Summers in Chicago** (Figure 2.15)). Those effects are similar to the ones described above.

An evaluation of the reductions in adverse health effects that could be achieved by 2020 in four major cities with a total population of 45 million found that GHG mitigation would "reduce particulate matter and ozone ambient concentrations by about 10% and avoid some 64,000 premature deaths, 65,000 person-chronic bronchitis case, and 37 million days of restricted activities (Cifuentes, Borja-Aburto, Gouveia, Thurston & Davis, 2001 (p. 47)). The cities' ozone levels are estimated to increase under predicted future climatic conditions, and this effect will be more extreme in cities that already suffer from high pollution. The estimates of elevated ozone levels could mean a 0.11% to 0.27% increase in daily total mortality (Bell et al., 2007 (p. 47)). Therefore, reduction of GHG emissions, along with actions to mitigate the effects of climate change are likely to reduce the public health outcomes associated with climate change.

2.5.5 Conclusions

The implications of climate change on public health are broad and vast. The interconnectedness of all of earth's systems and human health is an area that is a challenge to study; the climate change scenarios are variable. Public health is directly tied to the human ecosystem that we create through our unsustainable activities. The deterioration of public health on this planet is perhaps the most important consequence of our own unsustainable choices. Without good public health outcomes, human life on this planet is threatened and ultimately our actions could cause significant changes in human health, well-being and longevity. It is not the earth that is at stake - it is humanity.

2.5.6 Review Questions

Question 2.5.1
Think about the major sources of energy: coal, nuclear and petroleum. Name some health effects that are associated with each, as portrayed in recent world events. Find one popular and one scientific source to support this.

Question 2.5.2
Describe three health impacts of climate change.

Question 2.5.3
Modern farming practices are meant to increase productivity and feed the world solving the problems of malnutrition and starvation. How would you argue for or against this?

Question 2.5.4
What are some outcomes that could be measured to determine if a community is healthy?

2.5.7 Resources

Health Impacts of Climate Change – Society of Occupational and Environmental Health http://www.youtube.com/watch?v=aLfhwaS677c[107]

2.5.8 References

Bell, M. L., Goldberg, R., Hogrefe, C., Kinney, P. L., Knowlton, K., Lynn, B., . . . Patz, J. A. (2007). Climate change, ambient ozone, and health in 50 US cities. *Climatic Change, 82*, 61-76.

Besser L. M., & Dannenberg A. L. (2005, November). Walking to public transit steps to help meet physical activity recommendations. *American Journal of Preventive Medicine, 29*(4), 273-280.

Besser, L. M., Marcus, M., & Frumkin, H. (2008, March). Commute time and social capital in the U.S. *American Journal of Preventive Medicine, 34*(3), 207-211.

Blair S. N., Kampert, J. B., Kohl III, H. W., Barlow, C. E., Macera, C. A., Paffenbarger, Jr, R. S., & Gibbons, L. W. (1996). Influences of cardiorespiratory fitness and other precursors on cardiovascular disease and all-cause mortality in men and women. *Journal of American Medical Association, 276*(3), 205-210.

Cifuentes, L., Borja-Aburto, V. H., Gouveia, N., Thurston, G., & Davis, D. L. (2001). Hidden health benefits of greenhouse gas mitigation. *Science, 293*(5533), 1257-1259.

Ewing, R., Schmid, T., Killingsworth, R., Zlot, A., & Raudenbush, S. (2003, September/October). Relationship between urban sprawl and physical activity, obesity, and morbidity. *American Journal of Health Promotion, 18*(1), 49-57.

Friedman, M. S., Powell, K. E., Hutwagner, L., Graham, L. M., & Teague, W. G. (2001). Impact of changes in transportation and commuting behaviors during the 1996 Summer Olympic Games in Atlanta on air quality and childhood asthma. *JAMA: The Journal of the American Medical Association, 285*(7), 897–905.

Haines, A., Kovats, R. S., Campbell-Lendrum, D., & Corvalan, C. (2006). Climate change and human health: Impacts, vulnerability and public health. *Journal of the Royal Institute of Public Health. 120*, 585-596.

Hellmann, J., Lesht, B., & Nadelhoffer, K. (2007). Chapter Four – Health. In *Climate Change and Chicago: Projections and Potential Impacts.* Retrieved from http://www.chicagoclimateaction.org/filebin/pdf/report/Chicago_climate_impacts_report_Chapter_Four_Health.pdf[108]

Jentes, E. S., Davis, X. M., MacDonald, S., Snyman, P. J., Nelson, H., Quarry, D., . . . & Marano, N. (2010). Health risks and travel preparation among foreign visitors and expatriates during the 2008 Beijing Olympic and Paralympic Games. *American Journal of Tropical Medical Hygene, 82*, 466–472.

Lashof, D. A., & Patz, J. (2004). Heat advisory: How global warming causes more bad air days. Retrieved from http://www.nrdc.org/globalwarming/heatadvisory/heatadvisory.pdf[109] .

McMichael, A. J. (2006) Population health as the 'bottom-line' of sustainability: A contemporary challenge for public health researchers. *European Journal of Public Health, 16*(6), 579–582.

McMichael, A. J., Woodruff, R. E., & Hales, S. (2006). Climate change and human health: Present and future risks. *Lancet, 367*, 859-869.

Patz, J. A., Campbell-Lendrum, D., Holloway, T., & Foley, J. A. (2005). Impact of regional climate change on human health. *Nature, 438*, 310-317.

Pauly, D., & Alder, J. (2005). Marine Fisheries Systems. In R. Hassan, R. Scholes, & N. Ash (eds.), *Ecosystems and Human Well - being: Current State and Trends .* (Vol. 1). Washington, D.C., Island Press.

Plantinga, A. J., & Bernell, S. (2007). The association between urban sprawl and obesity: Is it a two-way street?, *Journal of Regional Science, 47*(5), 857-879.

Rosenzweig, C., Parry, M. L., Fischer, G., & Frohberg, K. (1993). Climate change and world food supply. Research Report No. 3. Oxford, U.K. : Oxford University, Environmental Change Unit.

---

[107] http://www.youtube.com/watch?v=aLfhwaS677c

[108] http://www.chicagoclimateaction.org/filebin/pdf/report/Chicago_climate_impacts_report_Chapter_Four_Health.pdf

[109] http://www.nrdc.org/globalwarming/heatadvisory/heatadvisory.pdf

Wang, X., Westerdahl, D., Chen, L., Wu, Y., Hao, J., Pan, X., Guo, X., & Zhang, K. M. (2009). Evaluating the air quality impacts of the 2008 Beijing Olympic Games: On-road emission factors and black carbon profiles. *Atmospheric Environment, 43*, 4535–4543.

Wei, M., Kampert, J. B. , Barlow, C. E. , Nichaman, M. Z. , Gibbons, L. W., Paffenbarger, Jr., R. S., & Blair, S. N. (1999). Relationship between low cardiorespiratory fitness and mortality in normal-weight, overweight, and obese men. *Journal of the American Medical Association, 282*(16), 1547-1553.

World Health Organization. (2009). Climate change and human health. Fact sheet, July 2005. Retrieved from http://www.who.int/globalchange/news/fsclimandhealth/en/index.html[110] .

---

[110]http://www.who.int/globalchange/news/fsclimandhealth/en/index.html

Chapter 3

Climate and Global Change

3.1 Climate and Global Change – Chapter Introduction[1]

Module by: Jonathan Tomkin

The Earth's climate is changing. The scientific consensus is that by altering the composition of the atmosphere humans are increasing the average temperature of the Earth's surface. This process has already begun – the planet is measurably warmer than it was at the start of the last century – but scientists predict the change that will occur over the 21st century will be even greater. This increase will have unpredictable impacts on weather patterns around the globe. We are all experiencing climate change. Our descendants will likely experience far more.

This chapter focuses on the science of climate change. We recognize that climate change can be a controversial subject, and that prescriptions for solutions quickly take on a political character, which can raise suspicions of bias. Some argue that the climate is too complicated to predict, and others suggest that natural variations can explain the observed changes in the climate.

These objections have some merit. It should be no surprise that the Earth's climate is a complicated subject. First, the atmosphere is vast: it extends over 600 km (370 miles) above the ground, and it weighs over five quadrillion tons (that's a five followed by 15 zeros). Second, the atmosphere is a dynamic system, creating blizzards, hurricanes, thunderstorms, and all the other weather we experience. And it is true that this dynamic system is largely controlled by natural processes – the Earth's climate has been changing continually since the atmosphere was produced.

And yet scientists can still confidently say that humans are responsible for the current warming. We can do this because this complicated system obeys underlying principles. In the modules **Climate Processes; External and Internal Controls** (Section 3.2) and **Milankovitch Cycles and the Climate of the Quaternary** (Section 3.3), we will describe how these principles work, and how they have been observed by scientists. We can then use these principles to understand how, by producing greenhouse gases, humans are altering the physical properties of the atmosphere in such a way as to increase its ability to retain heat.

In the module **Modern Climate Change** (Section 3.4) we show how this theoretical prediction of a warming world is borne out by ever stronger evidence. Temperatures have been measured, and are shown to be increasing. These increases in temperatures are significant and have observable effects on the world: glaciers are shrinking, sea ice is retreating, sea levels are rising – even cherry blossoms are blooming earlier in the year.

In the module **Climate Projections** (Section 3.5), we describe how we can attempt to predict the climate of the future. This is a doubly difficult problem, as it involves not only physics, but, harder yet, people. What will today's societies do with the foreknowledge of the consequences of our actions? The climate has become yet another natural system whose immediate fate is connected to our own. The reader may find it either reassuring or frightening that we hold the climate's future in our hands.

---

[1]This content is available online at <http://legacy.cnx.org/content/m41664/1.4/>.

3.2 Climate Processes; External and Internal Controls[2]

3.2.1 Learning Objectives

After reading this module, students should be able to

- define both "climate" and "weather" and explain how the two are related
- use the Celsius temperature scale to describe climate and weather
- discuss the role and mechanisms of the major controls on Earth's climate using the concepts of insolation, albedo and greenhouse gases
- identify and describe the mechanisms by which major external and internal changes to the climate (including solar output variation, volcanoes, biological processes, changes in glacial coverage, and meteorite impacts) operate
- know that the Earth's climate has changed greatly over its history as a result of changes in insolation, albedo, and atmospheric composition
- describe the processes that can lead to a "Snowball Earth" using the "positive feedback" concept, and be able to contrast the climate factors that influenced this period of Earth's history with others, including the dominant factors that operated during the Cretaceous
- state the major ways in which carbon dioxide is both added to and removed from the atmosphere, and be able to describe why levels of carbon dioxide and other greenhouse gases can be kept in balance

3.2.2 Introduction

The Earth's climate is continually changing. If we are to understand the current climate and predict the climate of the future, we need to be able to account for the processes that control the climate. One hundred million years ago, much of North America was arid and hot, with giant sand dunes common across the continent's interior. Six hundred and fifty million years ago it appears that the same land mass—along with the rest of the globe—was covered in a layer of snow and ice. What drives these enormous changes through Earth's history? If we understand these fundamental processes we can explain why the climate of today may also change.

In discussing climate in this chapter, we will be using degrees Celsius (°C) as the unit of temperature measurement.

---

[2]This content is available online at <http://legacy.cnx.org/content/m38482/1.18/>.

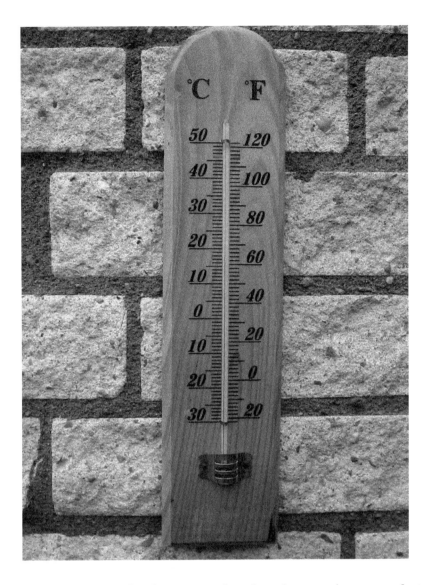

Figure 3.1: A Thermometer This thermometer shows how the two scales compare for typical atmospheric temperatures. A change of one degree Celsius (1 °C) is equivalent to a change of one and four fifths degrees Fahrenheit (1.8 °F). *Source: Michiel1972 at nl.wikipedia.*[3]

The Celsius scale is the standard international unit for temperature that scientists use when discussing the climate. In the Celsius scale, water freezes at 0 °C and boils at 100 °C. A comfortable room might be heated to 20 °C (which is equivalent to 68 °F). Temperatures can be converted from the Celsius scale to the Fahrenheit scale with the following equation:

$$°F = \frac{9}{5}°C + 32 \tag{3.1}$$

Weather describes the short term state of the atmosphere. This includes such conditions as wind, air pressure, precipitation, humidity and temperature. **Climate** describes the typical, or average, atmospheric

---

[3]http://en.wikipedia.org/wiki/File:Thermometer.jpg

conditions. Weather and climate are different as the short term state is always changing but the long-term average is not. On The 1ˢᵗ of January, 2011, Chicago recorded a high temperature of 6 °C; this is a measure of the weather. Measurements of climate include the averages of the daily, monthly, and yearly weather patterns, the seasons, and even a description of how often extraordinary events, such as hurricanes, occur. So if we consider the average Chicago high temperature for the 1ˢᵗ of January (a colder 0.5 °C) or the average high temperature for the entire year (a warmer 14.5 °C) we are comparing the city's weather with its climate. The **climate** is the average of the weather.

3.2.3 Insolation, Albedo and Greenhouse Gases

What controls the climate? The average temperature of the Earth is about 15 °C (which is the yearly average temperature for the city of San Francisco), so most of the Earth's water is in a liquid state. The average temperature of Mars is about -55 °C (about the same as the average winter temperature of the South Pole), so all of the water on the Martian surface is frozen. This is a big difference! One reason Earth is so much hotter than Mars is that Earth is closer to the Sun. Mars receives less than half as much energy from the Sun per unit area as Earth does. This difference in **insolation**, which is the measure of the amount of solar radiation falling on a surface, is a very important factor in determining the climate of the Earth.

On Earth, we notice the effects of varying insolation on our climate. Sunlight falls most directly on the equator, and only obliquely (at an angle) on the poles. This means that the sunlight is more concentrated at the equator. As shown in Figure **Insolation Angle** (Figure 3.2), the same amount of sunlight covers twice as much area when it strikes a surface at an angle of 30° compared to when it strikes a surface directly: the same energy is spread more thinly, weakening its ability to warm the Earth.

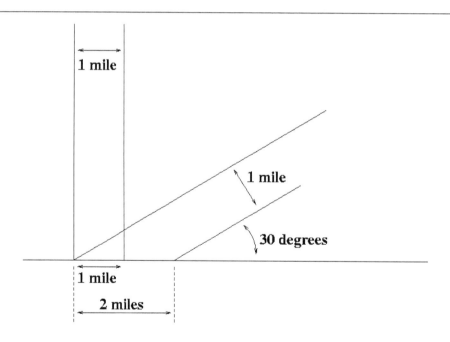

Figure 3.2: Insolation Angle Insolation is the effect of incidence angle on sunlight intensity. Note that the same amount of sunlight is spread out over twice the area when it strikes the surface at a 30-degree angle. *Source: Wikipedia*[4]

---

[4]http://en.wikipedia.org/wiki/File:Seasons.too.png

As a consequence, the tropics receive about twice the insolation as the area inside the Arctic Circle – see Figure **Insolation Comparison** (Figure 3.3). This difference in energy explains why the equator has a hot climate and the poles have a cold climate. Differences in insolation also explain the existence of seasons. The Earth's axis is tilted at 23° compared to its orbit, and so over the course of the year each hemisphere alternates between directly facing the Sun and obliquely facing the Sun. When the Northern hemisphere is most directly facing the Sun (the months of May, June and July) insolation is thus higher, and the climate is warmer. This variation in insolation explains why summer and winter occur (we get less energy from the Sun in winter then we do in summer), and why the timing of the seasons is opposite in the Southern and Northern hemispheres.

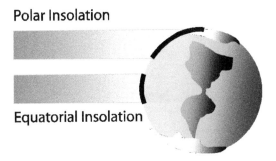

Figure 3.3: Insolation Comparison A cartoon of how latitude is important in determining the amount of insolation. The same amount of sunlight (yellow bars) is spread out over twice the planet's surface area when the rays strike the Earth at an angle (compare the length of the dark lines at the equator and at the poles). *Source: Jonathan H. Tomkin.*[5]

Figure **Insolation** (Figure 3.4) shows both the equatorial and seasonal impacts of insolation. High levels of insolation are shown in warm colors (red and pink) and low levels of insolation are shown in cold colors (blue). Notice that in January (top map) the maximum levels of insolation are in the Southern Hemisphere, as this is when the Southern Hemisphere is most directly facing the sun. The Arctic receives very little insolation at this time of year, as it experiences its long polar night. The reverse is true in April (bottom map).

[5]http://cnx.org/member_profile/tomkin

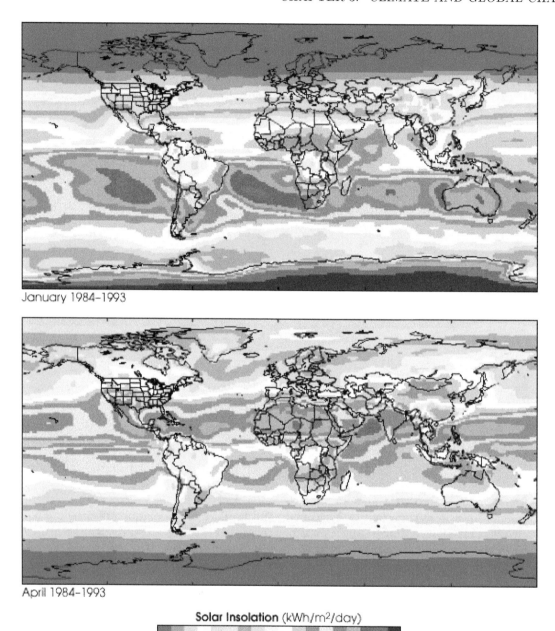

January 1984–1993

April 1984–1993

Solar Insolation (kWh/m²/day)

0   >8.5

Figure 3.4: Insolation Average insolation over ten years for the months of January (top) and April (bottom). *Source: Roberta DiPasquale, Surface Meteorology and Solar Energy Project, NASA Langley Research Center, and the ISCCP Project. Courtesy of NASA's Earth Observatory.*[6]

The equator always receives plenty of sunlight, however, and has a much higher average temperature as a consequence; compare the average temperature of the equator with that of the poles in Figure **Annual Mean Temperature** (Figure 3.5)

---

[6]http://earthobservatory.nasa.gov/IOTD/view.php?id=1355

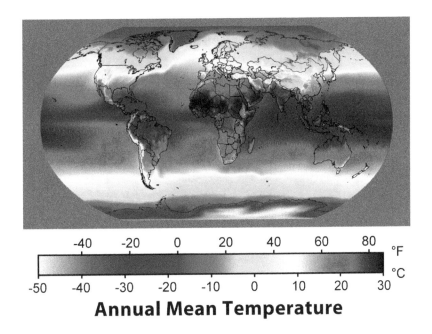

Annual Mean Temperature

Figure 3.5: Annual Mean Temperature The Earth's average annual temperature. *Source: Robert A. Rohde for Global Warming Art.*[7]

The level of insolation affecting Earth depends on the amount of light (or **solar radiation**) emitted by the Sun. Over the current geologic period, this is very slowly changing—solar radiation is increasing at a rate of around 10% every billion years. This change is much too slow to be noticeable to humans. The sun also goes through an 11-year solar cycle, in which the amount of solar radiation increases and decreases. At the solar cycle peak, the total solar radiation is about 0.1% higher than it is at the trough.

The Earth's orbit is not perfectly circular, so sometimes the Earth is closer to or further from the Sun than it is on average. This also changes the amount of insolation, as the closer the Earth is to the Sun the more concentrated the solar radiation. As we shall see in the next section, these orbital variations have made a big difference in conditions on the Earth during the period in which humans have inhabited it.

In addition to considering how much energy enters the Earth system via insolation, we also need to consider how much energy leaves. The climate of the Earth is controlled by the Earth's energy balance, which is the movement of energy into and out of the Earth system. Energy flows into the Earth from the Sun and flows out when it is radiated into space. The Earth's energy balance is determined by the amount of sunlight that shines on the Earth (the insolation) and the characteristics of the Earth's surface and atmosphere that act to reflect, circulate and re-radiate this energy. The more energy in the system the higher the temperature, so either increasing the amount of energy arriving or decreasing the rate at which it leaves would make the climate hotter.

One way to change how quickly energy exits the Earth system is to change the reflectivity of the surface. Compare the difference in dark surface of tilled soil (Figure **Reflectivity of Earth's Surface (a)** (Figure 3.6(a))) with the blinding brightness of snow-covered ice (Figure **Reflectivity of Earth's Surface (b)** (Figure 3.6(b))).

---

[7]http://en.wikipedia.org/wiki/File:Annual_Average_Temperature_Map.jpg

(a)

(b)

Figure 3.6: Reflectivity of Earth's Surface (a) Tilled soil. *Source: Tim Hallam.*[8] (b) The snow surface at Dome C Station, Antarctica *Source: Stephen Hudson*[9]

The dark soil is absorbing the sun's rays and in so doing is heating the Earth surface, while the brilliant snow is reflecting the sunlight back into space. **Albedo** is a measure of how reflective a surface is. The higher the albedo the more reflective the material: a perfectly black surface has zero albedo, while a perfectly white surface has an albedo of 1 - it reflects 100% of the incident light. If a planet has a high albedo, much of the radiation from the Sun is reflected back into space, lowering the average temperature. Today, Earth has an average albedo of just over 30%, but this value depends on how much cloud cover there is and what covers the surface. Covering soil with grass increases the amount of light reflected from 17% to 25%, while adding a layer of fresh snow can increase the amount reflected to over 80%. Figure **Surface of Earth with Cloud Cover Removed** (Figure 3.7) is a composite photograph of the Earth with the cloud cover removed. As you can see, forests and oceans are dark (low albedo) while snow and deserts are bright (high albedo).

---

[8]http://en.wikipedia.org/wiki/File:Tilled_soil_looking_towards_Admiralty_Point_-_geograph.org.uk_-_326568.jpg
[9]http://en.wikipedia.org/wiki/File:AntarcticaDomeCSnow.jpg

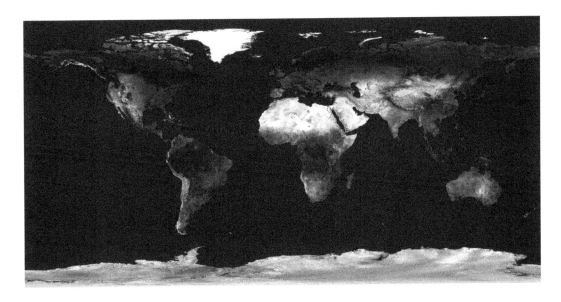

Figure 3.7: Surface of Earth with Cloud Cover Removed The surface of the Earth with cloud cover removed. The poles and deserts are much brighter than the oceans and forests. *Source: NASA Goddard Space Flight Center Image by Reto Stöckli. Courtesy of NASA's Earth Observatory.*[10]

Changes in albedo can create a **positive feedback** that reinforces a change in the climate. A positive feedback is a process which amplifies the effect of an initial change. If the climate cools, (the initial change), snow covers more of the surface of the land, and sea-ice covers more of the oceans. Because snow has a higher albedo than bare ground, and ice has a higher albedo than water, this initial cooling increases the amount of sunlight that is reflected back into space, cooling the Earth further (the amplification, or positive feedback). Compare the brightness of Figure **Surface of Earth with Cloud Cover Removed** (Figure 3.7) with a similar photo montage from February (Figure **Surface of the Earth in February with Cloud Cover Removed** (Figure 3.8)): the extra snow has increased the Earth's albedo. Imagine what would happen if the Earth produced even more snow and ice as a result of this further cooling. The Earth would then reflect more sunlight into space, cooling the planet further and producing yet more snow. If such a loop continued for long enough, this process could result in the entire Earth being covered in ice! Such a feedback loop is known as the **Snowball Earth** hypothesis, and scientists have found much supporting geological evidence. The most recent period in Earth's history when this could have occurred was around 650 Million years ago. Positive feedbacks are often described as "runaway" processes; once they are begun they continue without stopping.

---

[10]http://visibleearth.nasa.gov/view_rec.php?id=2433

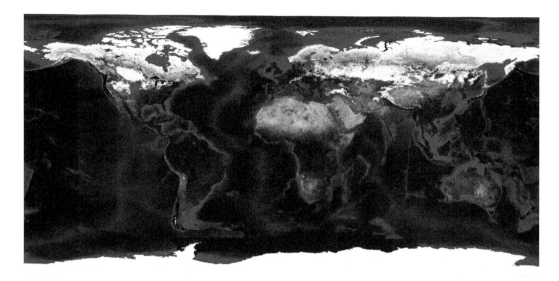

Figure 3.8: Surface of the Earth in February with Cloud Cover Removed This image shows the surface of the Earth in February (the Northern Hemisphere winter) with cloud cover removed. The seasonal snow cover is brighter (and so has a higher albedo) than the land surface it covers. *Source: NASA Goddard Space Flight Center Image by Reto Stöckli. Courtesy of NASA's Earth Observatory*[11]

Albedo does not explain everything, however. The Earth and the Moon both receive the same amount of insolation. Although the Moon is only slightly more reflective than the Earth, it is much colder. The average temperature on Earth is 15 °C, while the Moon's average temperature is -23 °C. Why the difference? A planet's energy balance is also regulated by its atmosphere. A thick atmosphere can act to trap the energy from sunlight, preventing it from escaping directly into space. Earth has an atmosphere while the Moon does not. If the Earth did not have an atmosphere, it would have an average temperature of -18 °C; slightly warmer than the Moon since it has a lower albedo.

How does the atmosphere trap the energy from the Sun? Shouldn't the Earth's atmosphere reflect as much incoming radiation as it traps? It is true the atmosphere reflects incoming solar radiation—in fact, only around half the insolation that strikes the top of the atmosphere reaches the Earth's surface. The reason an atmosphere generally acts to warm a planet is that the nature of light radiation changes as it reaches the planet's surface. Atmospheres trap more light than they reflect.

Humans see the Earth's atmosphere as largely transparent; that is, we can see a long way in air. This is because we see light in the **visible spectrum**, which is the light radiation in the range of wavelengths the human eye is able to perceive, and visible light is able to travel a long way through the Earth's atmosphere before it is absorbed. Light is also transmitted in wavelengths we can't see, such as in the **infrared spectrum**, which is sometimes referred to as infrared light, heat, or thermal radiation. Compared to visible light, infrared light cannot travel very far in the Earth's atmosphere before it is absorbed. Solar radiation striking the Earth is largely in the visible part of the spectrum. The surface of the Earth absorbs this energy and re-radiates it largely in the infrared part of the spectrum. This means that solar radiation enters the Earth in the form of visible light, unhindered, but tries to leave in the form of infrared light, which is trapped. Thicker atmospheres keep this infrared radiation trapped for longer, and so warm the Earth—just like an extra blanket makes you warmer in bed.

This effect is shown in Figure **Earth Atmosphere Cartoon** (Figure 3.9). The visible light radiation enters the atmosphere, and quickly exits as infrared radiation if there is no atmosphere (top Earth). With

---

[11]http://visibleearth.nasa.gov/view_rec.php?id=7101

our atmosphere (the middle Earth), visible light enters unhindered but the infrared light is partially reflected back to the surface, increasing the amount of energy and thus the temperature at the Earth's surface. If the atmosphere is made thicker (bottom Earth) the infrared radiation is trapped for longer, further warming the planet's surface.

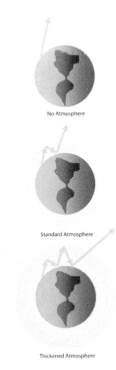

Figure 3.9: Earth Atmosphere Cartoon A cartoon of the greenhouse effect. (Top) Visible light radiation emitted by the sun (yellow arrows) strikes the Earth and reflects as infrared radiation (orange arrow); (middle) an atmosphere reflects some of the infrared radiation back toward the planet; (bottom) a thickened atmosphere reflects greater amounts of infrared radiation. *Source: Jonathan H. Tomkin.*[12]

The way the atmosphere acts to trap light radiation is referred to as the **greenhouse effect**, and the gases that prevent the thermal radiation from exiting the Earth system are described as **greenhouse gases**. The four most important greenhouse gases in the Earth's atmosphere are water vapor, carbon dioxide, methane, and ozone. All four are found naturally in the Earth's atmosphere. As we will discuss in Section 4.4, however, human activities are adding to the natural amount of carbon dioxide and methane, and even adding new greenhouse gases, such as chlorofluorocarbon (CFC).

3.2.4 Earth's Changing Atmosphere

The composition of Earth's atmosphere has changed over geologic time. The atmosphere has largely come from volcanic venting of gas from Earth's interior (see Figure **Volcanic Outgassing** (Figure 3.10)), but biology has also made important changes by producing oxygen and removing carbon dioxide. Greenhouse gases currently make up only a small fraction of the Earth's atmosphere—99% of air consists of nitrogen and oxygen molecules.

---

[12]http://cnx.org/member_profile/tomkin

Figure 3.10: Volcanic Outgassing The Mt. Bromo volcano in Indonesia emitting gas into the atmosphere. *Source: Jan-Pieter Nap, taken on July 11, 2004.*[13]

While volcanoes can warm the Earth by adding carbon dioxide to the atmosphere, which produces a greenhouse effect, they can also cool the Earth by injecting ash and sulfur into the atmosphere. These additions raise the albedo of the atmosphere, allowing less sunlight to reach the surface of the Earth. The effect lasts until the particles settle out of the atmosphere, typically within a few years. Volcanic eruptions have impacted human societies throughout history; the Mt. Tambora eruption in 1815 cooled the Earth so much that snow fell during June in New England, and the more recent Mt. Pinatubo eruption in 1991 (see Figure **Mt. Pinatubo Explosion** (Figure 3.11)) ejected so much sulfuric acid into the atmosphere that global temperatures were lowered by about 0.5 °C in the following year.

[13]http://en.wikipedia.org/wiki/File:Mahameru-volcano.jpeg

Figure 3.11: Mt. Pinatubo Explosion The 1991 eruption of Mt. Pinatubo. *Source: U.S. Geological Survey photograph, by Richard P. Hoblitt.*[14]

Evidence from the geologic past indicates that similar events have caused mass extinctions wherein a significant fraction of all species on Earth were wiped out in a relatively short amount of time. Sustained outgassing from continuous volcanic eruptions is thought to have produced so much ash and aerosols that light sufficient to support photosynthesis in plants was unable to penetrate the atmosphere, causing the food chain to collapse. The ash particles produced by extended eruptions would also have increased the Earth's albedo, making conditions inhospitably cool for plants and animals adapted to a warmer environment.

[14]http://en.wikipedia.org/wiki/File:Pinatubo91eruption_clark_air_base.jpg

Asteroid impacts can also cause the climate to suddenly cool. When large asteroids strike the Earth, ash is ejected into the atmosphere, which increases albedo in the same way as volcanic eruptions. Everyday clouds (made up of water droplets) both cool and warm the Earth. They can cool the Earth by increasing the planet's albedo, reflecting sunlight into space before it reaches the surface. Clouds can also warm the Earth, by reflecting infrared radiation emitted by the surface back towards the planet. Different types of clouds, and different conditions, determine which effect predominates. On a hot summer's day, for example, clouds cool us by shielding us from the sun's rays, but on a winter's night a layer of cloud can act as a warming blanket.

The composition of the Earth's atmosphere is not fixed; greenhouse gases can be added to and removed from the atmosphere over time. For example, carbon dioxide is added by volcanoes and the decay or burning of organic matter. It is removed by photosynthesis in plants, when it is dissolved in the oceans and when carbonate sediments (a type of rock) are produced. Over geologic time, these processes have significantly reduced the proportion of carbon dioxide in the atmosphere. Atmospheric carbon dioxide levels just prior to the industrial revolution are thought to have been only one twentieth of those of 500 million years ago. Natural processes also remove carbon dioxide added by human activity, but only very slowly. It is estimated that it would take the Earth around a thousand years to naturally remove most of the carbon dioxide released by the industrial consumption of fossil fuels up to the present.

Greenhouse gases other than carbon dioxide are shorter-lived: methane is removed from the atmosphere in around a decade, and chlorofluorocarbons break down within a century. Individual water molecules spend only a few days at a time in the atmosphere, but unlike the other greenhouse gases, the total amount of water vapor in the atmosphere remains constant. Water evaporated from the oceans replaces water lost by condensation and precipitation.

Changing the composition of the Earth's atmosphere also changes the climate. Do you remember the Snowball Earth (p. 57) — how increasing ice cover also increased the Earth's albedo, eventually covering the entire planet in ice and snow? Today's climate is temperate—so we must have escaped this frozen trap. But how? The leading hypothesis is that the composition of the Earth's atmosphere changed, with volcanoes slowly adding more and more carbon dioxide to it. Without access to the oceans, plants, or surface rocks, this carbon dioxide was not removed from the atmosphere and so continued to build up over millions of years. Eventually, the additional warming caused by the increase in greenhouse gases overcame the cooling caused by the snow's high albedo, and temperatures rose enough to melt the ice, freeing the Earth.

For most of Earth's history, carbon dioxide concentrations have been higher than they are today. As a consequence, past climates have often been very warm. During the late stage of the dinosaur era (the **Cretaceous**, a period that lasted between 65 and 145 million years ago), carbon dioxide levels were about 5 times higher than they are today, and the average global temperatures were more than 10 °C higher than today's. There were no large ice sheets, and dinosaur fossils from this period have been found as far north as Alaska. These animals would not survive the cold conditions found in the arctic today. Further south, fossil crocodiles from 60 million years ago have been found in North Dakota. The modern average winter temperature in North Dakota is around -10 °C –but being cold-blooded, crocodiles are most at home when the air temperature is around 30 °C! The climate was warmer in the past when the amount of carbon dioxide was higher.

3.2.5 Review Questions

Question 3.2.1

The text describes how the high albedo of snow acts as a positive feedback—if the Earth is made cooler, the highly reflective snow can act to further cool the Earth. Today, part of the Earth is covered with snow and ice. Can you describe a mechanism by which warmer temperatures would also produce a positive feedback—this time heating the Earth further—through a similar albedo mechanism?

Question 3.2.2

Mars is colder than the Earth. Venus, on the other hand, is much hotter, with average surface temperatures of around 450 °C. Venus is closer to the Sun than the Earth is, and so receives about twice as much solar radiation. Venus's atmosphere is also different than Earth's, as it is much thicker and mainly consists of carbon dioxide. Using the terms **insolation** and **greenhouse gases**, can you suggest reasons why Venus is so hot?

Question 3.2.3

Oxygen makes up over 20% of Earth's atmosphere, while carbon dioxide makes up less than 0.04%. Oxygen is largely transparent to both visible and infrared light. Explain why carbon dioxide is a more important greenhouse gas in the Earth's atmosphere than oxygen, even though there is much more oxygen than carbon dioxide.

Question 3.2.4

Figure Insolation (Figure 3.4) shows the insolation at the surface of the Earth. The Earth is spherical, so we would expect the values to be the same for places of the same latitude. But notice that this is not true – compare, for example, central Africa with the Atlantic Ocean at the same latitude. What feature of the atmosphere might explain this variation, and why?

3.2.6 Resources

The National Aeronautical and Space Administration (NASA) Earth Observatory website has an array of climate resources. For a more in-depth discussion of Earth's energy budget, go to http://earthobservatory.nasa.gov/Features/EnergyBalance/[15]

Are you interested in finding more about the controversial Snowball Earth hypothesis? The National Science foundation and Harvard University have set up a website with more about the hypothesis and the evidence. Go to http://www.snowballearth.org/[16]

3.3 Milankovitch Cycles and the Climate of the Quaternary[17]

3.3.1 Learning Objectives

After reading this module, students should be able to

- describe the changing climate of the Quaternary
- explain why Milankovitch cycles explain the variations of climate over the Quaternary, in terms of the similar periods of orbital variations and glacial cycles
- explain how the glacier/climate system is linked via albedo feedbacks
- describe how sediment and ice cores provide information about past climates
- use the mechanisms that cause stable isotope fractionation to predict the impact of changing climate on stable isotope records

3.3.2 Introduction

In Module **Climate Processes; External and Internal Controls** (Section 3.2) we saw the major drivers of the climate—the energy that comes from the Sun (insolation) and the properties of the planet that determine how long that energy stays in the Earth system (albedo, greenhouse gases). In this section, we will look at the recent natural changes in Earth's climate, and we will use these drivers to understand why the climate has changed.

---

[15]http://earthobservatory.nasa.gov/Features/EnergyBalance/

[16]http://www.snowballearth.org/

[17]This content is available online at <http://legacy.cnx.org/content/m38572/1.10/>.

The most recent period of Earth's geologic history—spanning the last 2.6 million years—is known as the **Quaternary period**. This is an important period for us because it encompasses the entire period over which humans have existed—our species evolved about 200,000 years ago. We will examine how the climate has changed over this period in detail. By understanding recent natural processes of climate change, we will be able to better understand why scientists attribute the currently observed changes in global climate as being the result of human activity.

3.3.3 Quaternary Climate — Information From Ice Cores

How do we know about the Quaternary climate? After all, most of the period predates human existence, and we have only been recording the conditions of climate for a few centuries. Scientists are able to make informed judgments about the climates of the deep past by using **proxy data**. Proxy data is information about the climate that accumulates through natural phenomena. In the previous module, for example, we discussed how 60-million-year-old crocodile fossils have been found in North Dakota. This gives us indirect information about the climate of the period—that the climate of the region was warmer than it is today. Although not as precise as climate data recorded by instruments (such as thermometers), proxy data has been recovered from a diverse array of natural sources, and provides a surprisingly precise picture of climate change through deep time.

One highly detailed record of past climate conditions has been recovered from the great **ice sheets** of Greenland and Antarctica. These ice sheets are built by snow falling on the ice surface and being covered by subsequent snowfalls. The compressed snow is transformed into ice. It is so cold in these polar locations that the ice doesn't melt even in the summers, so the ice is able to build up over hundreds of thousands of years. Because the ice at lower depths was produced by progressively earlier snowfalls, the age of the ice increases with depth, and the youngest ice is at the surface. The Antarctic ice sheet is up to three miles thick. It takes a long time to build up this much ice, and the oldest ice found at the bottom of the Antarctica ice sheet is around 800,000 years old.

Scientists drill into these ice sheets to extract *ice cores*, which record information about past climates. Figure **Ice Cores** (Figure 3.12) shows what these cores look like when they are cut open. Like tree rings, ice cores indicate years of growth. Note how the middle core (which required over a mile of drilling to extract!) has distinct layers—this is because the seasons leave an imprint in the layers of snow. Scientists can use this imprint to help calculate the age of the ice at different depths, although the task becomes more difficult the deeper the core sample, since the ice layers become more compressed. The ice records several different types of climate information: the temperature of the core, the properties of the water that make up the ice, trapped dust, and tiny entombed bubbles of ancient atmosphere.

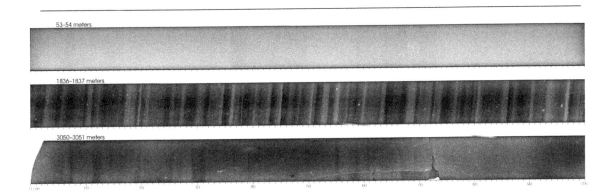

Figure 3.12: Ice Cores Three different sections of an ice core. The seasonal layers are most clear in the middle section (note the dark and light bands). The deepest section (bottom core) is taken from almost two miles down and is colored brown by rocky debris from the ground under the ice. *Source: National Ice Core Laboratory*[18]

The water molecules that make up the ice record information about the temperature of the atmosphere. Each water molecule is made up of two hydrogen atoms and one oxygen atom (and so has the chemical name H_2O). Not all oxygen atoms are the same however; some are "light" and some are "heavy". These different types of oxygen are called **isotopes**, which are atoms that have same number of protons but different numbers of neutrons. The heavy isotope of oxygen (oxygen-18, or ^{18}O) is more than 10% heavier than the light isotope (oxygen-16 or ^{16}O). This means that some water molecules weigh more than others. This is important because lighter water molecules are more easily evaporated from the ocean, and once in the atmosphere, heavier water molecules are more likely to condense and fall as precipitation. As we can see from Figure **Oxygen Schematic** (Figure 3.13), the water in the ice sheets is lighter (has a higher proportion of ^{16}O relative to ^{18}O) than the water in the oceans.

The process of differentiation between heavy and light water molecules is temperature dependent. If the atmosphere is warm, there is more energy available to evaporate and hold the heavier ^{18}O water in the atmosphere, so the snow that falls on the polar ice sheets is relatively higher in ^{18}O. When the atmosphere is cold, the amount of energy is less, and so less ^{18}O makes it to the poles to be turned into glacial ice. We can compare the amount of ^{18}O in different parts of the ice core to see how the atmosphere's temperature—the climate—has changed.

---

[18]http://nicl.usgs.gov/

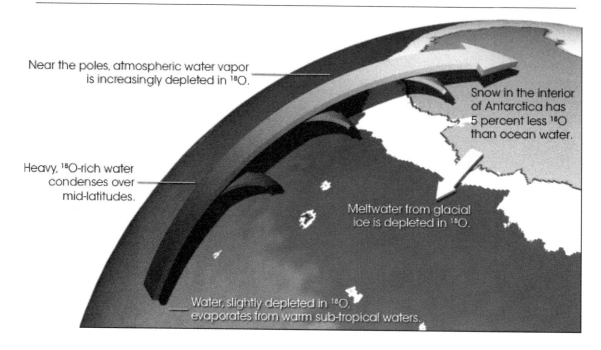

Figure 3.13: Oxygen Schematic Water becomes lighter as it travels toward the poles. The heavy (18O) water drops out of the atmosphere (as rain or snow) before reaching the ice sheet. This means that the snow that forms the glacial ice is lighter than the ocean water (has more 16O than 18O, compared to ocean water). *Source: Robert Simmon, NASA GSFC, NASA Earth Observatory*[19]

Figure **Ice Age Temperature** (Figure 3.14) shows what this record looks like over the last 400,000 years. The blue and green lines depict two different Antarctic ice cores (taken from ice about 350 miles apart) and the variations in oxygen isotopes are converted into temperature changes. The y-axis shows temperature change; today's climate is at zero—the dashed line. Notice that the Earth's climate has not been stable! Sometimes the temperature is higher than it is today—the blue and green lines are higher than the dashed about 120,000 years ago, for example. Most of the time the climate is much colder than today's, however: the most common value is around -6 °C (-13 °F). On average, the earth's temperature between 25,000 and 100,000 years ago was about 6 °C lower than it is today. These changes can be double-checked by measuring the temperature of the ice in the cores directly. Ice that is 30,000 years old is indeed colder than the ice made today, just as the isotope data predicts.

[19]http://earthobservatory.nasa.gov/Features/Paleoclimatology_OxygenBalance/oxygen_balance.php

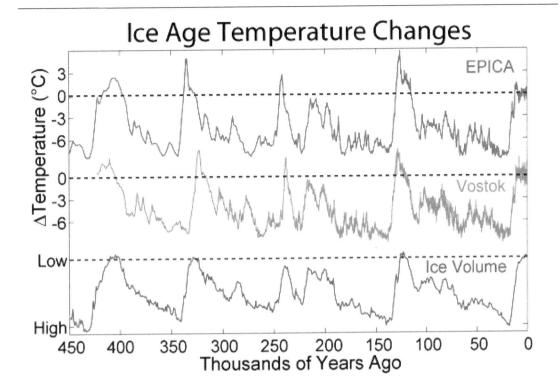

Figure 3.14: Ice Age Temperature The blue and green lines depict two different Antarctic ice cores (taken from ice about 350 miles apart) and the variations in oxygen isotopes are converted into temperature changes. The red line depicts global ice volume. The y-axis shows temperature change; today's climate is at zero – the dashed line. *Source: Robert A. Rohde*[20]

---

[20]http://en.wikipedia.org/wiki/User:Dragons_flight

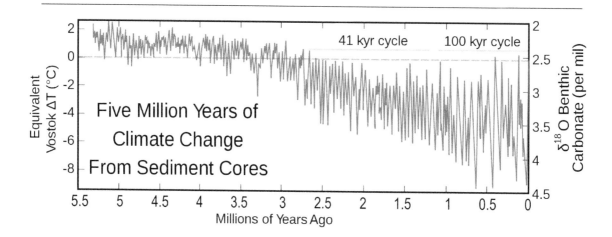

Figure 3.15: Five Myr Climate Change A comparison of the age of sediment (x-axis) and the change in temperature over time (left y-axis) as derived from oxygen isotope ratios (right y-axis). The dashed line shows today's climate. Note that the climate is cooling over the last few million years, but it is highly variable. In the last one million years the climate alternates between warm and cool conditions on a 100,000-year time scale ("100 kyr cycle"), before this it alternated on a 41,000 year cycle. Both these period lengths are the same as Milankovitch cycles. These cores suggest that today's temperature is higher than almost all of that of the Quaternary (the last 2.6 Million years). *Source: Jo Weber*[21]

The changes in climate recorded in ice sheets are thought to be worldwide. The same climate changes observed in Antarctica are also found in cores taken from Greenland, which is on the other side of the Earth. Isotope data can also be taken from sediment cored from the ocean floor—all over the planet—and these cores also show the same changes in climate, alternating between cold and warm. Because ocean sediment is deposited over millions of years, the sediment can give an indication of the climate across the whole of the Quaternary and beyond. Figure **Five Myr Climate Change** (Figure 3.15) shows how temperature has changed over time (blue line), compared with today (dashed line). The temperature has, on average, gotten colder over the Quaternary, but it also appears to oscillate between warm and cold periods. We'll investigate these periodic changes in the next section of this chapter.

As falling snow accumulates on the ground, tiny bubbles of air become trapped in it. These bubbles are retained as the snow transforms to ice, and constitute tiny samples of the ancient atmosphere that can be analyzed to find out if the changes in temperature (as recorded in the oxygen isotopes) are related to changes in the atmosphere. The temperature recorded by the isotopes in the ice is directly related to the amount of carbon dioxide in the trapped air (Figure **Vostok Petit Data** (Figure 3.16)): the times with higher carbon dioxide are also times of high temperature.

Falling snow also captures and entombs atmospheric dust, which is topsoil born aloft by the wind, and which is especially prevalent during droughts. The fact that more dust occurs in the ice accumulated during cold periods suggests that the glacial climate was dry, as well as cold.

---

[21]http://en.wikipedia.org/wiki/File:Five_Myr_Climate_Change.svg

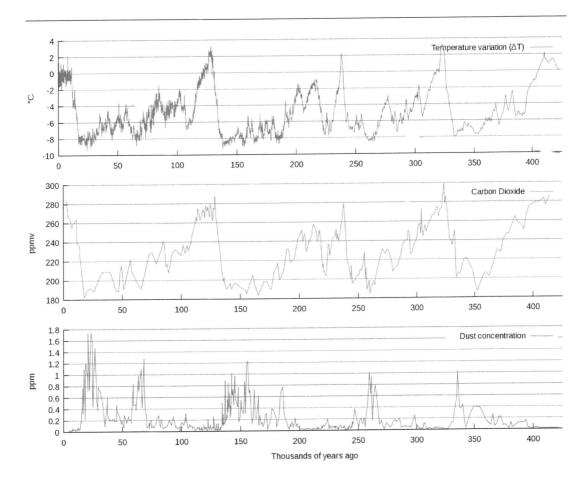

Figure 3.16: Vostok Petit Data These graphs depict how changes in temperature—inferred from changes in isotope ratios (blue line)–correspond to changes in atmospheric carbon dioxide (green line) and dust (red line) over the last 400,000 years as recorded in an ice core extracted from Antarctica. Carbon dioxide varies directly with temperature – the warmer the climate the higher the carbon dioxide level. Atmospheric dust is highest during the coolest periods (such as 25,000 and 150,000 years ago). *Source: William M. Connolley produced figure using data from the National Oceanic and Atmospheric Administration, U.S. Department of Commerce, Paleoclimatology branch, Vostok Ice Core Data.*[22]

---

[22]http://commons.wikimedia.org/wiki/File:Vostok-ice-core-petit.png

3.3.4 Quaternary Climate — Cycling Between Glacials and Interglacials

Figure 3.17: Ice Age Earth An artist's impression of the Earth during an ice age. Note that the Northern parts of North America and Europe (including Canada and Scandinavia) are entirely covered by ice-sheets. *Source: Ittiz*[23]

During the Quaternary, the Earth has cycled between **glacial periods** (sometimes referred to as "ice ages") and **interglacial periods**. The ice was at its most recent extreme around 20,000 years ago in a period known as the **Last Glacial Maximum**, or LGM. As we can see from the ice core record, the Quaternary climate is usually cold (see Figure **Ice Age Temperature** (Figure 3.14)), with long periods of cold punctuated with shorter (10,000 year long, or so) periods of warmer conditions, like those we experience today. In many ways, our current climate is exceptional—for most of human existence, the Earth has been a much colder place.

What was the Earth like during these glacial periods? Almost all the world was cold; average temperatures were around 6 °C (-13 °F) colder than today. Such conditions allow ice sheets to grow—much of North America, Asia and Europe were covered under mile-thick ice (see Figure **Ice Age Earth** (Figure 3.17)). Because this ice was made of water that was once in the oceans, sea levels were much lower. At the LGM, sea level was about 120 meters (or about 400 feet) lower than it is today. As the seas retreated, the continents grew larger, creating land bridges that joined Asia with North America, Britain with Europe, and Australia with Papua New Guinea.

[23]http://en.wikipedia.org/wiki/File:IceAgeEarth.jpg

During glacial periods the climate was also much drier, as evidenced by the increase in atmospheric dust (Figure **Vostok Petit Data** (Figure 3.16)). The lands at and near the poles were covered with ice, and dry grasslands occupied areas where temperate forests occur today. Deserts were much larger than they are now, and tropical rainforests, having less water and less warmth, were small. The animals and plants of glacial periods were different in their distribution than they are today, as they were adapted to these different conditions. Fossils of Mastodons (Figure **Knight Mastodon** (Figure 3.18)) have been found from all across what is now the United States, including from Florida, which currently enjoys a subtropical climate.

Figure 3.18: Knight Mastodon An artist's impression of a Mastodon, an elephant-like mammal with a thick wooly coat. Mastodon fossils dating from past glacial periods have been found across North America—from Florida to Alaska. *Source: Charles R. Knight*[24]

During glacial periods humans would have been unable to occupy the globe as they do today because all landmasses experienced different climactic conditions. Some countries of the present could not exist, as they would be almost completely covered by ice. As examples, look for Canada, Iceland and The United Kingdom in Figure **800pn Northern Icesheet** (Figure 3.20).

3.3.5 Milankovitch Cycles

Why has the Earth cycled through hot and cold climates throughout the Quaternary? As we learned in the previous module, the Earth's climate is controlled by several different factors—insolation, greenhouse gases, and albedo are all important. Scientists believe that changes in insolation are responsible for these climate swings, and the insolation varies as a result of wobbles in the Earth's orbit.

The Earth's orbit is not fixed – it changes regularly over time. These periodic changes in Earth's orbit named are referred to as **Milankovitch Cycles**, and are illustrated in Figure **Milankovitch Cycles** (Figure 3.19). Changes in the Earth's orbit alter the pattern of insolation that the Earth receives. There are three principle ways in which the Earth's orbit varies:

---

[24]http://en.wikipedia.org/wiki/File:Knight_Mastodon.jpg

Eccentricity (or *Orbital shape*). The Earth's orbit is not perfectly circular, but instead follows an ellipse. This means that the Earth is, through the course of the year, sometimes closer and sometimes further away from the Sun. Currently, the Earth is closest to the Sun in early January, and furthest from the Sun in Early July. This changes the amount of insolation by a few percent, so Northern Hemisphere seasons are slightly milder than they would be if the orbital was circular (cooler summers and warmer winters). The orbital shape changes over time: the Earth moves between being nearly circular and being mildly elliptical. There are two main periods over which this change occurs, one takes around 100,000 years (this is the time over which the orbit goes from being circular, to elliptic, and back to circular), another takes around 400,000 years.

2. **Axial Tilt** (or **Obliquity**). The Earth axis spins at an angle to its orbit around the Sun – currently this angle is 23.5 degrees (this angle is known as the *axial tilt*). This difference in orbit creates the seasons (as each hemisphere takes turns being tilted towards and away from the Sun over the course of the year). If the axis of spin lined up with the direction of the Earth's orbit (so that the tilt angle was zero) there would be no seasons! This axial tilt also changes over time, varying between 22.1 and 24.5 degrees. The larger the angle, the larger the temperature difference between summer and winter. It takes about 41,000 year for the axial tilt to change from one extreme to the other, and back again. Currently, the axial tilt is midway between the two extremes and is decreasing—which will make the seasons weaker (cooler summers and warmer winters) over the next 20,000 years.

3. **Axial Precession.** The direction of Earth's axis of rotation also changes over time relative to the stars. Currently, the North Pole points towards the star Polaris, but the axis of rotation cycles between pointing to that star and the star Vega. This impacts the Earth's climate as it determines when the seasons occur in Earth's orbit. When the axis is pointing at Vega, the Northern Hemisphere's peak summer is in January, not July. If this were true today, it would mean that the Northern Hemisphere would experience more extreme seasons, because January is when the Earth is closest to the Sun (as discussed above in eccentricity). This cycle takes around 20,000 years to complete.

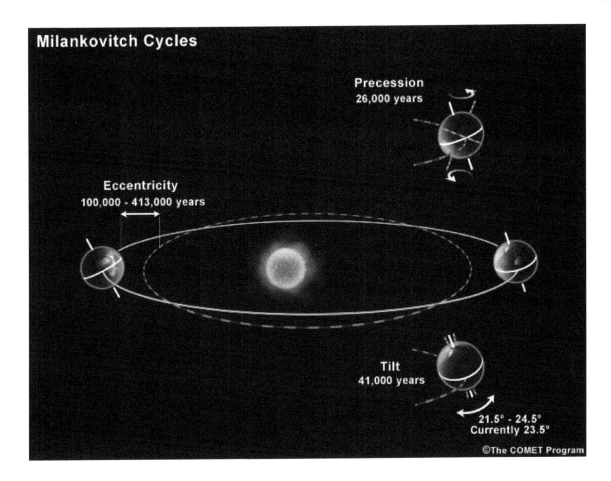

Figure 3.19: Milankovitch Cycles Illustration of the three variables in Earth's orbit, with periods of variation marked. *Source: COMET® at the University Corporation for Atmospheric Research (UCAR) pursuant to a Cooperative Agreements with the National Oceanic and Atmospheric Administration, U.S. Department of Commerce. ©1997-2009 University Corporation for Atmospheric Research. All Rights Reserved.*[25]

The three cycles described above have different periods, all of which are long by human standards: 20,000, 40,000, 100,000 and 400,000 years. If we look at the temperature data from ice and sediment cores, we see that these periods are reflected in Earth's climate. In the last million or so years, the 100,000-year eccentricity in the orbit has determined the timing of glaciations, and before that the 40,000-year axial tilt was dominant (Figure **Five Myr Climate Change** (Figure 3.15)). These cycles have been important for a long time; geologists have even found evidence of these periods in rocks that are hundreds of millions of years old.

But how do the Milankovitch Cycles change our climate? These orbital cycles do not have much impact on the *total* insolation the Earth receives: they change only the *timing* of that insolation. Since the total insolation does not change, these orbital variations have the power to make the Earth's seasons stronger or weaker, but the average annual temperature should stay the same. The best explanation for long term changes in average annual temperature is that the Milankovitch cycles initiate a positive feedback that amplifies the small change in insolation.

---

[25]http://meted.ucar.edu/

3.3.6 Insolation and the Albedo Feedback

Today, the Earth's orbit is not very eccentric (it is almost circular), but at the beginning of each of the recent ice age periods, the orbit was much more elliptical. This meant that the Earth was further away from the sun during the northern hemisphere summers, reducing the total insolation. Lower insolation meant that the summer months were milder than they would otherwise be, with cooler temperatures. Summer temperatures were also lower when the Earth's axial tilt was smaller, so the two different orbital parameters could reinforce one another's effects, in this case producing especially mild summers.

It is thought that these mild northern summers produced an albedo feedback that made the whole planet slip into an ice age. The northern hemisphere has continents near the poles—Europe, Asia, and North America. Today, these continents have largely temperate climates. During the winter, snow falls across much of the land (see Figure **Surface of the Earth in February with Cloud Cover Removed** (Figure 3.8) in the previous module) only to melt during the summer months. If the summers are not hot enough to melt all the snow and ice, glaciers can advance, covering more of the land. Because ice has a high albedo, more sunlight is reflected than before, and the Earth is made cooler. This creates a positive feedback, as the cooler conditions allow the ice to advance further—which, in turn, increases the albedo and cools the Earth! Eventually, a large proportion of the northern continents became covered in ice (Figure **800pn Northern Icesheet** (Figure 3.20)).

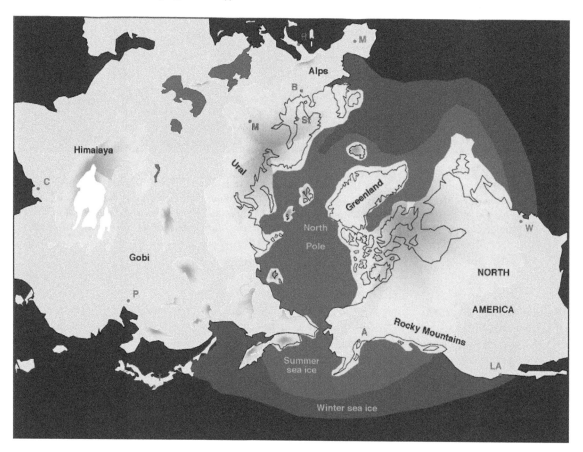

Figure 3.20: 800pn Northern Icesheet Glacial coverage (light blue) of the northern hemisphere during the ice ages. *Source: Hannes Grobe*[26]

This positive feedback process works in the other direction, as well. The interglacial periods are ushered in when the orbital parameters create summers that are unusually warm, which melts some of the ice. When the ice sheets shrink, the Earth's albedo decreases, which further warms the system. The giant northern ice sheets shriveled up in a few thousand years as warm summers and decreasing albedo worked together.

These cycles of alternating cooling and warming are also related to changes in the amount of greenhouse gases in the atmosphere. As we observed in Figure **Vostok Petit Data** (Figure 3.16), the climate contains higher levels of carbon dioxide during interglacial periods. Although this appears to make sense—carbon dioxide is a greenhouse gas, and so should produce warmer climates—it is also a puzzle, because it is not clear how changes in Milankovitch cycles lead to higher levels of carbon dioxide in the atmosphere. It is clear that these changes in carbon dioxide are important in making the change in temperature between interglacial and glacial periods so extreme. Several different hypotheses have been proposed to explain why glacial periods produce lower levels of carbon dioxide (it may be related to how the physical changes influence the Earth's ecosystems ability to absorb carbon dioxide: perhaps lower sea levels increase the nutrient supply in the ocean, or the drop in sea level destroys coral reefs, or iron-rich dust from new deserts fertilizes the oceans) but further work on this question remains to be done.

It is a concern for all of us that there are gaps in our understanding of how the feedbacks between insolation, albedo and greenhouse gases operate, as it makes it hard to predict what the consequences of any changes in the climate system might lead to. The current level of atmospheric carbon dioxide is unprecedented in human experience; it is at the highest level ever recorded in the Quaternary. Will the current increase in greenhouse gases lead to a positive feedback, warming the Earth even more?

3.3.7 Review Questions

Question 3.3.1
In the text, we discuss how polar ice has a smaller ^{18}O to ^{16}O ratio (that is, it has proportionally less heavy isotope water) than ocean water does. Hydrogen also has isotopes, the two most common being hydrogen-1 (^1H) and hydrogen-2 (^2H, also known as deuterium). Water is made up of both hydrogen and oxygen, and scientists analyze both elements when examining ice cores. Do you predict that polar ice sheets would have a higher ratio or a lower ratio of ^1H to ^2H than ocean water? Will colder global temperatures increase or decrease the amount of ^2H in polar ice?

Question 3.3.2
In the text, we discuss how polar ice has a smaller ^{18}O to ^{16}O ratio (that is, it has proportionally less heavy-isotope water) when the climate is cooler. We also discuss how changes in the ratio of ^{18}O to ^{16}O ratio in sediment cores can also be used to determine the climate's average temperature. In ocean sediments, the ratio of ^{18}O to ^{16}O increases when the climate is cooler (that is, it has proportionally more heavy isotope water). Explain why isotope ratios in ocean sediment have the opposite reaction to those in polar ice.

Question 3.3.3
There are three different ways in which the Earth's orbit changes through time. What combination of orbital parameters would be most likely to start an ice age? (Hint: Ice ages require cool northern summers.)

3.3.8 Resources

Do you want to know more about how ice cores are extracted and analyzed? NASA's Earth Observatory has details about the practical issues of drilling ice cores (deep ice needs to "relax" for as long as a year at the surface before being cut open – or it can shatter!) and how chemical data is interpreted. Go to

---

[26]http://en.wikipedia.org/wiki/File:Northern_icesheet_hg.png

http://earthobservatory.nasa.gov/Features/Paleoclimatology_IceCores/[27] for an in-depth article with great links.

3.4 Modern Climate Change[28]

3.4.1 Learning Objectives

After reading this module, students should be able to

- assess long-term global temperature records and place recent climate change into the context of historical temperature observations
- explain how changes in the Sun's energy output have impacted the last 1300 years of global temperature records
- analyze the human impact on the planetary albedo and relate these changes to recent climate change
- predict the response of the global average temperature when large volcanic eruptions occur
- explain the enhanced greenhouse effect
- discuss how recent observations of change measured within regional ecosystems are related to global climate change

3.4.2 Introduction

In previous modules, an examination of the geologic record of the earth's climate in the Quaternary Period revealed the primary drivers of climate change. The most important conclusions to be drawn from the Modules **Climate Processes; External and Internal Controls** (Section 3.2) and **Milankovitch Cycles and the Climate of the Quaternary** (Section 3.3) are the following:

1. In the past, Earth has been significantly warmer (and mostly ice free) and significantly colder (especially during the so-called "Snowball Earth" eras) than it is today.
2. Climate change occurs when there are changes in insolation, albedo, and composition of the atmosphere.
3. Climate is the average of weather, and changes to the earth's climate occur on long time scales.

Recent climate change, which has occurred during the modern instrument era, is the focus of this module. It is through the lens of long-term climate change (occurring on thousands to millions of years) that we will view earth's current climate and recent climate change. The goal is to investigate how the principles listed above are shaping current climate events.

3.4.3 Mechanisms

3.4.3.1 Temperature Records

Figure **Northern Hemisphere Surface Air** (Figure 3.21) clearly shows that the current global average temperature reflects an interglacial warm period. If we focus in on the end of this record we can observe some of the fine scale changes in the global temperature records. Figure **Northern Hemisphere Surface Air** (Figure 3.21) combines proxy data (i.e., information from ice cores and tree rings) with the modern instrument record to create a graph showing the last 1300 years of Northern Hemisphere (hereafter, NH) temperatures. Each line on the top two panels represents a different temperature data set collected in the NH and the bottom panel color codes the percentage of overlap among these data sets.

---

[27]http://earthobservatory.nasa.gov/Features/Paleoclimatology_IceCores/
[28]This content is available online at <http://legacy.cnx.org/content/m41579/1.6/>.

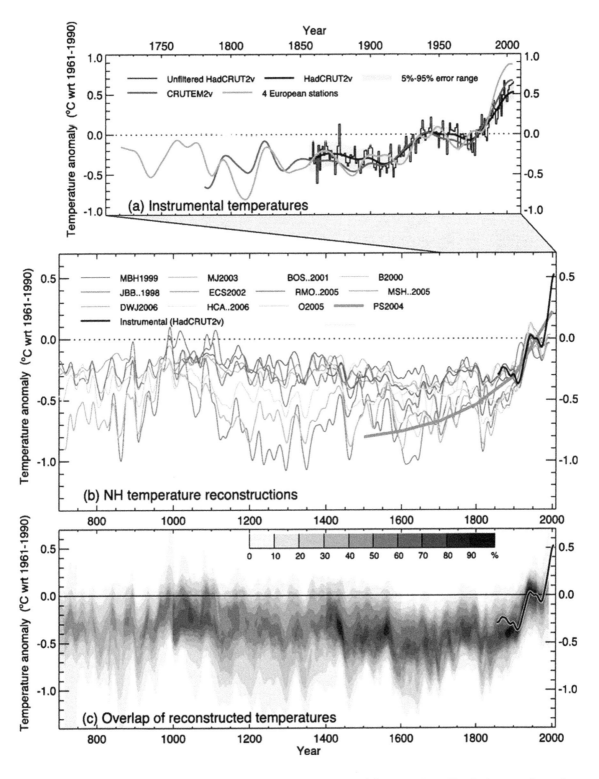

Figure 3.21: Northern Hemisphere Surface Air Panel (a) – Northern Hemisphere surface air temperature data from the modern instrument era from various sources. Panel (b) – Northern Hemisphere surface air temperature reconstruction dating back 1300 years from various sources. Panel (c) - Percent of overlap between the various sources of Panel (b). *Source: Climate Change 2007: The Physical Science Basis: Contribution of Working Group I to the Fourth Assessment Report of the Intergovernmental Panel on Climate Change, Cambridge University Press*[29]

Major features in these data include the **Medieval Warm Period** approximately 1,000 years ago and the **Little Ice Age** approximately 400 years ago. Even with these events, the bottom panel shows that most of the variability in the NH temperature fits within a 0.5 °C temperature range. Rarely has the temperature exceeded the 1961-1990 average, which is the dividing line on this graph. The only major fluctuation outside of this range is during the modern instrument era of the last 300 years, where confidence between the data sets is high. Beginning in the 1800s, the solid black line in each panel traces out approximately a 1 °C increase in global temperatures. It is this increase that is the central focus in recent climate change science. Remember from the previous chapter that a 1 °C change in the earth's temperature is a large change; reduce the global average by 4 °C to 6 °C and much of the NH will be covered with ice as it was 20,000 years ago.

There has been much debate over recent climate change, especially in the news media and among political parties around the world. This debate is centered on the cause of the recent 1 °C increase–is it a part of the natural variability in the climate system or have **anthropogenic**, which simply means human caused, influences played a major role? In a recent survey given to more than 3,000 college students at the University of Illinois at Urbana-Champaign, it was found the approximately two thirds of those surveyed agreed that recent climate change was due to reasons beyond natural variability in the climate system. (see Figure **Recent Climate Change Student Responses** (Figure 3.22)) Approximately 20% reported that the climate change is due to natural changes and the remainder was undecided. Let's investigate both sides of this argument!

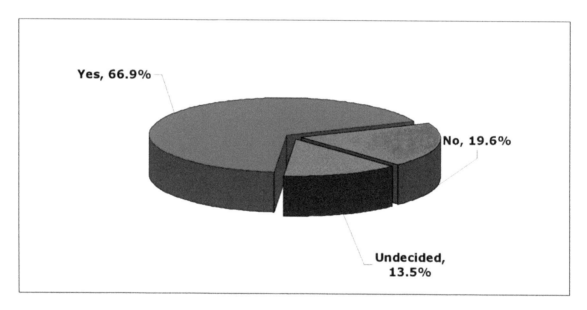

Figure 3.22: Recent Climate Change Student Responses Survey results from 3,000+ college students at the University of Illinois at Urbana-Champaign when asked if climate was changing beyond natural variability. *Source: Snodgrass, E.*[30]

Recall from the Module Milankovitch Cycles and the Climate of the Quaternary (Section 3.3) that global climate will change as a response to changes in insolation, albedo and the composition of the atmosphere. It was shown that the amount of energy entering the earth-atmosphere system from the sun varies less than 0.1% during the 11-year solar cycle in sunspot activity. Outside of this cycle, the amount of energy from the sun has increased 0.12 **Watts per square meter** (W/m^2) since 1750. Is this enough excess energy to

---

[29]http://www.ipcc.ch/publications_and_data/ar4/wg1/en/figure-6-10.html
[30]http://cnx.org/member_profile/snodgrss

produce the 1 °C increase in global temperatures that has been observed since the 1800s? As it turns out, the climate system needs nearly 8 times that amount of energy to warm by 1 °C. This essentially eliminates fluctuations in solar output as the culprit for recent climate change.

Has the earth's albedo changed since the 1800s? As we know from the Module **Climate Processes; External and Internal Controls** (Section 3.2), increases in the Earth's albedo lead to global cooling and decreases lead to warming. The net effect of human existence on Earth is to brighten the surface and increase the global albedo. This change is primarily accomplished through intensive agriculture where forest, marshland, and open prairie are cut down and crops like soybeans, corn, wheat, cotton, and rice are grown in their place. Add this to the current high rates of deforestation in South America and Africa and the evidence is clear that mankind has increased the Earth's albedo, which should have led to global cooling. (see Figure **Deforestation in the Amazon (2010)** (Figure 3.23)

Figure 3.23: Deforestation in the Amazon (2010) Satellite image shows the extent of deforestation in the Amazon as of 2010. *Source: NASA Earth Observatory*[31]

Outside of human influence, planetary albedo can also be changed by major volcanic eruptions. When volcanoes erupt, they spew enormous amounts of soot, ash, dust, sulfur, and other aerosols into the atmosphere. During major eruptions, like that of Mt. Pinatubo in 1991, some particles of this debris find their way into the stratosphere, where they reside for a few years. (see Figure **Mt. Pinatubo Erupting in 1991** (Figure 3.24)) The presence of these particles high in the earth's atmosphere acts like a shield that prevents sunlight from penetrating through the lower atmosphere to warm the earth's surface. Instead, the energy is either absorbed by the particles or reflected and scattered away. The net effect is that large volcanic

---

[31]http://earthobservatory.nasa.gov/Features/WorldOfChange/deforestation.php

eruptions can cool the planet for a few years by changing the earth's albedo.

Figure 3.24: Mt. Pinatubo Erupting in 1991 Photograph of Mt. Pinatubo erupting in the
Philippines in 1991. *Source: USGS/Cascades Volcano Observatory*[32]

3.4.3.2 Observations of Solar Output and Volcanic Eruptions

At first glance the Figure **Radiative Forcings & Simulated Temperatures** (Figure 3.25) looks quite
complicated, but let's break this graph down to understand how changes in the sun's output and volcanic
eruptions have contributed to recent climate change. In the top panel (a), changes in the amount of energy,
measured in W/m^2, are graphed against time to show how volcanic eruptions have impacted the amount of
energy the earth receives from the sun. Notice that around the year 1815, when Mt. Tambora erupted, there
is a large downward spike in the plot. Now, examine the bottom panel, which shows the NH temperatures,
just as Figure **Northern Hemisphere Surface Air** (Figure 3.21) displayed, and see how the temperatures
in the years following 1815 took a sharp downward turn. This is a direct consequence of the changes in
albedo caused by large volcanic eruptions. Next, look at the time period between 1000 and 1300 A.D., the
so-called Medieval Warm Period. In panel (b), changes in solar output are graphed against time; notice
that during the Medieval Warm Period, the amount of insolation was high compared to the average. The
opposite occurred during the Little Ice Age which peaked around 400 years ago.

---

[32]http://vulcan.wr.usgs.gov/Imgs/Jpg/Pinatubo/Images/Pinatubo91_eruption_plume_06-12-91.jpg

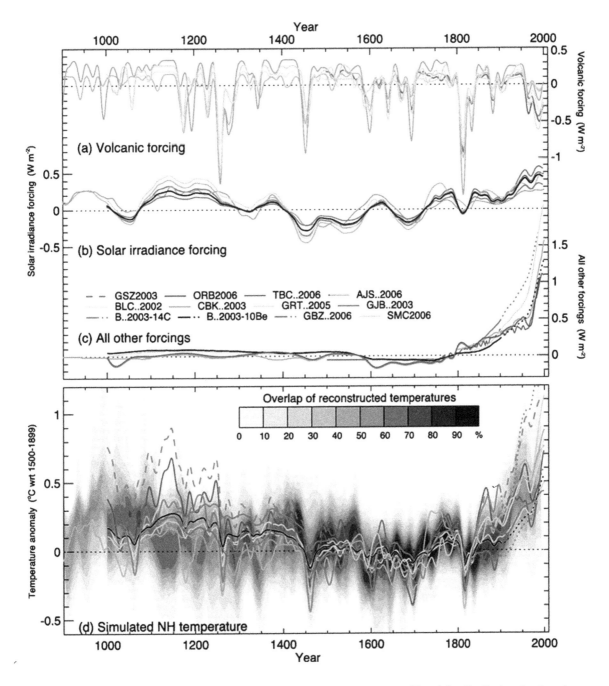

Figure 3.25: Radiative Forcings & Simulated Temperatures Plot (a) - Radiative forcing due to volcanic eruptions over the last 1,300 years. Plot (b) - Radiative forcing due to fluctuations in solar irradiance over the last 1,300 years. Plot (c) - Radiative forcing due to all other forcing over the last 1,300 years. Plot (d) – Northern Hemisphere temperature reconstruction with overlap (shading) over the last 1,300 years. *Source: Climate Change 2007: The Physical Science Basis: Contribution of Working Group I to the Fourth Assessment Report of the Intergovernmental Panel on Climate Change, Cambridge University Press*[33]

3.4.3.3 Alterations to the Natural Greenhouse Effect

We have ruled out the first two mechanisms (i.e., changes in albedo and insolation) as reasons for the recent increase in global temperatures. But when we look at panel (c) in Figure **Radiative Forcings & Simulated Temperatures** (Figure 3.25), we notice that the "all other forcing" curves point to a rapid increase in the amount of energy retained by the earth-atmosphere system over the last 200 years. What is responsible for the increasing tail on this graph? Have humans altered the composition of the Earth's atmosphere to make it more efficient at absorbing the infrared radiation that would have otherwise been lost to space? Is there proof of a human enhancement to the natural greenhouse effect? Can we explain the recent warming on an anthropogenic adjustment to the greenhouse gases like carbon dioxide (CO_2)? Is an "enhanced greenhouse effect" to blame for the fact that the top ten warmest years since the modern era of instrument measurements have occurred since 1995, as seen in Figure **Annual Global Temperature Anomalies** (Figure 3.26).

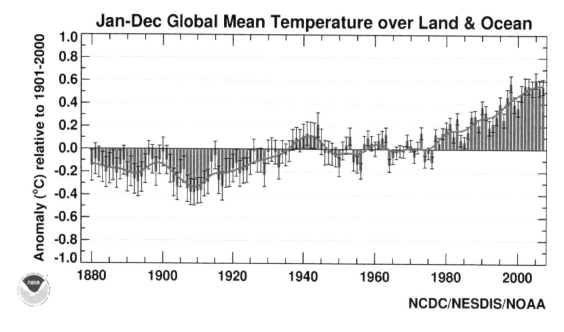

Figure 3.26: Annual Global Temperature Anomalies Global average surface temperature from 1880 to 2007. *Source: National Climate Data Center*[34]

Long before the term "global warming" became a common household phrase, nineteenth-century Irish physicist John Tyndall said, "Remove for a single summer-night the aqueous vapor from the air which overspreads this country, and you would assuredly destroy every plant capable of being destroyed by a freezing temperature." This now famous quote reveals the importance of greenhouse gases, like water vapor, in maintaining a balance between the incident solar radiation and the emitted terrestrial radiation. Tyndall understood that without greenhouse gases, water vapor being the most abundant, the earth's temperature would be markedly cooler. The global average surface temperature is approximately 15 °C (59 °F) but if the greenhouse gases were removed, the average global temperature would plummet to -18 °C (0 °F). Remember that these gases make up a small fraction of the composition of the atmosphere! Therefore, adjustments to their concentration will produce dramatic effects.

To understand why these gases are so efficient at keeping the planet warm, let's examine Figure **Atmospheric Transmission** (Figure 3.27). The top panel of this figure shows the normalized intensity of

---

[33]http://www.ipcc.ch/publications_and_data/ar4/wg1/en/ch6s6-6-3.html
[34]http://www.ncdc.noaa.gov/img/climate/research/2007/ann/global-jan-dec-error-bar-pg.gif

the radiation emitted by both the sun and earth as a function of wavelength. The middle panel shows the total atmospheric absorption spectrum and the bottom panel shows the individual gas absorption spectrum (excluding Nitrogen and Argon). Notice from the top panel that the sun's peak energy emission falls within the visible portion of the spectrum and suffers very little atmospheric absorption (middle panel). The peak emission wavelength for the earth is in the thermal infrared (IR), and it is effectively absorbed by water vapor (H_2O), carbon dioxide (CO_2), methane (CH_4) and nitrous oxide (NO_2). The primary purpose of this figure is to show that the gases in the earth's atmosphere are transparent to the sun's peak energy emission (visible light) but not the earth's peak emission (thermal IR). It is through the absorption of the earth's outgoing thermal infrared radiation that the global average temperature warms approximately $60\,°F$ over what it would be without greenhouse gases.

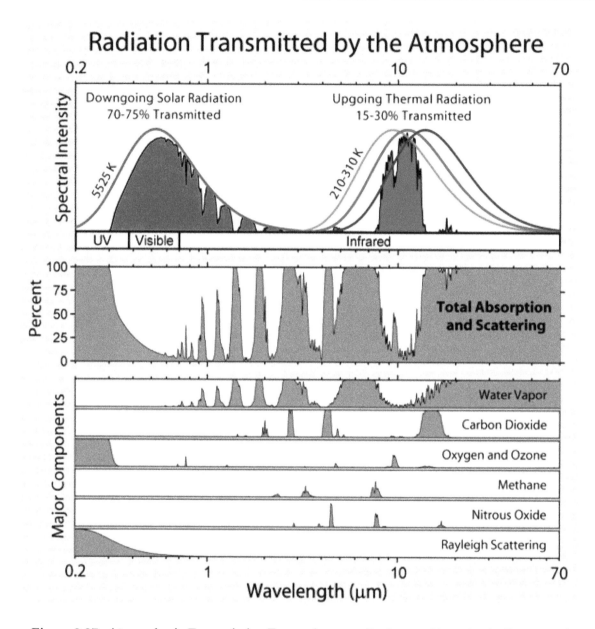

Figure 3.27: Atmospheric Transmission Top graph – normalized spectral intensity (radiant energy) emitted by the earth and sun as a function of wavelength. Middle graph – total atmospheric absorption as a function of wavelength. Bottom graph – individual gas absorption as a function of wavelength. *Source: R.A. Rohde for Global Warming Art Project*[35]

Are humans altering the natural greenhouse effect? Based upon our assessment so far, this is the final mechanism by which the global climate can be changed. Let's look into the alteration of the chemistry and composition of the earth's atmosphere. First are humans increasing the amount of water vapor, the most abundant but also weakest greenhouse gas in the atmosphere? As the air temperature increases, the amount of water vapor the atmosphere can hold also increases. However, a closer investigation of the

---

[35]http://en.wikipedia.org/wiki/File:Atmospheric_Transmission.png

water cycle is needed to understand what will happen to this increase in water vapor. In this cycle, the amount of evaporation must equal the amount of condensation and thus precipitation on a global scale. This equilibrium must be achieved or else water would end up entirely in its liquid form or in its vapor form. Also due to the speed at which the **hydrological cycle** operates, a large increase in water vapor would be quickly precipitated out of the atmosphere.

Other greenhouse gases progress through their respective cycles much more slowly than water. There are vast amounts of carbon and carbon dioxide in the earth-atmosphere system. Most carbon is locked up in rocks, where it may remain for millions of years. The carbon dioxide that is mobile, however, is mostly found in other places: the ocean, soils, vegetation, fossil fuels like coal, oil, and natural gas, and also in small concentrations in the atmosphere. These reservoirs of CO_2 can exchange mass like oceans and clouds do in the water cycle, but with one extremely important difference–the exchange rate is much slower. That means the system can get out of balance and remain out of balance for a long time, hundreds or thousands of years. There are two primary mechanisms for sequestering carbon dioxide that is released into the atmosphere: it can be captured by the respiration of plants, or dissolved in the ocean.

However, the rate at which plants and oceans can take CO_2 out of the atmosphere is fixed. Therefore, if a surplus of CO_2 is added to the atmosphere, it will stay there for a long time. This has major implications, given the fact that CO_2 is a powerful greenhouse gas. The question then to ask becomes, "is this exchange rate out of balance?"

The current average concentration of CO_2 in the atmosphere is about 390 parts per million (PPM), which means there are 390 parts of CO_2 per million parts of air. That does not seem like very much, but if that small amount of carbon dioxide were removed from the air, the global average temperature would plummet. Has this concentration been changing? To answer the question, we will turn to the findings of Richard Keeling, whose life's work was the observation of CO_2 concentrations at the Mauna Loa Observatory in Hawaii. Beginning in the early 1950s, observations of CO_2, a **well-mixed gas** in our atmosphere, have shown a remarkable climb in concentration. (see Figure **CO_2 Concentrations at the Mauna Loa Observatory** (Figure 3.28)) The "Keeling Curve," as it is sometimes called, clearly shows that since the 1950s CO_2 concentrations have increased steadily from 315 ppm to 390 ppm. The zigzag nature of this graph is due to life cycle of plants in the NH. The NH has much more land area that the SH, so when spring and summer arrive in the NH, the abundance of new plant life reduces the CO_2 concentrations in the atmosphere. When the plants die or become dormant in the fall and winter, CO_2 concentrations spike again.

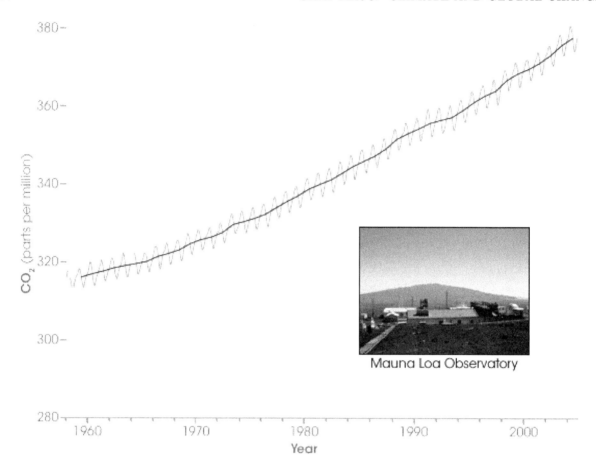

Figure 3.28: CO_2 Concentrations at the Mauna Loa Observatory The "Keeling Curve" of CO_2 concentrations measured in Mauna Loa, Hawaii, since the 1950s. *Source: NASA Earth Observatory*[36]

What is troublesome about this figure is that the carbon cycle is out of its normal rhythm and a surplus of CO_2, a known greenhouse gas, is building in the earth's atmosphere. Where is this surplus coming from? To answer this question, let's look at two historical records of CO_2 concentrations taken from ice core deposits. The top panel in Figure **Changes in Greenhouse Gases from Ice Core and Modern Data** (Figure 3.29) shows the past 10,000 years of atmospheric CO_2 concentrations. Before 1750, the amount of CO_2 in the atmosphere was relatively steady at 280 ppm. Since 1750 there has been a dramatic increase in CO_2 concentrations.

---

[36]http://earthobservatory.nasa.gov/images/imagerecords/5000/5620/maunaloa_2004.gif

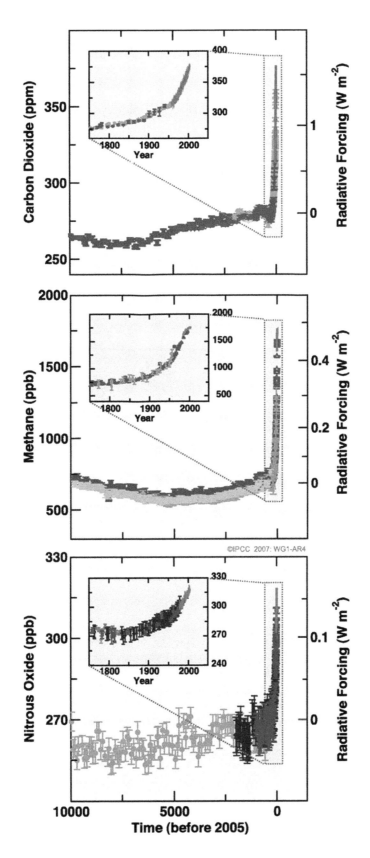

©IPCC 2007: WG1-AR4

Figure 3.29: Changes in Greenhouse Gases from Ice Core and Modern Data Top panel shoes
CO_2 concentrations (ppm) over the last 10,000 years. *Source: Climate Change 2007: The Physical Science
Basis:* [37] *Contribution of Working Group I to the Fourth Assessment Report of the Intergovernmental
Panel on Climate Change* [38]

If we look even further back in time, over the last half million years, we see a similar story. (see Figure **Evidence of Climate Change** (Figure 3.30)) The current concentration of CO_2 in the earth's atmosphere is higher than at any time in the past half million years. Where is this abundance of CO_2 coming from? Which reservoirs are being depleted of their CO_2 while the atmosphere takes on more? The answer lies in the burning of fossil fuels and in the deforestation of significant chunks of the earth's forest biomes. Notice the spike in CO_2 concentrations beginning around 1750. This time period marks the beginning of the industrial revolution, when fossil fuels overtook wood as the primary energy source on our planet. Over the subsequent two and a half centuries, oil, coal, and natural gas have been extracted from their underground reservoirs and burned to generate electricity and power modern forms of transportation. The exhaust from this process is currently adding 30 billions of tons, or gigatons (Gt), of carbon dioxide to the atmosphere each year. Combine this addition of CO_2, a known greenhouse gas, to the subtraction of one of the sinks of CO_2 through deforestation and the imbalance grows even further.

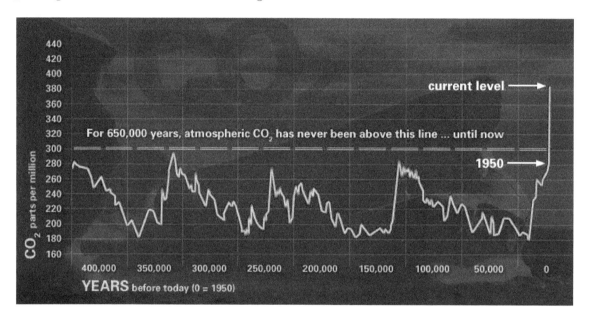

Figure 3.30: Evidence of Climate Change CO_2 concentrations over the last 400,000+ years. *Source: NASA/NOAA*[39]

What is the end result? By examining the earth's climate, both current and past and by investigating the three ways in which climate can change, we have arrived at the conclusion that the current warming is being caused by an imbalance in the carbon cycle that has been induced by human activity, namely the burning of fossil fuels. The record warmth over the last 1,300 years is very likely to have been caused by human decisions that have lead to a change in the chemistry of the atmosphere, and which has altered the natural climate variability toward warmer global temperatures. We are essentially changing the climate faster and in a different direction than natural processes have intended.

---

[37] http://www.ipcc.ch/publications_and_data/ar4/wg1/en/figure-spm-1.html
[38] http://www.ipcc.ch/publications_and_data/ar4/wg1/en/figure-spm-1.html
[39] http://climate.nasa.gov/evidence/

3.4.4 Observed Effects of Climate Change

3.4.4.1 Cherry Blossoms

In Japan each spring millions of people celebrate the blossoming of the cherry trees to mark the arrival of warmer weather. These celebrations have a long and storied history, and records of the cherry blossom festivals date back more than a thousand years. In fact, the record of the timing of the cherry blossoms in Japan is the oldest for any flowering plant! Two scientists and historians. Richard Primack and Hiroyoshi Higuchi recently analyzed this record and found that beginning in the early 1800s the mean air temperature in March has slowly risen, similar to the increase shown in Figure **Northern Hemisphere Surface Air** (Figure 3.21). During this same time period, the flowering date has slowly crept earlier in the season, and the trees are now flowering several days before they traditionally flowered. Although urbanization of Japan has lead to an increase in temperature, recent climate change is blamed for the earlier flowering of the Japanese cherry blossom tree. Primack and Higuchi show how Kyoto has warmed an average of 3.4 °C over the last 170 years. Climate change has contributed 18% to this total warming in Japan and Primack and Higuchi demonstrate the correlation of this warming with the industrial revolution.

Figure 3.31: Cherry Blossoms Photograph of cherry blossoms. *Source: Uberlemur via Wikimedia Commons*[40]

---

[40]http://commons.wikimedia.org/wiki/File:Yoshino_Sakura_Tidal_Basin_DC.jpg

3.4.4.2 Birds, Mosquitoes, and Fire Ants

A recent article[41] in the journal *Nature* discussed the response of plants and animals to current climate change. Phenologists, scientists who study how the periodic life cycle events of animals and plants are affected by variations in climate over the course of seasons and years, are finding that many species of birds are breeding and singing earlier in the year. Migrant birds are arriving earlier, butterflies are appearing earlier and some amphibians are spawning weeks ahead of their historical schedule. In addition, mountain tree lines, which are controlled by air temperature, have been advancing to higher altitudes in Europe, and Arctic shrubs are now found in regions that were once too cold for their existence in Alaska. While ecological changes such as these may not be threatening from a human perspective, others are. For example, malaria-carrying mosquitoes in Africa are now being found at altitudes that were once too cold for them, and outbreaks of malaria are showing up in towns and villages once thought to be out of their reach. In parts of California and Australia, fire ants are migrating to regions that historically have been too cold to support them.

---

[41]http://www.nature.com/nature/journal/v416/n6879/full/416389a.html

Figure 3.32: Fire Ants Photograph of fire ants on a piece of wood. *Source: Scott Bauer of the Agricultural Research Service, U.S. Department of Agriculture via Wikimedia Commons*[42]

---

[42]http://commons.wikimedia.org/wiki/File:Fire_ants02.jpg

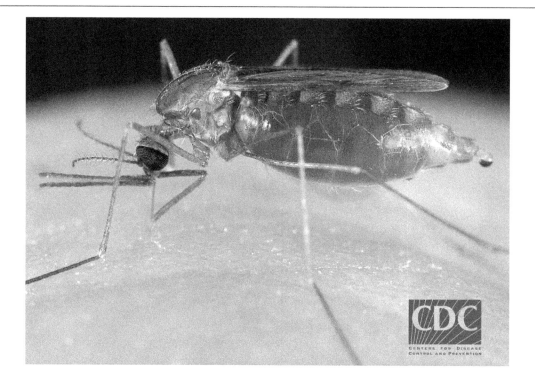

Figure 3.33: Mosquitos Photograph of a mosquito on skin. *Source: Centers for Disease Control and Prevention*[43]

3.4.4.3 Impacts of Change in the Arctic and the Antarctic

The Arctic and Antarctic are the regions experiencing the most rapid changes due to the recent warming of the earth's atmosphere. These two regions on Earth are a part of the cryosphere, which is defined as the part of the Earth that is occupied by sea ice, lake ice, ice caps and **permafrost**. (For a comprehensive overview of the current state of the cryosphere and an excellent archive of data, please check out "The Cryosphere Today[44] ") As explained in the Module **Milankovitch Cycles and the Climate of the Quaternary** (Section 3.3), these regions are most vulnerable due to the powerful ice-albedo effect. One amazing depiction of polar warming can be found in the drunken forests of Siberia. Larch and spruce trees there are often seen tilted over on their sides and growing at strange angles. Why? Because the once continually frozen soil, or permafrost, in which they are rooted has been melting in recent years. As the soil thaws it becomes more malleable and the trees begin to slant as the soil beneath them sinks. Farther north, Arctic sea ice has been decreasing both in extent and concentration. In 2007, the smallest extent of sea ice was measured since the 1970s, and the **Northwest Passage** opened for commerce and exploration. As the sea ice extent and concentration decreases, so does the habitat of polar bears. The sea ice is a vital part of their hunting grounds, and recent decreases of this ice have greatly reduced their access to certain prey. In addition to sea ice reductions, surface melt of the ice sheet on Greenland has increased in recent years, especially along its edges. This melt has lead to large pools and streams forming on top of this mile-thick sheet of ice. On the other side of the world, the Larsen B ice shelf in Antarctica recently collapsed, sending a large section

---

[43]http://www.cdc.gov/malaria/images/mosquitoes/freeborniwithlogo.jpg
[44]http://arctic.atmos.uiuc.edu/cryosphere/

of ice into the sea. This section of the Antarctic ice cap was roughly as large as the state of Rhode Island and it had been stably attached to the ice shelf for the past 12,000 years. Scientists are closely watching the Antarctic ice as nearly two-thirds of the world's fresh water resides there. Finally, alpine glacier retreat has been observed on every continent. With few exceptions, these glaciers have been retracting heavily since the 1960s, and over that time period NASA reports a global loss of 8,000 cubic kilometers of ice, which represents a what percentage reduction?

Figure 3.34: Drunken Forests of Siberia *Source: NASA Science blog*[45]

---

[45]http://en.wikipedia.org/wiki/File:20070801_forest.jpg

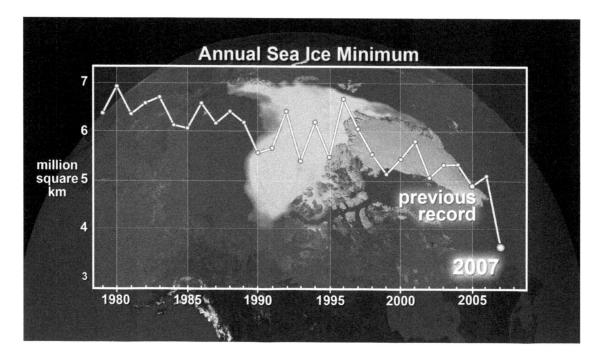

Figure 3.35: 2007 Sea Ice Extent in the Arctic *Source: NASA Goddard Space Flight Center*[46]

3.4.4.4 The Oceans' Response

Further dramatic changes brought on by recent warming have been observed by scientists concerned with the world's oceans. Observations of the world's coral reefs have revealed an alarming rate of coral bleaching (which is not caused by chlorine). As the oceans attempt to uptake the abundance of CO_2 and absorb nearly 80% of the heat added to the earth-atmosphere system from the enhanced greenhouse effect, the waters will inevitably warm. As these waters have warmed over the past 40 years, the delicate ecological balance within some of the world's coral reefs has been upset leading to coral bleaching. Under warmer waters the rate at which the algae, which is an important part of the coral ecosystem, undergoes photosynthesis is too much for the coral to manage. As a result, the coral rids itself of the algae, which leads to an exposure of the white skeleton of the coral. Another consequence of warming oceans is an increase in sea level. Since 1880, sea level has risen 20 cm (8 inches). The rise in sea level is associated both with an increase in glacial melt water and in the thermal expansion of the seawater. An interesting consequence of this rise in sea level has been the disappearance of the long-disputed New Moore Island between Bangladesh and India. Both countries laid claim to the shallow, uninhabited island due to the speculation that oil reserves may lie beneath it, but in 2010, the sea swallowed it. Scientists at the School of Oceanographic Studies at Jadavpur University, Kolkatta[47] , India suggest global warming played an important part.

---

[46]http://www.nasa.gov/centers/goddard/images/content/190555main_still_seaIce2007_0914.0730.jpg

[47]http://en.wikipedia.org/wiki/Kolkatta

Figure 3.36: Coral Bleaching A part of coral that has experienced coral bleaching. *Source: NOAA*[48]

Finally, as the planet has adjusted to warmer temperatures the proliferation of drought conditions in some regions has dramatically affected human populations. The Sahel, for example, is a border region between the Sahara Desert in the north of Africa and the tropical rainforests that occupy the central part of the continent. (see Figure **The Sahel in Africa** (Figure 3.37)) This region is experiencing desertification as the Sahara steadily expands southward. Since the 1970s, the amount of precipitation in this region has been steadily below normal. The combination of over irrigation and recent climate change has made the region uninhabitable and forced millions to relocate.

---

[48]http://www.noaa.gov/features/climate/images/fig2_bleach_fullsize.jpg

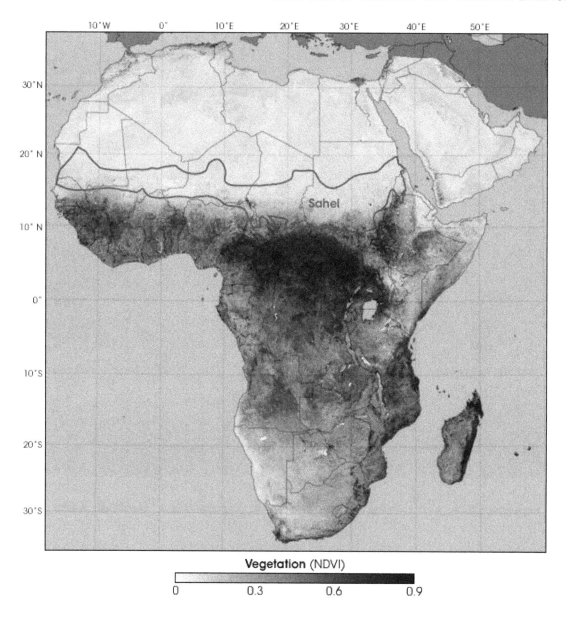

Figure 3.37: The Sahel in Africa *Source: NASA Earth Observatory*[49]

---

[49]http://earthobservatory.nasa.gov/Features/Desertification/Images/africa_ndvi_200511.jpg

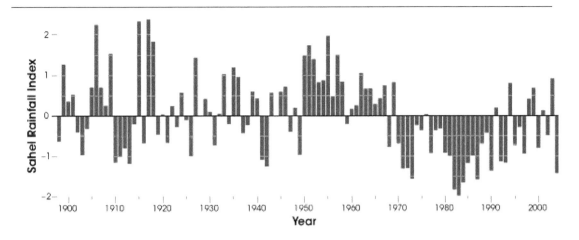

Figure 3.38: The Sahel Rainfall Index *Source: NASA Earth Observatory*[50]

3.4.5 Review Questions

Question 3.4.1
In Figure **Northern Hemisphere Surface Air** (Figure 3.21) the dividing line on the graph is the 1961-1990 average temperature. Explain the relevance of this line to the data presented in this figure.

Question 3.4.2
Explain how deforestation can lead to both a warming effect and cooling effect for global temperatures.

Question 3.4.3
In Figure **Atmospheric Transmission** (Figure 3.27), which gas is contributing the most to the absorption of ultra-violet light? If this gas were removed from the atmosphere, how might global temperatures respond?

Question 3.4.4
If the surface of the Greenland Ice Sheet continues to melt, how will this impact the albedo of this region and what impact will this have on the air temperature there?

Question 3.4.5
When sea ice melts, what happens to global sea level?

3.4.6 References

Walther, G. R., Post, E., Convey, P., Menzel, A., Parmesan, C., Beebee, T. J .C., et al. (2002, March 28). Ecological responses to recent climate change. *Nature*, 416, 389-395. doi: 10.1038/416389a

[50]http://earthobservatory.nasa.gov/Features/Desertification/Images/sahel_rainfall_timeseries.gif

3.5 Climate Projections[51]

3.5.1 Learning Objectives

After reading this module, students should be able to

- assess global CO_2 emissions and determine which countries and regions are responsible for the greatest emissions currently and historically
- explain the relationship between fossil fuel usage and CO_2 emissions
- link variables such as wealth, population, fuel imports, and deforestation to CO_2 emissions
- use IPCC future climate projections to assess future global temperature scenarios
- distinguish between weather events and climate change, and discuss the differences between weather forecasting and climate projections
- analyze the anthropogenic impact on climate by examining climate change without people
- assess the regional and global impacts of climate change on air temperature and precipitation

3.5.2 Introduction

In the Module **Modern Climate Change** (Section 3.4) we discovered that the global warming of approximately 1 °C over the past 200 years was human induced through an enhancement of the natural greenhouse effect. We learned that the burning of fossil fuels has upset the natural carbon cycle, which has steadily increased the amount of carbon dioxide (CO_2) in the atmosphere since the 1750s. Finally we looked at ancillary evidence of this warming to see the immediate impact of these changes. In this module we will investigate the findings of the Intergovernmental Panel on Climate Change (IPCC) and look at future climate projections. We will inspect these findings and analyze their impacts on a global scale.

3.5.3 Who is Responsible? Factors to Consider

In 2007, the IPCC was awarded a share of the Nobel Prize for its work in the area of global climate change. The IPCC is organized through the United Nations and is composed of over 3,000 scientists from around the world who are working together to understand current climate change and project future climate scenarios. As of 2011, the IPCC has released four comprehensive reports, and it has concluded, "Most of the observed increase in global average temperature since the mid-twentieth century is very likely due to the observed increase in anthropogenic greenhouse gas concentrations." This widely known statement essentially means that the probability of occurrence is greater than 90% that the current global warming is caused by humans burning fossil fuels. In response to these findings, the United Nations Framework Convention on Climate Change has called for numerous international meetings in cities including Kyoto, Bali, Copenhagen, and others where the leaders of world have gathered to discuss strategies to mitigate this looming disaster. At these meetings, scientists, politicians and world leaders review the current state of knowledge about the problem and strategize for the future. This chapter will take a large-scale view of the global challenges of climate change.

Over the past few years, China has surpassed the United States to become the nation that emits more greenhouse gasses than any other (see Figure **CO_2 Emissions for the United States and China** (Figure 3.39)). Currently, China is responsible for just over 25% of global CO_2 emissions, which are approximately 30 Gt per year, with the United States in a close second place. It is important to consider population when reviewing these numbers because there are over four times as many people living in China than in the United States. When you compare these two countries on a per capita basis, the average U.S. citizen emits approximately 19 metric tons of CO_2 per year while the average Chinese citizen emits approximately five metric tons. In 2009, the United States consumed more than double the amount oil than the second largest consumer, China, according to the U.S. Energy Information Administration. Topping the list in per capita

---

[51]This content is available online at <http://legacy.cnx.org/content/m41580/1.8/>.

CO_2 emissions is the oil rich nation of Qatar. This small country located on the Persian Gulf has the largest per capita production of oil and natural gas. It also has the world's highest gross domestic product (GDP) per capita. An average citizen in this country emits nearly 60 metric tons of CO_2 into the atmosphere each year.

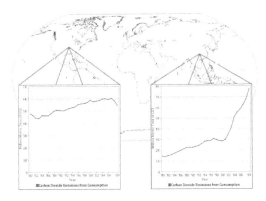

Figure 3.39: CO_2 Emissions for the United States and China CO_2 emissions in millions of metric tons graphed against time for the United States and China. *Source: Snodgrass, E.*[52] *created graphs using data from the U.S. Energy Information Association*[53]

Rather than point the finger at individual countries, let's examine the bigger problem. The maps in Figure **Global Influence Maps** (Figure 3.40) distort the size of each country based on a certain variable, like CO_2 emissions, with respect to the rest of the world. In the upper left panel, the map is based on population, which is why China and India appear so large. The upper right map distorts the size of the country based upon fuel imports. Notice that the United States, much of Europe, and Japan are expanded the most, while Africa, the Middle East, and much of South America are barely visible. Compare these two maps with absolute wealth and carbon emissions and the story is quite clear. The industrialized and wealthy nations are responsible for the largest quantities of carbon emissions and fuel imports. These societies are built on the foundation of energy production through the consumption of fossil fuels.

The bottom two panels tell another aspect of this story. Focus first on the graph in the lower right, which shows forest loss by country. The world's forest biomes are a large part of the CO_2 cycle and with deforestation, a large sink for atmospheric CO_2 is taken away. Notice that deforestation is most prevalent in Africa, South America, and Indonesia while the United States is barely visible on this map. In the United States, reforestation is practiced, but in the rainforests of the world, which are those areas in South America, Africa, and Indonesia that are ballooned on this map, deforestation is commonplace.

[52]http://cnx.org/member_profile/snodgrss
[53]http://www.eia.gov/

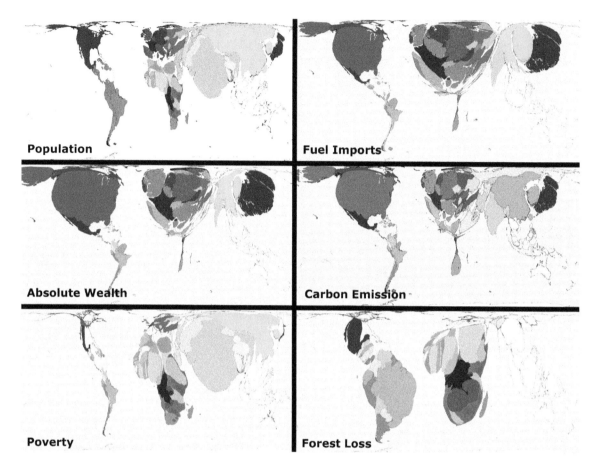

Figure 3.40: Global Influence Maps The variables labeled on each map are used to distort the size of each country to show their global influence. *Source: WorldMapper*[54], *©Copyright SASI Group (University of Sheffield) and Mark Newman (University of Michigan).*

The last graph in Figure **Global Influence Maps** (Figure 3.40) distorts each country's size according to poverty. Much of Asia and Africa are distorted the most, and it is in these regions that we need to pay close attention over the upcoming years. Many of the nations found within these countries are what economists and politicians call "emerging economies." Although much of the current abundance of CO_2 in the atmosphere is from developed countries such as the United States, CO_2 emissions from these countries are not increasing with time according to a 2008 report from the Energy Information Administration. In Figure **Global CO_2 Emissions from Coal Combustion** (Figure 3.41), the world's CO_2 emissions from coal combustion in billions of metric tons are plotted against time. Notice that countries of the Organization for Economic Co-operation and Development (OECD), which comprises a large group of developed and industrialized nations, have not increased their CO_2 emissions from coal combustion since 1990, and future projections also reveal a flat line in CO_2 emissions. Compare this to the non-OECD countries, many of which are emerging economies like China and India, and you see that CO_2 emissions are set to triple in the next 25 years. There is much debate over information like this now that recent climate change has been linked so closely to anthropogenic emission of CO_2. This debate revolves around the fact that developed nations used coal, oil, and natural gas during a time when the impacts of CO_2 and climate change were not

---

[54]http://www.worldmapper.org/index.html

well researched. This meant that during the time these countries, including the United States, industrialized there were no regulations on the emissions of CO_2. Now that CO_2 emissions have been shown to cause global warming, pressure is being applied to these emerging economies to regulate and control their CO_2 emissions. This is subject of much of the debate at the international climate summits at Kyoto, Bali, and Copenhagen. What is important to remember when discussing developed countries vs. emerging economies is that the per capita emissions of CO_2 in emerging economies are approximately one third of those for developed countries.

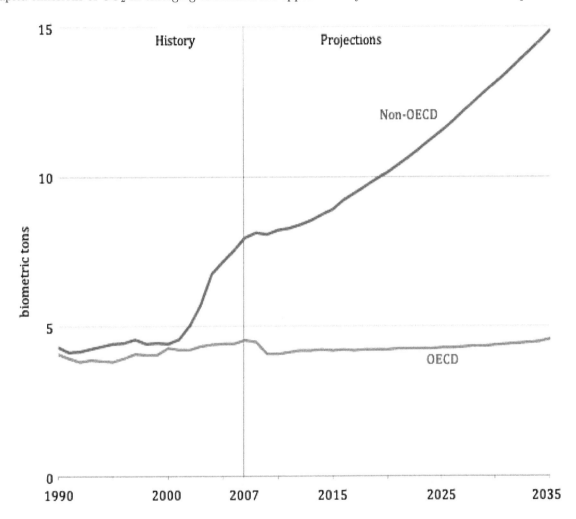

Figure 3.41: Global CO₂ Emissions from Coal Combustion The world's CO2 emissions from coal combustion in billions of metric tons are plotted against time for OECD countries and non-OECD countries. *Source: U.S. Energy Information Administration[55] (Oct 2008)*

---

[55]http://www.eia.doe.gov/oiaf/ieo/emissions.html

3.5.4 Climate Projections

One of the greatest obstacles climate scientists face in educating the public on issues of climate change is time. Most people take weather and climate to be one branch of scientific study. In reality, this could not be further from the truth. Weather and climate are two separate fields of study that are joined only by one definition—climate is the average of weather. It is important to understand this statement because people—news reporters, broadcast meteorologists, politicians, and even scientists—often make the mistake of attributing weather events, such as Hurricane Katrina (2005), to global climate change. Katrina was a weather event and, as such, it cannot be said to have been *caused* by global climate change. Are the ingredients for stronger hurricanes present in greater frequency now than they have been in the past? That's the type of question climate scientists seek to answer, and they do so by analyzing decades worth of data. Thirty years is the lowest value used in the denominator of climate calculations. In other words, 30 years is the shortest time period over which weather can be averaged to extract climate information. Therefore, it is impossible to blame a single weather event on climate change—this branch of science does not work that way.

To better understand the differences between weather and climate, take a look at Figure **High Temperature vs. Low Temperature, Champaign, IL** (Figure 3.42) which shows in red the actual high temperatures for each day in 2005 in Champaign, Illinois, compared to the average high temperature in black over a period beginning in 1899 and ending in 2009. It is completely normal for the temperature to vary $\pm 20\,°F$ around this average. In 2005 there were only a handful of days where the actual high was the same as the average high. This graph shows the highly variable and chaotic behavior of weather. But, when data from a long span of time is averaged, the climatological mean emerges.

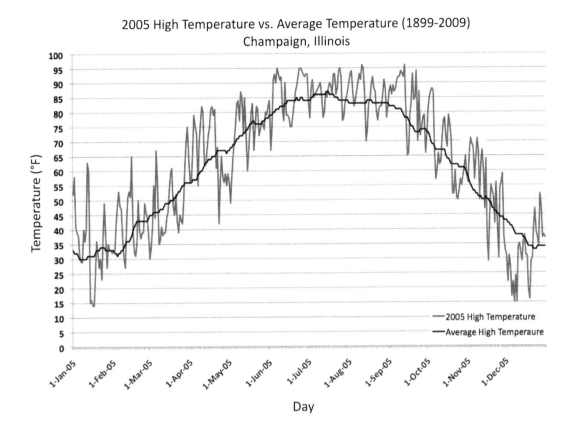

Figure 3.42: High Temperature vs. Low Temperature, Champaign, IL The average high temperature for Champaign-Urbana Illinois in black (1899-2009). The 2005 actual high temperature are graphed in red. *Source: E. Snodgrass[56] using data from the National Climate Data Center[57]*

To think of it another way, imagine you are in a large lecture hall with over 300 college students. If the professor were to call out one student and try to predict the course of her life over the next 70 years it would be nearly impossible! It would even be difficult to predict when that person would eat her next meal. However, the professor could project with great confidence that on average, most of the people in the room will eat dinner at 6:30PM on a given night. Beyond this meal, most of them will graduate from college by the time they are 22 years old. Many will be married by 27 years old and have their first children at 30. Most will have a job by the time they are 24 and most will have a job they like by 34. Most will have a total of 2.1 children by the time they are 36, and by the time they are 50 most will have gone to the doctor to have their first routine procedure. Most will retire at 67, and since they are college grads in the United States, there is a safe bet that they will retire with over a million dollars in assets. On average, the men in the room will die at 85 years old and most of the women will die before their ninetieth birthday. Now, if the professor were to single out one individual, the chances that her life would follow this path exactly are small, but when an entire class of 300 is averaged, this is the result. Weather is like the individual life. Climate is like the average of 300 lives. Weather and Climate are two separate branches of study in atmospheric science.

[56]http://cnx.org/member_profile/snodgrss
[57]http://www.ncdc.noaa.gov/oa/ncdc.html

In addition to keeping in mind the difference between weather and climate, remember that the focus of this chapter is *global* climate change. It is tempting to forget the global nature of this problem because it is happening very slowly on a large scale and it is averaged over long time periods. Recall the differences between weather and climate and remember that in conjunction with global warming there can still be weather events that take temperatures far below normal. The temptation during these events is to discount the science behind global climate change. For example, during the winter of 2009-2010, the weather patterns were such that the east coast of the United States experienced repeated record-setting snowstorms and cold air outbreaks. Many television news reports, weather broadcasts, and newspaper headlines scoffed at the idea of global warming during this winter and proclaimed that it was not happening or that it was a hoax. The shortsightedness of such responses is evidenced by the fact that *globally*, 2009 and 2010 were among the warmest years during the instrument record: 2009 ranked seventh, and 2010 tied for first. These were likely two of the warmest years of the last 1,300.

3.5.5 Climate Modeling and Future Climate Predictions

Sometimes people discount climate predictions based on their understanding of weather predictions. They will say something like, "Meteorologists can't even give me a reliable forecast of the weather over the next three days, how am I supposed to trust them to give me the forecast for the next 100 years." You're not! Climate scientists do not use weather forecast models to forecast climate conditions 100 years in advance. The computer models that are used to predict the weather over the next few days are entirely different from those used to predict the climate. Instead of predicting the highly chaotic nature of temperature, precipitation, and other common weather variables at very high spatial and temporal resolution, climate models forecast changes in the flux of energy between earth and its atmosphere and space. These two computer-modeling techniques differ substantially in their computational expense as well. Although weather forecast models are run on extremely fast computer systems at the National Center for Environmental Prediction, the fastest computers in the world, like the Earth Simulator in Japan and Blue Waters at the University of Illinois at Urbana-Champaign are charged with climate simulations (see Figure **Petascale Computing Facility** (Figure 3.43)).

Figure 3.43: Petascale Computing Facility The petascale computing facility "Blue Waters" located at the University of Illinois at Urbana-Champaign. *Source: HorsePunchKid via Wikimedia Commons*[58]

What are these climate models predicting will happen by the year 2100? First, we will look at the global average surface temperature projections. Figure **Climate Simulation Scenarios** (Figure 3.44) plots global surface warming against time with the present day in the middle of this chart. Recall that over the last 200 years, there has been a 1 °C increase in global temperatures, and that the rate of change has been extremely fast compared to natural changes in the earth's climate. The graphs in Figure **Climate Simulation Scenarios** (Figure 3.44) show the range of model projections from different climate simulation scenarios based upon various greenhouse gas emission scenarios (left graph). Focus on the top and bottom curves in the right panel, which show the most dramatic warming and the most conservative warming. The worst-case scenario, found in the top line, shows the "business as usual" projections. If nothing is done to mitigate the emission of greenhouse gases into the atmosphere, these climate models are predicting a 4 °C to 6 °C increase in global average temperature by 2100. The best-case scenario, from a climate change perspective, would be for a cessation of CO_2 emissions or for the current emission rates to not increase. In this case, there would still be a warming of 0.5° to 2 °C by 2100 as indicated by the bottom curves.

---

[58]http://en.wikipedia.org/wiki/File:NCSA_Blue_Waters.jpg

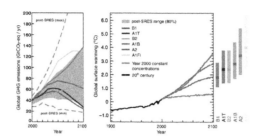

Figure 3.44: Climate Simulation Scenarios Left – multiple climate model projections (or scenarios) of greenhouse gas emissions (including CO2, CH4 and N2O) emissions in Gt-CO2-equivalent through 2100. Right – multiple climate model projections of globally averaged surface air temperature through 2100. *Source: Climate Change 2007: Synthesis Report, Contribution of Working Groups I, II and III to the Fourth Assessment Report of the Intergovernmental Panel on Climate Change*[59], *IPCC, figures 3.1 and 3.2, pages 44 and 46.*

In addition to predicting warming of the atmosphere, climate models also suggest that sea level will continue to rise. Since 1880, sea level has risen 20 cm (approximately 8 inches) as seen in Figure **Sea Levels since 1880** (Figure 3.45). This rise has been primarily the result of the water thermally expanding as it warms along with the atmosphere. Polar ice cap melt from land-based ice sheets and glaciers has also added to increase in sea level. The current projection is that sea level will rise at the rate of at least 2 mm per year over the next century, with an overall increase ranging from 15 to 60 inches cm.

---

[59]http://www.ipcc.ch/publications_and_data/ar4/syr/en/figure-spm-5.html

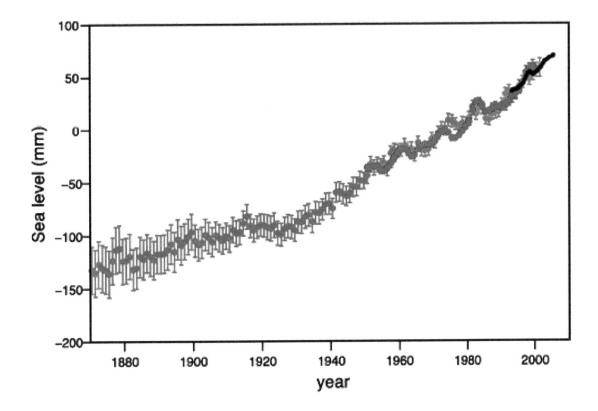

Figure 3.45: Sea Levels since 1880 Measured sea level rise since 1880. The different colors represent different data sets used to make this graph. *Source: Climate Change 2007: The Physical Science Basis:* [60] *Contribution of Working Group I to the Fourth Assessment Report of the Intergovernmental Panel on Climate Change, Cambridge University Press, figure 5.13, page 410* [61]

How much confidence can we place in predictions about temperature and sea level by climate scientists? Let's take a little detour before we address this important question directly. Imagine you are contemplating signing up with a psychic so you can better plan for the future—why save for retirement if money is tight and you're not sure how long you'll live? But you are uncertain about whether she can really see what lies ahead. You could pay her $20 a week for her predictions, and discover over time whether they come true or not. The trouble is, during this trial period you wouldn't know whether to spend your money as fast as you make it or put some aside. But you come up with a better plan. You'll pay the psychic $20 one time, but instead of asking her to predict your future, you'll ask her to tell what has happened to you in the past week. If she gets that right, she gets your business.

Along similar lines, climate scientists assess the trustworthiness of their models by checking how well they "predict" the past. In Figure **Model Simulations** (Figure 3.46), 58 different climate model simulations were tasked with predicting the past climate from 1900 to 2005. By comparing the model simulations to the observed temperature record the scientists with the IPCC tested the accuracy of their models. In Figure **Model Simulations** (Figure 3.46), the yellow lines in the top panel trace out the individual model simulations, the red line shows the model ensemble mean, and the black line represents the actual observed mean temperature. The models performed exceedingly well, as evidenced by the very small variability

---

[60]http://www.ipcc.ch/publications_and_data/ar4/wg1/en/figure-5-13.html
[61]http://www.ipcc.ch/publications_and_data/ar4/wg1/en/figure-5-13.html

around the observed temperature. The success of this test demonstrates the high-quality construction of these models and shows they are capable of accurately projecting the earth's future climate.

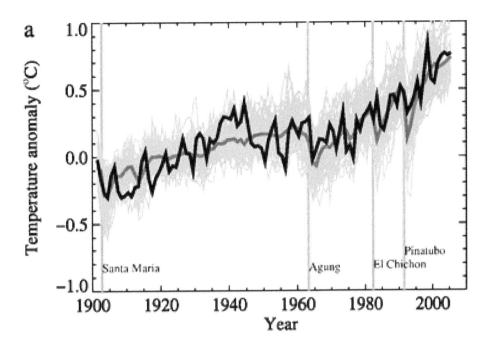

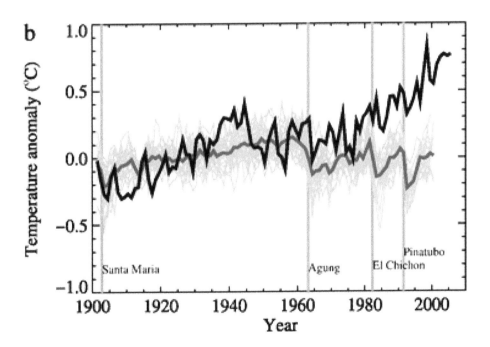

Figure 3.46: Model Simulations Top panel - Climate model simulations of the global mean surface temperature compared to the observed global mean surface temperature in black. Each yellow line is one of 58 climate model simulations of which the red line is the ensemble mean. Bottom panel – 19 climate model simulations in blue with the ensemble mean in dark blue. These simulations were run without anthropogenic influences. The thick black line is the observed global mean surface temperature. For a description of each scenario, please click here[62]. *Source: Climate Change 2007: The Physical Science Basis: Contribution of Working Group I to the Fourth Assessment Report of the Intergovernmental Panel on Climate Change, Cambridge University Press, figure 9.5, page 684*[63]

The bottom of Figure **Model Simulations** (Figure 3.46) and Figure **Global Surface Temperature Comparisons** (Figure 3.47) presents the most compelling argument that current climate change is caused in large part by humans. The bottom panel of Figure **Model Simulations** (Figure 3.46) shows 19 climate model simulations between 1900 and 2000 with human influences left out of the simulations. The thick black line represents the observed global mean surface temperature over this time. Compare this figure with that of Figure **Global Surface Temperature Comparisons** (Figure 3.47), which depicts a series of graphs that plot temperature anomalies against time from the early 1900s to 2000. The blue color shading on these graphs shows the computer model projections without anthropogenic effects, while the pink shading includes them. The black line represents the actual measured air temperatures in each of the locations over which the inlaid graphs are positioned. Notice that without humans the blue shading stays level or decreases with time. Compared with the pink shading and the black line, which both increase with time, and we find that these climate simulations cannot accurately represent the past climate without anthropogenic effects. Simply put, these models are unable to represent our current climate without greenhouse contributions from humans. Rigorous testing like this proves these models are robust and well-designed to simulate future climate conditions.

---

[62]http://www.ipcc.ch/pdf/special-reports/spm/sres-en.pdf
[63]http://www.ipcc.ch/publications_and_data/ar4/wg1/en/figure-9-5.html

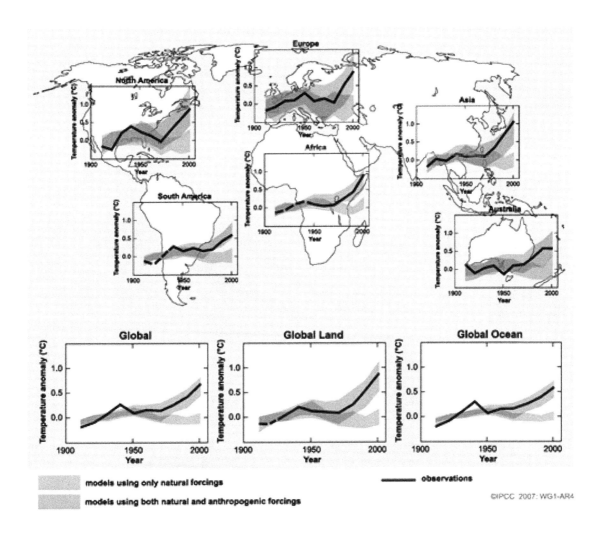

Figure 3.47: Global Surface Temperature Comparisons Comparison of regional and global scale surface temperature 1900-2000. Pink shading indicates the model predicted surface temperature using only natural forcings. The blue indicates model predicted surface temperature using natural and anthropogenic forcings. The black lines represent the actual observations. *Source: Climate Change 2007: The Physical Science Basis: Contribution of Working Group I to the Fourth Assessment Report of the Intergovernmental Panel on Climate Change, Cambridge University Press, FAQ 9.2, figure 1, page 121*[64]

The IPCC began its work in the early 1990's and they have released four reports on climate and climate change. In each report they have included evidence as shown in the sections above. Since a few decades have passed since their initial reports, we can compare the actual changes since 1990 to the IPCC forecasts. Figure **Observed Temperatures vs. Projected Temperatures** (Figure 3.48) compares the observed global average surface temperature to each of the first three reports (the fourth was released in 2007). This figure reveals that both the second (SAR) and third (TAR) reports have been conservative in the projection of globally averaged temperature. It also shows that the observed warming has fallen into the range of expected warming by the IPCC. Due to their success in accurately predicting changes in earth's climate over

---

[64]http://www.ipcc.ch/publications_and_data/ar4/wg1/en/figure-spm-4.html

this time period, the entire body of scientists shared a part of the 2007 Nobel Prize.

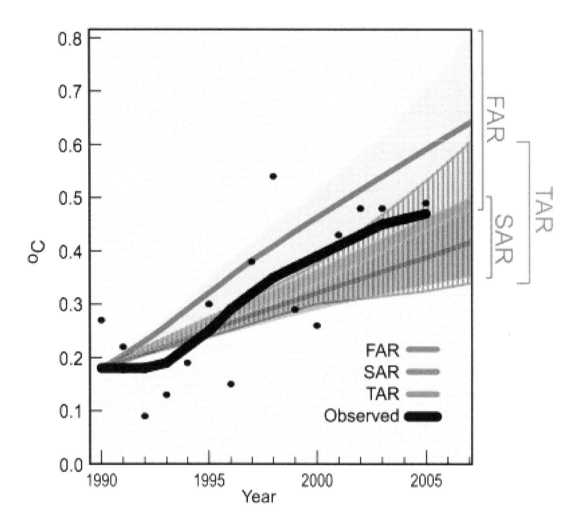

Figure 3.48: Observed Temperatures vs. Projected Temperatures Observed global average surface temperatures (black line) overlaid on the temperature projections of the first IPCC report (FAR), second report (SAR) and third report (TAR). *Source: Climate Change 2007: The Physical Science Basis: Contribution of Working Group I to the Fourth Assessment Report of the Intergovernmental Panel on Climate Change, Cambridge University Press, figure 1.1, page 98*[65]

3.5.6 Global Impacts of Climate Change

Globally, an increase of between $2\,°C$ and $6\,°C$ in mean surface temperature is expected by the year 2100. Regionally, these values may differ substantially, and some locations may actually cool over the next century. The hardest hit locations will be the in the high northerly latitudes of the Arctic. Figure **Projected Temperature Increases** (Figure 3.49) depicts the variation in expected increases in surface air temperature

---

[65]http://www.ipcc.ch/pdf/assessment-report/ar4/wg1/ar4-wg1-chapter1.pdf

for the time period of 2020-2029 and 2090-2099 with color shading. Notice that in all of these images, the greatest changes are expected to occur at high northerly latitudes. If these projections hold true, ice and snow cover will continue to retreat and enhance the ice-albedo effect discussed in Module **Climate Processes; External and Internal Controls** (Section 3.2). Since the 1980s, NH snow-covered area has shrunk by 3 million square kilometers, and many northerly lakes are spending less time each year covered in ice.

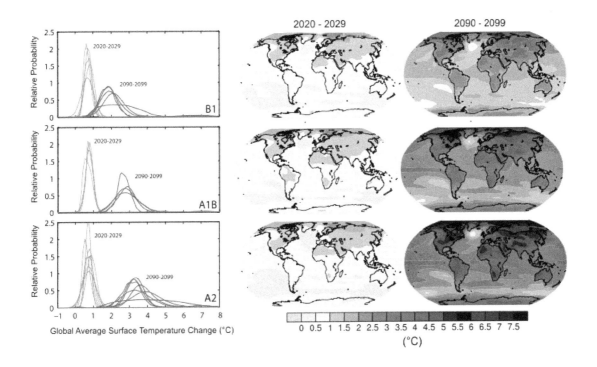

Figure 3.49: Projected Temperature Increases IPCC projected temperature increases for the years 2020-2029 and 2090-2099. *Source: Climate Change 2007: The Physical Science Basis: Contribution of Working Group I to the Fourth Assessment Report of the Intergovernmental Panel on Climate Change, Cambridge University Press, figure SPM.6, page 15*[66]

Aside from air temperature, global precipitation patterns and amounts are expected to change. As the atmosphere warms, its ability to hold water vapor increases, which leads to more evaporation from water on the earth's surface. As this water condenses in the earth's atmosphere to form clouds and precipitation, the distribution of the precipitation will vary greatly. Current projections forecast an increase in precipitation in the tropics and polar latitudes, with drier conditions over the mid-latitudes. Even though there will be more water vapor in the atmosphere, the distribution of precipitation may be such that large regions formerly unused to drought may be subjected to prolonged dry periods. Focus on the middle panels of Figure **Winter and Summer Precipitation Anomalies** (Figure 3.50), which shows the winter (top) and summer (bottom) precipitation anomalies. Notice that the tropics and polar regions are expected to have above normal precipitation, while the mid-latitudes have below normal precipitation. Although more areas are expected to experience prolonged drought, these projections suggest that when it does rain, rainfall will arrive in much greater amounts over shorter time periods. This will lead to increased flash flooding, the deadliest weather phenomenon in the United States.

---

[66]http://www.ipcc.ch/pdf/assessment-report/ar4/wg1/ar4-wg1-spm.pdf

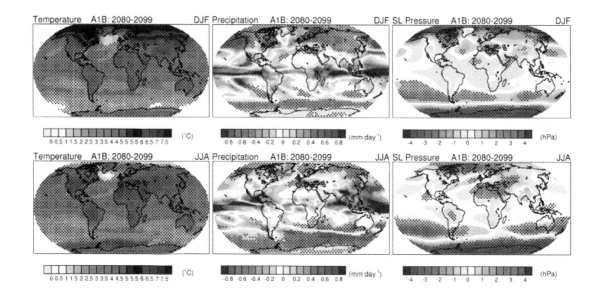

Figure 3.50: Winter and Summer Precipitation Anomalies Global temperature and precipitation projections for 2080-2099 using the A1B scenario. Top panels are temperature (left), precipitation (middle) and sea level pressure (right) for December-January-February. Bottom panels show the same variables for June-July-August. *Source: Climate Change 2007: The Physical Science Basis: Contribution of Working Group I to the Fourth Assessment Report of the Intergovernmental Panel on Climate Change, Cambridge University Press, figure 10.9, page 767*[67]

The goal of climate science is not to craft public policy on global warming. It is to provide the public and policymakers alike with reasonable projections about future climate conditions. This information should be used to show the potential impacts of our presence on the climate system so as to form the best possible mitigation plans. Current projections show that if we are able to slow greenhouse gas emissions, the climate system will respond with the least amount of warming. They also suggest that if we continue with "business as usual" the change in the global climate will be great in magnitude and occur very quickly—both beyond past "natural" change.

3.5.7 Review Questions

Question 3.5.1
How much CO_2 does the average world citizen release each year into the atmosphere? Assume a population of 7 billion people. Compare this number to the United States, China and Qatar.

Question 3.5.2
Explain why the April 2011 tornado outbreak, which set the record for the most tornadoes in a singe 24-hour period, cannot be blamed on climate change.

Question 3.5.3
In Illinois, during the summer of 2009 only two days topped $90\,°F$. In total it was the seventh coolest summer on record. Does this disprove climate change? In what context should we view this cold summer in Illinois?

Question 3.5.4
Why will there still be global warming if there is a complete cessation of CO_2 emissions?

---

[67]http://www.ipcc.ch/publications_and_data/ar4/wg1/en/figure-10-9.html

Question 3.5.5

Carbon cap and trade is one of many solutions proposed to reduce CO2 emissions. Make a list of pros and cons to a federally mandated cap and trade system. Be sure to consider what will happen to consumers, businesses and the federal government.

3.5.8 Resources

For further reading on global climate change, read *A Rough Guide to Climate Change: The Symptoms, The Science, The Solutions*, by Robert Henson (Penguin, 2011, ISBN-13: 978-1843537113)

For more information about the:

U.S. Global Change Research Program, visit http://www.globalchange.gov/publications/reports/scientific-assessments/us-impacts[68]

Global temperatures in the year 2010, visit http://www.yaleclimatemediaforum.org/2011/02/global-temperature-in-2010-hottest-year/[69]

---

[68]http://www.globalchange.gov/publications/reports/scientific-assessments/us-impacts
[69]http://www.yaleclimatemediaforum.org/2011/02/global-temperature-in-2010-hottest-year/

Chapter 4

Biosphere

4.1 Biosphere – Chapter Introduction[1]

4.1.1 Introduction

Humanity and the natural world are inextricably linked. A growing appreciation for the importance of this fact led to the formation and publication of the Millennium Ecosystem Assessment by the United Nations in 2005. It defines key concepts necessary for understanding how sustainable development can be achieved. In the terms of the Assessment, an **ecosystem** is a dynamic complex of plant, animal, and microorganism communities and the nonliving environment interacting as a functional unit, while **ecosystem services** are "the benefits people obtain from ecosystems." Ecosystem services are critical to human well-being and sufficiently diverse and numerous to justify classification into four major categories (see Figure **Ecosystem Services** (p. 117)). **Provisioning ecosystem services** are actively harvested by us from the natural world to meet our resource needs, e.g. food, water, timber, and fiber. **Regulating ecosystem services** are processes in the Earth system that control key physical and biological elements of our environment, e.g. climate regulation, flood regulation, disease regulation, water purification. **Cultural ecosystem services** reflect the aesthetic and spiritual values we place on nature, as well as the educational and recreational activities dependent on ecosystems. Finally, **supporting ecosystem services** are the biogeochemical cycles, as well as biological and physical processes that drive ecosystem function, e.g. soil formation, nutrient cycling, and photosynthesis.

---

[1] This content is available online at <http://legacy.cnx.org/content/m41617/1.5/>.

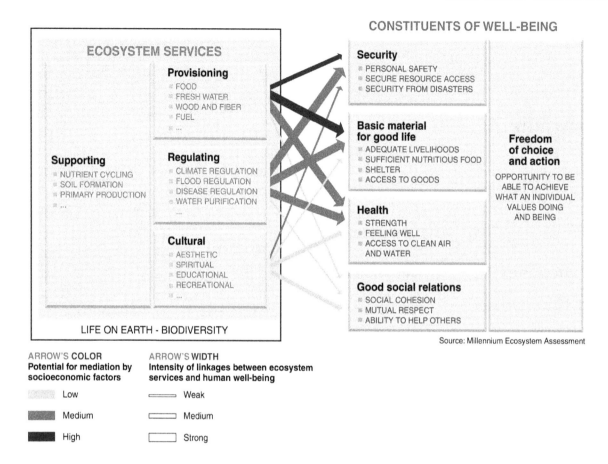

Figure 4.1: Ecosystem Services. Figure shows the linkages between ecosystem services and human well-being. *Source: Millennium Ecosystem Assessment, 2005. Ecosystems and Human Well-being: Synthesis*[2]. *Island Press, Washington, DC.*

We benefit from the services associated with both pristine, natural ecosystems, such as tropical rain forests or arctic tundra, and highly managed ecosystems, such as crop fields or urban landscapes. In all cases, ecosystems contribute to human well-being by influencing the attainability of basic material needs (e.g. food and shelter), health (e.g. clean air and water), good social relations and security (i.e. sufficient resources to avoid conflict, tolerate natural and man-made disasters, provide for children, and maintain social cohesion), as well as freedom of choice and action (an inherent component of the other elements of well-being is the right to live as one chooses). Linkages between some ecosystem services and human well-being vary in strength depending on socio-economic status (see Figure **Ecosystem Services** (p. 117)). For example, many people in developed countries can always afford to buy imported food without dependence on the yields of locally grown crops, thereby avoiding shortages when yields are low because of bad weather. However, in other cases our ability to control the impact of losing an ecosystem service on human well-being is limited. For example, despite major engineering efforts flooding still causes considerable human and economic damage in developed countries.

The challenge of sustainable development stems from the need to benefit from and manage ecosystem services without causing damage to the ecosystems and Earth system that will reduce their value in the longer term. People have long recognized that some ways of using natural resources are unsustainable, especially

---

[2]http://www.maweb.org/en/Synthesis.aspx

where ecosystems are rapidly exploited to the maximum extent possible and further access to the ecosystem services can be achieved only by moving on to previously unexploited areas, as in the case of slash and burn agriculture. Only more recently have we come to appreciate that human activity is altering global-scale phenomena, such as climate regulation, and this understanding raises a host of difficult questions. That is because the benefit of an ecosystem service may be realized by people in one locale, while the costs (in the form of negative environmental consequences) are imposed on people who live elsewhere, and who may be less equipped to withstand them.

The following sections discuss: (1) the natural biogeochemical cycling of carbon, water and nitrogen, the ecosystem services we derive from these biogeochemical cycles and human activities that are disturbing them; (2) species extinctions and ecosystem changes being caused by human activity; and (3) soil, how it is formed, its value to society, and practices that diminish or degrade it.

4.2 Biogeochemical Cycles and the Flow of Energy in the Earth System[3]

4.2.1 Learning Objectives

After reading this module, students should be able to

- explain the concept of a biogeochemical cycle, incorporating the terms "pool" and "flux"
- describe the natural cycles of carbon, water, and nitrogen
- name some of the important ways human activity disrupts those cycles

4.2.2 Introduction

If people are to live sustainably, they will need to understand the processes that control the availability and stability of the ecosystem services on which their well-being depends. Chief among these processes are the **biogeochemical cycles** that describehow chemical elements (e.g. nitrogen, carbon) or molecules (e.g. water) are transformed and stored by both physical and biological components of the Earth system. Storage occurs in **pools**, which are amounts of material that share some common characteristic and are relatively uniform in nature, e.g. the pool of carbon found as carbon dioxide (CO_2) in the atmosphere. Transformations or flows of materials from one pool to another in the cycle are described as **fluxes**; for example, the movement of water from the soil to the atmosphere resulting from evaporation is a flux. **Physical components of the earth system** are nonliving factors such as rocks, minerals, water, climate, air, and energy. **Biological components of the earth system** include all living organisms, e.g. plants, animals and microbes. Both the physical and biological components of the earth system have varied over geological time. Some landmark changes include the colonization of the land by plants ($\sim$400 million years ago), the evolution of mammals ($\sim$200 million years ago), the evolution of modern humans ($\sim$200 thousand years ago) and the end of the last ice age ($\sim$10 thousand years ago). The earth system and its biogeochemical cycles were relatively stable from the end of the last ice age until the Industrial Revolution of the eighteenth and nineteenth centuries initiated a significant and ongoing rise in human population and activity. Today, anthropogenic (human) activities are altering all major ecosystems and the biogeochemical cycles they drive. Many chemical elements and molecules are critical to life on earth, but the biogeochemical cycling of carbon, water, and nitrogen are most critical to human well-being and the natural world.

4.2.3 The Natural Carbon Cycle

Most of the carbon on Earth is stored in sedimentary rocks and does not play a significant role in the carbon cycle on the timescale of decades to centuries. The atmospheric pool of CO_2 is smaller [containing

---

[3]This content is available online at <http://legacy.cnx.org/content/m41618/1.6/>.

800 GtC (gigatonnes of carbon) = 800,000,000,000 tonnes] but is very important because it is a greenhouse gas. The sun emits short-wave radiation that passes through the atmosphere, is absorbed by the Earth, and re-emitted as long-wave radiation. **Greenhouse gases** in the atmosphere absorb this long-wave radiation causing them, and the atmosphere, to warm. The retention of heat in the atmosphere increases and stabilizes the average temperature, making Earth habitable for life. More than a quarter of the atmospheric CO_2 pool is absorbed each year through the process of photosynthesis by a combination of plants on land (120 GtC) and at sea (90 GtC). **Photosynthesis** is the process in which plants use energy from sunlight to combine CO_2 from the atmosphere with water to make sugars, and in turn build biomass. Almost as much carbon is stored in terrestrial plant biomass (550 GtC) as in the atmospheric CO_2 pool. On land, biomass that has been incorporated into soil forms a relatively large pool (2300 GtC). At sea, the phytoplankton that perform photosynthesis sink after they die, transporting organic carbon to deeper layers that then either are preserved in ocean sediments or decomposed into a very large dissolved inorganic carbon pool (37,000 GtC). Plants are called **primary producers** because they are the primary entry point of carbon into the biosphere. In other words, almost all animals and microbes depend either directly or indirectly on plants as a source of carbon for energy and growth. All organisms, including plants, release CO_2 to the atmosphere as a by-product of generating energy and synthesizing biomass through the process of **respiration**. The natural carbon cycle is balanced on both land and at sea, with plant respiration and microbial respiration (much of it associated with decomposition, or rotting of dead organisms) releasing the same amount of CO_2 as is removed from the atmosphere through photosynthesis.

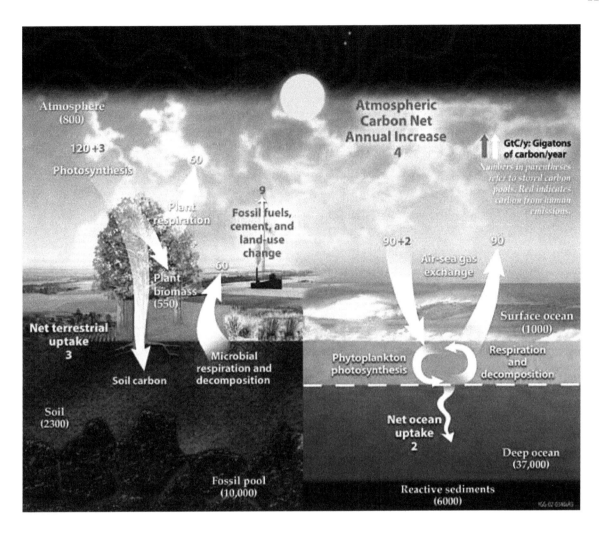

Figure 4.2: The Carbon Cycle. Figure illustrates the carbon cycle on, above, and below the Earth's surface. *Source: U.S. Department of Energy Genomic Science Program*[4].

4.2.3.1 Human Interactions with The Carbon Cycle

The global carbon cycle contributes substantially to the provisioning ecosystem services upon which humans depend. We harvest approximately 25% of the total plant biomass that is produced each year on the land surface to supply food, fuel wood and fiber from croplands, pastures and forests. In addition, the global carbon cycle plays a key role in regulating ecosystem services because it significantly influences climate via its effects on atmospheric CO_2 concentrations. Atmospheric CO_2 concentration increased from 280 parts per million (ppm) to 390 ppm between the start of industrial revolution in the late eighteenth century and 2010. This reflected a new flux in the global carbon cycle —**anthropogenic CO2 emissions**— where humans release CO_2 into the atmosphere by burning fossil fuels and changing land use. Fossil fuel burning takes carbon from coal, gas, and oil reserves, where it would be otherwise stored on very long time scales, and introduces it into the active carbon cycle. **Land use change** releases carbon from soil and plant biomass

[4]http://genomicscience.energy.gov/carboncycle/index.shtml#page=news

pools into the atmosphere, particularly through the process of deforestation for wood extraction or conversion of land to agriculture. In 2009, the additional flux of carbon into the atmosphere from anthropogenic sources was estimated to be 9 GtC—a significant disturbance to the natural carbon cycle that had been in balance for several thousand years previously. Slightly more than half of this anthropogenic CO_2 is currently being absorbed by greater photosynthesis by plants on land and at sea (5 GtC). However, that means 4 GtC is being added to the atmospheric pool each year and, while total emissions are increasing, the proportion absorbed by photosynthesis and stored on land and in the oceans is declining (Le Quere et al., 2009 (p. 126)). Rising atmospheric CO_2 concentrations in the twentieth century caused increases in temperature and started to alter other aspects of the global environment. Global environmental change has already caused a measurable decrease in the global harvest of certain crops. The scale and range of impacts from global environmental change of natural and agricultural ecosystems is projected to increase over the twenty-first century, and will pose a major challenge to human well-being.

4.2.4 The Natural Water Cycle

The vast majority of water on Earth is saline (salty) and stored in the oceans. Meanwhile, most of the world's fresh water is in the form of ice, snow, and groundwater. This means a significant fraction of the water pool is largely isolated from the water cycle. The major long-term stores of fresh water include ice sheets in Antarctica and Greenland, as well as groundwater pools that were filled during wetter periods of past geological history. In contrast, the water stored in rivers, lakes, and ocean surface is relatively rapidly cycled as it evaporates into the atmosphere and then falls back to the surface as precipitation. The atmospheric pool of water turns over most rapidly because it is small compared to the other pools (e.g. <15% of the freshwater lake pool). **Evaporation** is the process whereby water is converted from a liquid into a vapor as a result of absorbing energy (usually from solar radiation). Evaporation from vegetated land is referred to as **evapotranspiration** because it includes water transpired by plants, i.e. water taken up from the soil by roots, transported to leaves and evaporated from leaf surfaces into the atmosphere via stomatal pores. **Precipitation** is the conversion of atmospheric water from vapor into liquid (rain) or solid forms (snow, hail) that then fall to Earth's surface. Some water from precipitation moves over the land surface by **surface runoff** and **streamflow**, while other water from precipitation **infiltrates** the soil and moves below the surface as **groundwater discharge**. Water vapor in the atmosphere is commonly moved away from the source of evaporation by wind and the movement of air masses. Consequently, most water falling as precipitation comes from a source of evaporation that is located upwind. Nonetheless, local sources of evaporation can contribute as much as 25-33% of water in precipitation.

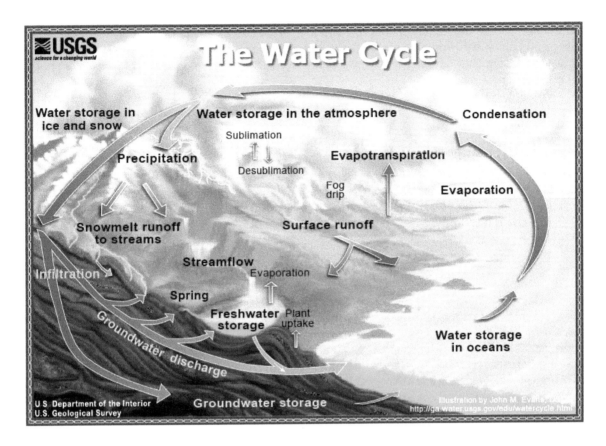

Figure 4.3: The Water Cycle. Figure illustrates the water cycle on, above, and below the Earth's surface. *Source: U.S. Department of the Interior and U.S. Geological Survey, The Water Cycle*[5].

4.2.4.1 Human Interactions with The Water Cycle

Freshwater supply is one of the most important provisioning ecosystem services on which human well-being depends. By 2000, the rate of our water extraction from rivers and aquifers had risen to almost 4000 cubic kilometers per year. The greatest use of this water is for irrigation in agriculture, but significant quantities of water are also extracted for public and municipal use, as well as industrial applications and power generation. Other major human interventions in the water cycle involve changes in land cover and infrastructure development of river networks. As we have deforested areas for wood supply and agricultural development we have reduced the amount of vegetation, which naturally acts to trap precipitation as it falls and slow the rate of infiltration into the ground. As a consequence, surface runoff has increased. This, in turn, means flood peaks are greater and erosion is increased. Erosion lowers soil quality and deposits sediment in river channels, where it can block navigation and harm aquatic plants and animals. Where agricultural land is also drained these effects can be magnified. Urbanization also accelerates streamflow by preventing precipitation from filtering into the soil and shunting it into drainage systems. Additional physical infrastructure has been added to river networks with the aim of altering the volume, timing, and direction of water flows for human benefit. This is achieved with reservoirs, weirs, and diversion channels. For example, so much water is removed or redirected from the Colorado River in the western United States that, despite its considerable size, in some years it is dry before reaching the sea in Mexico. We also exploit

---

[5]http://ga.water.usgs.gov/edu/watercycle.html

waterways through their use for navigation, recreation, hydroelectricity generation and waste disposal. These activities, especially waste disposal, do not necessarily involve removal of water, but do have impacts on water quality and water flow that have negative consequences for the physical and biological properties of aquatic ecosystems.

The water cycle is key to the ecosystem service of climate regulation as well as being an essential supporting service that impacts the function of all ecosystems. Consider the widespread impacts on diverse natural and human systems when major droughts or floods occur. Consequently, human disruptions of the natural water cycle have many undesirable effects and challenge sustainable development. There are two major concerns. First, the need to balance rising human demand with the need to make our water use sustainable by reversing ecosystem damage from excess removal and pollution of water. Traditionally, considerable emphasis has been on finding and accessing more supply, but the negative environmental impacts of this approach are now appreciated, and improving the efficiency of water use is now a major goal. Second, there is a need for a safe water supply in many parts of the world, which depends on reducing water pollution and improving water treatment facilities.

4.2.5 The Natural Nitrogen Cycle

The vast majority of nitrogen on Earth is held in rocks and plays a minor role in the nitrogen cycle. The second largest pool of nitrogen is in the atmosphere. Most atmospheric nitrogen is in the form of N_2 gas, and most organisms are unable to access it. This is significant because nitrogen is an essential component of all cells—for instance, in protein, RNA, and DNA—and nitrogen availability frequently limits the productivity of crops and natural vegetation. Atmospheric nitrogen is made available to plants in two ways. Certain microbes are capable of **biological nitrogen fixation**, whereby N_2 is converted into ammonium, a form of nitrogen that plants can access. Many of these microbes have formed symbiotic relationships with plants— they live within the plant tissue and use carbon supplied by the plant as an energy source, and in return they share ammonia produced by nitrogen fixation. Well-known examples of plants that do this are peas and beans. Some microbes that live in the soil are also capable of nitrogen fixation, but many are found in a zone very close to roots, where significant carbon sources are released from the plant. Together these biological nitrogen fixing processes on land, coupled with others that take place at sea, generate an annual flux out of the atmosphere of approximately 200 MtN (megatonnnes of nitrogen or 200,000,000 tonnes of nitrogen). Lightning causes nitrogen and oxygen in the atmosphere to react and produce nitrous oxides that fall or are washed out of the atmosphere by rain and into the soil, but the is flux is much smaller (30 MtN per year at most) than biological nitrogen fixation.

While the inputs of nitrogen from the atmosphere to the biosphere are important, the majority (90%) of nitrogen used by plants for growth each year comes from ammonification of organic material. Organic material is matter that comes from once-living organisms. **Ammonification** (or mineralization) is the release of ammonia by **decomposers** (bacteria and fungi) when they break down the complex nitrogen compounds in organic material. Plants are able to absorb (**assimilate**) this ammonia, as well as nitrates, which are made available by bacterial **nitrification**. The cycle of nitrogen incorporation in growing plant tissues and nitrogen release by bacteria from decomposing plant tissues is the dominant feature of the nitrogen cycle and occurs very efficiently. Nitrogen can be lost from the system in three main ways. First, **denitrifying bacteria** convert nitrates to nitrous oxide or N_2 gases that are released back to the atmosphere. Denitrification occurs when the bacteria grow under oxygen-depleted conditions, and is therefore favored by wet and waterlogged soils. Denitrification rates almost match biological nitrogen fixation rates, with wetlands making the greatest contribution. Second, nitrates are washed out of soil in drainage water (**leaching**) and into rivers and the ocean. Third, nitrogen is also cycled back into the atmosphere when organic material burns.

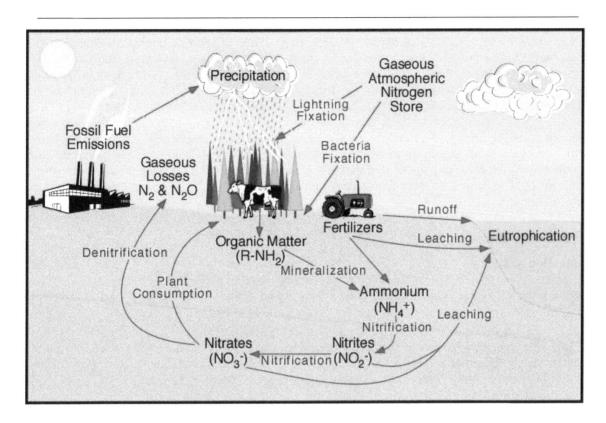

Figure 4.4: The Nitrogen Cycle. Figure illustrates the nitrogen cycle on, above, and below the Earth's surface. *Source: Physical Geography Fundamentals eBook*[6].

4.2.5.1 Human Interactions With The Nitrogen Cycle

Humans are primarily dependent on the nitrogen cycle as a supporting ecosystem service for crop and forest productivity. Nitrogen fertilizers are added to enhance the growth of many crops and plantations. The enhanced use of fertilizers in agriculture was a key feature of the green revolution that boosted global crop yields in the 1970s. The industrial production of nitrogen-rich fertilizers has increased substantially over time and now matches more than half of the input to the land from biological nitrogen fixation (90 MtN each year). If the nitrogen fixation from leguminous crops (e.g. beans, alfalfa) is included, then the anthropogenic flux of nitrogen from the atmosphere to the land exceeds natural fluxes to the land. As described above, most ecosystems naturally retain and recycle almost all of their nitrogen. The relatively little nitrogen that is being gained or lost by fluxes to the atmosphere and water cycle is also nearly being balanced. When humans make large additions of nitrogen to ecosystems leakage often results, with negative environmental consequences. When the amount of nitrate in the soil exceeds plant uptake, the excess nitrate is either leached in drainage water to streams, rivers, and the ocean or denitrified by bacteria and lost to the atmosphere. One of the main gases produced by denitrifying bacteria (nitrous oxide) is an important greenhouse gas that is contributing to human-induced global warming. Other gases released to the atmosphere by denitrifying bacteria, as well as ammonia released from livestock and sewage sludge, are later deposited from the atmosphere onto ecosystems. The additional nitrogen from this deposition,

---

[6]http://www.physicalgeography.net/fundamentals/9s.html

along with the nitrogen leaching into waterways, causes eutrophication. **Eutrophication** occurs when plant growth and then decay is accelerated by an unusually high supply of nitrogen, and it has knock-on effects, including the following: certain plant species out-competing other species, leading to biodiversity loss and altered ecosystem function; algal blooms that block light and therefore kill aquatic plants in rivers, lakes, and seas; exhaustion of oxygen supplies in water caused by rapid microbial decomposition at the end of algal blooms, which kills many aquatic organisms. Excess nitrates in water supplies have also been linked to human health problems. Efforts to reduce nitrogen pollution focus on increasing the efficiency of synthetic fertilizer use, altering feeding of animals to reduce nitrogen content in their excreta, and better processing of livestock waste and sewage sludge to reduce ammonia release. At the same time, increasing demand for food production from a growing global population with a greater appetite for meat is driving greater total fertilizer use, so there is no guarantee that better practices will lead to a reduction in the overall amount of nitrogen pollution.

4.2.6 Review Questions

Question 4.2.1
There is approximately 2,000 cubic kilometers of water stored in rivers around the world. Using the terms *water cycle*, *flux* and *pool*, describe under what conditions removing 1000 cubic kilometers per year from rivers for human use could be sustainable.

Question 4.2.2
Each year, around a quarter of the carbon dioxide found in the atmosphere is turned into plant matter via photosynthesis. Does this mean that, in the absence of human activity, all carbon dioxide would be removed from the atmosphere in around four years? Explain your answer.

Question 4.2.3
The water, carbon, and nitrogen cycles are all influenced by human activity. Can you describe a human activity that impacts all three cycles? In your example, which of the cycles is most significantly altered?

4.2.7 References

Le Quere, C., Raupach, M. R., Canadell, J. G., Marland, G., Bopp, L., Ciais, P., et al. (2009, December). Trends in the sources and sinks of carbon dioxide. *Nature Geoscience, 2*, 831-836. doi: 10.1038/ngeo689

Millennium Ecosystem Assessment (2005). Ecosystems and Human Well-Being: Synthesis. Washington DC. Retrieved from http://www.maweb.org/en/Reports.aspx[7]

4.3 Biodiversity, Species Loss, and Ecosystem Function[8]

4.3.1 Learning Objectives

After reading this module, students should be able to

- define biodiversity
- articulate current trends in biodiversity loss with reference to species and ecosystems
- explain some of the ways human activity affects biodiversity
- explain how biodiversity loss concerns people

---

[7]http://www.maweb.org/en/Reports.aspx
[8]This content is available online at <http://legacy.cnx.org/content/m41619/1.6/>.

4.3.2 What is Biodiversity?

You're probably familiar with the word, **biodiversity**, whether or not you can give an exact definition of it. It's common on the signs at zoos, parks, and nature centers, and it's often used without explanation or definition. Most people understand biodiversity in general terms as the number and mix of plant and animal species that occurs in a given place. Scientists are more precise and include more in their definition. The International Union for the Conservation of Nature (IUCN)[9] , which coordinates efforts to catalogue and preserve biodiversity worldwide, defines biodiversity as "the variability among living organisms from all sources including terrestrial, marine and other aquatic ecosystems, and the ecological complexes of which they are part; this includes diversity within species, between species, and of ecosystems." Rather than just species, biodiversity therefore includes variation from the level of genes and genomes to that of ecosystems to biomes.

Even within a single ecosystem, the numbers of species can be impressive. For example, there is a large region of dry forest and savanna in Brazil known as the Cerrado (see Figure **Cerrado Forest** (Figure 4.5)). This ecosystem alone hosts over 10,000 species of plants, almost 200 species of mammals, over 600 species of birds, and about 800 species of fish.

Figure 4.5: Cerrado Forest. Photograph of the Cerrado Forest. *Source: C2rik via Wikimedia Commons*[10].

---

[9]http://www.iucn.org/

Generally, biodiversity is greatest in tropical areas–especially "rainforests"—but there are terrestrial biodiversity "hotspots" on all the major continents. (View an interactive map of hotspots[11] .)

4.3.3 Current Trends: Species Loss and Decline

One way scientists gauge trends in biodiversity is by monitoring the fate of individual species of animals and plants. For more than 40 years, the IUCN has compiled information in the "Red List of Threatened Species," which "provides a snapshot of what is happening to species around the world." Updates to the Red List are released every four years. Here is how the authors of the most recent one, released in 2008, characterize the news it holds: "The overwhelming message" from the 2008 Red List, they write, "is that the world is losing species and that the rate of loss appears to be accelerating in many taxonomic groups" (Vie, Hilton-Taylor, & Stuart, 2008, p. 38 (p. 134)).

---

[10]http://en.wikipedia.org/wiki/File:Cerrado.jpg
[11]http://www.biodiversityhotspots.org/xp/hotspots/Pages/default.aspx

	Estimated Number of described species[7]	Number of species evaluated	Number of threatened species[8]	Number threatened, as % of species described[8]	Number threatened, as % of species evaluated[8,9]
Vertebrates					
Mammals[1]	5,488	5,488	1,141	21%	21%
Birds	9,990	9,990	1,222	12%	12%
Reptiles	8,734	1,385	423	5%	31%
Amphibians[2]	6,347	6,260	1,905	30%	30%
Fishes	30,700	3,481	1,275	4%	37%
Subtotal	**61,259**	**26,604**	**5,966**	**10%**	**22%**
Invertebrates					
Insects	950,000	1,259	626	0%	50%
Molluscs	81,000	2,212	978	1%	44%
Crustaceans	40,000	1,735	606	2%	35%
Corals	2,175	856	235	11%	27%
Arachnids	98,000	32	18	0%	56%
Velvet Worms	165	11	9	5%	82%
Horseshoe Crabs	4	4	0	0%	0%
Others	61,040	52	24	0%	46%
Subtotal	**1,232,384**	**6,161**	**2,496**	**0.20%**	**41%**
Plants[3]					
Mosses[4]	16,000	95	82	1%	86%
Ferns and allies[5]	12,838	211	139	1%	66%
Gymnosperms	980	910	323	33%	35%
Dicotyledons	199,350	9,624	7,122	4%	74%
Monocotyledons	59,300	1,155	782	1%	68%
Green Algae[6]	3,962	2	0	0%	0%
Red Algae[6]	6,076	58	9	0%	16%
Subtotal	**298,506**	**12,055**	**8,457**	**3%**	**70%**
Others					
Lichens	17,000	2	2	0%	100%
Mushrooms	30,000	1	1	0%	100%
Brown Algae[6]	3,040	15	6	0%	40%
Subtotal	**50,040**	**18**	**9**	**0.02%**	**50%**
TOTAL	**1,642,189**	**44,838**	**16,928**	**1%**	**38%**

Figure 4.6: **Summary of Threatened Species**. Table lists the numbers and proportions of species assessed as threatened on the 2008 IUCN Red List by major taxonomic group. *Source: IUCN Red List, Wildlife in a Changing World 2008*[12], *p. 17. Please see IUCN Terms of Use*[13] *for copyright restrictions.*

4.3.3.1 Vertebrates

Scientists know much more about the state of vertebrates—especially mammals, birds, and amphibians—than they do about other forms of animal life. Every one of the 5,488 species of mammals that have been

---

[12]http://iucn.org/about/work/programmes/species/red_list/review/
[13]http://www.iucnredlist.org/info/terms-of-use

described, for example, has been evaluated for purposes of the Red List. Of them, 76 species have become **extinct** since 1500, and two, Pere David's deer, which is native to China, and the scimitar oryx from Africa survive only in managed facilities. Another 29 of the mammal species listed as critically endangered are also tagged as "possibly extinct;" they are very likely gone, but the sort of exhaustive surveys required to confirm that fact have not been conducted. Overall, approximately 22% of mammal species worldwide are known to be threatened or extinct. (In the terms of the Red List, the broad designation "threatened" includes three levels of risk for extinction in the wild: Vulnerable [high], Endangered [higher], and Critically Endangered [highest].)

The Red List categorizes a smaller proportion of the world's 9,990 described bird species—14%—as threatened or extinct. But the raw number of species lost since 1500 is at least 134, and four more species persist only in zoos. Another 15 species of birds are considered possibly extinct. The fact that 86% of bird species are categorized as "not threatened" is good news in the context of the Red List.

Figure 4.7: Passenger Pigeons. North American passenger pigeons lived in enormous flocks and were once the most numerous birds on earth. Market hunting on a massive scale and habitat destruction combined to extinguish them as a species in the early twentieth century. *Source: Ltshears via Wikimedia Commons*[14]

Among the well-studied vertebrates, amphibians are faring especially poorly. Of the more than 6,000 known species of amphibians, 38 have become extinct worldwide since 1500, and another one, the Wyoming toad, survives only in captivity. Another 120 species are considered possibly extinct. Overall, 2,030, or

---

[14]http://commons.wikimedia.org/wiki/File:Passenger_Pigeon_065.jpg

one-third of the world's amphibian species are known to be threatened or extinct. More troubling still, many amphibian species—42.5%—are reported to be declining, and that number is probably low, since trend information is unavailable for 30.4% of species.

Figure 4.8: Monteverde Golden Toad. The golden toad of Monteverde, Costa Rica, is one of 11 species of amphibians to become extinct since 1980. Habitat loss and chytrid fungus. *Source: U.S. Fish and Wildlife Service via Wikimedia Commons*[15].

Only small proportions of the world's species of reptiles and fish have been evaluated for purposes of the Red List. Among those, the numbers of species that fall into the threatened category are very high: 1,275 of the 3,481 evaluated species, or 37%, for fish; and 423 of 1,385 evaluated species, or 31%, for reptiles. It should be noted, however, that these percentages are likely overestimates, since species of concern are more likely to be selected for evaluation than others.

4.3.3.2 Invertebrates

The category "invertebrates" lumps together the vast majority of multi-cellular animals, an estimated 97% of all species. It includes everything from insects and arachnids, to mollusks, crustaceans, corals, and more. Few of these groups have been assessed in a comprehensive way, and so as with fish and reptiles, the Red List percentages of threatened species are skewed high. But assessments within some groups call attention to disturbing, large-scale trends. For example, 27% of the world's reef-building corals are already considered threatened, and many more of them are experiencing rates of decline that move them toward threatened

---

[15]http://en.wikipedia.org/wiki/File:Bufo_periglenes2.jpg

status. The demise of reef-building corals has magnified ecological impacts, since so much other marine life depends on them.

Figure 4.9: Pink Soft Coral with Reef Fish. Photograph shows some pink, soft coral with reef fish nearby. *Source: Linda Wade via National Oceanic & Atmospheric Administration (NOAA)*[16].

It should be understood that information about familiar creatures such as amphibians, mammals, and birds is just a beginning, and that even with the inclusion of some invertebrates the Red List does not provide a comprehensive picture of life on Earth. Scientists have described fewer than 2 million of the 8-9 million species of organisms thought to exist, most of which are insects. And of those 2 million, the status of only 44,838 has been assessed by IUCN.

---

[16]http://www.photolib.noaa.gov/htmls/reef0484.htm

In addition, it should be understood that among the species that have been assessed so far, there is a strong bias toward terrestrial vertebrates and plants, especially the ones that occur where biologists have visited frequently. Red List assessments also tend to focus on species that are likely to be threatened, since the effort also has the aim of enabling people to conserve species.

Whereas extinction is the global loss of a species, the elimination of species at a local level–known as **extirpation** – also poses threats to the integrity and sustainability of ecosystems. Widespread extirpation obviously leads to threatened or endangered status, but absence of species, even at a local scale, can affect **ecosystem function**. For example, by the mid-1920s wolves had been extirpated from Yellowstone National Park, although they continued to thrive elsewhere. When wolves were reintroduced to the park in the mid 1990s, numbers of elk (a main prey item) decreased significantly. This, in turn, reduced browsing pressure and had a significant effect on the vegetation and plant communities. What mattered for ecosystem function in Yellowstone was whether wolves were present *there*, not just whether the species survived somewhere.

The human activities that account for extinction and extirpation vary considerably from one species to another, but they fall into a few broad categories: habitat destruction and fragmentation; intentional and unintentional movement of species that become invasive (including disease-causing organisms); over-exploitation (unsustainable hunting, logging, etc.); habitat/ecosystem degradation (e.g. pollution, climate change).

4.3.4 Current Trends: Ecosystem Loss and Alteration

Another way of gauging biodiversity involves assessment on the scale of ecosystems. The causes of wholesale losses of ecosystems are much the same as those driving extinction or endangerment of species, with habitat loss and fragmentation being the primary agent. Worldwide, for example, the conversion of land to agriculture and cultivation have led to significant losses in grassland ecosystems. In North America, nearly 70% of the tallgrass prairie ecosystem (which once covered 142 million acres) has been converted to agriculture, and losses from other causes, such as urban development, have brought the total to about 90%. Current estimates indicate that agricultural activity and cultivation systems now cover nearly 25% of the Earth's surface.

Tropical rainforests, which are the habitats for nearly half of the world's plant and animal species, covered about 4 billion acres in past centuries, but only 2.5 billion acres remain and nearly 1% is being lost annually. Losses have been especially severe in the "paleo" or old world tropics that include Africa and Southeast Asia.

The category "wetlands" includes many types of ecosystems, but current estimates indicate that about 50% of the world's wetland habitat has been lost. The former extent of wetland habitats worldwide (fresh, brackish and salt) is difficult to determine but certainly exceeded a billion acres.

4.3.5 Species and Ecosystem Loss in Perspective

To understand why biologists talk about ongoing losses of species and ecosystems as the "biodiversity crisis," it is useful to put current and projected rates of species loss into historical perspective. Over the history of life on Earth—a span of 3.5 *billion* years—nearly all species that existed eventually became extinct. This, of course, is coupled with the processes of speciation and biological diversification. Rates of extinction and diversification have fluctuated significantly over geologic time. For extinction, paleontologists have detected five episodes of mass extinction over the last 540 million years. These periods contrast with the relatively constant "background rate" of extinction observed over the geologic record, and include the relatively well-known event 65 million years ago when most of the extant dinosaurs went extinct. By definition, these episodes are characterized by the comparatively rapid loss of at least three-fourths of the species thought to exist at the onset of the event.

Recently, the question has been posed whether present-day rates of species loss constitute a sixth episode of mass extinction (Barnosky, et al., 2011 (p. 134)). Even with caveats about uncertainty in how many species there are today (only a fraction of the estimated total have been described, especially for plants, invertebrates, and microbes) and about comparisons of the fossil record with modern data, it appears that estimated rates of loss in the near future could rival those of past mass extinctions. Some estimates indicate that we will see a 30% loss of species within decades. Put another way, forecasted rates of species loss could be as much as 1000 to 10,000 times higher than background rates.

4.3.6 How Does Loss of Biodiversity Concern People?

As we learn more about biodiversity, it is becoming clear that there is often a positive association between biodiversity and the integrity of biological systems. This is not to say more diverse systems are "better;" rather, this means that systems with a relatively pristine complement of biological and abiotic or physical components tend to be more resilient and robust. Whereas this is rather nebulous, there is little doubt that the integrity of ecosystems is of fundamental importance to nearly all phases of human life and culture.

Often called **ecological services**, the products and processes associated with biological systems are of immense value to the well being of people. An incomplete list of these services and products includes the formation of soil and cycling of nutrients; provisioning of food, fresh water, fuel, fiber, and recreation opportunities; the regulation of climate, flooding, and disease. The value of these services is often overlooked or simply taken for granted, but one global estimate puts it somewhere between $16-64 trillion annually. From global food security, to a source of medicines, to even the oxygen in our air, we are dependent on biodiversity and the sustained integrity of ecological systems. Nature is also the basis for a significant part of aesthetic and spiritual values held by many cultures.

Given this dependence, it is astounding that many are unaware or—even worse—apathetic about what is occurring and what will likely happen in the near future to our biological resources. We do not contend that any loss of species will affect productivity or function at the ecosystem level. The function of one species can be redundant with others and its loss may not lead to a significant change at the ecosystem level. Whereas redundancy can contribute to the resiliency of natural systems, that should not be a source of comfort. Much ecological theory posits thresholds of species loss beyond which the integrity of ecosystems is threatened; unexpected and possibly permanent new "states" may result. Once a community or ecosystem reaches an alternative state, there may be little that can be done to restore or remediate the system. Therefore, even under optimistic scenarios for rates of species loss (from the local to global scale) we are facing an uncertain environment.

4.3.7 Review Questions

Question 4.3.1
What is the difference between extinction and extirpation?

Question 4.3.2
What are some human activities that impact species diversity and ecosystem function?

Question 4.3.3
Does the loss of one species lead to loss of ecosystem function? Why or why not?

Question 4.3.4
How does biodiversity promote sustainability?

4.3.8 References

Barnosky, A.D., Matzke, N., Tomiya, S., Wogan, G.O.U., Swartz, B., Quental, T.B., et al. (2011, March). Has the Earth's sixth mass extinction already arrived? *Nature, 471,* 51-57. doi:10.1038/nature09678

Vie, J-C, Hilton-Taylor, C. & Stuart S.N. (Eds.). (2009). *Wildlife in a Changing World: An Analysis of the 2008 IUCN Red List of Threatened Species*™. Gland, Switzerland: IUCN. Retrieved from http://data.iucn.org/dbtw-wpd/edocs/RL-2009-001.pdf[17] .

[17]http://data.iucn.org/dbtw-wpd/edocs/RL-2009-001.pdf

4.4 Soil and Sustainability[18]

4.4.1 Learning Objectives

After reading this module, students should be able to

- define soil and comment on its importance to society
- describe how soil profiles form
- explain the importance of soil constituents for plant growth and nutrient uptake
- understand the importance of soil to agricultural sustainability and ecological processes

4.4.2 Soil Profiles and Processes

4.4.2.1 What Is Soil?

The word "soil" has been defined differently by different scientific disciplines. In agriculture and horticulture, soil generally refers to the medium for plant growth, typically material within the upper meter or two (see Figure **Soil Profile** (Figure 4.10)).

---

[18]This content is available online at <http://legacy.cnx.org/content/m41620/1.8/>.

Figure 4.10: Soil Profile. Photograph shows a soil profile from South Dakota with A, E, and Bt horizons. The yellow arrows symbolize translocation of fine clays to the Bt horizon. The scale is in feet. *Source: University of Idaho*[19] *and modified by D. Grimley.*

We will use this definition in this chapter. In common usage, the term soil is sometimes restricted to only the dark topsoil in which we plant our seeds or vegetables. In a more broad definition, civil engineers use the term soil for any unconsolidated (soft when wet) material that is not considered bedrock. Under this definition, soil can be as much as several hundred feet thick! Ancient soils, sometimes buried and preserved in the subsurface, are referred to as paleosols (see Figure **Modern versus Buried Soil Profiles** (Figure 4.11)) and reflect past climatic and environmental conditions.

---

[19] http://soils.cals.uidaho.edu/soilorders/i/Moll_02b.jpg

Figure 4.11: Modern versus Buried Soil Profiles. A buried soil profile, or paleosol (above geologist 's head), represents soil development during the last interglacial period. A modern soil profile (Alfisol) occurs near the land surface. *Source: D. Grimley.*

From a somewhat philosophical standpoint, soil can be viewed as the interface between the atmosphere and the earth's crust, and is sometimes referred to as the skin of the earth. Soil also incorporates aspects of the biosphere and the hydrosphere. From a physical standpoint, soil contains solid, liquid, and gaseous phases. The solid portion of the soil consists predominantly of mineral matter, but also contains organic matter (humus) and living organisms. The pore spaces between mineral grains are filled with varying proportions of water and air.

4.4.2.2 Importance of Soil

Soil is important to our society as it provides the foundation for most of the critical aspects of civilization. Our building structures and homes, food, agricultural products, and wood products all rely on soil. Forests, prairies, and wetlands all have a dependence on soil. Of course, soil is also a critical component for terrestrial life on earth, including most animals, plants, and many microorganisms.

Soil plays a role in nearly all natural cycles on the earth's surface. Global cycling of key nutrients, such as Carbon (C), Nitrogen (N), Sulfur (S), and Phosphorous (P), all pass through soil. In the hydrologic cycle, soil helps to mediate the flow of precipitation from the land surface into the groundwater or can control stormwater runoff into lakes, streams, bays, and oceans. Soil microorganisms or microflora can help to modify or destroy environmental pollutants.

4.4.2.3 Soil Forming Factors

The fundamental factors that affect soil genesis can be categorized into five elements: climate, organisms, relief, parent material, and time. One could say that the landscape *relief*, *climate*, and *organisms* dictate the local soil environment, and act together to cause weathering and mixing of the soil *parent material* over *time*. The soil forming factors are interrelated and interdependent, but considered independently they provide a useful framework for discussion and categorization.

As soil is formed it often has distinct layers, which are formally described as "horizons." Upper horizons (labeled as the A and O horizons) are richer in organic material and so are important in plant growth, while deeper layers (such as the B and C horizons) retain more of the original features of the bedrock below.

4.4.2.3.1 Climate

The role of climate in soil development includes aspects of temperature and precipitation.Soils in very cold areas with permafrost conditions (*Gelisols*) tend to be shallow and weakly developed due to the short growing season. Organic rich surface horizons are common in low-lying areas due to limited chemical decomposition. In warm, tropical soils (*Ultisols, Oxisols*), other factors being equal, soils tend to be thicker, with extensive leaching and mineral alteration. In such climates, organic matter decomposition and chemical weathering occur at an accelerated rate.

4.4.2.3.2 Organisms

Animals, plants, and microorganisms all have important roles in soil development processes, in providing a supply of organic matter, and/or in nutrient cycling. Worms, nematodes, termites, ants, gophers, moles, crayfish, etc. all cause considerable mixing of soil and help to blend soil, aerate and lighten the soil by creating porosity, and create characteristic natural soil structure over time. Animal life, such as insects and mammals, can cause irregularities in the soil horizons.

Plant life provides much organic matter to soil and helps to recycle nutrients with uptake by roots in the subsurface. The type of plant life that occurs in a given area, such as types of trees or grasses, depends on the climate, along with parent material and soil type. So there are clearly feedbacks among the soil forming factors. With the annual dropping of leaves and needles, trees tend to add organic matter to soil surfaces, helping to create a thin, organic-rich A or O horizon over time. Grasses, on the other hand, have a considerable root mass, in addition to surficial organic material, that is released into the soil each fall for annuals and short-lived perennials. For this reason, grassland soils (*Mollisols*) have much thicker A horizons with higher organic matter contents, and are more agriculturally productive than forest soils. Grasses release organic matter to soils that is more rich in base cations, whereas leaf and needle litter result in release of acids into the soil.

Microorganisms aid in the oxidation of organic residues and in production of humus material. They also play a role in iron oxidation-reduction cycles, fine-grained mineral dissolution (providing nutrients to soil solutions), and mineral neoformation. New research is continually expanding our knowledge of the role of microorganisms in plant growth, nutrient cycling, and mineral transformations.

4.4.2.3.3 Relief (Topography and Drainage)

The local landscape can have a surprisingly strong effect on the soils that form on site. The local topography can have important microclimatic effects as well as affecting rates of soil erosion. In comparison to flat regions, areas with steep slopes overall have more soil erosion, more runoff of rainwater, and less water infiltration, all of which lead to more limited soil development in very hilly or mountainous areas. In the northern hemisphere, south-facing slopes are exposed to more direct sunlight angles and are thus warmer and drier than north-facing slopes. The cooler, moister north-facing slopes have a more dynamic plant community due to less evapotranspiration and, consequently, experience less erosion because of plant rooting of soil and have thicker soil development.

Soil drainage affects iron oxidation-reduction states, organic matter accumulation and preservation, and local vegetation types. Well-drained soils, generally on hills or sideslopes, are more brownish or reddish due to conversion of ferrous iron (Fe^{2+}) to minerals with ferric (Fe^{3+}) iron. More poorly drained soils, in lowland, alluvial plains or upland depressions, tend more be more greyish, greenish-grey (gleyed), or dark colored, due to iron reduction (to Fe^{2+}) and accumulation and preservation of organic matter in areas tending towards anoxic. Areas with poor drainage also tend to be lowlands into which soil material may wash and accumulate from surrounding uplands, often resulting in overthickened A or O horizons. In contrast, steeply sloping areas in highlands may experience erosion and have thinner surface horizons.

4.4.2.3.4 Parent Material

The parent material of a soil is the material from which the soil has developed, whether it be river sands, lake clays, windblown loess, shoreline deposits, glacial deposits, or various types of bedrock. In youthful soils, the parent material has a clear connection to the soil type and has significant influence. Over time, as weathering processes deepen, mix, and alter the soil, the parent material becomes less recognizable as chemical, physical, and biological processes take their effect. The type of parent material may also affect the rapidity of soil development. Parent materials that are highly weatherable (such as volcanic ash) will transform more quickly into highly developed soils, whereas parent materials that are quartz-rich, for example, will take longer to develop. Parent materials also provide nutrients to plants and can affect soil internal drainage (e.g. clay is more impermeable than sand and impedes drainage).

4.4.2.3.5 Time

In general, soil profiles tend to become thicker (deeper), more developed, and more altered over time. However, the rate of change is greater for soils in youthful stages of development. The degree of soil alteration and deepening slows with time and at some point, after tens or hundreds of thousands of years, may approach an equilibrium condition where erosion and deepening (removals and additions) become balanced. Young soils (< 10,000 years old) are strongly influenced by parent material and typically develop horizons and character rapidly. Moderate age soils (roughly 10,000 to 500,000 years old) are slowing in profile development and deepening, and may begin to approach equilibrium conditions. Old soils (>500,000 years old) have generally reached their limit as far as soil horizonation and physical structure, but may continue to alter chemically or mineralogically.

To be sure, soil development is not always continual. Geologic events can rapidly bury soils (landslides, glacier advance, lake transgression), can cause removal or truncation of soils (rivers, shorelines) or can cause soil renewal with additions of slowly deposited sediment that add to the soil (wind or floodplain deposits). Biological mixing can sometimes cause soil regression, a reversal or bump in the road for the normal path of increasing development over time.

4.4.3 Ecological and Societal Aspects of Soil

As the medium for native plant growth, agriculture, building construction, waste disposal, and a pathway for groundwater infiltration, soil plays an important role for many key activities of our society. Soil scientists, agronomists, foresters, plant biologists, land-use planners, engineers, archeologists, and geologists, among others, all consider soil type (composition, texture, structure, density, etc.) in many aspects of their research or work. Below are some examples of the importance of soils in natural plant growth, in agriculture, and related societal issues. The long-term sustainability of soil is vital to both human ecology, even in modern society, and the ecology of our natural surroundings.

4.4.3.1 Soil-Plant Relations: Natural Processes

Soil plays a key role in plant growth. Beneficial aspects to plants include providing physical support, heat, water, nutrients, and oxygen. Heat, light, and oxygen are also obtained by the atmosphere, but the roots of many plants also require oxygen. Elemental nutrients, dissolved in soil water solution, are derived from soil minerals and organic material (see Figure **Soil-Plant Nutrient Cycle** (Figure 4.12)).

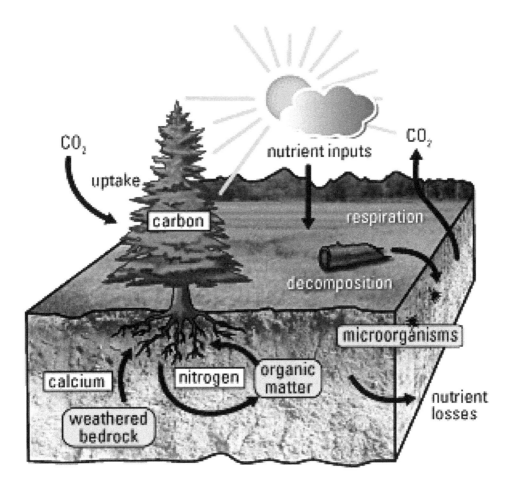

Figure 4.12: Soil-Plant Nutrient Cycle. Figure illustrates the uptake of nutrients by plants in the forest" soil ecosystem. *Source: U.S. Geological Survey*[20].

Plants mainly obtain nutrients from dissolved soil solutions. Though many aspects of soil are beneficial to plants, excessively high levels of trace metals (either naturally occurring or anthropogenically added) or applied herbicides can be toxic to some plants.

The ratio of solids/water/air in soil is also critically important to plants for proper oxygenation levels and water availability. Too much porosity with air space, such as in sandy or gravelly soils, can lead to less available water to plants, especially during dry seasons when the water table is low. Too much water, in poorly drained regions, can lead to anoxic conditions in the soil, which may be toxic to some plants. Hydrophytic vegetation can handle anoxic conditions and is thus suitable to poorly drained soils in wetland areas.

4.4.3.1.1 Nutrient Uptake by Plants

Several elements obtained from soil are considered essential for plant growth. Macronutrients, including C, H, O, N, P, K, Ca, Mg, and S, are needed by plants in significant quantities. C, H, and O are mainly obtained from the atmosphere or from rainwater. These three elements are the main components of most organic compounds, such as proteins, lipids, carbohydrates, and nucleic acids. Oxygen generally serves as an electron acceptor and is required by roots of many plants. The other six elements (N, P, K, Ca, Mg, and S) are obtained by plant roots from the soil and are variously used for protein synthesis, chlorophyll synthesis, energy transfer, cell division, enzyme reactions, and osmotic or ionic regulation.

Micronutrients are essential elements that are needed only in small quantities, but can still be limiting to plant growth since these nutrients are not so abundant in nature. Micronutrients include iron (Fe), manganese (Mn), boron (B), molybdenum (Mo), chlorine (Cl), zinc (Zn), and copper (Cu). There are some other elements that tend to aid plant growth but are not absolutely essential.

Micronutrients and macronutrients are desirable in particular concentrations and can be detrimental to plant growth when concentrations in soil solution are either too low (limiting) or too high (toxicity). Elemental nutrients are useful to plants only if they are in an extractable form in soil solutions, such as an exchangeable cation, rather than in a solid mineral grain. As nutrients are used up in the microenvironment surrounding a plant's roots, the replenishment of nutrients in soil solution is dependent on three aspects: (a) the rate of dissolution/alteration of soil minerals into elemental constituents, (b) the release rate of organically bound nutrients, and (c) the rate of diffusion of nutrients through the soil solution to the area of root uptake.

Many nutrients move through the soil and into the root system as a result of concentration gradients, moving by diffusion from high to low concentrations. However, some nutrients are selectively absorbed by the root membranes, such that elemental concentrations of solutions within plants may differ from that in soil solutions. Most nutrients exist as exchangeable cations that are acquired by roots from the soil solution— rather than from mineral or particle surfaces. Inorganic chemical processes and organic processes, such as the action of soil microorganisms, can help to release elemental nutrients from mineral grains into the soil environment.

4.4.3.2 Soil Health and Agricultural Impacts: Soil as a Sustainable Resource

4.4.3.2.1 Soil Health and Sustainability

Overall soil health can generally be defined as the capacity of the soil to function in a way that infiltrates water and cycles nutrients to support plant growth. Long term health of native soil is in many cases improved by disturbing the soil less, growing a greater diversity of crops, maintaining living roots in the soil, and keeping the soil covered with residue. Stable soil aggregates are important for soil health as they promote proper infiltration and thus limit the amount of water runoff —this has the added benefit of reducing soil erosion and downstream flooding and sedimentation.

Management of soil on farms may include use of tillage, fertilizer, pesticides, and other tools that may improve soil health if used correctly; however, significant damage to soil may result otherwise. Tillage with

---

[20]http://pubs.usgs.gov/fs/2009/3078/

a plow or disk is can be physically disruptive to soil fauna and microbes. The complex relations between soil and plant life, which have evolved into a sustainable relationship in the natural world, can be disturbed chemically by misuse or overuse of fertilizers or pesticides. Thus, to maintain soil health, one needs to understand the chemical, biological, and physical processes that operate in the natural soil profile. To the extent possible, we must work with the complexity of processes that function in a healthy soil and limit our disturbances to only those that are clear, practical necessity. Biodiversity is another important aspect to consider, because increasing the biodiversity of plants that are grown in soil can limit disease and pest problems and allow for a better functioning food web. More diversity in plants above ground leads to more diversity in the subsurface food web. Consequently, increasing the diversity of appropriate crop rotation in agricultural lands can ultimately lead to better soil health and limit problems in the long run.

4.4.3.2.2 Agriculture and Food Capacity

Soils on arable lands globally are a resource to society with potential use for food production. Production is ultimately limited by soil type, climate, hydrology, and land management. The native soil type is what has been provided by the land, from centuries or millennia of soil development, typically under mostly natural conditions under native plant vegetation. The effect of human populations may have been to drain land for cultivation (affecting hydrology), to modify the landscape, build structures, and to remove native vegetation. Some modifications have aided with food production. Others have had unintended consequences of causing land degradation, such as salinization, topsoil erosion, compaction, pollution, desertification, or depletion of soil nutrients.

Some of these issues are of serious concern in developing countries where oversight and regulations protecting the land may not be in place. For instance, overgrazing and rapid deforestation of the land, and generally poor land management, can lower the organic matter content of surface soils, thus lowering fertility and increasing the likelihood of topsoil erosion due to removal of the protective vegetative covering. As the world's population continues to increase, we will need to find ways to continually increase (or more effectively utilize) food production capacity from an essentially fixed amount of arable land worldwide. As population density has increased, crop yields and the numbers of acres in production have been continually increasing, with technological advances and more land in agriculture. This is not a sustainable trend, though, since the land area on earth is finite. In fact, some prime farmland is even being removed from production in developed countries as urbanization and land development occur on the ever-expanding edges of population centers. Efforts will need to be made to preserve enough high yield farmland to be sustainable for future generations.

4.4.3.2.3 Soil Compaction, Tillage, and Sustainable Practices

In modern agricultural practices, heavy machinery is used to prepare the seedbed, for planting, to control weeds, and to harvest the crop. The use of heavy equipment has many advantages in saving time and labor, but can cause compaction of soil and disruption of the natural soil biota. Much compaction is reversible and some is unavoidable with modern practices; however, serious compaction issues can occur with excessive passage of equipment during times when the soil has a high water content. The problem with soil compaction is that increased soil density limits root penetration depth and may inhibit proper plant growth.

Current practices generally encourage minimal tillage or no tillage in order to reduce the number of trips across the field. With proper planning, this can simultaneously limit compaction, protect soil biota, reduce costs (if performed correctly), promote water infiltration, and help to prevent topsoil erosion (see below). Tillage of fields does help to break up clods that were previously compacted, so best practices may vary at sites with different soil textures and composition. Crop rotation can also help to reduce bulk density with planting of crops with different root depth penetration. Another aspect of soil tillage is that it may lead to more rapid decomposition of organic matter due to greater soil aeration. Over large areas of farmland, this has the unintended consequence of releasing more carbon and nitrous oxides (greenhouse gases) into the atmosphere, thereby contributing to global warming effects. In no-till farming, carbon can actually become sequestered into the soil. Thus, no-till farming may be advantageous to sustainability issues on the local scale and the global scale.

4.4.3.2.4 Soil Erosion

Accelerated erosion of topsoil due to human activities and poor agricultural land management is a potentially serious issue. The areas most vulnerable to soil erosion include locations with thin organic (A and O) horizons and hilly terrains (see Figure **Water Erosion Vulnerability** (Figure 4.13)).

Figure 4.13: Water Erosion Vulnerability. Figure shows a global map of soil erosion vulnerability and includes a photograph of water and wind erosion. *Source: U.S. Department of Agriculture, National Resource Conservation Service[21], Rodney Burton via Wikimedia Commons[22], and Jim Bain via Wikimedia Commons[23].*

Some amount of soil erosion is a natural process along sloping areas and/or in areas with soft or non-cohesive materials susceptible to movement by water, wind, or gravity. For instance, soil material can be mobilized in strong windstorms, along the banks of rivers, in landslides, or by wave action along coastlines. Yet most topsoil erosion results from water influenced processes such as in rivers, creeks, ravines, small gullies, and overland flow or sheetwash from stormwater runoff. Although some soil erosion is natural, anthropogenic (human-induced) processes have greatly accelerated the erosion rate in many areas. Construction and agriculture are two of the more significant activities in our modern society that have increased

---

[21]http://soils.usda.gov/use/worldsoils/mapindex/erosh2o.html
[22]http://commons.wikimedia.org/wiki/File:Soil_erosion,_Wigborough,_Somerset_-_geograph.org.uk_-_133839.jpg
[23]http://commons.wikimedia.org/wiki/File:Soil_erosion,_brownout_-_geograph.org.uk_-_367915.jpg

erosion rates. In both cases, the erosion of topsoil can be significant if poor land management practices are used or if the area is geologically sensitive. For instance, in the 1930's, drought conditions and poor land management methods (lack of cover crops and rotation) combined to result in severe wind erosion and dust storms in the Great Plains of the United States, which came to be known as the Dust Bowl. Deep plowing of soil and displacement of the original prairie grasses (that once held the soil together) also contributed to the crisis. Once the natural topsoil is eroded by wind or water, it is only slowly renewable to its former pre-eroded condition. It may take anywhere from several decades to hundreds of years to millennia, under replanted native vegetation, to restore the soil to a relatively natural (pre-disturbed) state with its original physical, chemical, and biological characteristics. Furthermore, when soil is eroded, the particles become sedimented downstream in streams, rivers, lakes, and reservoirs. If rapid, this sedimentation can deteriorate the water quality with sediment and agricultural chemicals. Better land management practices, such as more limited tillage or no-till practices, can help to greatly limit soil erosion to a rate that is sustainable over the long term. Practices today are somewhat improved overall, but more improvement in agricultural practices are needed over large areas of farmland in the United States and other countries to bring us on a path to long-term sustainability of agricultural lands.

Deforestation due to logging, construction, or increased fire occurrences can also cause significant increases in soil erosion in many areas globally and may be a particular problem in developing countries. Removal of the natural cover of vegetation enhances erosion since plant foliage tends to buffer the intensity of rainfall and roots hold soil together and prevent breakup and erosion. Furthermore, decomposing plant material provides a protective cover of organic material on the soil surface. Watersheds with large areas of construction or deforestation can experience several times the natural erosion rate. In such watersheds, streams can become clogged with unwanted sediment that disturbs the natural ecosystem and infills valuable wetland areas, in addition to the problem of valuable topsoil loss from upland areas.

4.4.3.2.5 Fertilizer Runoff, Ecological Effects, and Dead Zones

Nutrients in soil and water are generally beneficial when they exist at naturally occurring levels. Nitrogen fertilizers have been applied to farm fields for decades in order to maximize production of agricultural lands. However, an unintended consequence is that the same nutrients can be detrimental to aquatic ecosystems when introduced excessively for agricultural or other purposes. Nitrogen (N) and Phosphorus (P) are introduced by fertilizers that are used intensively in agriculture, as well as golf courses and some lawns and gardens. Farm animal waste and sewage also provide large amounts of reactive N and P. Phosphorus was formerly used heavily as an additive in laundry and dishwater detergents, but since the 1970's it has been phased out in both through a combination of state and federal regulations. Overall, our modern society has altered the global N and P cycles such that there is an overabundance in many settings.

Although atmospheric nitrogen gas is abundant, the gas is neither reactive nor utilized by most plants. Reactive nitrogen, in nitrate and ammonia fertilizers, is utilized by plants at some rate. However, excessive nutrients (not utilized) are often washed into drainage ways, streams, and rivers during rainfall and storm events. High N and P levels in surface water runoff have the effect of dramatically increasing algae growth downstream due to eutrophic conditions. The algal blooms have the unwanted effect of strong decreases in dissolved oxygen, which is needed for survival of fish and other aquatic life. Enhanced algae growth can thus disrupt normal functioning of the ecosystem and cause what are known as "dead zones" (see Figure **Aquatic Dead Zones** (Figure 4.14)). The waters may locally become cloudy and colored a shade of green, brown, or red. Eutrophication can occur naturally, but it has been greatly enhanced due to the use of fertilizers. As a result of eutrophication, many coastal waters contain increasingly problematic dead zones where major rivers discharge nutrient-rich agricultural runoff or poorly treated sewage and wastewater (e.g. Gulf of Mexico, Chesapeake Bay, Baltic Sea, East China Sea) (see Figure **Aquatic Dead Zones** (Figure 4.14)). This issue is of great importance because the dead zones are near inhabited coastlines with commercially and ecologically vital aquatic life.

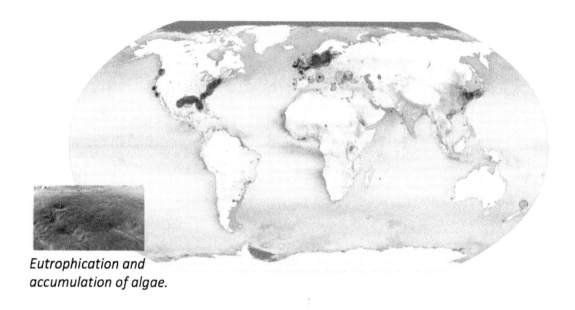

Figure 4.14: Aquatic Dead Zones. The red circles show the size of many of our planet's dead
(hypoxia) zones, whereas the plain black dots are dead zones of unknown size. Darker blue colors show
high concentrations of particulate organic matter, an indication of overly fertile waters (high in N and
P). Most dead zones occur in downriver of agricultural areas (with overused fertilizer) or areas of high
population density with poorly treated wastewater. *Source: NASA Earth Observatory via Wikimedia
Commons*[24] *and Lamiot via Wikimedia Commons*[25].

One of the most notorious dead zones (second to the Baltic Sea) is an 8,500 square mile region in the Gulf
of Mexico (see Figure **Aquatic Dead Zones** (Figure 4.14)). The Mississippi River dumps high-nutrient
runoff from its drainage basin that includes vast agricultural lands in the American Midwest. Increased
algal growth produced by these nutrients has affected important shrimp fishing grounds in the Gulf. The
primary source of the nutrients is the heavily tile-drained areas of farmland in the Midwest corn and soybean
belt (SW Minnesota, N Iowa, NE Illinois, N Indiana and NW Ohio). Improved soil drainage systems over
the past century or more have allowed for effective transport of nitrate compounds as stormwater runoff
into drainage basins (Ohio River, Wabash River, Illinois River, Missouri River, etc.) that feed into the
Mississippi River. In other words, the same drainage tiles that allow for the agricultural benefit of having
rich bottomland/wetland soils in production, have the disadvantage of increased and more rapid movements
of nitrate solutes to the Gulf of Mexico. Such large-scale problems, across state governmental boundaries,
can only be fully addressed in the future with a national system of incentives, regulations, or laws.

In addition to fertilizers, Nitrogen inputs to watersheds can also include atmospheric deposition, livestock waste, and sewage, but nitrogen fertilizers comprise a significant majority of the input to monitored
streams, particularly in springtime when much fertilizer is applied. Possible solutions to this problem include
encouraging farmers to apply a more limited quantity of fertilizer in the spring (only as much as necessary),
rather than in the fall, to allow for considerably less time for stormwater or meltwater runoff. Other solutions
include maintaining cover crops, or restoring wetlands in key locations to contain nitrate losses. An overall
strategy that limits the excess capacity of nutrients can simultaneously benefit farmers (by limiting cost), the
ecology of stream watersheds and coastal ecosystems (also locally stressed by oil spills and other pollution).

---

[24]http://en.wikipedia.org/wiki/File:Aquatic_Dead_Zones.jpg
[25]http://legacy.cnx.org/content/m41620/latest/

Over the long term, more efforts will need to be made in the Mississippi River Basin, and globally in similarly stressed agricultural or urban watersheds (see Figure **Aquatic Dead Zones** (Figure 4.14)), to improve the health and sustainability of our soil, land, and aquatic ecosystems.

4.4.4 Review Questions

Question 4.4.1
What is the importance of soil to our society today?

Question 4.4.2
How has human activity changed the physical, chemical, or biological character of native soil?

Question 4.4.3
What practices can be used to improve the long-term sustainability of soil health?

4.4.5 Further Reading

Hassett, J.J. & Banwart, W.L. (1992). *Soils and Their Environment*. New Jersey: Prentice-Hall.

Birkeland, P.W. (1999). *Soils and Geomorphology*. London: Oxford University Press.

A wealth of information may be obtained from your local county soil report (USDA) or online[26], including detailed interactive soil maps, along with useful data concerning soil types and their physical and chemical properties (useful for home owners, in construction, land-use planning, agriculture, etc.).

---

[26]http://websoilsurvey.nrcs.usda.gov/app/HomePage.htm

Chapter 5

Physical Resources: Water, Pollution, and Minerals

5.1 Physical Resources: Water, Pollution, and Minerals - Chapter Introduction[1]

5.1.1 Introduction

Water, air, and food are the most important natural resources to people. Humans can live only a few minutes without oxygen, about a week without water, and about a month without food. Water also is essential for our oxygen and food supply. Plants, which require water to survive, provide oxygen through photosynthesis and form the base of our food supply. Plants grow in soil, which forms by weathering reactions between water and rock.

Water is the most essential compound for Earth's life in general. Human babies are approximately 75% water and adults are 50–60% water. Our brain is about 85% water, blood and kidneys are 83% water, muscles are 76% water, and even bones are 22% water. We constantly lose water by perspiration; in temperate climates we should drink about 2 quarts of water per day and people in hot desert climates should drink up to 10 quarts of water per day. Loss of 15% of body-water usually causes death. Earth is truly the "Water Planet" (see Figure **Planet Earth from Space** (Figure 5.1)). The abundance of water on Earth distinguishes us from other bodies in the solar system. About 70% of Earth's surface is covered by oceans and approximately half of Earth's surface is obscured by clouds at any time. There is a very large volume of water on our planet, about 1.4 billion cubic kilometers (km3) (330 million cubic miles) or about 53 billion gallons per person on Earth. All of Earth's water could cover the United States to a depth of 145 km (90 mi). From a human perspective, the problem is that over 97% of it is seawater, which is too salty to drink or use for irrigation. The most commonly used water sources are rivers and lakes, which contain less than 0.01% of the world's water!

---

[1]This content is available online at <http://legacy.cnx.org/content/m41523/1.3/>.

Figure 5.1: **Planet Earth from Space** *Source: Created by Marvel, based on a Nasa image via Wikimedia Commons*[2]

One of our most important environmental goals is to provide a clean, sufficient, and sustainable water supply for the world. Fortunately, water is a renewable resource, and it is difficult to destroy. Evaporation and precipitation combine to replenish our fresh water supply constantly and quickly; however, water availability is complicated by its uneven distribution over the Earth. Arid climate and densely populated areas have combined in many parts of the world to create water shortages, which are projected to worsen significantly in the coming years. Human activities such as water overuse and water pollution have compounded the water crisis that exists today. Hundreds of millions of people lack access to safe drinking water, and billions

[2]http://commons.wikimedia.org/wiki/File:Rotating_earth_(large).gif

of people lack access to improved sanitation as simple as a pit latrine. As a result, nearly two million people die every year from diarrheal diseases and 90% of those deaths occur among children under the age of 5. Most of these are easily prevented deaths.

Although few minerals are absolutely essential for human life, the things that define modern society require a wide range of them: iron ore for steel, phosphate minerals for fertilizer, limestone rock for concrete, rare earth elements for night-vision goggles and phosphors in computer monitors, and lithium minerals for batteries in our laptops, cell phones, and electric cars. As global population grows and emerging large economies expand, we will face a crisis in the supply of many important minerals because they are nonrenewable, which is to say we consume them far more quickly than nature creates them. As we consume minerals from larger and lower grade mineral deposits there will be greater environmental impacts from mineral mining and processing. The impending mineral crisis may be more challenging to address than the water crisis.

This chapter introduces basic principles in water supply, water pollution, and mineral resources. The emphasis, however, is on environmental issues and sustainable solutions for each problem.

5.2 Water Cycle and Fresh Water Supply[3]

5.2.1 Learning Objectives

After reading this module, students should be able to

- understand how the water cycle operates
- understand the principles controlling groundwater resources and how they also can affect surface water resources
- know the causes and effects of depletion in different water reservoirs
- understand how we can work toward solving the water supply crisis

5.2.2 Water Reservoirs and Water Cycle

Water is the only substance that occurs naturally on earth in three forms: solid, liquid and gas. It is distributed in various locations, called **water reservoirs**. The oceans are by far the largest of the reservoirs with about 97% of all water but that water is too saline for most human uses (see Figure **Earth's Water Reservoirs** (Figure 5.2)). Ice caps and glaciers are the largest reservoirs of fresh water but this water is inconveniently located, mostly in Antarctica and Greenland. Shallow groundwater is the largest reservoir of usable fresh water. Although rivers and lakes are the most heavily used water resources, they represent only a tiny amount of the world's water. If all of world's water was shrunk to the size of 1 gallon, then the total amount of fresh water would be about 1/3 cup, and the amount of readily usable fresh water would be 2 tablespoons.

---

[3]This content is available online at <http://legacy.cnx.org/content/m41397/1.5/>.

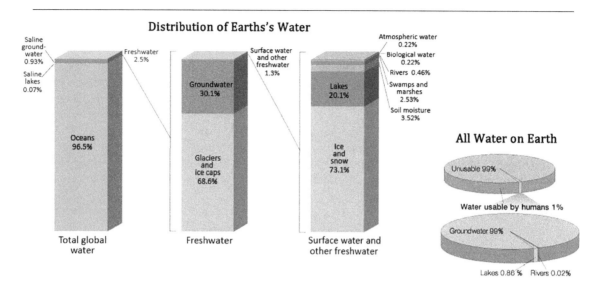

Figure 5.2: Earth's Water Reservoirs Bar chart Distribution of Earth's water including total global water, fresh water, and surface water and other fresh water and Pie chart Water usable by humans and sources of usable water. *Source: United States Geographical Survey[4] Igor Skiklomanov's chapter "World fresh water resources" in Peter H. Gleick (editor), 1993, Water in Crisis: A Guide to the World's Fresh Water Resources*

The **water cycle** shows the movement of water through different reservoirs, which include oceans, atmosphere, glaciers, groundwater, lakes, rivers, and biosphere (see Figure **The Water Cycle** (Figure 5.3)). Solar energy and gravity drive the motion of water in the water cycle. Simply put, the water cycle involves water moving from the ocean to the atmosphere by evaporation, forming clouds. From clouds, it falls as precipitation (rain and snow) on both water and land, where it can move in a variety of ways. The water on land can either return to the ocean by **surface runoff** (unchannelized overland flow), rivers, glaciers, and subsurface groundwater flow, or return to the atmosphere by evaporation or **transpiration** (loss of water by plants to the atmosphere).

---

[4]http://ga.water.usgs.gov/edu/earthwherewater.html

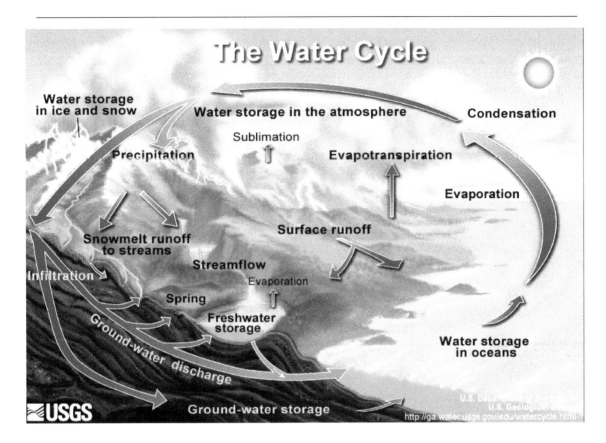

Figure 5.3: The Water Cycle Arrows depict movement of water to different reservoirs located above, at, and below Earth's surface. *Source: United States Geological Survey*[5]

An important part of the water cycle is how water varies in salinity, which is the abundance of dissolved ions in water. Ocean water is called salt water because it is highly saline, with about 35,000 mg of dissolved ions per liter of seawater. **Evaporation** (where water changes from liquid to gas at ambient temperatures) is a distillation process that produces nearly pure water with almost no dissolved ions. As water vaporizes, it leaves the dissolved ions in the original liquid phase. Eventually, **condensation** (where water changes from gas to liquid) forms clouds and sometimes precipitation (rain and snow). After rainwater falls onto land, it dissolves minerals, which increases its salinity. Most lakes, rivers, and near-surface groundwater have a relatively low salinity and are called fresh water. The next several sections discuss important parts of the water cycle relative to fresh water resources.

5.2.3 Primary Fresh Water Resources: Precipitation

Precipitation is a major control of fresh water availability, and it is unevenly distributed around the globe (see Figure **World Rainfall Map** (Figure 5.4)). More precipitation falls near the equator, and landmasses there are characterized by a tropical rainforest climate. Less precipitation tends to fall near 20–30 ° north and south latitude, where the world's largest deserts are located. These rainfall and climate patterns are related to global wind circulation cells. The intense sunlight at the equator heats air, causing it to rise and cool,

---

[5]http://commons.wikimedia.org/wiki/File:Water_cycle.png

which decreases the ability of the air mass to hold water vapor and results in frequent rainstorms. Around 30° north and south latitude, descending air conditions produce warmer air, which increases its ability to hold water vapor and results in dry conditions. Both the dry air conditions and the warm temperatures of these latitude belts favor evaporation. Global precipitation and climate patterns are also affected by the size of continents, major ocean currents, and mountains.

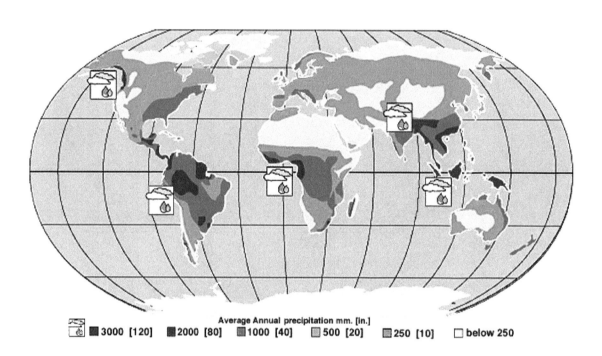

Figure 5.4: World Rainfall Map The false-color map above shows the amount of rain that falls around the world. Areas of high rainfall include Central and South America, western Africa, and Southeast Asia. Since these areas receive so much rainfall, they are where most of the world's rainforests grow. Areas with very little rainfall usually turn into deserts. The desert areas include North Africa, the Middle East, western North America, and Central Asia. *Source: United States Geological Survey*[6] *Earth Forum, Houston Museum Natural Science*

5.2.4 Surface Water Resources: Rivers, Lakes, Glaciers

Flowing water from rain and melted snow on land enters river channels by surface runoff (see Figure **Surface Runoff** (Figure 5.5)) and groundwater seepage (see Figure **Groundwater Seepage** (Figure 5.6)). **River discharge** describes the volume of water moving through a river channel over time (see Figure **River Discharge** (Figure 5.7)). The relative contributions of surface runoff vs. groundwater seepage to river discharge depend on precipitation patterns, vegetation, topography, land use, and soil characteristics. Soon after a heavy rainstorm, river discharge increases due to surface runoff. The steady normal flow of river water is mainly from groundwater that discharges into the river. Gravity pulls river water downhill toward the ocean. Along the way the moving water of a river can erode soil particles and dissolve minerals, creating

---

[6]http://ga.water.usgs.gov/edu/watercyclesummary.html

the river's load of moving sediment grains and dissolved ions. Groundwater also contributes a large amount of the dissolved ions in river water. The geographic area drained by a river and its tributaries is called a **drainage basin**. The Mississippi River drainage basin includes approximately 40% of the U.S., a measure that includes the smaller drainage basins (also called watersheds), such as the Ohio River and Missouri River that help to comprise it. Rivers are an important water resource for irrigation and many cities around the world. Some of the world's rivers that have had international disputes over water supply include the Colorado (Mexico, southwest U.S.), Nile (Egypt, Ethiopia, Sudan), Euphrates (Iraq, Syria, Turkey), Ganges (Bangladesh, India), and Jordan (Israel, Jordan, Syria).

Figure 5.5: Surface Runoff Surface runoff, part of overland flow in the water cycle *Source: James M. Pease*[7] *at Wikimedia Commons*

---

[7]http://commons.wikimedia.org/wiki/File:Runoff.jpg

Figure 5.6: Groundwater Seepage Groundwater seepage can be seen in Box Canyon in Idaho, where approximately 10 cubic meters per second of seepage emanates from its vertical headwall. *Source: NASA*[8]

---

[8]http://astrobiology.nasa.gov/articles/erosion-on-earth-and-mars-mere-seepage-or-megaflood/

Figure 5.7: River Discharge Colorado River, U.S.. Rivers are part of overland flow in the water cycle and an important surface water resource. *Source: Gonzo fan2007[9] at Wikimedia Commons*

Lakes can also be an excellent source of fresh water for human use. They usually receive water from surface runoff and groundwater discharge. They tend to be short-lived on a geological time-scale because they are constantly filling in with sediment supplied by rivers. Lakes form in a variety of ways including glaciation (Great Lakes, North America, See Figure **Great Lakes from Space** (Figure 5.8)), recent tectonic uplift (Lake Tanganyika, Africa), and volcanic eruptions (Crater Lake, Oregon). People also create artificial lakes (**reservoirs**) by damming rivers. Large changes in climate can result in major changes in a lake's size. As Earth was coming out of the last Ice Age about fifteen thousand years ago, the climate in the western U.S. changed from cool and moist to warm and arid, which caused more than100 large lakes to disappear. The Great Salt Lake in Utah is a remnant of a much larger lake called Lake Bonneville.

[9]http://commons.wikimedia.org/wiki/File:Overlook_over_the_Colorado.JPG

Figure 5.8: Great Lakes from Space The Great Lakes hold 21% of the world's surface fresh water. Lakes are an important surface water resource. *Source: SeaWiFS Project, NASA/Goddard Space Flight Center, and ORBIMAGE*[10]

Although glaciers represent the largest reservoir of fresh water, they generally are not used as a water source because they are located too far from most people (see Figure **Mountain Glacier in Argentina** (Figure 5.9)). Melting glaciers do provide a natural source of river water and groundwater. During the last Ice Age there was as much as 50% more water in glaciers than there is today, which caused sea level to be about 100 m lower. Over the past century, sea level has been rising in part due to melting glaciers. If Earth's climate continues to warm, the melting glaciers will cause an additional rise in sea level.

[10]http://commons.wikimedia.org/wiki/File:Great_Lakes_from_space.jpg

Figure 5.9: Mountain Glacier in Argentina Glaciers are the largest reservoir of fresh water but they are not used much as a water resource directly by society because of their distance from most people. *Source: Luca Galuzzi - www.galuzzi.it[11]*

5.2.5 Groundwater Resources

Although most people in the U.S. and the world use surface water, groundwater is a much larger reservoir of usable fresh water, containing more than 30 times more water than rivers and lakes combined. Groundwater is a particularly important resource in arid climates, where surface water may be scarce. In addition, groundwater is the primary water source for rural homeowners, providing 98% of that water demand in the U.S.. **Groundwater** is water located in small spaces, called **pore space**, between mineral grains and fractures in subsurface earth materials (rock or sediment, i.e., loose grains). Groundwater is not located in underground rivers or lakes except where there are caves, which are relatively rare. Between the land surface and the depth where there is groundwater is the **unsaturated zone**, where pore spaces contain only air and water films on mineral grains (see Figure **Subsurface Water Terminology** (Figure 5.10)).[12] Below the unsaturated zone is the **saturated zone**, where groundwater completely fills pore spaces in earth materials. The interface between the unsaturated zone and saturated zone is the **water table**. Most groundwater originates from rain or snowmelt, which infiltrates the ground and moves downward until it reaches the

[11]http://en.wikipedia.org/wiki/File:Perito_Moreno_Glacier_Patagonia_Argentina_Luca_Galuzzi_2005.JPG

[12]Groundwater is the name for water in the saturated zone and **soil moisture** describes water in the unsaturated zone. Therefore, groundwater is the underground water resource used by society but soil moisture is the principal water supply for most plants and is an important factor in agricultural productivity.

saturated zone. Other sources of groundwater include seepage from surface water (lakes, rivers, reservoirs, and swamps), surface water deliberately pumped into the ground, irrigation, and underground wastewater treatment systems, i.e., septic tanks. **Recharge areas** are locations where surface water infiltrates the ground rather than running off into rivers or evaporating. Wetlands and flat vegetated areas in general are excellent recharge areas.

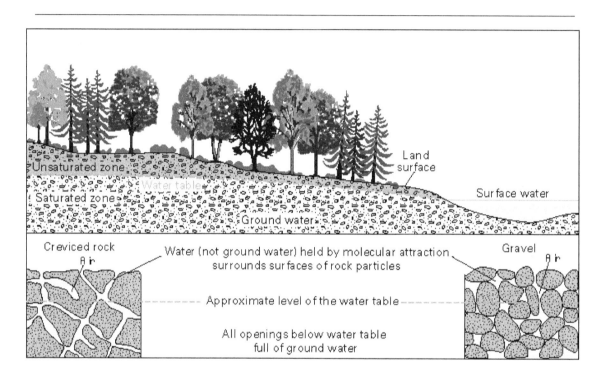

Figure 5.10: Subsurface Water Terminology Groundwater in pore spaces and fractures of earth materials, saturated zone, unsaturated zone, and water table, which follows land surface but in a more subdued way. *Source: United States Geological Survey*[13]

Groundwater is in constant motion due to interconnection between pore spaces. **Porosity** is the percentage of pore space in an earth material and it gives a measure of how much groundwater an earth material can hold. **Permeability** is a measure of the speed that groundwater can flow through an earth material, and it depends on the size and degree of interconnection among pores. An earth material that is capable of supplying groundwater from a well at a useful rate—i.e., it has relatively high permeability and medium to high porosity—is called an **aquifer**. Examples of aquifers are earth materials with abundant, large, well-connected pore spaces such as sand, gravel, uncemented sandstone, and any highly fractured rock. An earth material with low hydraulic conductivity is an **aquitard**. Examples of aquitards include clay, shale (sedimentary rock with abundant clay), and igneous and metamorphic rock, if they contain few fractures.

As discussed above, groundwater flows because most earth materials near the surface have finite (nonzero) porosity and permeability values. Another reason for groundwater movement is that the surface of the water table commonly is not completely flat but mimics the topography of the land surface, especially in humid climates. There is "topography" to the water table because groundwater moves slowly through rock and soil, so it builds up in higher elevation areas. In fact, when groundwater flows slowly through

---

[13]http://ga.water.usgs.gov/edu/gwhowtofind.html

aquitards and deep underground, it can take many thousands of years to move relatively short distances. An **unconfined aquifer** has no aquitard above it and, therefore, it is exposed to the atmosphere and surface waters through interconnected pores (See Figure **Flowing Groundwater** (Figure 5.11)). In an unconfined aquifer, groundwater flows because of gravity to lower water table levels, where it eventually may **discharge** or leave the groundwater flow system. Discharge areas include rivers, lakes, swamps, reservoirs, water wells, and **springs** (see Figure **Fatzael Springs in Jordan Valley** (Figure 5.12)). Springs are rivers that emerge from underground due to an abrupt intersection of the land surface and the water table caused by joints, caves, or faults that bring permeable earth materials to the surface. A **confined aquifer** is bounded by aquitards below and above, which prevents recharge from the surface immediately above. Instead, the major recharge occurs where the confined aquifer intercepts the land surface, which may be a long distance from water wells and discharge areas (see Figure **Schematic Cross Section of Aquifer Types** (Figure 5.13)). Confined aquifers are commonly inclined away from recharge areas, so groundwater in a confined aquifer is under greater-than-atmospheric pressure due to the weight of water in the upslope direction. Similar to river discharge, groundwater discharge describes the volume of water moving through an aquifer over time. Total groundwater discharge depends on the permeability of the earth material, the pressure that drives groundwater flow, and the size of the aquifer. It is important to determine groundwater discharge to evaluate whether an aquifer can meet the water needs of an area.

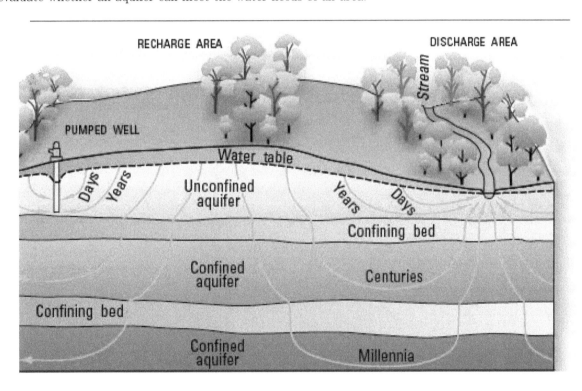

Figure 5.11: Flowing Groundwater Blue lines show the direction of groundwater in unconfined aquifers, confined aquifers, and confining beds. Deep groundwater moves very slowly especially through low permeability layers.*Source: United States Geological Survey*[14]

[14]http://ga.water.usgs.gov/edu/watercyclegwdischarge.html

Figure 5.12: Fatzael Springs in Jordan Valley A spring is a river that emerges from underground due to an abrupt intersection of the water table with the land surface such as alongside a hill. *Source: Hanay*[15] *at Mediawiki Commons*

---

[15]http://commons.wikimedia.org/wiki/File:Fatzael_Springs_and_water_system_017.JPG

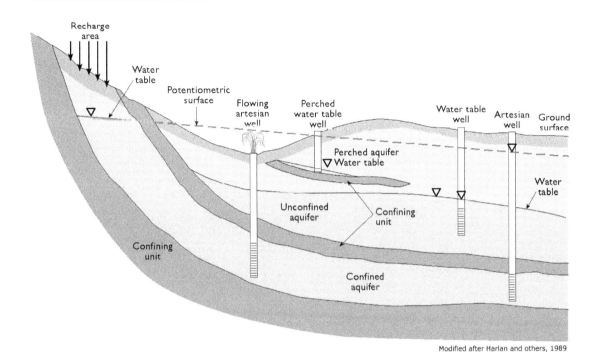

Modified after Harlan and others, 1989

Figure 5.13: Schematic Cross Section of Aquifer Types This figure shows different types of aquifers and water wells, including unconfined aquifer, confined aquifer, water table well, artesian well, and flowing artesian well. Point of triangle is water level in each well and water table in other parts of figure. Water level in artesian well is at potentiometric surface and above local water table (dashed blue line) due to extra pressure on groundwater in confined aquifer. Water in flowing artesian well moves above land surface. *Source: Colorado Geological Survey*[16]

Most shallow water wells are drilled into unconfined aquifers. These are called **water table wells** because the water level in the well coincides with the water table (See Figure **Schematic Cross Section of Aquifer Types** (Figure 5.13)). 90% of all aquifers for water supply are unconfined aquifers composed of sand or gravel. To produce water from a well, you simply need to drill a hole that reaches the saturated zone and then pump water to the surface. Attempting to pump water from the unsaturated zone is like drinking root beer with a straw immersed only in the foam at the top.

To find a large aquifer for a city, hydrogeologists (geologists who specialize in groundwater) use a variety of information including knowledge of earth materials at the surface and sub-surface as well as test wells. Some people search for water by dowsing, where someone holds a forked stick or wire (called a divining rod) while walking over an area. The stick supposedly rotates or deflects downward when the dowser passes over water. Controlled tests show that a dowser's success is equal to or less than random chance. Nevertheless, in many areas water wells are still drilled on dowser's advice sometimes for considerable money. There is no scientific basis to dowsing.

Wells into confined aquifers typically are deeper than those into unconfined aquifers because they must penetrate a confining layer. The water level in a well drilled into a confined aquifer, which is an **artesian well**, (see Figure **Schematic Cross Section of Aquifer Types** (Figure 5.13)), moves above the local

---

[16]http://geosurvey.state.co.us/apps/wateratlas/chapter2page2.asp

water table to a level called the potentiometric surface because of the greater pressure on the groundwater. Water in a flowing well (see Figure **A Flowing Well** (Figure 5.14)) moves all of the way to the land surface without pumping.

Figure 5.14: A Flowing Well Flowing artesian well where water moves above the land surface due to extra pressure on the groundwater in a confined aquifer. *Source: Environment Canada*[17]

A confined aquifer tends to be depleted from groundwater pumping more quickly than an unconfined aquifer, assuming similar aquifer properties and precipitation levels. This is because confined aquifers have smaller recharge areas, which may be far from the pumping well. Conversely, an unconfined aquifer tends to be more susceptible to pollution because it is hydrologically connected to the surface, which is the source of most pollution.

Groundwater and surface water (rivers, lakes, swamps, and reservoirs) are strongly interrelated because both are part of the same overall resource. Major groundwater removal (from pumping or drought) can lower the levels of surface water and vice versa. We can define two types of streams: gaining (effluent) streams and losing (influent) streams (see Figure **Interaction of Streams and Ground Water** (Figure 5.15)). Gaining streams tend to be perennial (flow year round), are characteristic of humid climates, have the water table sloping towards the river, and therefore gain water from groundwater discharge. Losing streams tend to be ephemeral (flow only after significant rain), are characteristic of arid climates, are located above the water table (which slopes away from the river), and therefore lose water to groundwater recharge. Pollution that is dumped into a losing stream will tend to move into the ground and could also contaminate local groundwater.

---

[17]http://tw.gs/4bx0

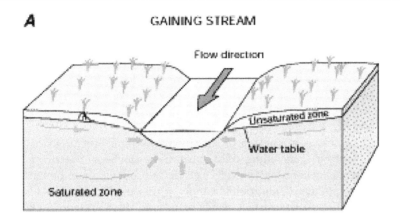

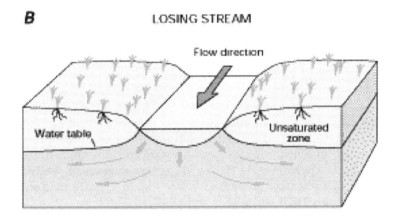

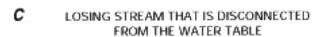

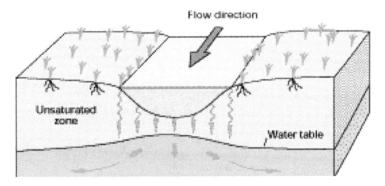

Figure 5.15: Interaction of Streams and Ground Water A) Gaining stream where water table slopes toward river and groundwater discharges into river, B) Losing stream where water table slopes away from river and river water discharges into groundwater, C) Losing stream where water table is separated from and below river. *Source: United States Geological Survey*[18]

5.2.6 Water Use in the U.S. and World

People need water to produce the food, energy, and mineral resources they use—commonly large amounts of it. Consider, for example, these approximate water requirements for some things people in the developed world use every day: one tomato = 3 gallons; one kilowatt-hour of electricity (from a thermoelectric power plant) = 21 gallons; one loaf of bread = 150 gallons; one pound of beef = 1,600 gallons; and one ton of steel = 63,000 gallons. Human beings require only about 1 gallon per day to survive, but a typical person in a U.S. household uses approximately 100 gallons per day, which includes cooking, washing dishes and clothes, flushing the toilet, and bathing.

The water demand of an area is a function of the population and other uses of water. There are several general categories of water use, including **offstream use**, which removes water from its source, e.g., irrigation, thermoelectric power generation (cooling electricity-producing equipment in fossil fuel, nuclear, and geothermal power plants), industry, and public supply; **consumptive use**, which is a type of offstream use where water does not return to the surface water or groundwater system immediately after use, e.g., irrigation water that evaporates or goes to plant growth; and **instream use**, which is water used but not removed from a river, mostly for hydroelectric power generation. The relative size of these three categories are instream use ≫ offstream use > consumptive use. In 2005, the U.S. used approximately 3,300 billion gallons per day for instream use, 410 billion gallons per day for offstream use, and 100 billion gallons per day for consumptive use. The major offstream uses of that water were thermoelectric (49%), irrigation (31%), public supply (11%), and industry (4%, see Figure **Trends in Total Water Withdrawals by Water-use Category, 1950-2005** (Figure 5.16)). About 15% of the total water withdrawals in the U.S. in 2005 were saline water, which was used almost entirely for thermoelectric power generation. Almost all of the water used for thermoelectric power generation is returned to the river, lake, or ocean from where it came but about half of irrigation water does not return to the original source due to evaporation, plant transpiration, and loss during transport, e.g., leaking pipes. Total withdrawals of water in the U.S. actually decreased slightly from 1980 to 2005, despite a steadily increasing population. This is because the two largest categories of water use (thermoelectric and irrigation) stabilized or decreased over that time period due to better water management and conservation. In contrast, public supply water demand increased steadily from 1950 (when estimates began) through 2005. Approximately 77% of the water for offstream use in the U.S. in 2005 came from surface water and the rest was from groundwater (see Figure **Trends in Source of Fresh Water Withdrawals in the U.S. from 1950 to 2005** (Figure 5.17)).

---

[18] http://pubs.usgs.gov/circ/circ1186/html/gw_effect.html

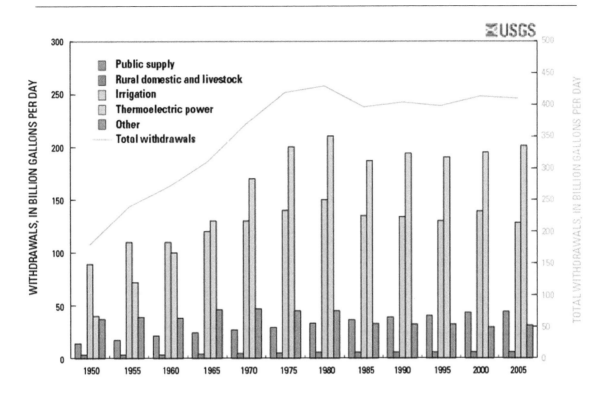

Figure 5.16: Trends in Total Water Withdrawals by Water-use Category, 1950-2005 Trends in total water withdrawals in the U.S. from 1950 to 2005 by water use category, including bars for thermo-electric power, irrigation, public water supply, and rural domestic and livestock. Thin blue line represents total water withdrawals using vertical scale on right. *Source: United States Geological Survey*[19]

[19]http://ga.water.usgs.gov/edu/wateruse-trends.html

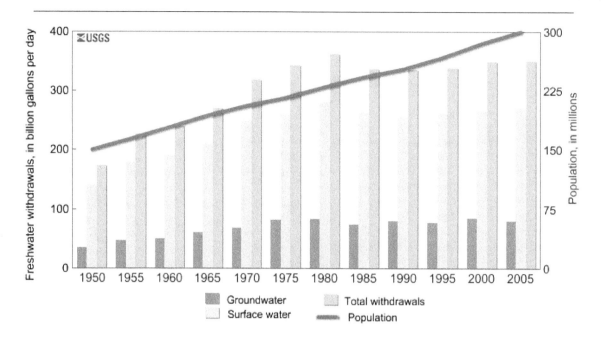

Figure 5.17: Trends in Source of Fresh Water Withdrawals in the U.S. from 1950 to 2005
Trends in source of fresh water withdrawals in the U.S. from 1950 to 2005, including bars for surface
water, groundwater, and total water. Red line gives U.S. population using vertical scale on right. *Source:
United States Geological Survey*[20]

In contrast to trends in the U.S., global total water use is steadily increasing at a rate greater than world
population growth (see Figure **Trends in World Water Use from 1900 to 2000 and Projected to
2025** (Figure 5.18)). During the twentieth century global population tripled and water demand grew by a
factor of six. The increase in global water demand beyond the rate of population growth is due to improved
standard of living without an offset by water conservation. Increased production of goods and energy entails
a large increase in water demand. The major global offstream water uses are irrigation (68%), public supply
(21%), and industry (11%).

---

[20]http://ga.water.usgs.gov/edu/wateruse-trends.html

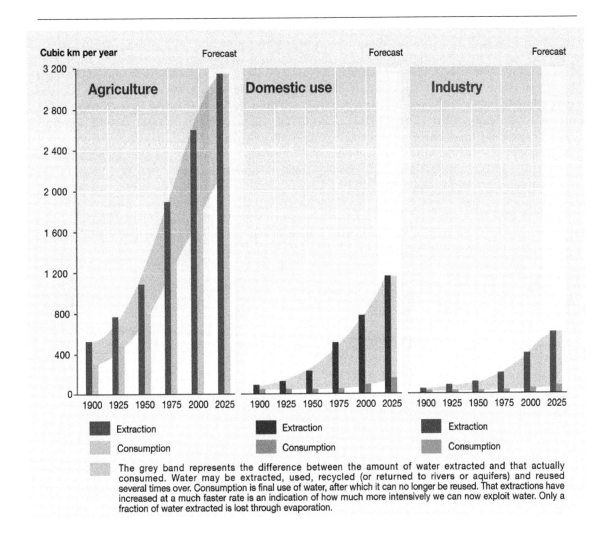

Figure 5.18: **Trends in World Water Use from 1900 to 2000 and Projected to 2025** For each water major use category, including trends for agriculture, domestic use, and industry. Darker colored bar represents total water extracted for that use category and lighter colored bar represents water consumed (i.e., water that is not quickly returned to surface water or groundwater system) for that use category. *Source: Igor A. Shiklomanow, State Hydrological Institute (SHI, St. Petersburg) and United Nations Educational, Scientific and Cultural Organisation (UNESCO, Paris), 1999*[21]

5.2.7 Water Supply Problems: Resource Depletion

As groundwater is pumped from water wells, there usually is a localized drop in the water table around the well called a **cone of depression** (see Figure **Formation of a Cone of Depression around a Pumping Water Well** (Figure 5.19)). When there are a large number of wells that have been pumping water for a long time, the regional water table can drop significantly. This is called **groundwater mining**, which can force the drilling of deeper, more expensive wells that commonly encounter more saline groundwater.

---

[21]http://maps.grida.no/go/graphic/trends-in-global-water-use-by-sector

The occurrence of mining does not mean that groundwater will *never* be recharged, but in many cases the recharge rate is negligible on a human time-scale. Confined aquifers are more susceptible to groundwater mining due to their limited recharge areas. Urban development usually worsens groundwater mining because natural recharge rates drop with the proliferation of impermeable pavement, buildings, and roads. Extensive groundwater pumping around Chicago has created a gigantic cone of depression there. Because the water table dropped up to 250 m (800 ft) in the area (see Figure **Drop in Water Table in a Confined Aquifer in the Area of Chicago, Illinois and Milwaukee, Wisconsin, U.S. from 1864 - 1980** (Figure 5.20)), many local public water suppliers have switched to Lake Michigan water. Chicago is fortunate to have a large alternate supply of fresh water; many arid locations don't have that luxury. Other places where groundwater mining is a serious problem include the High Plains (Ogallala Aquifer) and the Desert Southwest of the U.S., Mexico, the Middle East, India, and China. Rivers, lakes, and artificial lakes (reservoirs) can also be depleted due to overuse. Some large rivers, such as the Colorado in the U.S. and Yellow in China, run dry in some years. The case history of the Aral Sea discussed below involves depletion of a lake. Finally, glaciers are being depleted due to accelerated melting associated with global warming over the past century.

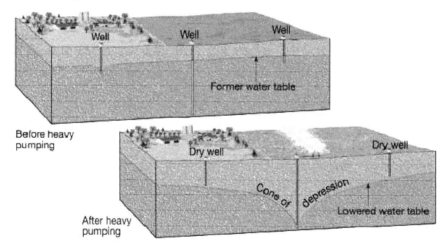

Figure 5.19: Formation of a Cone of Depression around a Pumping Water Well *Source: Fayette County Groundwater Conservation District, TX*[22]

---

[22]http://www.fayettecountygroundwater.com/educational_info.htm

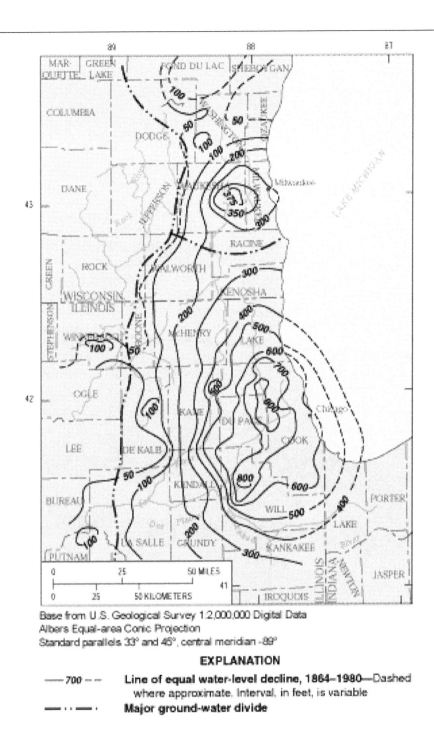

Base from U.S. Geological Survey 1:2,000,000 Digital Data
Albers Equal-area Conic Projection
Standard parallels 33° and 45°, central meridian -89°

EXPLANATION

—— 700 — — **Line of equal water-level decline, 1864–1980—Dashed**
where approximate. Interval, in feet, is variable

—— ·· —— · **Major ground-water divide**

Figure 5.20: Drop in Water Table in a Confined Aquifer in the Area of Chicago, Illinois and Milwaukee, Wisconsin, U.S. from 1864 - 1980 *Source: United States Geological Survey*[23]

---

[23]http://pubs.usgs.gov/circ/circ1186/html/gw_storage.html

Another water resource problem associated with groundwater mining is **saltwater intrusion**, where overpumping of fresh water aquifers near ocean coastlines causes saltwater to enter fresh water zones. Saltwater intrusion is a significant problem in many coastal areas of the U.S. including Long Island, New York; Cape Cod, Massachusetts; and southeastern and Gulf Coastal states. The drop of the water table around a cone of depression in an unconfined aquifer can change the regional groundwater flow direction, which could send nearby pollution toward the pumping well instead of away from it. Finally, problems of subsidence (gradual sinking of the land surface over a large area) and sinkholes (rapid sinking of the land surface over a small area) can develop due to a drop in the water table.

5.2.8 The Water Supply Crisis

The **water crisis** refers to a global situation where people in many areas lack access to sufficient water or clean water or both. This section describes the global situation involving water shortages, also called water stress. The next section covers the water crisis involving water pollution. Figure **Countries Facing Water Stress in 1995 and Projected in 2025** (Figure 5.21) shows areas of the world experiencing water stress as defined by a high percentage of water withdrawal compared to total available water. Due to population growth the 2025 projection for global water stress is significantly worse than water stress levels in 1995. In general, water stress is greatest in areas with very low precipitation (major deserts) or large population density (e.g., India) or both. Future global warming could worsen the water crisis by shifting precipitation patterns away from humid areas and by melting mountain glaciers that recharge rivers downstream. Melting glaciers will also contribute to rising sea level, which will worsen saltwater intrusion in aquifers near ocean coastlines. Compounding the water crisis is the issue of social injustice; poor people generally get less access to clean water and commonly pay more for water than wealthy people.

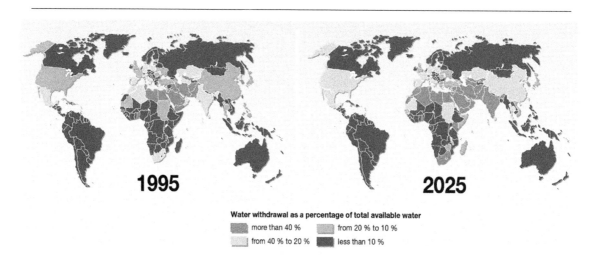

Figure 5.21: Countries Facing Water Stress in 1995 and Projected in 2025 Water stress is defined as having a high percentage of water withdrawal compared to total available water in the area. *Source: Philippe Rekacewicz*[24] *(Le Monde diplomatique), February 2006*

According to a 2006 report by the United Nations Development Programme, in 2005, 700 million people

---

[24]http://maps.grida.no/go/graphic/increased-global-water-stress

(11% of the world's population) lived under water stress with a per capita water supply below 1,700 m^3/year[25] (Watkins, 2006 (p. 179)). Most of them live in the Middle East and North Africa. By 2025, the report projects that more than 3 billion people (about 40% of the world's population) will live in water-stressed areas with the large increase coming mainly from China and India. The water crisis will also impact food production and our ability to feed the ever-growing population. We can expect future global tension and even conflict associated with water shortages and pollution. Historic and future areas of water conflict include the Middle East (Euphrates and Tigris River conflict among Turkey, Syria, and Iraq; Jordan River conflict among Israel, Lebanon, Jordan, and the Palestinian territories), Africa (Nile River conflict among Egypt, Ethiopia, and Sudan), Central Asia (Aral Sea conflict among Kazakhstan, Uzbekistan, Turkmenistan, Tajikistan, and Kyrgyzstan), and south Asia (Ganges River conflict between India and Pakistan).

5.2.9 Sustainable Solutions to the Water Supply Crisis?

The current and future water crisis described above requires multiple approaches to extending our fresh water supply and moving towards sustainability. Some of the longstanding traditional approaches include **dams** and **aqueducts**. Reservoirs that form behind dams in rivers can collect water during wet times and store it for use during dry spells (see Figure **Hoover Dam, Nevada, U.S.** (Figure 5.22)). They also can be used for urban water supplies. New York City has a large number of reservoirs and controlled lakes up to 200 km away to meet the water demands of its large population. Other benefits of dams and reservoirs are hydroelectricity, flood control, and recreation. Some of the drawbacks are evaporative loss of reservoir water in arid climates, downstream river channel erosion, and impact on the ecosystem including a change from a river to lake habitat and interference with fish migration and spawning. Aqueducts can move water from where it is plentiful to where it is needed (see Figure **The California Aqueduct** (Figure 5.23)). Southern California has a large and controversial network of aqueducts that brings in water from the Sierra Nevada Mountains in the north, the valleys in northern and central California, and the Colorado River to the east (see Figure **Map of California Aqueducts** (Figure 5.24)). Aqueducts can be controversial and politically difficult especially if the water transfer distances are large. One drawback is the water diversion can cause drought in the area from where the water is drawn. For example, Owens Lake and Mono Lake in central California began to disappear after their river inflow was diverted to the Los Angeles aqueduct. Owens Lake remains almost completely dry, but Mono Lake has recovered more significantly due to legal intervention.

---

[25]Although 1,700 m^3/year sounds like a lot of water for every person, it is the minimum amount that hydrologists consider is needed to grow food, support industry, and maintain the environment in general.

Figure 5.22: Hoover Dam, Nevada, U.S. Hoover Dam, Nevada, U.S.. Behind the dam is Lake Mead, the largest reservoir in U.S.. White band reflects the lowered water levels in the reservoir due to drought conditions from 2000 - 2010. *Source: Cygnusloop99*[26] *at Wikimedia Commons*

Figure 5.23: The California Aqueduct California Aqueduct in southern California, U.S. *Source: David Jordan*[27] *at en.wikipedia*

---

[26] http://commons.wikimedia.org/wiki/File:Hoover_Dam_-_2010-12-10_-_View_from_bridge.jpg
[27] http://en.wikipedia.org/wiki/File:Tupman_California_California_Aqueduct_Mile_236.JPG

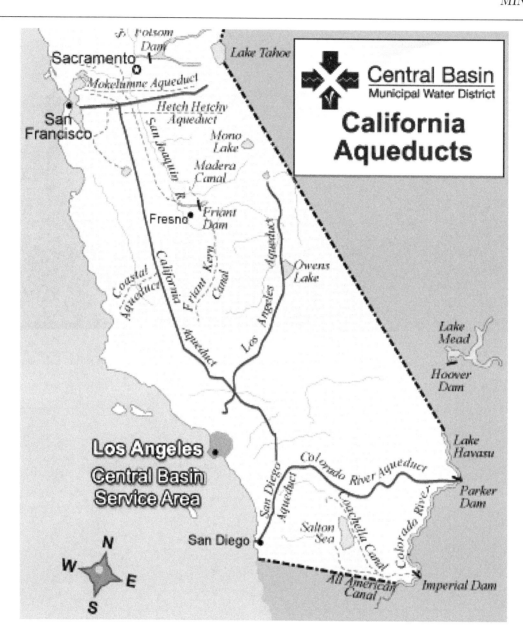

Figure 5.24: **Map of California Aqueducts** Map of California aqueducts that bring water to southern California from central and northern California and from the Colorado River to the east. *Source: Central Basin Municipal Water District*[28]

The Colorado River, probably the most exploited river in the U.S., has many dams, some huge reservoirs, and several large aqueducts so that it can provide large amounts of fresh water to 7 states in the arid southwestern U.S. and Mexico. The primary use for the water is for a few large cities (Las Vegas, Phoenix, and Tuscon) and irrigation. Allocation of Colorado River water is strictly regulated. Fortunately, not all

---

[28]http://www.centralbasin.org/waterSupplySystem.html

states use all of their water allocation because the total amount of allocated water is more than the typical Colorado River discharge. Colorado River water gets so saline due to evaporation along its course that the U.S. was forced to build a desalination plant near the border with Mexico so that it could be used for drinking and irrigation. The wetlands of the Colorado River delta and its associated ecosystem have been sadly degraded by the water overuse; some years, no river flow even reaches the ocean.

One method that actually can increase the amount of fresh water on Earth is **desalination**, which involves removing dissolved salt from seawater or saline groundwater. There are several ways to desalinate seawater including boiling, filtration, electrodialysis, and freezing. All of these procedures are moderately to very expensive and require considerable energy input, making the produced water much more expensive than fresh water from conventional sources. In addition, the processes create highly saline wastewater, which must be disposed of. Desalination is most common in the Middle East, where energy from oil is abundant but water is scarce.

Conservation means using less water and using it more efficiently. Around the home, conservation can involve both engineered features, such as high-efficiency clothes washers and low-flow showers and toilets, as well as behavioral decisions, such as growing native vegetation that require little irrigation in desert climates, turning off the water while you brush your teeth, and fixing leaky faucets. **Rainwater harvesting** involves catching and storing rainwater for reuse before it reaches the ground. Efficient irrigation is extremely important because irrigation accounts for a much larger water demand than public water supply. **Water conservation** strategies in agriculture include growing crops in areas where the natural rainfall can support them, more efficient irrigation systems such as drip systems that minimize losses due to evaporation, no-till farming that reduces evaporative losses by covering the soil, and reusing treated wastewater from sewage treatment plants. Recycled wastewater has also been used to recharge aquifers. There are a great many other specific water conservation strategies. Sustainable solutions to the water crisis must use a variety of approaches but they should have water conservation as a high priority.

5.2.10 Review Questions

Question 5.2.1
What is the water cycle and why is it important to fresh water resources?

Question 5.2.2
What are the relative merits of using surface water vs. groundwater as a water resource?

Question 5.2.3
What should society learn from the case history of the Aral Sea?

Question 5.2.4
Why is society facing a crisis involving water supply and how can we solve it?

5.2.11 References

Watkins, K. (2006). Beyond scarcity: Power, poverty and the global water crisis. *Human Development Report 2006, United Nations Development Programme.* Retrieved from http://hdr.undp.org/en/reports/global/hdr2006/[29]

5.3 Case Study: The Aral Sea - Going, Going, Gone[30]

The Aral Sea is a lake located east of the Caspian Sea between Uzbekistan and Kazakhstan in central Asia (see Figure **Map of Aral Sea Area** (Figure 5.25)). This area is part of the Turkestan desert, which is the fourth largest desert in the world; it is produced from a rain shadow effect by Afghanistan's high mountains

[29]http://hdr.undp.org/en/reports/global/hdr2006/
[30]This content is available online at <http://legacy.cnx.org/content/m41400/1.4/>.

to the south. Due to the arid and seasonally hot climate there is extensive evaporation and limited surface waters in general. Summer temperatures can reach 60 ° C (140 ° F)! The water supply to the Aral Sea is mainly from two rivers, the Amu Darya and Syr Darya, which carry snowmelt from mountainous areas. In the early 1960s the then-Soviet Union diverted the Amu Darya and Syr Darya Rivers for irrigation of one of the driest parts of Asia to produce rice, melons, cereals, and especially cotton. The Soviets wanted cotton or "white gold" to become a major export. They were successful and today Uzbekistan is one of the world's largest exporters of cotton. Unfortunately this action essentially eliminated any river inflow to the Aral Sea and caused it to disappear almost completely.

Figure 5.25: Map of Aral Sea Area Map shows lake size in 1960 and political boundaries of 2011. Countries in yellow are at least partially in Aral Sea drainage basin. *Source: Wikimedia Commons*[31]

In 1960 Aral Sea was the fourth largest inland water body; only the Caspian Sea, Lake Superior, and Lake Victoria were larger. Since then, it has progressively shrunk due to evaporation and lack of recharge by rivers (see Figure **Shrinking Aral Sea Blue** (Figure 5.26)). Before 1965 the Aral Sea received 20–60 km^3 of fresh water per year from rivers and by the early 1980s it received none. By 2007 the Aral Sea shrank to about 10% of its original size and its salinity increased from about 1% dissolved salt to about 10% dissolved salt, which is 3 times more saline than seawater. These changes caused an enormous environmental impact. A once thriving fishing industry is dead as are the 24 species of fish that used to live there; the fish could not adapt to the more saline waters. The current shoreline is tens of kilometers from former fishing

---

[31]http://commons.wikimedia.org/wiki/File:Aral_map.png

towns and commercial ports. Large fishing boats lie in the dried up lakebed of dust and salt (see Figure **An Abandoned Ship** (Figure 5.27)). A frustrating part of the river diversion project is that many of the irrigation canals were poorly built, allowing abundant water to leak or evaporate. An increasing number of dust storms blow salt, pesticides, and herbicides into nearby towns causing a variety of respiratory illnesses including tuberculosis.

Figure 5.26: Shrinking Aral Sea Blue area gives size of Aral Sea in 1960, 1970, 1980, 1990, 2000, 2004, 2008, and 2009 *Source: NordNordWest*[32] *at Wikimedia Commons*

Figure 5.27: An Abandoned Ship This abandoned ship lies in a dried up lake bed that was the Aral Sea near Aral, Kazakhstan *Source: Staecker*[33] *at Wikimedia Commons*

The wetlands of the two river deltas and their associated ecosystems have disappeared. The regional climate is drier and has greater temperature extremes due to the absence of moisture and moderating influence from the lake. In 2003 some lake restoration work began on the northern part of the Aral Sea and it provided some relief by raising water levels and reducing salinity somewhat. The southern part of the Aral Sea has seen no relief and remains nearly completely dry. The destruction of the Aral Sea is one of the planet's biggest environmental disasters and it is caused entirely by humans. Lake Chad in Africa is another example of a massive lake that has nearly disappeared for the same reasons as the Aral Sea. Aral Sea and Lake Chad are the most extreme examples of large lakes destroyed by unsustainable diversions of river water. Other lakes that have shrunk significantly due to human diversions of water include the Dead Sea in the Middle East, Lake Manchar in Pakistan, and Owens Lake and Mono Lake, both in California.

[32]http://commons.wikimedia.org/wiki/File:Aralsee.gif
[33]http://commons.wikimedia.org/wiki/File:Aralship2.jpg

5.4 Water Pollution[34]

5.4.1 Learning Objectives

After reading this module, students should be able to

- understand the major kinds of water pollutants and how they degrade water quality
- understand how and why the lack of safe drinking water in some parts of the world is a major problem
- know what sewage treatment does and why it is important
- know why it is more difficult to remediate groundwater pollution than surface water pollution
- understand how we can work toward solving the crisis involving water pollution

5.4.2 The Water Pollution Crisis

The Module **Water Cycle and Fresh Water Supply** (Section 5.2) described one aspect of the global water crisis, the water shortages that afflict many arid and densely populated areas. The global water crisis also involves water pollution, because to be useful for drinking and irrigation, water must not be polluted beyond certain thresholds. According to the World Health Organization, in 2008 approximately 880 million people in the world (or 13% of world population) did not have access to improved (safe) drinking water (World Health Statistics, 2010 (p. 209)) (See Figure **Proportion of Population by Country Using Improved Drinking Water Sources in 2008** (Figure 5.28)). At the same time, about 2.6 billion people (or 40% of world population) lived without improved sanitation (see Figure **Proportion of Population by Country Using Improved Sanitation Facilities in 2008** (Figure 5.29)), which is defined as having access to a public sewage system, septic tank, or even a simple pit latrine. Each year approximately 1.7 million people die from diarrheal diseases associated with unsafe drinking water, inadequate sanitation, and poor hygiene, e.g., hand washing with soap. Almost all of these deaths are in developing countries, and around 90% of them occur among children under the age of 5 (see Figure **Deaths by Country from Diarrhea Caused by Unsafe Water, Unimproved Sanitation, and Poor Hygiene in Children Less than 5 Years Old, 2004** (Figure 5.30)). Compounding the water crisis is the issue of social justice; poor people more commonly lack clean water and sanitation than wealthy people in similar areas. Globally, improving water, sanitation, and hygiene could prevent up to 9% of all disease and 6% of all deaths. In addition to the global waterborne disease crisis, chemical pollution from agriculture, industry, cities, and mining threatens global water quality. Some chemical pollutants have serious and well-known health effects; however, many others have poorly known long-term health effects. In the U.S. currently more than 40,000 water bodies fit the definition of "impaired" set by EPA (See Figure **Percentage of Impaired Water Bodies in a Watershed by State in USA Based on US EPA Data in 2000** (Figure 5.31)), which means they could neither support a healthy ecosystem nor meet water quality standards. In Gallup public polls conducted over the past decade Americans consistently put water pollution and water supply as the top environmental concerns over issues such as air pollution, deforestation, species extinction, and global warming.

---

[34]This content is available online at <http://legacy.cnx.org/content/m41441/1.8/>.

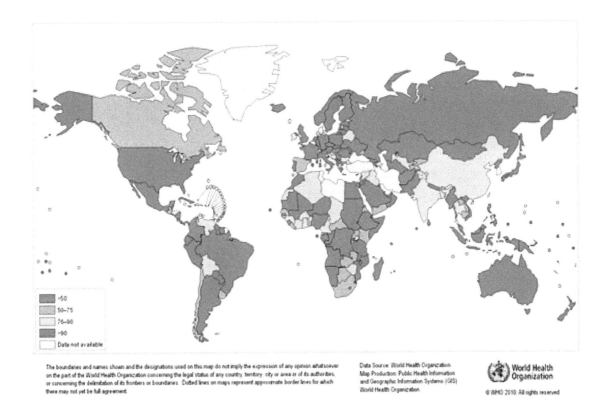

The boundaries and names shown and the designations used on this map do not imply the expression of any opinion whatsoever on the part of the World Health Organization concerning the legal status of any country, territory, city or area or of its authorities, or concerning the delimitation of its frontiers or boundaries. Dotted lines on maps represent approximate border lines for which there may not yet be full agreement.

Data Source: World Health Organization
Map Production: Public Health Information
and Geographic Information Systems (GIS)
World Health Organization

World Health Organization

© WHO 2010. All rights reserved

Figure 5.28:   Proportion of Population by Country Using Improved Drinking Water Sources in 2008 Improved drinking water sources, e.g., household connections, public standpipes, boreholes, protected dug wells and springs, and rainwater collections, are defined as those more likely to provide safe water than unimproved water sources, e.g., unprotected wells and springs, vendor-provided water, bottled water (unless water for other uses is available from an improved source), and tanker truck-provided water. *Source: World Health Organization*[35]

---

[35]http://gamapserver.who.int/mapLibrary/Files/Maps/phe_water_08.png

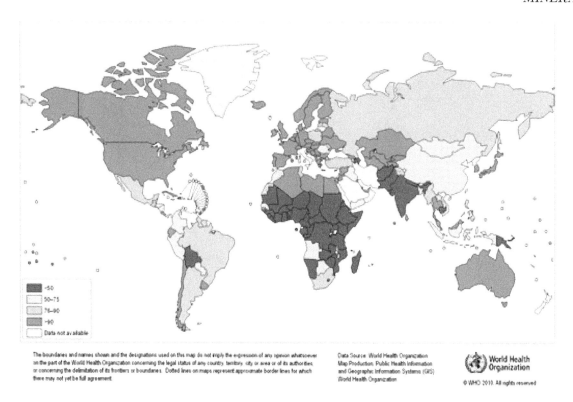

**Figure 5.29:   Proportion of Population by Country Using Improved Sanitation Facilities
in 2008** Improved sanitation facilities, e.g., connection to public sewers or septic systems, pour-flush
latrines, pit latrines, and ventilated improved pit latrines, are defined as those more likely to be sanitary
than unimproved facilities, e.g., bucket latrines, public latrines, and open pit latrines. *Source: World
Health Organization*[36]

---

[36]http://gamapserver.who.int/mapLibrary/Files/Maps/MDG7_sanitation_08.png

187

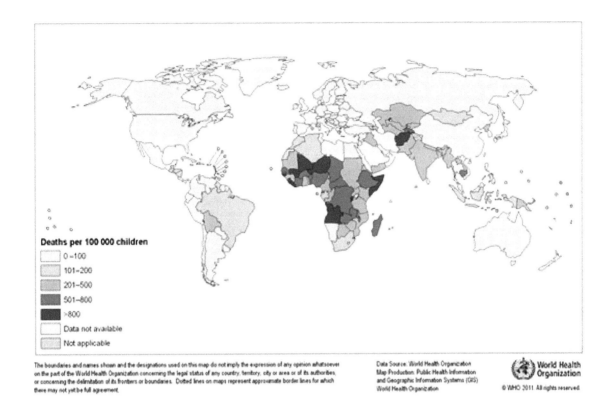

Figure 5.30: Deaths by Country from Diarrhea Caused by Unsafe Water, Unimproved Sanitation, and Poor Hygiene in Children Less than 5 Years Old, 2004 *Source: World Health Organization*[37]

---

[37]http://gamapserver.who.int/mapLibrary/Files/Maps/Global_wsh_death_under5_2004.png

Figure 5.31:   Percentage of Impaired Water Bodies in a Watershed by State in USA
Based on US EPA Data in 2000 Map of watersheds containing impaired water bodies from the U.S.
Environmental Protection Agency's 1998 list of impaired waters *Source: U.S. Geological Survey*[38]

5.4.3 Water Chemistry Overview

Compared to other molecules of similar molecular weight, water (H_2O) has unique physical properties including high values for melting and boiling point, surface tension (water's cohesion, or "stickiness"), and
capacity to dissolve soluble minerals, i.e., act as a **solvent**. These properties are related to its asymmetrical
structure and *polar nature*, which means it is electrically neutral overall but it has a net positive charge on
the side with the two hydrogen atoms and a net negative charge on the oxygen side (see Figure **Structure of
Water, Polar Charge of Water, and Hydrogen Bonds between Water Molecules** (Figure 5.32)).
This separation of the electrical charge within a water molecule results in *hydrogen bonds* with other water
molecules, mineral surfaces (hydrogen bonding produces the water films on minerals in the unsaturated zone
of the subsurface), and *dissolved ions* (atoms with a negative or positive charge). Many minerals and pollutants dissolve readily in water because water forms *hydration shells* (spheres of loosely coordinated, oriented
water molecules) around ions.

---

[38]http://pubs.usgs.gov/fs/FS-130-01/

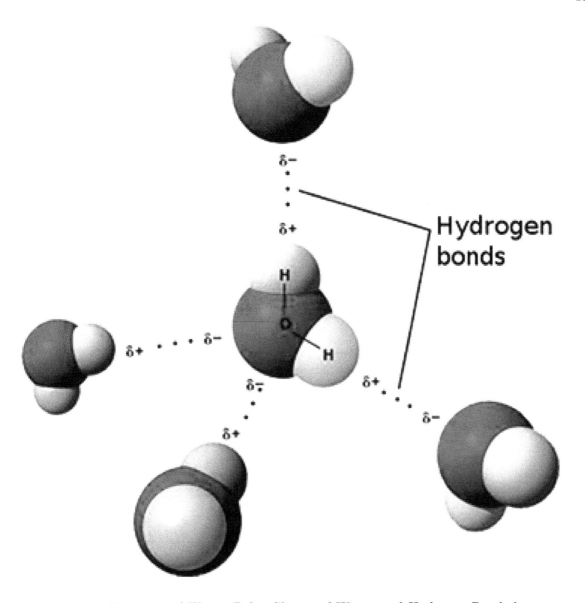

Figure 5.32: Structure of Water, Polar Charge of Water, and Hydrogen Bonds between Water Molecules *Source: Michal Maňas[39] at Wikimedia Commons*

Any natural water contains dissolved chemicals; some of these are important human nutrients, while others can be harmful to human health. The abundance of a water pollutant is commonly given in very small concentration units such as parts per million (ppm) or even parts per billion (ppb). An arsenic concentration of 1 ppm means 1 part of arsenic per million parts of water. This is equivalent to one drop of arsenic in 50 liters of water. To give you a different perspective on appreciating small concentration units, converting 1 ppm to length units is 1 cm (0.4 in) in 10 km (6 miles) and converting 1 ppm to time units is 30 seconds in a year. **Total dissolved solids** (TDS) represent the total amount of dissolved material in water. Average TDS (salinity) values for rainwater, river water, and seawater are about 4 ppm, 120 ppm, and 35,000 ppm. As discussed in Module **Climate Processes; External and Internal Controls** (Section 3.2), the

---

[39]http://commons.wikimedia.org/wiki/File:3D_model_hydrogen_bonds_in_water.jpg

most important processes that affect the salinity of natural waters are evaporation, which distills nearly pure water and leaves the dissolved ions in the original water, and chemical weathering, which involves mineral dissolution that adds dissolved ions to water. Fresh water is commonly defined as containing less than either 1,000 or 500 ppm TDS, but the US Environmental Protection Agency (EPA) recommends that drinking water not exceed 500 ppm TDS or else it will have an unpleasant salty taste.

5.4.4 Water Pollution Overview

Water pollution is the contamination of water by an excess amount of a substance that can cause harm to human beings and the ecosystem. The level of water pollution depends on the abundance of the pollutant, the ecological impact of the pollutant, and the use of the water. Pollutants are derived from biological, chemical, or physical processes. Although natural processes such as volcanic eruptions or evaporation sometimes can cause water pollution, most pollution is derived from human, land-based activities (see Figure **Water Pollution** (Figure 5.33)). Water pollutants can move through different water reservoirs, as the water carrying them progresses through stages of the water cycle (see Figure **Sources of Water Contamination** (Figure 5.34)). Water residence time (the average time that a water molecule spends in a water reservoir) is very important to pollution problems because it affects pollution potential. Water in rivers has a relatively short residence time, so pollution usually is there only briefly. Of course, pollution in rivers may simply move to another reservoir, such as the ocean, where it can cause further problems. Groundwater is typically characterized by slow flow and longer residence time, which can make groundwater pollution particularly problematic. Finally, pollution residence time can be much greater than the water residence time because a pollutant may be taken up for a long time within the ecosystem or absorbed onto sediment.

Figure 5.33: Water Pollution Obvious water pollution in the form of floating debris; invisible water pollutants sometimes can be much more harmful than visible ones. *Source: Stephen Codrington*[40] *at Wikimedia Commons*

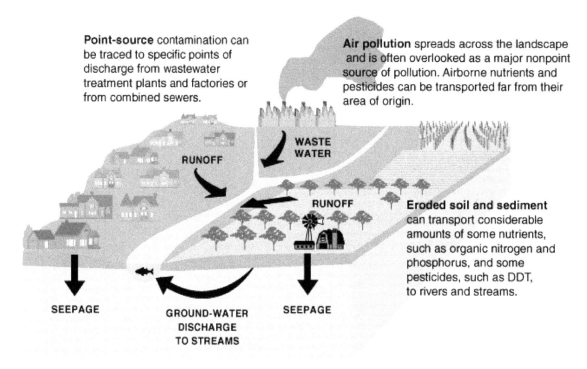

Figure 5.34: Sources of Water Contamination Sources of some water pollutants and movement of pollutants into different water reservoirs of the water cycle. *Source: U.S. Geological Survey*[41]

Pollutants enter water supplies from **point sources**, which are readily identifiable and relatively small locations, or **nonpoint sources**, which are large and more diffuse areas. Point sources of pollution include animal "factory" farms that raise a large number and high density of livestock such as cows, pigs, and chickens (see Figure **A Commercial Meat Chicken Production House** (Figure 5.35)) and discharge pipes from a factories or sewage treatment plants. **Combined sewer systems** that have a single set of underground pipes to collect both sewage and storm water runoff from streets for wastewater treatment can be major point sources of pollutants. During heavy rain, storm water runoff may exceed sewer capacity, causing it to back up and spilling untreated sewage into surface waters (see Figure **Combined Sewer System** (Figure 5.36)). Nonpoint sources of pollution include agricultural fields, cities, and abandoned mines. Rainfall runs over the land and through the ground, picking up pollutants such as herbicides, pesticides, and fertilizer from agricultural fields and lawns; oil, antifreeze, car detergent, animal waste, and road salt from urban areas; and acid and toxic elements from abandoned mines. Then, this pollution is carried into surface water bodies and groundwater. Nonpoint source pollution, which is the leading cause of water pollution in the U.S., is usually much more difficult and expensive to control than point source pollution because of its low concentration, multiple sources, and much greater volume of water.

---

[40]http://commons.wikimedia.org/?title=File:Obvious_water_pollution.jpeg
[41]http://ga.water.usgs.gov/edu/waterquality.html

Figure 5.35: A Commercial Meat Chicken Production House This chicken factory farm is a possible major point source of water pollution. *Source: Larry Rana*[42] *at Wikimedia Commons*

---

[42]http://commons.wikimedia.org/wiki/File:Florida_chicken_house.jpg

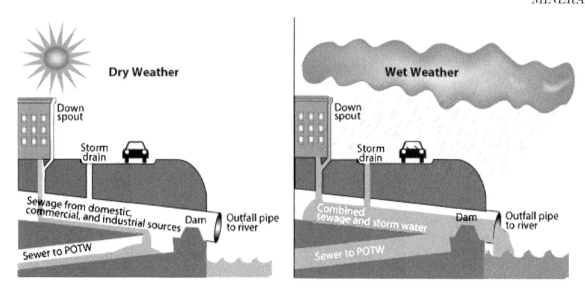

Figure 5.36: Combined Sewer System A combined sewer system is a possible major point source of water pollution during heavy rain due to overflow of untreated sewage. During dry weather (and small storms), all flows are handled by the publicly owned treatment works (POTW). During large storms, the relief structure allows some of the combined stormwater and sewage to be discharged untreated to an adjacent water body. *Source: U.S. Environmental Protection Agency*[43] *at Wikimedia Commons*

5.4.5 Types of Water Pollutants

Oxygen-demanding waste is an extremely important pollutant to ecosystems. Most surface water in contact with the atmosphere has a small amount of dissolved oxygen, which is needed by aquatic organisms for cellular respiration. Bacteria decompose dead organic matter (chemically represented in a simplified way as CH_2O) and remove dissolved oxygen (O_2) according to the following reaction:

$$CH_2O + O_2 \rightarrow CO_2 + H_2O \tag{5.1}$$

Too much decaying organic matter in water is a pollutant because it removes oxygen from water, which can kill fish, shellfish, and aquatic insects. The amount of oxygen used by aerobic (in the presence of oxygen) bacterial decomposition of organic matter is called **biochemical oxygen demand** (BOD). The major source of dead organic matter in most natural waters is sewage; grass and leaves are smaller sources. An unpolluted water body with respect to oxygen is a turbulent river that flows through a natural forest. Turbulence continually brings water in contact with the atmosphere where the O_2 content is restored. The dissolved oxygen content in such a river ranges from 10 to 14 ppm O_2, BOD is low, and clean-water fish, e.g., bass, trout, and perch dominate. A polluted water body with respect to oxygen is a stagnant deep lake in an urban setting with a combined sewer system. This system favors a high input of dead organic carbon from sewage overflows and limited chance for water circulation and contact with the atmosphere. In such a lake, the dissolved O_2 content is ≤ 5 ppm O_2, BOD is high, and low O_2-tolerant fish, e.g., carp and catfish dominate.

Excessive plant nutrients, particularly nitrogen (N) and phosphorous (P), are pollutants closely related to oxygen-demanding waste. Aquatic plants require about 15 nutrients for growth, most of which are plentiful in water. N and P are called *limiting nutrients*, because they usually are present in water at low

---

[43]http://commons.wikimedia.org/wiki/File:CSO_diagram_US_EPA.jpg

concentrations and therefore restrict the total amount of plant growth. This explains why N and P are major ingredients in most fertilizer. High concentrations of N and P from human sources (mostly agricultural and urban runoff including fertilizer, sewage, and P-based detergent) can cause **cultural eutrophication**, which involves the rapid growth of aquatic plants, particularly algae, called an *algal bloom*. Thick mats of floating and rooted green or sometimes red algae (see Figure **Algal Bloom in River in Sichuan, China** (Figure 5.37)) create water pollution, damage the ecosystem by clogging fish gills and blocking sunlight, and damage lake aesthetics by making recreation difficult and creating an eyesore. A small percentage of algal species produce toxins that can kill fish, mammals, and birds, and may cause human illness; explosive growths of these algae are called *harmful algal blooms* (see Figure **Harmful Algal Bloom** (Figure 5.38)). When the prolific algal layer dies, it becomes oxygen-demanding waste, which can create very low O_2 water ($< {\sim}2$ ppm O_2), called **hypoxia** or dead zone because it causes death to organisms that are unable to leave that environment. An estimated 50% of lakes in North America, Europe, and Asia are negatively impacted by cultural eutrophication. In addition, the size and number of marine hypoxic zones have grown dramatically over the past 50 years (see Figure **Aquatic Dead Zones** (Figure 5.39)), including a very large dead zone located offshore Louisiana in the Gulf of Mexico. Cultural eutrophication and hypoxia are difficult to combat, because they are caused primarily by nonpoint source pollution, which is difficult to regulate, and N and P, which are difficult to remove from wastewater.

Figure 5.37:   Algal Bloom in River in Sichuan, China Algal blooms can present problems for
ecosystems and human society. *Source: Felix Andrews*[44] *via Wikimedia Commons*

Figure 5.38: **Harmful Algal Bloom** Harmful algal bloom with deep red color. *Source: Kai Schumann*[45] *via National Oceanic and Atmospheric Administration*

---

[44]http://commons.wikimedia.org/wiki/File:River_algae_Sichuan.jpg
[45]http://oceanservice.noaa.gov/hazards/hab/

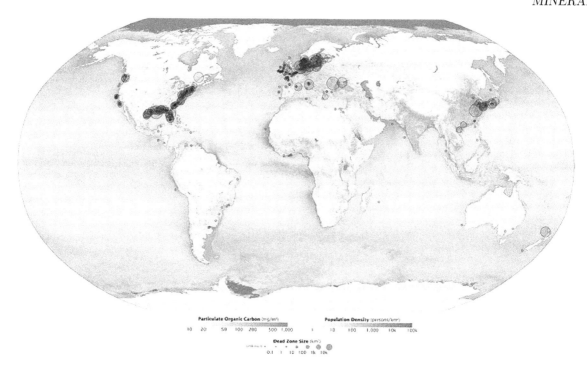

Figure 5.39: Aquatic Dead Zones Zones of hypoxia shown as red circles. Black dots show hypoxia zones of unknown size, brown shading shows population density, and blue shading shows density of particulate organic carbon, an indicator of organic productivity. *Source: Robert Simmon & Jesse Allen*[46] *at NASA Earth Observatory via Wikimedia Commons*

Pathogens are disease-causing microorganisms, e.g., viruses, bacteria, parasitic worms, and protozoa, which cause a variety of intestinal diseases such as dysentery, typhoid fever, hepatitis, and cholera. Pathogens are the major cause of the water pollution crisis discussed at the beginning of this section. Unfortunately nearly a billion people around the world are exposed to waterborne pathogen pollution daily and around 1.5 million children mainly in underdeveloped countries die every year of waterborne diseases from pathogens (see Figure **Deaths by Country from Diarrhea Caused by Unsafe Water, Unimproved Sanitation, and Poor Hygiene in Children Less than 5 Years Old, 2004** (Figure 5.30)). Pathogens enter water primarily from human and animal fecal waste due to inadequate sewage treatment. In many underdeveloped countries, sewage is discharged into local waters either untreated or after only rudimentary treatment. In developed countries untreated sewage discharge can occur from overflows of combined sewer systems, poorly managed livestock factory farms, and leaky or broken sewage collection systems (see Figure **Overflowing Sanitary Sewer** (Figure 5.40)). Water with pathogens can be remediated by adding chlorine or ozone, by boiling, or by treating the sewage in the first place.

---

[46]http://commons.wikimedia.org/wiki/File:Aquatic_Dead_Zones.jpg

Figure 5.40: Overflowing Sanitary Sewer A manhole cover blown off by a June 2006 sanitary sewer overflow in Rhode Island. *Source: U.S. Environmental Protection Agency*[47] *via Wikimedia Commons*

Oil spills are another kind of organic pollution. Oil spills can result from supertanker accidents such as the Exxon Valdez in 1989, which spilled 10 million gallons of oil into the rich ecosystem of offshore south Alaska and killed massive numbers of animals. The largest marine oil spill was the Deepwater Horizon disaster, which began with a natural gas explosion (see Figure **Deepwater Horizon Explosion** (Figure 5.41)) at an oil well 65 km offshore of Louisiana and flowed for 3 months in 2010, releasing an estimated 200 million gallons of oil. The worst oil spill ever occurred during the Persian Gulf war of 1991, when Iraq deliberately dumped approximately 200 million gallons of oil in offshore Kuwait and set more than 700 oil well fires that released enormous clouds of smoke and acid rain for over nine months. During an oil spill on water, oil floats to the surface because it is less dense than water, and the lightest hydrocarbons evaporate, decreasing the size of the spill but polluting the air. Then, bacteria begin to decompose the remaining oil, in a process that can take many years. After several months only about 15% of the original volume may remain, but it is in thick asphalt lumps, a form that is particularly harmful to birds, fish, and shellfish. Cleanup operations can include *skimmer ships* that vacuum oil from the water surface (effective only for small spills), *controlled burning* (works only in early stages before the light, ignitable part evaporates but also pollutes the air), *dispersants* (detergents that break up oil to accelerate its decomposition, but some dispersants may be toxic to the ecosystem), and *bioremediation* (adding microorganisms that specialize in quickly decomposing oil, but this can disrupt the natural ecosystem).

---

[47]http://commons.wikimedia.org/wiki/File:Sewer_overflow_RI_EPA.jpg

Figure 5.41:   Deepwater Horizon Explosion Boats fighting the fire from an explosion at the Deepwater Horizon drilling rig in Gulf of Mexico offshore Louisiana on April 20, 2010. *Source: United States Coast Guard*[48] *via Wikimedia Commons*

Toxic chemicals involve many different kinds and sources, primarily from industry and mining. General kinds of toxic chemicals include *hazardous chemicals*, which are a wide variety of synthetic organic and inorganic chemicals such as acids, bases, cyanide, and a class of compounds called **persistent organic pollutants** that includes *DDT* (pesticide), *dioxin* (herbicide by-product), and *PCBs* (polychlorinated biphenyls, which were used as a liquid insulator in electric transformers). Persistent organic pollutants are long-lived in the environment, accumulate through the food chain (bioaccumulation), and can be toxic. Another category of toxic chemicals includes *radioactive materials* such as cesium, iodine, uranium, and radon gas, which can result in long-term exposure to radioactivity if it gets into the body. A final group of toxic chemicals is **heavy metals** such as lead, mercury, arsenic, cadmium, and chromium, which can accumulate through the food chain. Heavy metals are commonly produced by industry and at metallic ore mines. Arsenic and mercury are discussed in more detail below. The US EPA regulates 83 contaminants in drinking water to ensure a safe public water supply. Similarly, at the international level the World Health Organization has drinking water standards for a variety of contaminants.

Arsenic (As) has been famous as an agent of death for many centuries. In large doses arsenic causes cancer and can be fatal. Only recently have scientists recognized that health problems can be caused by drinking small arsenic concentrations in water over a long time. It attacks the central nervous system

---

[48]http://commons.wikimedia.org/wiki/File:Deepwater_Horizon_offshore_drilling_unit_on_fire_2010.jpg

and can damage the respiratory system, bladder, lungs, liver, and kidneys. It enters the water supply naturally from weathering of As-rich minerals and from human activities such as coal burning and smelting of metallic ores. The worst case of arsenic poisoning occurred in the densely populated impoverished country of Bangladesh, which had experienced 100,000s of deaths from diarrhea and cholera each year from drinking surface water contaminated with pathogens due to improper sewage treatment. In the 1970s the United Nations provided aid for millions of shallow water wells, which resulted in a dramatic drop in pathogenic diseases. Unfortunately, many of the wells produced water naturally rich in arsenic. Tragically, there are an estimated 77 million people (about half of the population) who inadvertently may have been exposed to toxic levels of arsenic in Bangladesh as a result. The World Health Organization has called it the largest mass poisoning of a population in history.

Mercury (Hg) is used in a variety of electrical products, such as dry cell batteries, fluorescent light bulbs, and switches, as well as in the manufacture of paint, paper, vinyl chloride, and fungicides. In the methylmercury form (CH_3Hg^+) it is highly toxic; ≥ 1 ppb of methylmercury represents water contaminated with mercury. Mercury concentrates in the food chain, especially in fish, in a process caused biomagnification (see Sidebar **Biomagnification** (Biomagnification, p. 201)). It acts on the central nervous system and can cause loss of sight, feeling, and hearing as well as nervousness, shakiness, and death. Like arsenic, mercury enters the water supply naturally from weathering of Hg-rich minerals and from human activities such as coal burning and metal processing. A famous mercury poisoning case in Minamata, Japan involved methylmercury-rich industrial discharge that caused high Hg levels in fish. People in the local fishing villages ate fish up to three times per day for over 30 years, which resulted in over 2,000 deaths. During that time the responsible company and national government did little to mitigate, help alleviate, or even acknowledge the problem.

SIDEBAR: Biomagnification represents the processes in an ecosystem that cause greater concentrations of a chemical, such as methylmercury, in organisms higher up the food chain. Mercury and methylmercury are present in only very small concentrations in seawater; however, at the base of the food chain algae absorb methylmercury. Then, small fish eat the algae, large fish and other organisms higher in the food chain eat the small fish, and so on. Fish and other aquatic organisms absorb methylmercury rapidly but eliminate it slowly from the body. Therefore, each step up the food chain increases the concentration from the step below (see Figure **Biomagnification** (Figure 5.42)). Largemouth bass can concentrate methylmercury up to 10 million times over the water concentration and fish-eating birds can concentrate it even higher. Other chemicals that exhibit biomagnification are DDT, PCBs, and arsenic.

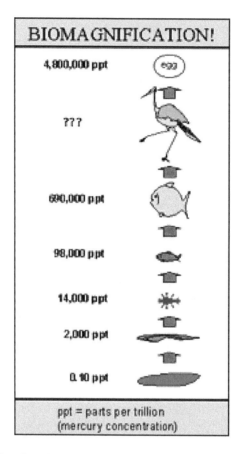

Figure 5.42: Biomagnification An illustrative example of biomagnification of mercury from water
through the food chain and into a bird's egg. *Source: U.S. Geological Survey*[49]

Other water pollutants include **sediment** and **heat**. Muddy water is bad for drinking but even worse for
underwater plants that need sunlight for photosynthesis. Much of the sediment in water bodies is derived
from the erosion of soil, so it also represents a loss of agricultural productivity. Thermal pollution involves
the release of heated waters from power plants and industry to surface water, causing a drop in the dissolved
O_2 content, which can stress fish.

   Hard water contains abundant calcium and magnesium, which reduces its ability to develop soapsuds
and enhances *scale* (calcium and magnesium carbonate minerals) formation on hot water equipment. Water
softeners remove calcium and magnesium, which allows the water to lather easily and resist scale formation.
Hard water develops naturally from the dissolution of calcium and magnesium carbonate minerals in soil; it
does not have negative health effects in people.

   Groundwater pollution can occur from underground sources and all of the pollution sources that contaminate surface waters. Common sources of groundwater pollution are leaking underground storage tanks
for fuel, septic tanks, agricultural activity, and landfills. Common groundwater pollutants include nitrate,
pesticides, volatile organic compounds, and petroleum products. Polluted groundwater can be a more serious
problem than polluted surface water because the pollution in groundwater may go undetected for a long time
because usually it moves very slowly. As a result, the pollution in groundwater may create a **contaminant
plume**, a large body of flowing polluted groundwater (see Figure **Contaminant Plume in Groundwater** (p. 203)), making cleanup very costly. By the time groundwater contamination is detected, the entity

---
[49]http://sofia.usgs.gov/sfrsf/rooms/mercury/achilles_heel/cause.html

responsible for the pollution may be bankrupt or nonexistent. Another troublesome feature of groundwater pollution is that small amounts of certain pollutants, e.g., petroleum products and organic solvents, can contaminate large areas. In Denver, Colorado 80 liters of several organic solvents contaminated 4.5 trillion liters of groundwater and produced a 5 km long contaminant plume. Most groundwater contamination occurs in shallow, unconfined aquifers located near the contamination source. Confined aquifers are less susceptible to pollution from the surface because of protection by the confining layer. A major threat to groundwater quality is from **underground fuel storage tanks**. Fuel tanks commonly are stored underground at gas stations to reduce explosion hazards. Before 1988 in the U.S. these storage tanks could be made of metal, which can corrode, leak, and quickly contaminate local groundwater. Now, leak detectors are required and the metal storage tanks are supposed to be protected from corrosion or replaced with fiberglass tanks. Currently there are around 600,000 underground fuel storage tanks in the U.S. and over 30% still do not comply with EPA regulations regarding either release prevention or leak detection.

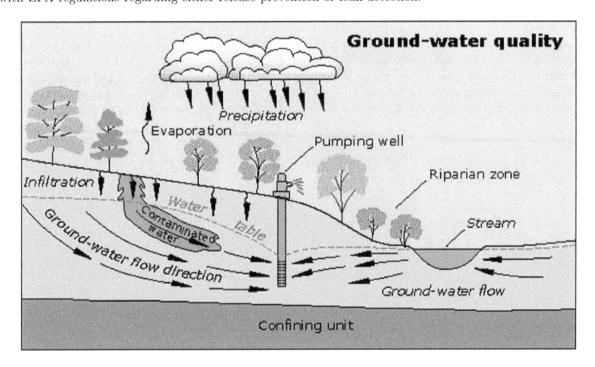

Figure 5.43: Contaminant Plume in Groundwater Mapping how a contaminant plume will migrate once it reaches groundwater requires understanding of the pollutant's chemical properties, local soil characteristics, and how permeable the aquifer is. *Source: United States Geological Survey*[50]

5.4.6 Sustainable Solutions to the Water Pollution Crisis?

Resolution of the global water pollution crisis described at the beginning of this section requires multiple approaches to improve the quality of our fresh water and move towards sustainability. The most deadly form of water pollution, pathogenic microorganisms that cause waterborne diseases, kills almost 2 million people in underdeveloped countries every year. The best strategy for addressing this problem is proper sewage (wastewater) treatment. Untreated sewage is not only a major cause of pathogenic diseases, but also a major source of other pollutants, including oxygen-demanding waste, plant nutrients (N and P), and toxic

---

[50]http://www.learner.org/courses/envsci/visual/visual.php?shortname=contaminant_flow

heavy metals. Wastewater treatment is done at a **sewage treatment plant** in urban areas and through a **septic tank system** in rural areas.

The main purpose of a sewage treatment plant is to remove organic matter (oxygen-demanding waste) and kill bacteria; special methods also can be used to remove plant nutrients and other pollutants. The numerous processing steps at a conventional sewage treatment plant (see Figure **Steps at a Sewage Treatment Plant** (Figure 5.44)) include *pretreatment* (screening and removal of sand and gravel), *primary treatment* (settling or floatation to remove organic solids, fat, and grease), *secondary treatment* (aerobic bacterial decomposition of organic solids), *tertiary treatment* (bacterial decomposition of nutrients and filtration), *disinfection* (treatment with chlorine, ozone, ultraviolet light, or bleach), and either *discharge* to surface waters (usually a local river) or *reuse* for some other purpose, such as irrigation, habitat preservation, and artificial groundwater recharge. The concentrated organic solid produced during primary and secondary-treatment is called **sludge**, which is treated in a variety of ways including landfill disposal, incineration, use as fertilizer, and anaerobic bacterial decomposition, which is done in the absence of oxygen. Anaerobic decomposition of sludge produces methane gas, which can be used as an energy source. To reduce water pollution problems, separate sewer systems (where street runoff goes to rivers and only wastewater goes to a wastewater treatment plant) are much better than combined sewer systems, which can overflow and release untreated sewage into surface waters during heavy rain. Some cities such as Chicago, Illinois have constructed large underground caverns and also use abandoned rock quarries to hold storm sewer overflow. After the rain stops, the stored water goes to the sewage treatment plant for processing.

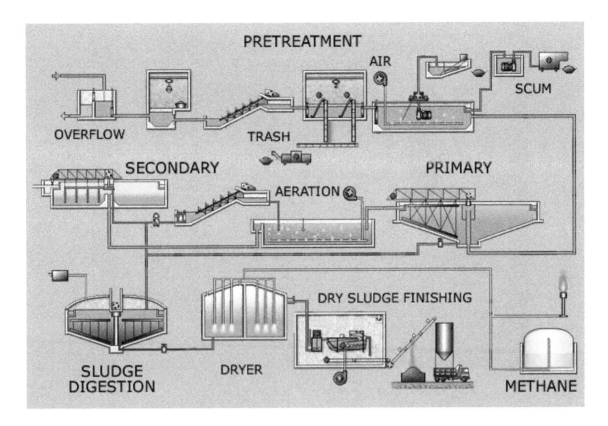

Figure 5.44: Steps at a Sewage Treatment Plant The numerous processing steps at a conventional sewage treatment plant include pretreatment (screening and removal of sand and gravel), primary treatment (settling or floatation to remove organic solids, fat, and grease), secondary treatment (aerobic bacterial decomposition of organic solids), tertiary treatment (bacterial decomposition of nutrients and filtration), disinfection (treatment with chlorine, ozone, ultraviolet light, or bleach), and either discharge to surface waters (usually a local river) or reuse for some other purpose, such as irrigation, habitat preservation, and artificial groundwater recharge. *Source: Leonard G.*[51] *via Wikipedia*

A septic tank system is an individual sewage treatment system for homes in rural and even some urban settings. The basic components of a septic tank system (see Figure **Septic System** (Figure 5.45)) include a sewer line from the house, a *septic tank* (a large container where sludge settles to the bottom and microorganisms decompose the organic solids anaerobically), and the drain field (network of perforated pipes where the clarified water seeps into the soil and is further purified by bacteria). Water pollution problems occur if the septic tank malfunctions, which usually occurs when a system is established in the wrong type of soil or maintained poorly.

---

[51]http://en.wikipedia.org/wiki/File:ESQUEMPEQUE-EN.jpg

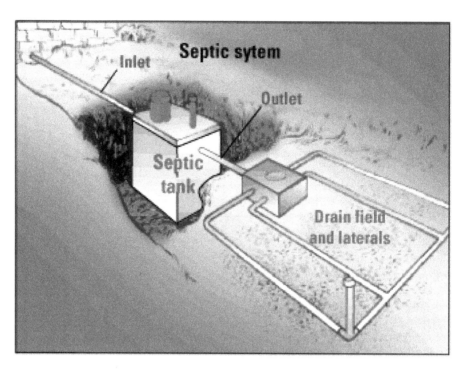

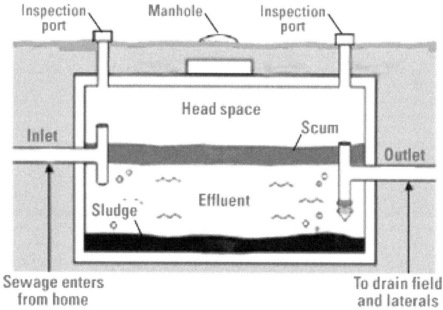

Figure 5.45:   **Septic System** Septic tank system for sewage treatment. *Source: United States Geological Survey*[52]

For many developing countries, financial aid is necessary to build adequate sewage treatment facilities;

[52]http://pubs.usgs.gov/fs/fs07203/

however, the World Health Organization estimates an estimated cost savings of between \$3 and \$34 for every \$1 invested in clean water delivery and sanitation (Water for Life, 2005 (p. 209)). The cost savings are from health care savings, gains in work and school productivity, and deaths prevented. Simple and inexpensive techniques for treating water at home include chlorination, filters, and solar disinfection. Another alternative is to use **constructed wetlands** technology (marshes built to treat contaminated water), which is simpler and cheaper than a conventional sewage treatment plant.

Bottled water is *not* a sustainable solution to the water crisis, despite exponential growth in popularity in the U.S. and the world. Bottled water is not necessarily any safer than the U.S. public water supply, it costs on average about 700 times more than U.S. tap water, and every year it uses approximately 200 billion plastic and glass bottles that have a relatively low rate of recycling. Compared to tap water, it uses much more energy, mainly in bottle manufacturing and long-distance transportation. If you don't like the taste of your tap water, then please use a water filter instead of bottled water!

Figure 5.46: **Storm Drain** Curbside storm drain receiving urban runoff. *Source: By Robert Lawton*[53] *via Wikimedia Commons*

Additional sustainable solutions to the water pollution crisis include legislation to eliminate or greatly reduce point sources of water pollution. In the U.S., the Clean Water Act of 1972 and later amendments led to major improvements in water quality (see Sidebar **Clean Water Act** (Clean Water Act, p. 208)). Nonpoint sources of water pollution, e.g., agricultural runoff and urban runoff (see Figure **Storm Drain** (p. 207)), are much harder to regulate because of their widespread, diffuse nature. There are many construction and agricultural practices that reduce polluted runoff including no-till farming and sediment traps. Artificial aeration or mechanical mixing can remediate lakes with oxygen depletion. Specific things that we can do

---

[53]http://commons.wikimedia.org/wiki/File:Storm_Drain.JPG

to reduce urban runoff include the following: keep soil, leaves, and grass clippings off driveways, sidewalks, and streets; don't pour used motor oil, antifreeze, paints, pesticides, or any household hazardous chemical down the storm sewer or drain; recycle used motor oil; use hazardous waste disposal programs offered by the community; compost your organic waste; don't use fertilizers and herbicides on your lawn; and flush pet waste down the toilet.

SIDEBAR: During the early 1900s rapid industrialization in the U.S. resulted in widespread water pollution due to free discharge of waste into surface waters. The Cuyahoga River in northeast Ohio caught fire numerous times (see Figure **Cuyahoga River on Fire** (Figure 5.47)), including a famous fire in 1969 that caught the nation's attention. In 1972 Congress passed one of the most important environmental laws in U.S. history, the Federal Water Pollution Control Act, which is more commonly called the Clean Water Act. The purpose of the Clean Water Act and later amendments is to maintain and restore water quality, or in simpler terms to make our water swimmable and fishable. It became illegal to dump pollution into surface water unless there was formal permission and U.S. water quality improved significantly as a result. More progress is needed because currently the EPA considers over 40,000 U.S. water bodies as impaired, most commonly due to pathogens, metals, plant nutrients, and oxygen depletion. Another concern is protecting groundwater quality, which is not yet addressed sufficiently by federal law.

Figure 5.47: Cuyahoga River on Fire *Source: National Oceanic and Atmospheric*[54]

---

[54]http://oceanservice.noaa.gov/education/kits/pollution/media/supp_pol02d.html

Sometimes slow flow through a soil can naturally purify groundwater because some pollutants, such as P, pesticides, and heavy metals, chemically bind with surfaces of soil clays and iron oxides. Other pollutants are not retained by soil particles: These include N, road salt, gasoline fuel, the herbicide atrazine, tetrachloroethylene (a carcinogenic cleaning solvent used in dry cleaning), and vinyl chloride. In other cases, slow groundwater flow can allow bacteria to decompose dead organic matter and certain pesticides. There are many other ways to remediate polluted groundwater. Sometimes the best solution is to stop the pollution source and allow natural cleanup. Specific treatment methods depend on the geology, hydrology, and pollutant because some light contaminants flow on top of groundwater, others dissolve and flow with groundwater, and dense contaminants can sink below groundwater. A common cleanup method called pump and treat involves pumping out the contaminated groundwater and treating it by oxidation, filtration, or biological methods. Sometimes soil must be excavated and sent to a landfill. In-situ treatment methods include adding chemicals to immobilize heavy metals, creating a permeable reaction zone with metallic iron that can destroy organic solvents, or using **bioremediation** by adding oxygen or nutrients to stimulate growth of microorganisms.

5.4.7 Review Questions

Question 5.4.1
What are the major kinds of water pollutants and how do they degrade water quality?

Question 5.4.2
How would you rank the water pollution problems described in this chapter? Why?

Question 5.4.3
Why is untreated sewage such an important water pollutant to remediate?

Question 5.4.4
What should society learn from the case history of Love Canal?

Question 5.4.5
Why are people facing a crisis involving water pollution and how can we solve it?

5.4.8 References

Water for Life: Making it Happen (2005) World Health Organization and UNICEF. Retrieved from http://www.who.int/water_sanitation_health/waterforlife.pdf[55]

World Health Statistics (2010) World Health Organization. Retrieved from http://www.who.int/whosis/whostat/EN_WHS10_Full.pdf[56]

5.5 Case Study: The Love Canal Disaster[57]

One of the most famous and important examples of groundwater pollution in the U.S. is the Love Canal tragedy in Niagara Falls, New York. It is important because the pollution disaster at Love Canal, along with similar pollution calamities at that time (Times Beach, Missouri and Valley of Drums, Kentucky), helped to create **Superfund**, a federal program instituted in 1980 and designed to identify and clean up the worst of the hazardous chemical waste sites in the U.S.

Love Canal is a neighborhood in Niagara Falls named after a large ditch (approximately 15 m wide, 3–12 m deep, and 1600 m long) that was dug in the 1890s for hydroelectric power. The ditch was abandoned before it actually generated any power and went mostly unused for decades, except for swimming by local residents. In the 1920s Niagara Falls began dumping urban waste into Love Canal, and in the 1940s the

[55]http://www.who.int/water_sanitation_health/waterforlife.pdf
[56]http://www.who.int/whosis/whostat/EN_WHS10_Full.pd
[57]This content is available online at <http://legacy.cnx.org/content/m41444/1.5/>.

U.S. Army dumped waste from World War II there, including waste from the frantic effort to build a nuclear bomb. Hooker Chemical purchased the land in 1942 and lined it with clay. Then, the company put into Love Canal an estimated 21,000 tons of hazardous chemical waste, including the carcinogens benzene, dioxin, and PCBs in large metal barrels and covered them with more clay. In 1953, Hooker sold the land to the Niagara Falls school board for \$1, and included a clause in the sales contract that both described the land use (filled with chemical waste) and absolved them from any future damage claims from the buried waste. The school board promptly built a public school on the site and sold the surrounding land for a housing project that built 200 or so homes along the canal banks and another 1,000 in the neighborhood (see Figure **Love Canal** (Figure 5.48)). During construction, the canal's clay cap and walls were breached, damaging some of the metal barrels.

Figure 5.48: Love Canal *Source: US Environmental Protection Agency*[58]

Eventually, the chemical waste seeped into people's basements, and the metal barrels worked their way to the surface. Trees and gardens began to die; bicycle tires and the rubber soles of children's shoes disintegrated in noxious puddles. From the 1950s to the late 1970s, residents repeatedly complained of strange odors and substances that surfaced in their yards. City officials investigated the area, but did not act to solve the problem. Local residents allegedly experienced major health problems including high rates of miscarriages, birth defects, and chromosome damage, but studies by the New York State Health Department disputed that. Finally, in 1978 President Carter declared a state of emergency at Love Canal, making it the first human-

[58]http://www.epa.gov/region2/superfund/npl/lovecanal/images.html

caused environmental problem to be designated that way. The Love Canal incident became a symbol of improperly stored chemical waste. Clean up of Love Canal, which was funded by Superfund and completely finished in 2004, involved removing contaminated soil, installing drainage pipes to capture contaminated groundwater for treatment, and covering it with clay and plastic. In 1995, Occidental Chemical (the modern name for Hooker Chemical) paid $102 million to Superfund for cleanup and $27 million to Federal Emergency Management Association for the relocation of more than 1,000 families. New York State paid $98 million to EPA and the US government paid $8 million for pollution by the Army. The total clean up cost was estimated to be $275 million. The only good thing about the Love Canal tragedy is that it helped to create Superfund, which has analyzed tens of thousands of hazardous waste sites in the U.S. and cleaned up hundreds of the worst ones. Nevertheless, over 1,000 major hazardous waste sites with a significant risk to human health or the environment are still in the process of being cleaned.

5.6 Mineral Resources: Formation, Mining, Environmental Impact[59]

5.6.1 Learning Objectives

After reading this module, students should be able to

- know the importance of minerals to society
- know factors that control availability of mineral resources
- know why future world mineral supply and demand is an important issue
- understand the environmental impact of mining and processing of minerals
- understand how we can work toward solving the crisis involving mineral supply

5.6.2 Importance of Minerals

Mineral resources are essential to our modern industrial society and they are used everywhere. For example, at breakfast you drink some juice in a glass (made from melted quartz sand), eat from a ceramic plate (created from clay minerals heated at high temperatures), sprinkle salt (halite) on your eggs, use steel utensils (from iron ore and other minerals), read a magazine (coated with up to 50% kaolinite clay to give the glossy look), and answer your cellphone (containing over 40 different minerals including copper, silver, gold, and platinum). We need minerals to make cars, computers, appliances, concrete roads, houses, tractors, fertilizer, electrical transmission lines, and jewelry. Without mineral resources, industry would collapse and living standards would plummet. In 2010, the average person in the U.S. consumed more than 16,000 pounds of mineral resources[60] (see Table **Per Capita Consumption of Minerals** (Table 5.1)). With an average life expectancy of 78 years, that translates to about 1.3 million pounds of mineral resources over such a person's lifetime. Here are a few statistics that help to explain these large values of mineral use: an average American house contains about 250,000 pounds of minerals (see Figure **Mineral Use in the Kitchen** (Figure 5.49) for examples of mineral use in the kitchen), one mile of Interstate highway uses 170 million pounds of earth materials, and the U.S. has nearly 4 million miles of roads. All of these mineral resources are nonrenewable, because nature usually takes hundreds of thousands to millions of years to produce mineral deposits. Early hominids used rocks as simple tools as early as 2.6 million years ago. At least 500,000 years ago prehistoric people used flint (fine-grained quartz) for knives and arrowheads. Other important early uses of minerals include mineral pigments such as manganese oxides and iron oxides for art, salt for food preservation, stone for pyramids, and metals such as bronze (typically tin and copper), which is stronger than pure copper and iron for steel, which is stronger than bronze.

---

[59]This content is available online at <http://legacy.cnx.org/content/m41470/1.5/>.

[60]Americans also consumed more than 21,000 pounds of energy resources from the Earth including coal, oil, natural gas, and uranium.

1. RADIO: Includes aluminum, copper, gold, iron, and petroleum products.
2. TOASTER: Includes copper, iron, nickel, mica, chromium, and petroleum products.
3. ELECTRICAL WIRING: Includes copper, aluminum, and petroleum products.
4. MICROWAVE: Includes copper, gold, iron, nickel, and silica.
5. STOVE: Includes aluminum, copper, iron, nickel, and silica.
6. REFRIGERATOR: Includes aluminum, copper, iron, nickel, petroleum products, and zinc.
7. TABLE SALT: Includes halite; light salt can be made from sylvite. Most salt has added iodine.
8. PLATES: Includes clays, silica, and feldspar.
9. CUTLERY: Includes iron, nickel, silver, and chromium.
10. CLOCK: Includes iron, nickel, petroleum products, and silica.
11. STAINLESS STEEL SINK: Includes iron and nickel.
12. BLACKBOARD: Includes clays. Chalk includes limestone or petroleum products.
13. MAGNET: Includes cobalt.
14. DISH RACK: Made of petroleum products.

Figure 5.49: Mineral Use in the Kitchen *Source: U.S. Geological Survey*[61]

Mineral	Per Capita Consumption of Minerals – 2010 (Pounds per Person)	Per Capita Consumption of Minerals - Lifetime (Pounds Per Person)
Bauxite (Aluminum)	65	5,090
Cement	496	38,837
Clays	164	12,841
Copper	12	939.6
Iron Ore	357	27,953
Lead	11	861
Manganese	5	392
Phosphate Rock	217	16,991
Potash	37	2,897
Salt	421	32,964
		continued on next page

[61]http://minerals.usgs.gov/granted.html

Sand, Gravel, Stone	14,108	1,104,656
Soda Ash	36	2,819
Sulfur	86	6,734
Zinc	6	470
Other Metals	24	1,879
Other Nonmetals	332	25,996
Total	**16,377**	**1,282,319**

Table 5.1: Per capita consumption of nonenergy related minerals and metals in the U.S. for 2010 and for a lifetime of 78.3 years assuming 2010 mineral consumption rates *Sources: US Geological Survey, National Mining Association, and U.S. Census Bureau*

5.6.3 Mineral Resource Principles

A geologist defines a **mineral** as a naturally occurring inorganic solid with a defined chemical composition and crystal structure (regular arrangement of atoms). Minerals are the ingredients of **rock**, which is a solid coherent (i.e., will not fall apart) piece of planet Earth. There are three classes of rock, igneous, sedimentary, and metamorphic. **Igneous rocks** form by cooling and solidification of hot molten rock called lava or magma. Lava solidifies at the surface after it is ejected by a volcano, and magma cools underground. **Sedimentary rocks** form by hardening of layers of sediment (loose grains such as sand or mud) deposited at Earth's surface or by mineral precipitation, i.e., formation of minerals in water from dissolved mineral matter. **Metamorphic rocks** form when the shape or type of minerals in a preexisting rock changes due to intense heat and pressure deep within the Earth. **Ore** is rock with an enrichment of minerals that can be mined for profit. Sometimes **ore deposits** (locations with abundant ore) can be beautiful, such as the giant gypsum crystals at the amazing Cave of the Crystals in Mexico (see Figure **Giant Gypsum Crystals** (Figure 5.50)). The **enrichment factor**, which is the ratio of the metal concentration needed for an economic ore deposit over the average abundance of that metal in Earth's crust, is listed for several important metals in the Table **Enrichment Factor** (Table 5.2: Enrichment Factor). Mining of some metals, such as aluminum and iron, is profitable at relatively small concentration factors, whereas for others, such as lead and mercury, it is profitable only at very large concentration factors. The metal concentration in ore (column 3 in Table **Enrichment Factor** (Table 5.2: Enrichment Factor)) can also be expressed in terms of the proportion of metal and waste rock produced after processing one metric ton (1,000 kg) of ore. Iron is at one extreme, with up to 690 kg of Fe metal and only 310 kg of waste rock produced from pure iron ore, and gold is at the other extreme with only one gram (.03 troy oz) of Au metal and 999.999 kg of waste rock produced from gold ore.

Figure 5.50: Giant Gypsum Crystals Giant gypsum crystals in the Cave of Crystals in Naica, Mexico. There are crystals up to 11 m long in this cave, which is located about 1 km underground. *Source: National Geographic via Wikipedia*[62]

---

[62]http://en.wikipedia.org/wiki/File:Caveofcrystals.jpg

Enrichment Factor

Metal	Average Concentration in Crust (%)	Concentration Needed for Economic Mine (%)	Approximate Enrichment Factor
Aluminum	8	35	4
Iron	5	20 - 69	4 - 14
Copper	0.005	0.4 - 0.8	80 - 160
Gold	0.0000004	0.0001[68]	250
Lead	0.0015	4	2,500
Mercury	0.00001	0.1	10,500

Table 5.2: Approximate enrichment factors of selected metals needed before profitable mining is possible.
Source: US Geological Survey Professional Paper 820, 1973

5.6.4 Formation of Ore Deposits

Ore deposits form when minerals are concentrated—sometimes by a factor of many thousands—in rock, usually by one of six major processes. These include the following: (a) **igneous crystallization**, where molten rock cools to form igneous rock. This process forms building stone such as granite, a variety of gemstones, sulfur ore, and metallic ores, which involve dense chromium or platinum minerals that sink to the bottom of liquid magma. Diamonds form in rare Mg-rich igneous rock called kimberlite that originates as molten rock at 150–200 km depth (where the diamonds form) and later moves very quickly to the surface, where it erupts explosively. The cooled magma forms a narrow, carrot-shaped feature called a pipe. Diamond mines in kimberlite pipes can be relatively narrow but deep (see Figure **A Diamond Mine** (Figure 5.51)). (b) **Hydrothermal** is the most common ore-forming process. It involves hot, salty water that dissolves metallic elements from a large area and then precipitates ore minerals in a smaller area, commonly along rock fractures and faults. Molten rock commonly provides the heat and the water is from groundwater, the ocean, or the magma itself. The ore minerals usually contain sulfide (S^{2-}) bonded to metals such as copper, lead, zinc, mercury, and silver. Actively forming hydrothermal ore deposits occur at undersea mountain ranges, called oceanic ridges, where new ocean crust is produced. Here, mineral-rich waters up to $350\,^{\circ}C$ sometimes discharge from cracks in the crust and precipitate a variety of metallic sulfide minerals that make the water appear black; they are called **black smokers** (see Figure **Black Smokers** (Figure 5.52)). (c) **Metamorphism** occurs deep in the earth under very high temperature and pressure and produces several building stones, including marble and slate, as well as some nonmetallic ore, including asbestos, talc, and graphite. (d) **Sedimentary processes** occur in rivers that concentrate sand and gravel (used in construction), as well as dense gold particles and diamonds that weathered away from bedrock. These gold and diamond ore bodies are called **placer deposits**. Other sedimentary ore deposits include the deep ocean floor, which contains manganese and cobalt ore deposits and evaporated lakes or seawater, which produce halite and a variety of other salts. (e) **Biological processes** involve the action of living organisms and are responsible for the formation of pearls in oysters, as well as phosphorous ore in the feces of birds and the bones and teeth of fish. (f) **Weathering** in tropical rain forest environments involves soil water that concentrates insoluble elements such as aluminum (bauxite) by dissolving away the soluble elements.

---

[69] Economic concentration value for gold comes from Craig, Vaughan, Skinner (2011).

Figure 5.51: A Diamond Mine Udachnaya Pipe, an open-pit diamond mine in Russia, is more than
600 meters (1,970 ft) deep, making it the third deepest open-pit mine in the world. *Source: Stapanov
Alexander via Wikimedia Commons*[70]

---

[70]http://commons.wikimedia.org/wiki/File:Udachnaya_pipe.JPG

Figure 5.52: Black Smoker A billowing discharge of superheated mineral-rich water at an oceanic ridge, in the Atlantic Ocean. Black "smoke" is actually from metallic sulfide minerals that form modern ore deposits. *Source: P. Rona of U.S. National Oceanic and Atmospheric Administration via Wikimedia Commons*[71]

5.6.5 Mining and Processing Ore

There are two kinds of mineral mines, **surface mines** and **underground mines**. The kind of mine used depends on the quality of the ore, i.e., concentration of mineral and its distance from the surface. Surface mines include **open-pit mines**, which commonly involve large holes that extract relatively low-grade metallic ore (see Figure **Open Pit Mine** (Figure 5.53)), **strip mines**, which extract horizontal layers of ore or rock, and **placer mines**, where gold or diamonds are extracted from river and beach sediment by scooping up (dredging) the sediment and then separating the ore by density. Large, open-pit mines can create huge piles of rock (called overburden) that was removed to expose the ore as well as huge piles of ore for processing. Underground mines, which are used when relatively high-grade ore is too deep for surface mining, involve a network of tunnels to access and extract the ore. Processing metallic ore (e.g., gold, silver, iron, copper, zinc, nickel, and lead) can involve numerous steps including crushing, grinding with water, physically separating the ore minerals from non-ore minerals often by density, and chemically separating the metal from the ore minerals using methods such as **smelting** (heating the ore minerals with different chemicals to extract the metal) and **leaching** (using chemicals to dissolve the metal from a large volume of crushed rock). The fine-grained waste produced from processing ore is called **tailings**. **Slag** is the glassy unwanted by-product of smelting ore. Many of the nonmetallic minerals and rocks do not require chemical separation techniques.

---

[71]http://commons.wikimedia.org/wiki/File:Blacksmoker_in_Atlantic_Ocean.jpg

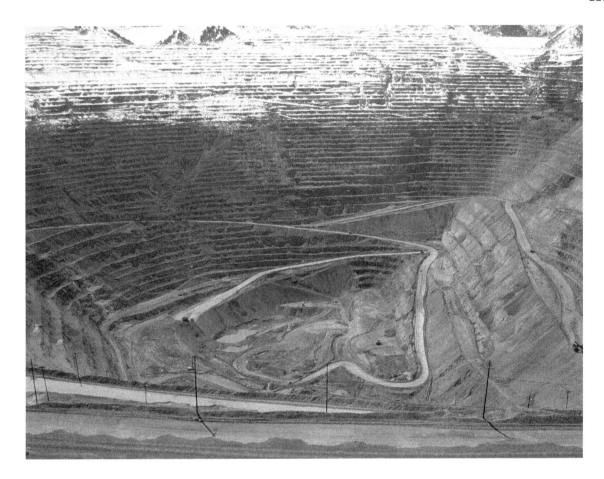

Figure 5.53: Open Pit Mine Bingham Canyon copper mine in Utah, USA. At 4 km wide and 1.2 km deep, it is the world's deepest open-pit mine. It began operations in 1906. *Source: Tim Jarrett via Wikimedia Commons*[72]

5.6.6 Mineral Resources and Sustainability Issues

Our heavy dependence on mineral resources presents humanity with some difficult challenges related to sustainability, including how to cope with finite supplies and how to mitigate the enormous environmental impacts of mining and processing ore. As global population growth continues—and perhaps more importantly, as standards of living rise around the world—demand for products made from minerals will increase. In particular, the economies of China, India, Brazil, and a few other countries are growing very quickly, and their demand for critical mineral resources also is accelerating. That means we are depleting our known mineral deposits at an increasing rate, requiring that new deposits be found and put into production. Figure **Demand for Nonfuel Minerals Materials** (Figure 5.54) shows the large increase in US mineral consumption between 1900 and 2006. Considering that mineral resources are nonrenewable, it is reasonable to ask how long they will last. The Table **Strategic Minerals** (Table 5.3: Strategic Minerals) gives a greatly approximated answer to that question for a variety of important and **strategic minerals** based on the current production and the estimated **mineral reserves**. Based on this simplified analysis, the estimated life of these important mineral reserves varies from more than 800 to 20 years. It is important to realize that

[72]http://commons.wikimedia.org/wiki/File:Bingham_Canyon_April_2005.jpg

we will not completely run out of any of these minerals but rather the economically viable mineral deposits
will be used up. Additional complications arise if only a few countries produce the mineral and they decide
not to export it. This situation is looming for rare earth elements, which currently are produced mainly by
China, which is threatening to limit exports of these strategic minerals.

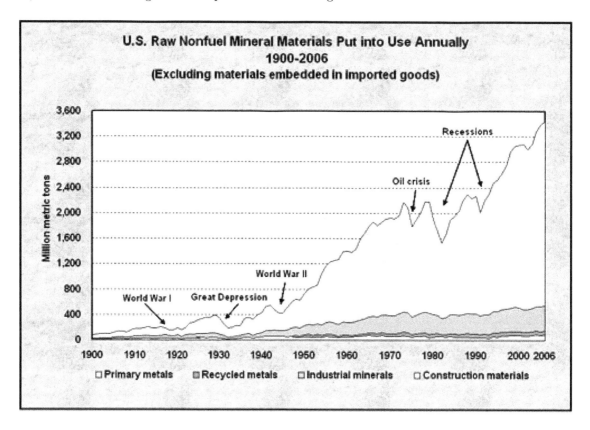

Figure 5.54: Demand for Nonfuel Minerals Materials US mineral consumption from 1900 - 2006,
excluding energy-related minerals *Source: U.S. Geological Survey*[73]

Strategic Minerals

Mineral	Uses	2010 Production (thousands of metric tons)	2010 Reserves (thousands of metric tons)	Estimated Life of Reserves (years)
				continued on next page

---

[73]http://minerals.usgs.gov/granted.html

Rare earths	catalysts, alloys, electronics, phosphors, magnets	130	110,000	846
Lithium	ceramics, glass, lithium-ion batteries in electronics and electric cars	25.3	13,000	514
Phosphate rock	fertilizer, animal feed supplement	176,000	65,000,000	369
Platinum Group	catalysts, electronics, glass, jewelry	0.4	66	178
Aluminum ore	Al cans, airplanes, building, electrical	211,000	28,000,000	133
Titanium minerals	white pigment, metal in airplanes and human joint replacements	6,300	690,000	110
Cobalt	airplane engines, metals, chemicals	88	7,300	83
Iron ore	main ingredient in steel	2,400,000	180,000,000	75
Nickel	important alloy in steel, electroplating	1,550	76,000	49
Manganese	important alloy in steel	13,000	630,000	48
Copper	electrical wire, electronics, pipes, ingredient in brass	16,200	630,000	39
Silver	industry, coins, jewelry, photography	22.2	510	23
Zinc	galvanized steel, alloys, brass	12,000	250,000	21
Lead	batteries	4,100	80,000	20
Tin	electrical, cans, construction,	261	5,200	20
			continued on next page	

Gold	jewelry, arts, electronics, dental	2.5	51	20

Table 5.3: Uses, world production in 2010, and estimated projected lifetime of reserves (ore that is profitable to mine under current conditions) for selected minerals *Source: US Geological Survey Mineral Commodity Summaries, 2011*

A more complex analysis of future depletions of our mineral supplies predicts that 20 out of 23 minerals studied will likely experience a permanent shortfall in global supply by 2030 where global production is less than global demand (Clugston, 2010 (p. 226)). Specifically this study concludes the following: for cadmium, gold, mercury, tellurium, and tungsten—they have already passed their global production peak, their future production only will decline, and it is nearly certain that there will be a permanent global supply shortfall by 2030; for cobalt, lead, molybdenum, platinum group metals, phosphate rock, silver, titanium, and zinc—they are likely at or near their global production peak and there is a very high probability that there will be a permanent global supply shortfall by 2030; for chromium, copper, indium, iron ore, lithium, magnesium compounds, nickel, and phosphate rock—they are expected to reach their global production peak between 2010 and 2030 and there is a high probability that there will be a permanent global supply shortfall by 2030; and for bauxite, rare earth minerals, and tin—they are not expected to reach their global production peak before 2030 and there is a low probability that there will be a permanent global supply shortfall by 2030. It is important to note that these kinds of predictions of future mineral shortages are difficult and controversial. Other scientists disagree with Clugston's predictions of mineral shortages in the near future. Predictions similar to Clugston were made in the 1970s and they were wrong. It is difficult to know exactly the future demand for minerals and the size of future mineral reserves. The remaining life for specific minerals will decrease if future demand increases. On the other hand, mineral reserves can increase if new mineral deposits are found (increasing the known amount of ore) or if currently unprofitable mineral deposits become profitable ones due to either a mineral price increase or technological improvements that make mining or processing cheaper. **Mineral resources**, a much larger category than mineral reserves, are the total amount of a mineral that is not necessarily profitable to mine today but that has some sort of economic potential.

Mining and processing ore can have considerable impact on the environment. Surface mines can create enormous pits (see Figure **Open Pit Mine** (Figure 5.53)) in the ground as well as large piles of overburden and tailings that need to be **reclaimed**, i.e., restored to a useful landscape. Since 1977 surface mines in U.S. are required to be reclaimed, and commonly reclamation is relatively well done in this country. Unfortunately, surface mine reclamation is not done everywhere, especially in underdeveloped countries, due to lack of regulations or lax enforcement of regulations. Unreclaimed surface mines and active surface mines can be major sources of water and sediment pollution. Metallic ore minerals (e.g., copper, lead, zinc, mercury, and silver) commonly include abundant sulfide, and many metallic ore deposits contain abundant pyrite (iron sulfide). The sulfide in these minerals oxidizes quickly when exposed to air at the surface producing sulfuric acid, called **acid mine drainage**. As a result streams, ponds, and soil water contaminated with this drainage can be highly acidic, reaching pH values of zero or less (see Figure Acid Mine Drainage)! The acidic water can leach heavy metals such as nickel, copper, lead, arsenic, aluminum, and manganese from mine tailings and slag. The acidic contaminated water can be highly toxic to the ecosystem. Plants usually will not regrow in such acidic soil water, and therefore soil erosion rates skyrocket due to the persistence of bare, unvegetated surfaces. With a smaller amount of tailings and no overburden, underground mines usually are much easier to reclaim, and they produce much less acid mine drainage. The major environmental problem with underground mining is the hazardous working environment for miners primarily caused by cave-ins and lung disease due to prolonged inhalation of dust particles. Underground cave-ins also can damage the surface from subsidence. Smelting can be a major source of air pollution, especially SO_2 gas. The case history below examines the environmental impact of mining and processing gold ore.

Figure 5.55: Acid Mine Drainage The water in Rio Tinto River, Spain is highly acidic (pH = ~2) and the orange color is from iron in the water. A location along this river has been mined beginning some 5,000 years ago primarily for copper and more recently for silver and gold. *Source: Sean Mack of NASA via Wikimedia Commons*[74]

5.6.7 Sustainable Solutions to the Mineral Crisis?

Providing sustainable solutions to the problem of a dwindling supply of a nonrenewable resource such as minerals seems contradictory. Nevertheless, it is extremely important to consider strategies that move towards sustainability even if true sustainability is not possible for most minerals. The general approach towards mineral sustainability should include **mineral conservation** at the top of the list. We also need to *maximize exploration for new mineral resources* while at the same time we *minimize the environmental impact of mineral mining and processing*.

Conservation of mineral resources includes improved efficiency, substitution, and the 3 Rs of sustainability, reduce, reuse, and recycle. Improved efficiency applies to all features of mineral use including mining, processing, and creation of mineral products. Substituting a rare nonrenewable resource with either a more abundant nonrenewable resource or a renewable resource can help. Examples include substituting glass fiber optic cables for copper in telephone wires and wood for aluminum in construction. Reducing global demand for mineral resources will be a challenge, considering projections of continuing population growth

---

[74]http://commons.wikimedia.org/wiki/File:Rio_tinto_river_CarolStoker_NASA_Ames_Research_Center.jpg

and the rapid economic growth of very large countries such as China, India, and Brazil. Historically economic growth is intimately tied to increased mineral consumption, and therefore it will be difficult for those rapidly developing countries to decrease their future demand for minerals. In theory, it should be easier for countries with a high mineral consumption rate such as the U.S. to reduce their demand for minerals but it will take a significant change in mindset to accomplish that. Technology can help some with some avenues to reducing mineral consumption. For example, digital cameras have virtually eliminated the photographic demand for silver, which is used for film development. Using stronger and more durable alloys of steel can translate to fewer construction materials needed. Examples of natural resource reuse include everything at an antique store and yard sale. Recycling can extend the lifetime of mineral reserves, especially metals. Recycling is easiest for pure metals such as copper pipes and aluminum cans, but much harder for alloys (mixtures of metals) and complex manufactured goods, such as computers. Many nonmetals cannot be recycled; examples include road salt and fertilizer. Recycling is easier for a wealthy country because there are more financial resources to use for recycling and more goods to recycle. Additional significant benefits of mineral resource conservation are less pollution and environmental degradation from new mineral mining and processing as well as reductions in energy use and waste production.

Because demand for new minerals will likely increase in the future, we must continue to search for new minerals, even though we probably have already found many of the "easy" targets, i.e., high-grade ore deposits close to the surface and in convenient locations. To find more difficult ore targets, we will need to apply many technologies including geophysical methods (seismic, gravity, magnetic, and electrical measurements, as well as remote sensing, which uses satellite-based measurements of electromagnetic radiation from Earth's surface), geochemical methods (looking for chemical enrichments in soil, water, air, and plants), and geological information including knowledge of plate tectonics theory. We also may need to consider exploring and mining unconventional areas such as continental margins (submerged edges of continents), the ocean floor (where there are large deposits of manganese ore and other metals in rocks called manganese nodules), and oceanic ridges (undersea mountains that have copper, zinc, and lead ore bodies).

Finally, we need to explore for, mine, and process new minerals while minimizing pollution and other environmental impacts. Regulations and good engineering practices are necessary to ensure adequate mine reclamation and pollution reduction, including acid mine drainage. The emerging field of biotechnology may provide some sustainable solutions to metal extraction. Specific methods include **biooxidation** (microbial enrichment of metals in a solid phase), **bioleaching** (microbial dissolution of metals), **biosorption** (attachment of metals to cells), and **genetic engineering of microbes** (creating microorganisms specialized in extracting metal from ore).

5.6.8 Review Questions

Question 5.6.1
Name some important ways mineral resources are used. Why are they important to society?

Question 5.6.2
What are the major environmental issues associated with mineral resources?

Question 5.6.3
What should society learn from the case history of gold?

Question 5.6.4
Why is society facing a crisis involving mineral supply and how might we work to solve it?

5.6.9 References

Clugston, C. (2010) Increasing Global Nonrenewable Natural Resource Scarcity - An Analysis, The Oil Drum. Retrieved from http://www.theoildrum.com/node/6345[75]

---

[75]http://www.theoildrum.com/node/6345

Craig J, Vaughan D, and Skinner B (2011) Earth Resources and the Environment (4th ed.). Pearson Prentice Hall, p. 92

5.7 Case Study: Gold: Worth its Weight?[76]

Gold is a symbol of wealth, prestige, and royalty that has attracted and fascinated people for many thousands of years (see Figure **Native Gold** (Figure 5.56)). Gold is considered by many to be the most desirable precious metal because it has been sought after for coins, jewelry, and other arts since long before the beginning of recorded history. Historically its value was used as a currency standard (the gold standard) although not anymore. Gold is very dense but also very malleable; a gram of gold can be hammered into a 1 m^2 sheet of gold leaf. Gold is extremely resistant to corrosion and chemical attack, making it almost indestructible. It is also very rare and costly to produce. Today the primary uses of gold are jewelry and the arts, electronics, and dentistry. The major use in electronics is gold plating of electrical contacts to provide a corrosion-resistant conductive layer on copper. Most gold is easily recycled except for gold plating due to combinations with other compounds such as cyanide. About half of the world's gold ever produced has been produced since 1965 (see Figure **World Gold Production** (Figure 5.57)). At the current consumption rate today's gold reserves are expected to last only 20 more years.

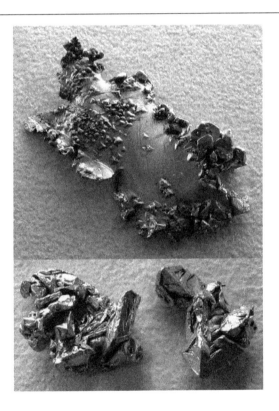

Figure 5.56: Native Gold A collage of 2 photos, showing 3 pieces of native gold. The top piece is from the Washington mining district, California, and the bottom two are from Victoria, Australia. *Source: Aram Dulyan via Wikimedia Commons*[77]

---

[76]This content is available online at <http://legacy.cnx.org/content/m41467/1.5/>.

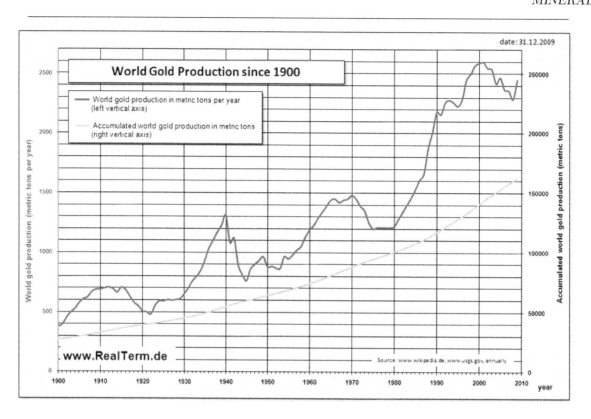

Figure 5.57: World Gold Production World gold production from 1900 to 2009 including annual (blue line) and cumulative data (gray line) *Source: Realterm via Wikimedia Commons*[78]

There are two types of gold ore deposits: (1) *hydrothermal*, where magma-heated groundwater dissolves gold from a large volume of rock and deposits it in rock fractures and (2) *placer*, where rivers erode a gold ore deposit of hydrothermal origin and deposit the heavy gold grains at the bottom of river channels. Although gold's resistance to chemical attack makes it extremely durable and reusable, that same property also makes gold difficult to extract from rock. As a result, some gold mining methods can have an enormous environmental impact. The first discovered gold ore was from placer deposits, which are relatively simple to mine. The method of extracting gold in a placer deposit involves density settling of gold grains in moving water, similar to how placer deposits form. Specific variations of placer mining include **hushing** (developed by the ancient Romans where a torrent of water is sent through a landscape via an aqueduct), **sluice box** (where running water passes through a wooden box with riffles on the bottom), **panning** (a hand-held conical metal pan where water swirls around) and hydraulic (where high pressure hoses cut into natural landscapes, see Figure **Hydraulic Mining** (Figure 5.58)). **Hydraulic mining**, developed during the California Gold Rush in the middle 1800s, can destroy natural settings, accelerate soil erosion, and create sediment-rich rivers that later flood due to sediment infilling the channel. The largest gold ore body ever discovered is an ancient, lithified (i.e., hardened) placer deposit. Nearly half of the world's gold ever mined has come from South Africa's Witwatersrand deposits, which also have the world's deepest underground mine at about 4,000 m. To increase the efficiency of gold panning, liquid mercury is added to gold pans because mercury can form an alloy with gold in a method called **mercury amalgamation**. The mercury-gold amalgam is then collected

---

[77]http://commons.wikimedia.org/wiki/File:Native_gold_nuggets.jpg

[78]http://commons.wikimedia.org/wiki/File:Gold_world_production.png

and heated to vaporize the mercury and concentrate the gold. Although mercury amalgamation is no longer used commercially, it is still used by amateur gold panners. Unfortunately, considerable mercury has been released to the environment with this method, which is problematic because mercury bioaccumulates and it is easily converted to methylmercury, which is highly toxic.

Figure 5.58: Hydraulic Mining Gold hydraulic mining in New Zealand, 1880s *Source: James Ring via Wikimedia Commons*[79]

Today most gold mining is done by a method called **heap leaching**, where cyanide-rich water percolates through finely ground gold ore and dissolves the gold over a period of months; eventually the water is collected and treated to remove the gold. This process revolutionized gold mining because it allowed economic recovery of gold from very low-grade ore (down to 1 ppm) and even from gold ore tailings that previously were considered waste. On the other hand, heap leaching is controversial because of the toxic nature of cyanide. The world's largest cyanide spill to date occurred at Baia Mare in northern Romania (see Figure **Baia Mare** (Figure 5.59)). In January 2000 after a period of heavy rain and snowmelt, a dam surrounding a gold tailings pond collapsed and sent into the drainage basin of the Danube River 100,000 m^3 (100 million liters) of water with 500 - 1,000 ppm cyanide[80], killing more than a thousand metric tons of fish (see Figure **Baia Mare Cyanide Spill** (Figure 5.60)). Considering the large environmental impact of gold mining, this may take some of the glitter from gold.

---

[79]http://commons.wikimedia.org/wiki/File:Gold_sluicing,_Dillman_Town,_West_Coast,_188-%3F.jpg
[80]The U.S. EPA allows no more than 0.2 ppm cyanide in drinking water.

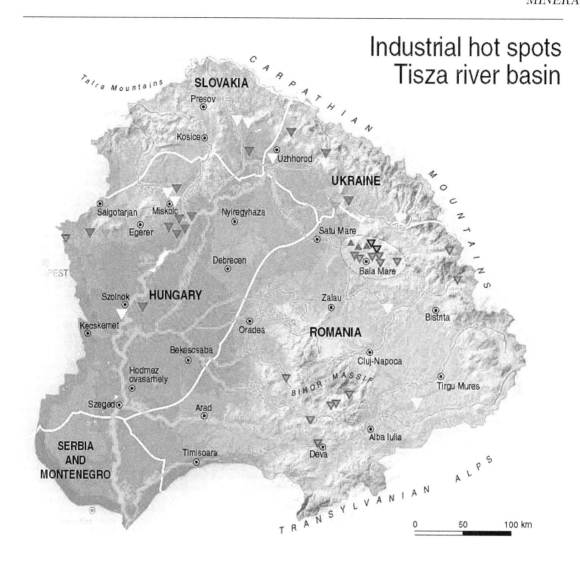

Figure 5.59: **Baia Mare** Map of Tisza River drainage basin with pollution hot spots including Baia Mare, Romania, which is the location of a cyanide spill disaster in 2000 *Source: United Nations Environment Program - GRID-Arendal*[81]

[81]http://www.grida.no/publications/et/ep3/page/2589.aspx

Figure 5.60: Baia Mare Cyanide Spill Dead fish from cyanide spill disaster Baia Mare, Romania, the location of a in 2000 *Source: Toxipedia*[82]

[82]http://toxipedia.org/display/toxipedia/Baia+Mare+Cyanide+Spill;jsessionid=5F173E794FFED4E912DD437314468B20

Chapter 6

Environmental and Resource Economics

6.1 Environmental and Resource Economics - Chapter Introduction[1]

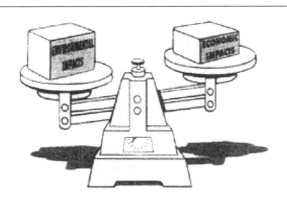

Figure 6.1: *Source: The NEED Project*[2]

6.1.1 Introduction

The field of environmental and natural resource economics sounds to many like an oxymoron. Most people think economists study money, finance, and business—so what does that have to do with the environment? Economics is really broadly defined as the study of the allocation of scarce resources. In other words, economics is a social science that helps people understand how to make hard choices when there are unavoidable tradeoffs. For example, a company can make and sell more cars, which brings in revenue, but doing so also increases production costs. Or a student can choose to have a part-time job to reduce the size of the loan she needs to pay for college, but that reduces the time she has for studying and makes it harder for her to get good grades. Some economists do study business, helping companies and industries design production, marketing, and investment strategies that maximize their profits. Other economists work to understand and inform the choices individuals make about their investments in education and how to divide their time between work, leisure, and family in order to make themselves and their families better off. Environmental and

---

[1]This content is available online at <http://legacy.cnx.org/content/m38598/1.7/>.
[2]http://www.need.org/

natural resource economists study the tradeoffs associated with one of the most important scarce resources we have—nature.

Economists contribute to the study of environmental problems with two kinds of work. First, they do **normative** studies of how people should manage resources and invest in environmental quality to make themselves and/or society as well off as possible. Second, they do **positive analyses** of how human agents—individuals, firms, and so forth—actually do behave. Normative studies give recommendations and guidance for people and policy makers to follow. Positive studies of human behavior help us to understand what causes environmental problems and which policies are most likely to work well to alleviate them.

This chapter gives an overview of a few of the key ideas that have been developed in this field. First, we will learn the economic theories that help us understand where environmental problems come from and what makes something a problem that actually needs to be fixed. This section of the chapter will introduce the concepts of externalities, public goods, and open access resources, and explain how in situations with those features we often end up with too much pollution and excessive rates of natural resource exploitation. Second, we will learn the tools economists have developed to quantify the value of environmental amenities. It is very difficult to identify a monetary value for things like clean air and wildlife, which are not traded in a marketplace, but such value estimates are often helpful inputs for public discussions about environmental policies and investments. Third, we will discuss a set of approaches economists use to evaluate environmental policies and projects. We want to design policies that are "good," but what exactly does that mean? Finally, we will learn about the different policy tools that can be used to solve problems of excess environmental degradation and resource exploitation, including a set of incentive policies that were designed by economists to work *with* rather than against the way that people really behave, and we will discuss the strengths and weaknesses of those different tools.

6.2 Tragedy of the Commons[3]

6.2.1 Learning Objectives

After reading this module, students should be able to

- know how economists define environmental outcomes that make society as well off as possible.
- understand what externalities are, and how they can lead to outcomes with too much pollution and resource exploitation.
- be able to define public goods and common-property resources, and understand how those things are prone to under-provision and over-exploitation, respectively.

6.2.2 Introduction

To identify and solve environmental problems, we need to understand what situations are actually problems (somehow formally defined) and what circumstances and behaviors cause them. We might think that it is easy to recognize a problem—pollution is bad, saving natural resources is good. However, critical thinking often reveals snap judgments to be overly simplistic. Some examples help to illustrate this point.

- *Running out!* Oil is a depletable resource, and many people worry that rapid extraction and use of oil might cause us to run out. But would it really be a bad thing to use up all the oil as long as we developed alternative energy technologies to which we could turn when the oil was gone? Is there any intrinsic value to keeping a stock of oil unused in the ground? Running out of oil someday may not be a problem. However, subsidies for oil extraction might cause us to run out more quickly than is socially optimal. Other inefficiencies arise if multiple companies own wells that tap the same pool of oil, and each ends up racing to extract the oil before the others can take it away—that kind of race can increase total pumping costs and reduce the total amount of oil that can be gleaned from the pool.

---

[3]This content is available online at <http://legacy.cnx.org/content/m38612/1.6/>.

- *Biological pollution!* Horror stories abound in the news about the havoc raised by some nonnative animal and plant species in the United States. Zebra mussels clog boats and industrial pipes, yellow star thistle is toxic to horses and reduces native biodiversity in the American West, and the emerald ash borer kills ash trees as it marches across the landscape. From the current tone of much media and scientific discourse about nonnative species, one could conclude that all nonnative species are problems. But does that mean we should forbid farmers in the U.S from growing watermelons, which come from Africa? Or should we ship all the ring-necked pheasants back to Eurasia whence they originally came, and tell North Dakota to choose a new state bird? The costs and benefits of nonnative species vary greatly – one policy approach is not likely to apply well to them all.

This section first explains the way economists think about whether an outcome is good. Then it describes some of the features of natural resources and environmental quality that often trigger problematic human behaviors related to the environment.

6.2.3 Efficiency and Deadweight Loss

Ask anyone who lived during the centrally-planned, nonmarket economy years of the Soviet Union—markets are very good at many things. When a product becomes scarcer or more costly to produce we would like to send signals to consumers that would cause them to buy less of that thing. If an input is more valuable when used to produce one good than another, we would like to send signals to firms to make sure that input is put to its best use. If conditions are right, market prices do these useful things and more. Markets distribute inputs efficiently through the production side of the economy: they ensure that plant managers don't need to hoard inputs and then drive around bartering with each other for the things they need to make their products, and they arrange for efficient quantities of goods to be produced. Markets also distribute outputs among consumers without surpluses, shortages, or large numbers of bathing suits being foisted upon consumers in Siberia.

Economists mean something very specific when they use the word **efficient**. In general, an allocation is efficient if it maximizes social well-being, or welfare. Traditional economics defines **welfare** as total **net benefits**—the difference between the total benefits all people in society get from market goods and services and the total costs of producing those things. Environmental economists enhance the definition of welfare. The values of environmental goods like wildlife count on the "benefit" side of net benefits and damages to environmental quality from production and consumptive processes count as costs.

Under ideal circumstances, market outcomes are efficient. In perfect markets for regular goods, goods are produced at the point where the cost to society of producing the last unit, the **marginal cost**, is just equal to the amount a consumer is willing to pay for that last unit, the **marginal benefit**, which means that the net benefits in the market are maximized. Regular goods are supplied by industry such that supply is equivalent to the marginal production costs to the firms, and they are demanded by consumers in such a way that we can read the marginal benefit to consumers off the demand curve; when the market equilibrates at a price that causes quantity demanded to equal quantity supplied at that price (Q_{market} in Figure **Market Equilibrium** (Figure 6.2)), it is also true that marginal benefit equals marginal cost.

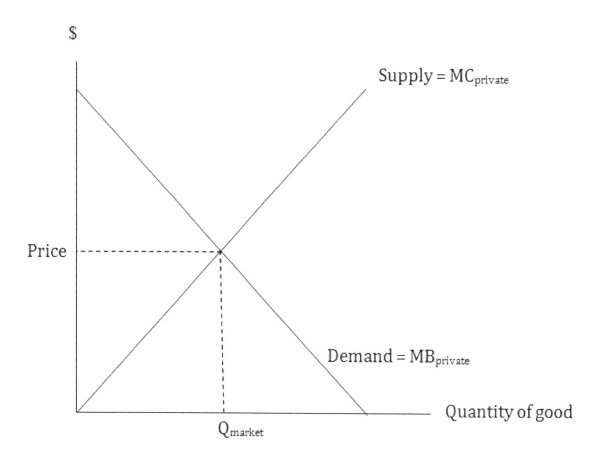

Figure 6.2: Market Equilibrium A private market equilibrates at a price such that the quantity supplied equals the quantity demanded, and thus private marginal cost equals private marginal benefit. *Source: Amy Ando*[4]

Even depletable resources such as oil would be used efficiently by a well-functioning market. It is socially efficient to use a depletable resource over time such that the price rises at the same rate as the rate of interest. Increasing scarcity pushes the price up, which stimulates efforts to use less of the resource and to invest in research to make "backstop" alternatives more cost-effective. Eventually, the cost of the resource rises to the point where the backstop technology is competitive, and the market switches from the depletable resource to the backstop. We see this with copper; high prices of depletable copper trigger substitution to other materials, like fiber optics for telephone cables and plastics for pipes. We would surely see the same thing happen with fossil fuels; if prices are allowed to rise with scarcity, firms have more incentives to engage in research that lowers the cost of backstop technologies like solar and wind power, and we will eventually just switch.

Unfortunately, many conditions can lead to **market failure** such that the market outcome does not maximize social welfare. The extent to which net benefits fall short of their potential is called **deadweight loss**. Deadweight loss can exist when not enough of a good is produced, or too much of a good is produced, or production is not done in the most **cost-effective** (least expensive) way possible, where costs include environmental damages. Some types of market failures (and thus deadweight loss) are extremely common

---
[4]http://cnx.org/member_profile/amyando

in environmental settings.

6.2.4 Externalities

In a market economy, people and companies make choices to balance the costs and benefits that accrue to them. That behavior can sometimes yield outcomes that maximize total social welfare even if individual agents are only seeking to maximize their own personal well-being, because self-interested trades lead the market to settle where aggregate marginal benefits equal aggregate marginal costs and thus total net benefits are maximized.

However, people and companies do not always bear the full costs and benefits associated with the actions they take. When this is true economists say there are externalities, and individual actions do not typically yield efficient outcomes.

A **negative externality** is a cost associated with an action that is not borne by the person who chooses to take that action. For example, if a student cheats on an exam, that student might get a higher grade. However, if the class is graded on a curve, all the other students will get lower grades. And if the professor learns that cheating happened, she might take steps to prevent cheating on the next exam that make the testing environment more unpleasant for all the students (no calculators allowed, no bathroom breaks, id checks, etc.). Negative externalities are rampant in environmental settings:

- Companies that spill oil into the ocean do not bear the full costs of the resulting harm to the marine environment, which include everything from degraded commercial fisheries to reduced endangered sea turtle populations).
- Commuters generate emissions of air pollution, which lowers the ambient quality of the air in areas they pass through and causes health problems for other people.
- Developers who build houses in bucolic exurban settings cause habitat fragmentation and biodiversity loss, inflicting a cost on the public at large.

Figure 6.3: Negative Externality: Smog A NASA photograph of the atmosphere over upstate New York, with Lake Eire (top) and Lake Ontario (bottom) featured. Both natural, white clouds and man-made smog (grey clouds below) are visible. The smog is an example of a negative externality, as the cost of the pollution is borne by everyone in the region, not just by the producers. *Source: Image Science and Analysis Laboratory, NASA-Johnson Space Center*[5]

In situations where an action or good has a negative externality, the private marginal cost that shapes the behavior of an agent is lower than the marginal cost to society as a whole, which includes the private marginal cost and the external environmental marginal cost. The efficient outcome would be where the social marginal cost equals the social marginal benefit (labeled $Q_{efficient}$ in Figure **Inefficiency from Negative Externality** (Figure 6.4)). Unfortunately, the free-market outcome (labeled Q_{market} in Figure **Inefficiency**

---

[5]http://earth.jsc.nasa.gov/sseop/EFS/printinfo.pl?PHOTO=STS092-713-32

from **Negative Externality** (Figure 6.4)) will tend to have more of the good or activity than is socially optimal because the agents are not paying attention to all the costs. Too much oil will be shipped, and with insufficient care; people will drive too many miles on their daily commutes; developers will build too many new homes in sensitive habitats. Thus, there is deadweight loss (the shaded triangle in the figure); the marginal social cost associated with units in excess of the social optimum is greater than the marginal benefit society gets from those units. Public policy that reduces the amount of the harmful good or activity could make society as a whole better off.

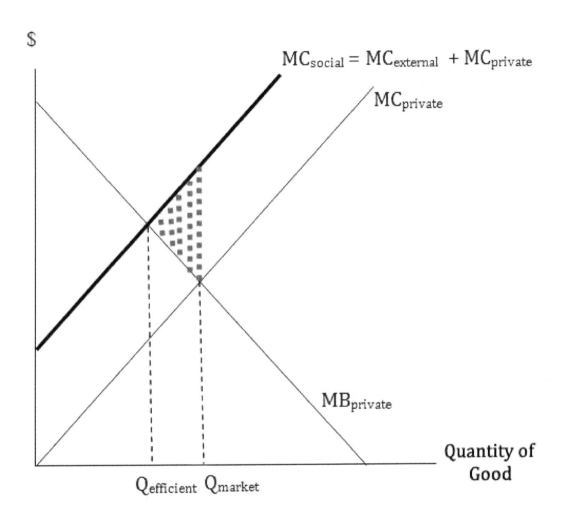

Figure 6.4: Inefficiency from Negative Externality When there is a negative externality, the market equilibrates where the total social marginal cost exceeds the marginal benefit of the last unit of a good and society is not as well off as it could be if less were produced. *Source: Amy Ando*[6]

Conversely, a **positive externality** is a benefit associated with an action that is not borne by the person who chooses to take that action. Students who get flu shots in October, for example, gain a private benefit because they are less likely to get the flu during the winter months. However, their classmates, roommates, and relatives also gain some benefit from that action because inoculated students are less likely to pass the flu

---

[6]http://cnx.org/member_profile/amyando

along to them. Positive externalities exist in the world of actions and products that affect the environment:

- A homeowner who installs a rain barrel to collect unchlorinated rainwater for her garden also improves stream habitat in her watershed by reducing stormwater runoff.
- A delivery company that re-optimizes its routing system to cut fuel costs also improves local air quality by cutting its vehicle air pollution emissions.
- A farmer who plants winter cover crops to increase the productivity of his soil will also improve water quality in local streams by reducing erosion.

In situations where an action or good has a positive externality, the private marginal benefit that shapes the behavior of an agent is lower than the marginal benefit to society as a whole, which includes the private marginal benefit and the external environmental marginal benefit. The efficient outcome would be where the social marginal cost equals the social marginal benefit (labeled $Q_{efficient}$ in Figure **Positive Externality** (Figure 6.5)). In the presence of a positive externality, the free-market outcome will tend to promote less of the good or activity than is socially optimal because the agents do not reap all the benefits. Too few rain barrels will be installed; not enough delivery routes will be re-optimized; too few acres of agricultural fields will have cover crops in the winter months. Again there is deadweight loss (the shaded triangle in the figure), but this time because the marginal social benefit associated with some of the units not produced would have been greater than the marginal costs of producing them. Just because an externality is positive rather than negative doesn't mean there isn't a problem; public policy could still make society as a whole better off.

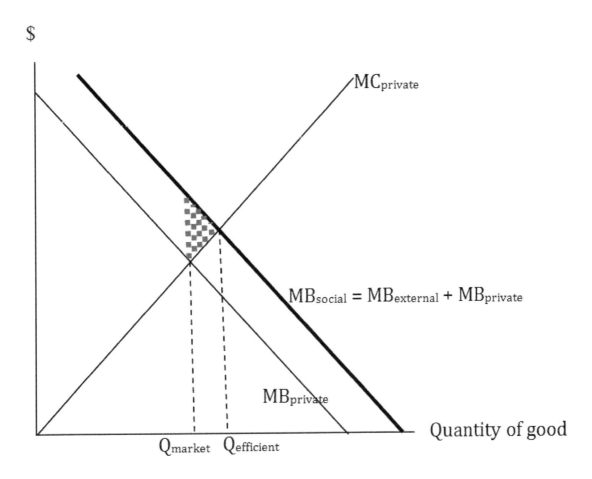

Figure 6.5: Positive Externality When there is a a positive externality, the market equilibrates where the total social marginal benefit exceeds the marginal cost of the last unit of a good and society is not as well off as it could be if more were produced. *Source: Amy Ando*[7]

6.2.5 Public Goods and Common-pool Resources

Market outcomes are almost never efficient in two broad kinds of cases: public goods and common-pool resources. The market failures in these settings are related to the problems we saw with negative and positive externalities.

A pure **public good** is defined as being nonexclusive and nonrival in consumption. If something is nonexclusive, people cannot be prevented from enjoying its benefits. A private house is exclusive because doors, windows, and an alarm system can be used to keep nonowners out. A lighthouse, on the other hand, is non-exclusive because ships at sea cannot be prevented from seeing its light. A good that is nonrival in consumption has a marginal benefit that does not decline with the number of people who consume it. A hot dog is completely rival in consumption: if I eat it, you cannot. On the other hand, the beauty of a fireworks display is completely unaffected by the number of people who look at it. Some elements of the environment are pure public goods:

---

[7]http://cnx.org/member_profile/amyando

- Clean air in a city provides health benefits to everyone, and people cannot be prevented from breathing
- The stratospheric ozone layer protects everyone on earth from solar UV radiation

The efficient amount of a public good is still where social marginal benefit equals the marginal cost of provision. However, the social marginal benefit of one unit of a public good is often very large because many people in society can benefit from that unit simultaneously. One lighthouse prevents all the ships in an area from running aground in a storm. In contrast, the social marginal benefit of a hot dog is just the marginal benefit gained by the one person who gets to eat it.

Society could figure out the efficient amount of a public good to provide—say, how much to spend on cleaner cars that reduce air pollution in a city. Unfortunately, private individuals acting on their own are unlikely to provide the efficient amount of the public good because of the **free rider** problem. If my neighbors reduce pollution by buying clean electric cars or commuting via train, I can benefit from that cleaner air; thus, I might try to avoid doing anything costly myself in hopes that everyone else will clean the air for me. Evidence suggests that people do not behave entirely like free riders – they contribute voluntarily to environmental groups and public radio stations. However, the levels of public-good provision generated by a free market are lower than would be efficient. The ozone layer is too thin; the air is too dirty. Public goods have big multilateral positive externality problems.

In contrast, a **common-pool resource** (also sometimes called an open-access resource) suffers from big multilateral negative externality problems. This situation is sometimes called the "tragedy of the commons." Like public goods, common-pool resources are nonexcludable. However, they are highly rival in use. Many natural resources have common-pool features:

- Water in a river can be removed by anyone near it for irrigation, drinking, or industrial use; the more water one set of users removes, the less water there is available for others.
- Swordfish in the ocean can be caught by anyone with the right boat and gear, and the more fish are caught by one fleet of boats, the fewer remain for other fishers to catch.
- Old growth timber in a developing country can be cut down by many people, and slow regrowth means that the more timber one person cuts the less there is available for others.

One person's use of a common-pool resource has negative effects on all the other users. Thus, these resources are prone to overexploitation. One person in Indonesia might want to try to harvest tropical hardwood timber slowly and sustainably, but the trees they forebear from cutting today might be cut down by someone else tomorrow. The difficulty of managing common-pool resources is evident around the world in rapid rates of tropical deforestation, dangerous overharvesting of fisheries (see Case study: Marine Fisheries (Section 6.3)), and battles fought over mighty rivers that have been reduced to dirty trickles.

The tragedy of the commons occurs most often when the value of the resource is great, the number of users is large, and the users do not have social ties to one another, but common-pool resources are not always abused. Elinor Ostrom's Nobel prize-winning body of work, for example, has studied cases of common-pool resources that were not over-exploited because of informal social institutions.

6.2.6 Review Questions

Question 6.2.1
What does it mean for an outcome to be efficient?

Question 6.2.2
How do externalities cause market outcomes not to be efficient?

Question 6.2.3
How are the free rider problem and the common pool resource problem related to basic problems of externalities?

6.3 Case Study: Marine Fisheries[8]

Fisheries are classic common-pool resources. The details of the legal institutions that govern access to fisheries vary around the globe. However, the physical nature of marine fisheries makes them prone to overexploitation. Anyone with a boat and some gear can enter the ocean. One boat's catch reduces the fish available to all the other boats and reduces the stock available to reproduce and sustain the stock available in the following year. Economic theory predicts that the market failure associated with open access to a fishery will yield socially excessive levels of entry into the fishery (too many boats) and annual catch (too many fish caught) and inefficiently low stocks of fish (Beddington, Agnew, & Clark, 2007 (p. 246)).

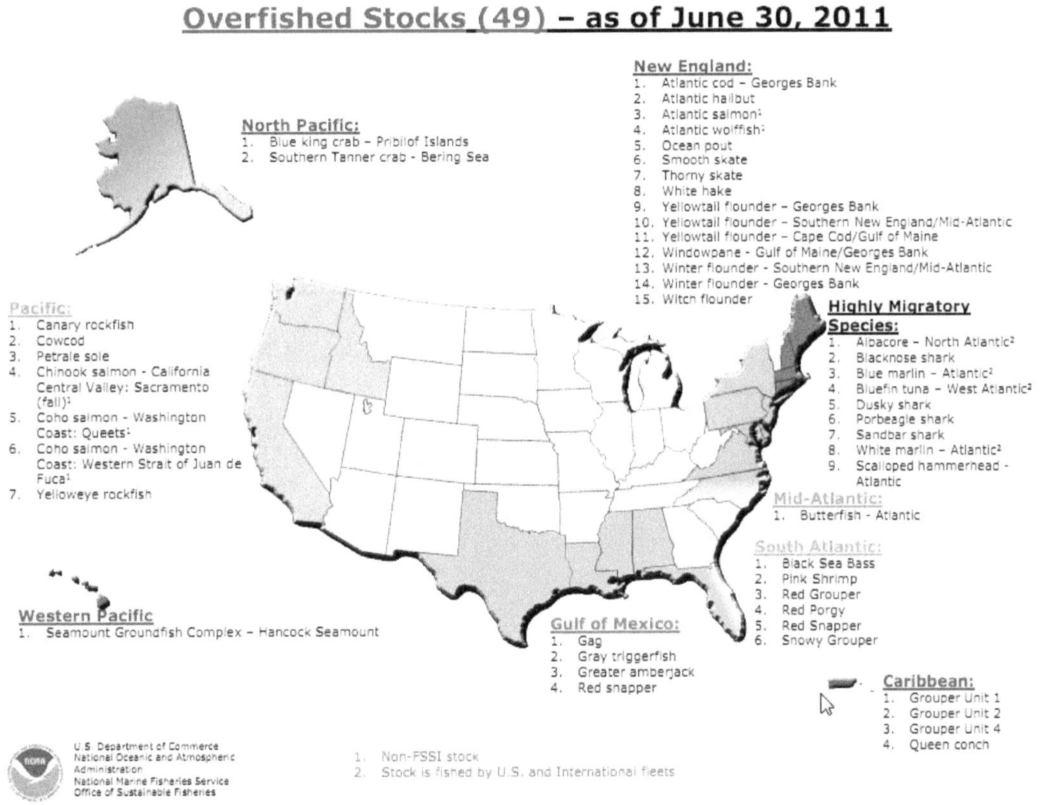

Overfished Stocks (49) – as of June 30, 2011

North Pacific:
1. Blue king crab - Pribilof Islands
2. Southern Tanner crab - Bering Sea

New England:
1. Atlantic cod – Georges Bank
2. Atlantic halibut
3. Atlantic salmon[1]
4. Atlantic wolffish[1]
5. Ocean pout
6. Smooth skate
7. Thorny skate
8. White hake
9. Yellowtail flounder – Georges Bank
10. Yellowtail flounder – Southern New England/Mid-Atlantic
11. Yellowtail flounder – Cape Cod/Gulf of Maine
12. Windowpane - Gulf of Maine/Georges Bank
13. Winter flounder - Southern New England/Mid-Atlantic
14. Winter flounder - Georges Bank
15. Witch flounder

Pacific:
1. Canary rockfish
2. Cowcod
3. Petrale sole
4. Chinook salmon - California Central Valley: Sacramento (fall)[1]
5. Coho salmon - Washington Coast: Queets[1]
6. Coho salmon - Washington Coast: Western Strait of Juan de Fuca[1]
7. Yelloweye rockfish

Highly Migratory Species:
1. Albacore – North Atlantic[2]
2. Blacknose shark
3. Blue marlin – Atlantic[2]
4. Bluefin tuna – West Atlantic[2]
5. Dusky shark
6. Porbeagle shark
7. Sandbar shark
8. White marlin – Atlantic[2]
9. Scalloped hammerhead - Atlantic

Mid-Atlantic:
1. Butterfish - Atlantic

South Atlantic:
1. Black Sea Bass
2. Pink Shrimp
3. Red Grouper
4. Red Porgy
5. Red Snapper
6. Snowy Grouper

Western Pacific
1. Seamount Groundfish Complex – Hancock Seamount

Gulf of Mexico:
1. Gag
2. Gray triggerfish
3. Greater amberjack
4. Red snapper

Caribbean:
1. Grouper Unit 1
2. Grouper Unit 2
3. Grouper Unit 4
4. Queen conch

U.S. Department of Commerce
National Oceanic and Atmospheric Administration
National Marine Fisheries Service
Office of Sustainable Fisheries

1. Non-FSSI stock
2. Stock is fished by U.S. and International fleets

Figure 6.6: *Source: National Oceanic and Atmospheric Administration*[9]

Unfortunately, the state of fisheries around the globe seems to indicate that the predictions of that theory are being borne out. Bluefin tuna are in danger of extinction. Stocks of fish in once-abundant fisheries such as North Atlantic cod and Mediterranean swordfish have been depleted to commercial (and sometimes biological) exhaustion (Montaigne, 2007 (p. 246)). Scientists have documented widespread collapse of fish stocks and associated loss of marine biodiversity from overfishing; this devastates the ability of coastal and open-ocean ecosystems to provide a wide range of ecosystem services such as food provisioning, water filtration, and detoxification (Worm et al., 2006 (p. 246)). Scholars have documented isolated cases such as

---

[8]This content is available online at <http://legacy.cnx.org/content/m38878/1.5/>.

[9]http://www.nmfs.noaa.gov/sfa/statusoffisheries/2011/second/MapOverfishedStocksCY_Q2_2011.pdf

the "lobster gangs" of coastal Maine where communal informal management prevented overexploitation of the resource (Acheson, 1988 (p. 246)), but such cases are the exception rather than the rule.

Early efforts to control overfishing used several kinds of regulations on quotas, fishing effort, and gear. For example, fishing boats are forbidden in some places from using conventional longlines because that gear yields high levels of bycatch and kills endangered leatherback turtles. Some forms of fishery management limit the number of fish that can be caught in an entire fishery. Under a total allowable catch (TAC) system, fishers can fish when and how they want, but once the quota for the fishery has been met, fishing must stop until the next season. Unfortunately, TAC policies do not solve the underlying problem that fishermen compete for the fish, and often yield perverse incentives and undesirable outcomes such as overcapitalization of the industry (Beddington, Agnew, & Clark, 2007 (p. 246)) and races between fishing boat crews to catch fish before the quota is reached. In the well-known case of the Alaskan halibut fishery, the race became so extreme that the fishing season was reduced to a single 24-hour mad dash; given that fish are perishable, this temporal clumping of the catch is not a desirable outcome.

Figure 6.7: Marine Fisheries: Fishing Boats Alaskan waters have been fished by people for thousands of years, but they are under pressure from modern fishing technologies and large-scale extraction. *Source: National Oceanic and Atmospheric Administration*[10]

Resource economists developed the idea of a tradable permit scheme to help manage fisheries. Individual tradable quota (ITQ) schemes are cap-and-trade policies for fish, where total catch is limited but fishers in the fishery are given permits that guarantee them a right to a share of that catch. Players in the fishery can sell their quota shares to each other (helping the catch to flow voluntarily to the most efficient boats in the industry) and there is no incentive for captains to buy excessively large boats or fish too rapidly to beat the other boats to the catch. ITQ policies have rationalized the Alaskan halibut fishery completely: the fish stock is thriving, overcapitalization is gone, and the fish catch is spread out over time (Levy, 2010 (p. 246)). ITQs have also been implemented in the fisheries of New Zealand, yielding large improvements in the biological status of the stocks (Annala, 1996 (p. 246)). There is some general evidence that ITQ systems have been relatively successful in improving fishery outcomes (Costello, Gaines, & Lynham et al. 2008 (p. 246)), though other research implies that evidence of the superiority of the ITQ approach is more mixed (Beddington 2007 (p. 246)) Scholars and fishery managers continue to work to identify the details of ITQ management that make such systems work most effectively, and to identify what needs to be done to promote more widespread adoption of good fishery management policy worldwide.

6.3.1 References

Acheson, J. M. (1988). The Lobster Gangs of Maine. Lebanon, NH: University of New England Press.

Annala, J. H. (1996). New Zealand's ITQ system: have the first eight years been a success or a failure? Reviews in Fish Biology and Fisheries. 6(1), 43–62. doi: 10.1007/BF00058519

Beddington, J. R., Agnew, D.J., & Clark, C. W. (2007). Current problems in the management of marine fisheries. Science, 316(5832), 1713-1716. doi:10.1126/science.1137362

Costello, C., Gaines, S. D., & Lynham, J. (2008). Can catch shares prevent fisheries collapse? Science, 321(5896), 1678 – 1681. doi10.1126/science.1159478

Levy, S. (2010). Catch shares management. BioScience, 60(10), 780–785. doi:10.1525/bio.2010.60.10.3

Montaigne, F. (2007, April). Still waters, the global fish crisis. National Geographic Magazine. Retrieved from http://ngm.nationalgeographic.com/print/2007/04/global-fisheries-crisis/montaigne-text[11] .

Worm, B., Barbier, E. B., Beaumont, N., Duffy, J. E., Folke, C., Halpern, B. S., Hackson, J. B. C., Lotze, H. K., Micheli, F., Palumbi, S. R., Sala, E., Selkoe, K. A., Stachowicz, J. J., & Watson, R. (2006). Impacts of biodiversity loss on ocean ecosystem services. Science, 314(5800), 787 – 790. doi:10.1126/science.1132294

6.4 Environmental Valuation[12]

6.4.1 Learning Objectives

After reading this module, students should be able to

1. understand why it might be useful to develop estimates of the values of environmental goods in dollar terms.
2. know the difference between the two economic measures of value, willingness to pay and willingness to accept.
3. be familiar with valuation methods in all three parts of the environmental valuation toolkit: direct, revealed preference, and stated preference methods.
4. understand the strengths and weaknesses of those valuation methods.

---

[10]http://www.photolib.noaa.gov/htmls/line0488.htm

[11]http://ngm.nationalgeographic.com/print/2007/04/global-fisheries-crisis/montaigne-text

[12]This content is available online at <http://legacy.cnx.org/content/m38954/1.5/>.

6.4.2 Use Values

Externality, public good, and common-pool resource problems yield suboptimal levels of environmental quality and excessive rates of resource exploitation. Many factors complicate the process of deciding what to do about these problems. One is that environmental goods are not traded in any marketplace, and hence analysts struggle to identify quantitative measures of their values to society.

Environmental **valuation** is controversial. Some environmentalists object to efforts to place dollar values on elements of the environment that might be viewed as priceless. Such values are important, however, for making sure that society does not fail to take the value of nature into account when making policy and investment choices. All U.S. government regulations, for example, are subjected to benefit-cost analyses to make sure that government actions don't inadvertently make society worse off (see Module **Evaluating Projects and Policies** (Section 6.5)). If we do not have dollar values for the environmental benefits of things like clean water and air, then estimates of the benefits of pollution control will be consistently lower than the true social benefits, and government policy will chronically underinvest in efforts to control pollution.

Environmental and natural resource economists have worked for decades to develop valuation methods that can be used to generate reasonable estimates of the dollar values of environmental amenities. Thousands of journal articles have been published in this effort to refine valuation methodology. In the early years of valuation studies, most of the work was focused on generating estimates of the social values of water and air quality. Over time, economists broadened their focus to study how to value a broader range of amenities such as wetland habitat and endangered species.

The United Nations launched an international effort in 2000 called the Millennium Ecosystem Assessment which was to evaluate the current state of earth's ecosystems (and the services that flow from nature to humans) and identify strategies for conservation and sustainable use. Reports from this effort[13]) have helped scientists and policy makers develop a new framework for thinking about how nature has value to humans by providing a wide range of **ecosystem services**. Since then, a surge of multidisciplinary research has emerged to quantify the physical services provided by the environment and estimate the values to humanity of those services. Economists recognize two broad categories of environmental values: use and non-use. **Use values** flow from services that affect people directly, such as food production, flood regulation, recreation opportunities, and potable water provision. **Non-use values** are less tangible: the desire for endangered tigers to continue to exist even on the part of people who will never see them in the wild; concern about bequeathing future generations a planet with healthy fish populations; a sense that people have an ethical responsibility to be good stewards of the earth. Economic valuation methods exist to capture all of these environmental values.

---

[13]http://www.maweb.org/en/index.aspx

Figure 6.8: Use Value: Recreational Angler A fisherman takes advantage of the use value of the natural environment of Four Springs Lake, Tasmania. *Source: Photo by Peripitus*[14]

---

[14]http://en.wikipedia.org/wiki/File:Four_Springs_Lake_and_fisherman.JPG

Figure 6.9: Non-use Value: Sumatran Tiger Although wild tigers do not directly impact people living in the United States, many Americans wish for the species to continue existing in their natural environment. This is an example of a non-use value. *Source: Photo by Nevit Dilman*[15]

---

[15]http://en.wikipedia.org/wiki/File:Sumatran-tiger-new.jpg

6.4.3 Willingness to Pay/Accept

Economists use measures of value that are anthropocentric, or human centered. A rigorous body of theory about consumer choice lies beneath those measures. Mathematical complexity can make that theory seem like unreliable trickery, but in truth, consumer theory rests on only a very small number of fundamental assumptions:

- People have preferences over things.
- People are able to rank any two bundles of goods to identify which one they prefer.
- People are rational in that they will choose the bundle they prefer (over bundles they do not prefer) if they can afford it.

Those uncontroversial axioms are actually enough to derive all the results economists use when working with valuation methodology. However, the derivations are easier and sometimes more intuitive with a little more structure added to our hypothetical consumer choice problem:

- People face budget constraints (total expenditures can't exceed their income).
- People make choices to make themselves as well off as possible ("maximize their utility") within the rationing forced by their budget constraints.

This framework yields two ways to think about the values of changes to the quality or quantity of environmental goods. Consider first a situation where we are trying to determine the value of a project that yields an environmental improvement—say, for example, water in the Chicago River will be cleaner. The social benefit of that project turns out to be what people are willing to pay for it. The second measure of value is appropriate if we want to measure the value of environmental goods that will be lost or degraded by a deleterious change—say, for example, climate change leading to the extinction of polar bears. In that context, the value of the change is given by the amount of money you would have to pay people in order to make them willing to accept it.

"**Willingness to pay**" (WTP) is a budget-constrained measure of a change in welfare; a person cannot be willing to pay more money for a change than they have income. In contrast, "**willingness to accept**" (WTA) is not a budget constrained measure of value—you might have to increase a person's income many times over in order to fully compensate them for the loss of an environmental amenity they hold dear—and can theoretically approach infinity. Empirical studies tend to find that WTA value estimates are larger than equivalent estimates of WTP.

Analysts usually choose whether to use WTA or WTP approaches as a function of the context of the analysis. The "right" measure to use may depend on whether you want value estimates to inform a policy that would improve conditions relative to the current legal status quo, or to understand the consequences of a change that would cause deterioration of some environmental good citizens currently enjoy. Another factor in choosing a valuation method is that WTP is budget constrained while WTA is not. WTP estimates of value tend to be lower in places where people have lower incomes. That variation captures a realistic pattern in the size of willingness to pay for environmental improvements. However, equity problems clearly plague a study that concludes, for example, that improvements in air quality are more valuable to society if they happen in rich areas rather than poor.

All valuation methodologies—WTP and WTA—are designed to estimate values of fairly small changes in the environment, and those values are often setting-specific. Careful analysts can do **benefit transfer** studies in which they use the results of one valuation study to inform value estimates in a different place. However, such applications must be carried out carefully. The value of a unit change in a measure of environmental integrity is not an immutable constant, and the values of very large changes in either quantity or quality of an environmental amenity usually cannot be estimated. A cautionary example is an influential but widely criticized paper published in *Nature* by Robert Costanza and colleagues that carried out sweeping benefit transfer estimates of the total social values of a number of Earth's biomes (open oceans, forests, wetlands, etc.). The resulting estimates were too large to be correct estimates of WTP because they exceeded the value of the whole world's GDP, and too small to be correct estimates of WTA because life on earth would cease to exist if oceans disappeared, so WTA for that change should be infinity (Costanza et al., 1997 (p. 253)).

6.4.4 An Economist's Environmental Valuation Toolkit: Direct, Revealed Preference, and Stated Preference Methods

Early work on environmental valuation estimated the benefits of improved environmental quality using **direct methods** that exploit easily obtained information about the monetary damage costs of pollution. These methods are still sometimes used (most often by people who are not environmental economists) because of their simple intuitive appeal. An analyst can measure costs associated with pollution; the benefits of environmental cleanup are then the reductions in those costs. Following are some examples:

- *Production damage measures*: Pollution has a deleterious effect on many production processes. For example, air pollution lowers corn yields, thus increasing the cost of producing a bushel of corn. An analyst could try to measure the benefits of eliminating air pollution by calculating the increase in net social benefits that would flow from the corn market as a result of higher yields.

- *Avoided cost measures*: Environmental degradation often forces people to spend money on efforts to mitigate the harm caused by that degradation. One benefit of reversing the degradation is not having to spend that money on mitigation—the **avoided cost**. For example, hydrological disruption from impervious surfaces in urban areas forces cities to spend money on expensive storm sewer infrastructure to try to reduce floods. A benefit of installing rain gardens and green roofs to manage stormwater might be avoided storm sewer infrastructure costs.

- *Health cost measures*: Pollution has adverse effects on human health. For example, toxic chemicals can cause cancer, and ground level ozone causes asthma. Some measures of the damages caused by pollution simply count the financial costs of such illnesses, including the costs of cancer treatment and lost wages from adults missing work during asthma attacks.

These measures seem appealing, but are in fact deeply problematic. One of the most serious problems with direct measures is that they often yield woefully incomplete estimates of the benefits of environmental cleanup. Consider the example of cancer above. Suppose a woman gets cancer from drinking contaminated well water. By the time her illness is diagnosed, the cancer is so advanced that doctors can do little to treat her, and she dies a few months later. The medical expenditures associated with this illness are not very large; she and her family would surely have been willing to pay much more money to have eliminated the toxins so she did not ever get sick. The direct health cost measure of the benefits of cleaning up the contaminated water is a serious underestimate of the true benefit to society of that environmental improvement.

A second set of valuation tools called **revealed preference** methods work to estimate WTP for environmental amenities and quality by exploiting data on actual behaviors and market choices that are related to the environmental good in question. People reveal their WTP for environmental goods with their actions. Three examples of such methods are below.

- *Hedonic price analysis*: We often cannot observe individuals taking direct action to change the quality of the environment to which they are exposed in a given location because they simply cannot effect such change; no one person, for example, can reduce the concentration of fine particles in the air near his house. We do, however, observe market data about the choices people make about where to live. If two houses are otherwise identical but one house is situated in a place with much cleaner air than the other, the benefit of breathing cleaner air will get capitalized in the value of that house. All else equal, neighborhoods with better environments will have more expensive homes. Analysts can gather data on housing prices and house characteristics (both environmental and nonenvironmental) and use a statistical analysis to estimate marginal WTP for elements of environmental quality that vary among the houses in the data set. The **hedonic price analysis** approach has been used to value amenities such as air quality, hazardous waste site cleanup, and open space.

- *Hedonic wage analysis*: Some forms of pollution cause people to face higher risk of death in any given year. Thus, one important goal of valuation is to estimate a dollar value of reduced mortality resulting from pollution cleanup. Except in the movies, we rarely observe people choosing how much money they are willing to pay to save a specific person from certain death. However, all of us make choices every day that affect our risk of death. One important choice is which job to accept. Elementary school teachers face little job-related mortality risk. In contrast, coal miners, offshore oil rig workers, and deep sea fishermen accept high rates of accidental death when they take their jobs. By analyzing data on wage rates and worker death rates in a variety of different industries, we can estimate WTP to reduce the risk of death. Using such **hedonic wage analysis**, economists have developed measures of the **value of a statistical life** (VSL), which can be applied to physical estimates of reductions in pollution-related deaths to find the benefits of reduced mortality.

- *Travel cost analysis*: Many natural amenities, such as forests, lakes, and parks are enjoyed by the public free of charge. While there is no formal market for "hours of quality outdoor recreation," people do incur costs associated with such recreation—gas purchased to drive to the site, hotel expenses for overnight trips, and the opportunity cost of the time spent on the trip. If environmental quality is valued, people will be willing to pay higher travel costs to visit recreation sites with higher levels of environmental quality (e.g., cleaner water in the lake, more fish to catch, a better view from a mountain with low air pollution). In **travel cost analysis**, researchers gather data on the environmental features of a set of recreation sites and the choices people make about visiting those sites—which they choose to visit, and how often—and apply statistical analysis to those data to estimate WTP for improved quality of natural amenities.

One of the greatest strengths of revealed preference valuation methods is that they use information about real behavior rather than hypothetical choices. These approaches also yield estimates of WTP that are often more complete than the results of direct market measure studies.

Revealed preference studies do, however, have weaknesses and limitations. First, they only give good estimates of WTP for environmental goods if people have full and accurate information about environmental quality and associated risks. For example, hedonic estimates of WTP to avoid living with polluted air will be biased downward if people in a city do not know how air pollution varies among neighborhoods. Second, some revealed preference approaches are only valid if the relevant markets (labor markets for a wage study, housing markets for a hedonic price study) are not plagued by market power and transaction costs that prevent efficient equilibria from being reached. For example, if workers find it too daunting and costly to move from one region to another, then coal miners may fail to earn the wage premium that would be associated with such a risky job in the absence of relocation hurdles. Third, revealed preference approaches cannot be used to estimate values for levels of environmental quality that are not observed in real-world data. If all the lakes in a region are terribly polluted, we cannot use a travel cost study of lake site choice to identify WTP for very clean lakes. Fourth, revealed preference methods can capture only use values, not non-use values.

The limitations of revealed preference valuation tools motivated environmental and natural resource economists to develop valuation methods that do not require analysts to be able to observe real-world behavior related to the amenity being valued. These **stated preference** methods are now highly refined, but the essential idea is simple. These studies design a survey that presents people with information about hypothetical scenarios involving an environmental good, gather data on their responses to questions about how much they would pay for something or whether they would choose one scenario over another, and then analyze the data to estimate WTP for the good or WTA compensation for elimination or degradation of the good.

- *Contingent valuation*: The methodology called contingent valuation (or CV) gained prominent attention when it was used by economists to estimate the damage done to society by the oil spilled by Exxon's *Valdez* oil tanker in Prince William Sound in 1989 (Carson et al., 2003 (p. 253)). A CV survey gives a clear description of a single environmental amenity to be valued, such as a wetland restoration, whale populations, or improved water quality in a local lake. The description includes details about how the amenity would be created, and how the survey respondent would pay any money they claim to be willing to pay in support of the amenity. Respondents are then asked a question to elicit their WTP. This value elicitation question can be open ended ("How much would you be willing to pay in taxes to increase whale populations?) or closed ended ("Would you be willing to pay $30 to increase whale populations?). The resulting data set is analyzed to find the average WTP of people in the sample population.

- *Conjoint analysis*: Conjoint analysis is also referred to as choice experiment survey analysis. It was developed first by analysts in business marketing and psychology, and only later adopted by economists for environmental valuation. The main difference between conjoint analysis and CV is that CV elicits WTP for an environmental amenity with a single fixed bundle of features, or attributes. Conjoint analysis estimates separate values for each of a set of attributes of a composite environmental amenity. For example, grasslands can vary in bird species diversity, wildflower coverage, and distance from human population centers. A conjoint analysis of grassland ecosystems would construct a set of hypothetical grasslands with varied combinations of attributes (including the cost to the respondent of a chosen grassland). The survey would present respondents with several choice questions; in each choice, the respondent would be asked to pick which of several hypothetical grasslands they would prefer. The resulting data would be analyzed to find how each attribute affects the likelihood that one grassland is preferred over another. This would yield estimates of marginal values for each attribute; those values could then be used to find WTP for composite grasslands with many different combinations of features.

Both CV and conjoint analysis methods can be designed to estimate WTP for improvement or WTA degradation depending on which context is most appropriate for the problem at hand. These stated preference methods have two main strengths. First, they can capture non-use values. Second, their hypothetical nature allows analysts to estimate WTP for improvements out of the range of current experience (or WTA for degradation we have fortunately not yet experienced).

However, stated preferences approaches do have weaknesses and limitations. For example, many economists are uncomfortable using value estimates derived from hypothetical choices, worrying whether consumers would make the same choices regarding payment for public environmental goods if the payments were real. Scholars also worry about whether people give responses to stated preference surveys that are deliberately skewed from their true WTP. Understatements of value could arise to protest a government policy ("Why should I have to pay to clean up the environment when someone else made it dirty in the first place?") or out of a desire to free ride. Finally, the hypothetical nature of stated preference surveys can mean that some respondents are not familiar with the thing being valued, and thus may have trouble giving meaningful responses to the questions. Stated preference surveys must be designed to give respondents enough information without biasing their responses.

6.4.5 References

Carson, R. T., Mitchell, R. C., Hanemann, M., Kopp, R. J., Presser, S., and Ruud, P. A. (2003). Contingent valuation and lost passive use: Damages from the Exxon Valdez oil spill. *Environmental and Resource Economics, 25*(3), 257-286. DOI: 10.1023/A:1024486702104.

Costanza, R., d'Arge, R., de Groot, R., Farber, S., Grasso, M., Hannon, B., Limburg, K., Naeem, S., O'Neill, R. V., Paruelo, J., Raskin, R. G., Sutton, P., & van den Bel, M. (1997). The value of the world's ecosystem services and natural capital. *Nature, 387*, 253–260. doi:10.1038/387253a0

6.4.6 Review Questions

Question 6.4.1
Why might it be useful to estimate dollar values for features of the environment?

Question 6.4.2
What are the three types of valuation tools? List at least one strength and one weakness of each.

6.5 Evaluating Projects and Policies[16]

6.5.1 Learning Objectives

After reading this module, students should be able to

- know five important features of how economists think about costs
- understand why discounting is both important and controversial, and be able to calculate the net present value of a project or policy
- know what cost-benefit analysis is, and be aware of some of its limitations
- think about four criteria for evaluating a project that are not captured in a basic cost-benefit analysis

6.5.2 Introduction

Environmental valuation methods help analysts to evaluate the benefits society would gain from policies or cleanup and restoration projects that improve environmental quality or better steward our natural resources. Another set of tools can yield information about the costs of such actions (a brief description is below). But even if we have plausible estimates of the costs and benefits of something, more work needs to be done to put all that information together and make some rational choices about public policy and investments. This module discusses the challenges of policy evaluation when costs and benefits accrue over time, outlines the main features of cost-benefit analysis, and presents several other criteria for policy evaluation.

6.5.3 Net Present Value, Discounting, and Cost-benefit Analysis

Cost estimation has not generated the same amount of scholarly research as benefit valuation because the process of estimating the costs of environmental improvement is usually more straightforward than the process of estimating the benefits. Economists do think differently about costs than engineers or other physical scientists, and several key insights about the economics of cost evaluation are important for policy analysis. Viewed through an inverse lens, all these ideas are important for benefit estimation as well.

6.5.3.1 Opportunity Cost

Not all costs involve actual outlays of money. An opportunity cost is the foregone benefit of something that we choose (or are forced) not to do. The **opportunity cost** of a year of graduate school is the money you could have made if you had instead gotten a full-time job right after college. Endangered species protection has many opportunity costs: timber in old-growth forests can't be cut and sold; critical habitat in urban areas can't be developed into housing and sold to people who want to live in the area. Opportunity costs do not appear on firms' or governments' accounting sheets and are thus often overlooked in estimates of the costs of a policy. Studies of U.S. expenditures on endangered species' recoveries have used only information about costs like direct government expenditures because opportunity costs are so challenging to measure (e.g. Dawson and Shogren, 2001 (p. 260)).

---

[16]This content is available online at <http://legacy.cnx.org/content/m38611/1.7/>.

Figure 6.10: A Redwood Forest in California Forests can't both be cut down and preserved for habitat. The dollar cost of lumber is straightforward to quantify, but it is more difficult to quantify the value of ecosystems. Cutting down the forest therefore has an opportunity cost that is hard to measure, and this can bias people and governments towards resource extraction. *Source: Photo by Michael Barera*[17]

6.5.3.2 Transfers Are Not Costs

Cost totals should only include real changes in behavior or resource use, and not transfers of money from one party to another. For example, imagine a program in which a wastewater treatment plant can pay a

---

[17]http://en.wikipedia.org/wiki/File:Redwoods_in_Muir_Woods_2.JPG

farmer for the cost of taking land out of production and installing a wetland on the land that will soak up nutrients that would otherwise flow into a local river. The cost of those nutrient reductions is the cost of installing the wetland and the opportunity cost of the foregone farming activity. If payments for multiple services are permitted, the farmer might also be able to get paid by a conservation group for the wildlife benefit associated with the new wetland. However, that additional payment to the farmer is a pure transfer. The social cost of the wetland has not gone up just because the farmer was paid more for it.

6.5.3.3 Use the Correct Counterfactual

Many cursory analyses of the costs of a policy find the difference between the cost of something before and after the policy was put in place and claim that any increase was caused by the policy. For example, the U.S. government put temporary restrictions on offshore oil drilling after the Deepwater Horizon explosion and oil spill to consider new environmental regulations on such drilling. After those restrictions were put in place, the price of crude oil in the U.S. went up. A sloppy analysis would attribute all the costs of that price increase to the drilling restrictions. However, during the same period of 2010, the U.S. economy was beginning to pull out of a very deep recession; this caused increased manufacturing activity and consumer driving, and thus an increased call for fossil-fuel energy. Therefore, some of the increase in oil prices might have been driven by the increased demand for oil. A careful analysis would compare the price of oil with the restrictions in place to what the price of oil would have been during the same time period if the restrictions had not been implemented—that hypothetical scenario is the true **counterfactual**.

6.5.3.4 Additionality

A careful analysis of the costs of a program includes only costs that are additional, that is, new additions to costs that would have existed even in the absence of the program. For example, current regulations require developers to use temporary controls while constructing a new building to prevent large amounts of sediment from being washed into local rivers and lakes. Suppose EPA wants to estimate the costs of a new regulation that further requires new development to be designed such that stormwater doesn't run off the site after the building is finished. A proper analysis would not include the costs of the temporary stormwater controls in the estimate of the cost of the new regulation, because those temporary controls would be required even in the absence of the new regulation (Braden and Ando, 2011 (p. 260)). The concept of **additionality** has been made famous in the context of benefit estimation by a debate over whether programs that pay landowners not to deforest their lands have benefits that are additional; some of those lands might not have been deforested even without the payments, or the landowners may receive conservation payments from multiple sources for the same activity.

6.5.3.5 Control for Associated Market Changes

A careful cost analysis must pay attention to market changes associated with cost increases. To illustrate, suppose the government is thinking of passing a ban on agricultural use of methyl bromide. This ozone-depleting chemical is widely used as an agricultural fumigant, and is particularly important in strawberry production and shipping. A ban on methyl bromide might, therefore, increase the marginal cost of producing strawberries. A simple approach to estimating the cost of the proposed methyl bromide ban would be to find out how many strawberries were sold before the ban and calculate the increase in the total cost of producing that many strawberries. However, the increase in production costs will drive up the price of strawberries and lower the number of strawberries sold in the marketplace. There is a cost to society with two parts: (a) deadweight loss associated with the net benefits of the strawberries not sold, and (b) the increased cost of producing the strawberries that still are sold. That total social cost is lower, however, than the estimate yielded by the simple approach outlined above because the simple approach includes increased production costs for strawberries that are not sold. An accurate cost estimate must take into account market changes.

The concept of net benefits was introduced above; in the context of policy or project evaluation, net benefits are, quite simply, the difference between the benefits and the costs of a policy in a given year.

However, environmental policies typically have benefits and costs that play out over a long period of time, and those flows are often not the same in every year. For example, wetland restoration in agricultural areas has a large fixed cost at the beginning of the project when the wetland is constructed and planted. Every year after that there is an opportunity cost associated with foregone farm income from the land in the wetland, but that annual cost is probably lower than the fixed construction cost. The wetland will yield benefits to society by preventing the flow of some nitrogen and phosphorus into nearby streams and by providing habitat for waterfowl and other animals. However, the wildlife benefits will be low in the early years, increasing over time as the restored wetland vegetation grows and matures. It is not too difficult to calculate the net benefits of the restoration project in each year, but a different methodology is needed to evaluate the net benefits of the project over its lifetime.

Some analysts simply add up all the costs and benefits for the years that they accrue. However, that approach assumes implicitly that we are indifferent between costs and benefits we experience now and those we experience in the future. That assumption is invalid for two reasons. First, empirical evidence has shown that humans are impatient and prefer benefits today over benefits tomorrow. One need only ask a child whether they want to eat a candy bar today or next week in order to see that behavior at work. Second, the world is full of investment opportunities (both financial and physical). Money today is worth more than money tomorrow because we could invest the money today and earn a rate of return. Thus, if there is a cost to environmental cleanup, we would rather pay those costs in the future than pay them now.

Economists have developed a tool for comparing net benefits at different points in time called **discounting**. Discounting converts a quantity of money received at some point in the future into a quantity that can be directly compared to money received today, controlling for the time preference described above. To do this, an analyst assumes a discount rate r, where r ranges commonly between zero and ten percent depending on the application. If we denote the net benefits t years from now as Vt (in the current year, $t=0$), then we say the **present discounted value** of Vt is $PDV(V_t) = \frac{V_t}{(1+r)^t}$. Figure 6.4.2 shows how the present value of $10,000 declines with time, and how the rate of the decrease varies with the choice of discount rate r. If a project has costs and benefits every year for T years, then the **net present value** of the entire project is given by $NPV = \sum_{t=0}^{T} \frac{V_t}{(1+r)^t}$.

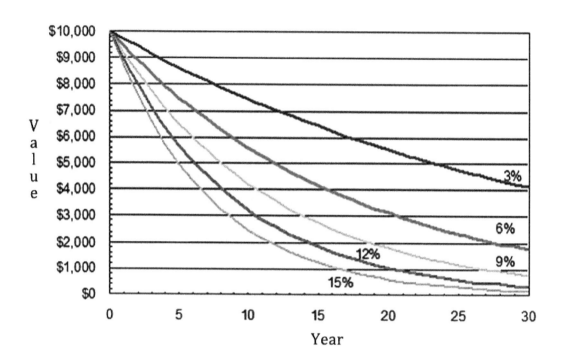

Figure 6.11: The Impact of a Discount Rate on Present Value Estimates *Source: California Department of Transportation*[18]

A particular cost or benefit is worth less in present value terms the farther into the future it accrues and the higher the value of the discount rate. These fundamental features of discounting create controversy over the use of discounting because they make projects to deal with long-term environmental problems seem unappealing. The most pressing example of such controversy swirls around analysis of climate-change policy. Climate-change mitigation policies typically incur immediate economic costs (e.g. switching from fossil fuels to more expensive forms of energy) to prevent environmental damages from climate change several decades in the future. Discounting lowers the present value of the future improved environment while leaving the present value of current costs largely unchanged.

Cost-benefit analysis is just that: analysis of the costs and benefits of a proposed policy or project. To carry out a cost-benefit analysis, one carefully specifies the change to be evaluated, measures the costs and benefits of that change for all years that will be affected by the change, finds the totals of the presented discounted values of those costs and benefits, and compares them. Some studies look at the difference between the benefits and the costs (the net present value), while others look at the ratio of benefits to costs. A "good" project is one with a net present value greater than zero and a benefit/cost ratio greater than one.

The result of a cost-benefit analysis depends on a large number of choices and assumptions. What discount rate is assumed? What is the status quo counterfactual against which the policy is evaluated? How are the physical effects of the policy being modeled? Which costs and benefits are included in the analysis—are non-use benefits left out? Good cost-benefit analyses should make all their assumptions clear and transparent. Even better practice explores whether the results of the analysis are sensitive to assumptions about things like the discount rate (a practice called **sensitivity analysis**). Scandal erupted in 2000 when

---

[18]http://www.dot.ca.gov/hq/tpp/offices/ote/benefit_cost/calculations/discount_rate.html

a whistle-blower revealed that the Army Corps of Engineers was pressuring its staff to alter assumptions to make sure a cost-benefit analysis yielded a particular result (EDV&CBN, 2000 (p. 260)). Transparency and sensitivity analysis can help to prevent such abuses.

6.5.4 Efficiency, Cost Effectiveness, Innovation, and Equity

Cost-benefit analysis gives us a rough sense of whether or not a project is a good idea. However, it has many limitations. Here we discuss several other measures of whether a project is desirable. Economists use all these criteria and more when evaluating whether a policy is the right approach for solving a problem with externalities, public goods, and common-pool resources.

6.5.4.1 Efficiency

A policy is efficient if it maximizes the net benefits society could get from an action of that kind. Many projects and policies can pass a cost-benefit test but still not be efficient. Several levels of carbon dioxide emission reduction, for example, could have benefits exceeding costs, but only one will have the largest difference between benefits and costs possible. Such efficiency will occur when the marginal benefits of the policy are equal to its marginal costs. Sometimes a cost-benefit analysis will try to estimate the total costs and benefits for several policies with different degrees of stringency to try to see if one is better than the others. However, only information about the marginal benefit and marginal cost curves will ensure that the analyst has found the efficient policy. Unfortunately, such information is often very hard to find or estimate.

6.5.4.2 Cost Effectiveness

As we saw in the Module **Environmental Valuation** (Section 6.4), it can be particularly difficult to estimate the benefits of environmental policy, and benefit estimates are necessary for finding efficient policies. Sometimes policy goals are just set through political processes—reducing sulfur dioxide emissions by 10 million tons below 1980 levels in the Clean Air Act acid rain provisions, cutting carbon dioxide emissions by 5% from 1990 levels in the Kyoto protocol—without being able to know whether those targets are efficient. However, we can still evaluate whether a policy will be **cost effective** and achieve its goal in the least expensive way possible. For example, for total pollution reduction to be distributed cost-effectively between all the sources that contribute pollution to an area (e.g. a lake or an urban airshed), it must be true that each of the sources is cleaning up such that they all face the same marginal costs of further abatement. If one source had a high marginal cost and another's marginal cost was very low, total cost could be reduced by switching some of the cleanup from the first source to the second.

6.5.4.3 Incentives to Innovate:

At any one point in time, the cost of pollution control or resource recovery depends on the current state of technology and knowledge. For example, the cost of reducing carbon dioxide emissions from fossil fuels depends in part on how expensive solar and wind power are, and the cost of wetland restoration depends on how quickly ecologists are able to get new wetland plants to be established. Everyone in society benefits if those technologies improve and the marginal cost of any given level of environmental stewardship declines. Thus, economists think a lot about which kinds of policies do the best job of giving people incentives to develop cheaper ways to clean and steward the environment.

6.5.4.4 Fairness

A project can have very high aggregate net benefits, but distribute the costs and benefits very unevenly within society. We may have both ethical and practical reasons not to want a policy that is highly unfair. Some people have strong moral or philosophical preferences for policies that are equitable. In addition, if the costs of a policy are borne disproportionately by a single group of people or firms, that group is likely to fight against it in the political process. Simple cost-benefit analyses do not speak to issues of equity.

However, it is common for policy analyses to break total costs and benefits down among subgroups to see if uneven patterns exist in their distribution. Studies can break down policy effects by income category to see if a policy helps or hurts people disproportionately depending on whether they are wealthy or poor. Other analyses carry out regional analyses of policy effects. . For example, climate-change mitigation policy increases costs disproportionately for poor households because of patterns in energy consumption across income groups. Furthermore, the benefits and costs of such policy are not uniform across space in the U.S. The benefits of reducing the severity of climate change will accrue largely to those areas that would be hurt most by global warming (coastal states hit by sea level rise and more hurricanes, Western states hit by severe water shortages) while the costs will fall most heavily on regions of the country with economies dependent on sales of oil and coal.

Some of our evaluative criteria are closely related to each other; a policy cannot be efficient if it is not cost-effective. However, other criteria have nothing to do with each other; a policy can be efficient but not equitable, and vice versa. Cost-benefit analyses provide crude litmus tests—we surely do not want to adopt policies that have costs exceeding their benefits. However, good policy development and evaluation considers a broader array of criteria.

6.5.5 Review Questions

Question 6.5.1
What are some common mistakes people make in evaluating the costs of a policy or project, and what should you do to avoid them?

Question 6.5.2
What is discounting, and how do we use it in calculating the costs and the benefits of a project that has effects over a long period of time?

Question 6.5.3
Why is discounting controversial?

Question 6.5.4
How does cost-benefit analysis complement some of the other measures people use to evaluate a policy or project?

6.5.6 References

Braden, J. B. & A. W. Ando. 2011. Economic costs, benefits, and achievability of low-impact development based stormwater regulations, in *Economic Incentives for Stormwater Control*, Hale W. Thurston, ed., Taylor & Francis, Boca Raton, FL.

Carson, R. T., Mitchell, R. C., Hanemann, M., Kopp, R. J., Presser, S., and Ruud, P. A. (2003).Contingent valuation and lost passive use: Damages from the Exxon Valdez oil spill. *Environmental and Resource Economics, 25*(3), 257-286. DOI: 10.1023/A:1024486702104.

Dawson, D. & Shogren, J. F. (2001). An update on priorities and expenditures under the Endangered Species Act. *Land Economics, 77*(4), 527-532.

EDV&CBN (2000). Environmental groups protest alteration of U.S. Army Corps cost benefit analysis. *Environmental Damage Valuation and Cost Benefit News*, 7(4), 1-3. http://www.costbenefitanalysis.org/newsletters/nws00apr.pdf[19] .

---

[19]http://www.costbenefitanalysis.org/newsletters/nws00apr.pdf

6.6 Solutions: Property Rights, Regulations, and Incentive Policies[20]

6.6.1 Learning Objectives

After reading this module, students should be able to

- know why having clearly defined property rights might improve environmental outcomes and be aware of the limitations of that approach
- define several different types of command and control regulations, and understand their comparative advantages
- know what incentive policies (taxes and tradable permits) are, what they do, and what their strengths and weaknesses are

6.6.2 Introduction

Governments have implemented many policies to solve problems with environmental quality and natural resource depletion. Every policy is unique and deserves detailed individual analysis in the policymaking process—the devil is always in the details. However, economists have developed a taxonomy of policy types. This taxonomy helps us to understand general principles about how policies of different types are likely to perform and under which circumstances they are likely to work best. Policies are broadly characterized as either command-and-control or incentive policies. Command and control includes several types of standards. Incentive policies include taxes, tradable permits, and liability.

6.6.3 Property Rights

In 1960, Ronald Coase wrote the pioneering article "The Problem of Social Cost" in which he put forth ideas about externalities that have come to be known as the **Coase theorem** (Coase, 1960 (p. 266)). The basic idea of the Coase theorem is that if property rights over a resource are well specified, and if the parties with an interest in that resource can bargain freely, then the parties will negotiate an outcome that is efficient regardless of who has the rights over the resource. The initial allocation of rights will not affect the efficiency of the outcome, but it will affect the distribution of wealth between the parties because the party with the property rights can extract payment from the other parties as part of the agreement.

To bring this abstract idea to life, we will draw on the classic example employed by generations of economists to think about the Coase theorem. Suppose a farmer and a rancher live next door to each other. There is land between them on which the farmer wants to plant crops, but the rancher's cows keep eating the crops. The farmer would like to have no cows on the land, and the rancher would like the farmer to stop planting crops so the cows could eat as much grass as they like. The efficient outcome is where the marginal benefit of a cow to the rancher is just equal to the marginal cost to the farmer of that cow's grazing. If the farmer is given property rights over the land, the rancher will have an incentive to pay the farmer to allow the efficient number of cows rather than zero; if the rancher has the rights, then the farmer will have to pay the rancher to limit the herd to just the efficient size. Either way they have incentives to negotiate to the efficient outcome because otherwise both of them could be made better off.

The Coase theorem is invoked by some scholars and policy analysts to argue that government policy is not needed to correct problems of externalities; all you need is property rights, and private negotiations will take care of the rest. However, Coase himself recognized in his writing that often the real world does not have the frictionless perfect negotiation on which the conclusions of the theorem rest. For example, there are transaction costs in bargaining, and those transaction costs can be prohibitively large when many people are involved, as in the case of air pollution from a factory. Furthermore, perfect bargaining requires perfect information. People often are unaware of the threats posed to their health by air and water pollution, and thus do not know what kind of bargaining would actually be in their own best interests.

---

[20]This content is available online at <http://legacy.cnx.org/content/m38956/1.6/>.

Despite these limitations, there is a move afoot to use property right development to effect environmental improvement and improve natural resource stewardship, particularly in developing countries. In parts of Africa, new systems have given villages property rights over wildlife on their lands, yielding stronger incentives to manage wildlife well and demonstrably increasing wildlife populations. In South America, land-tenure reform is promoted as a way to reduce deforestation.

6.6.4 Command and Control Regulations

Most environmental policy in the United States is much more rigid and controlling than property-rights reform. Our policies for things like clean air and water, toxic waste cleanup, and endangered species protection have largely been composed of rigid rules and regulations. Under such policies, people are given strict and specific rules about things they must or must not do regarding some facet of pollution control or natural resource use, and then a government agency enforces the rules. Here we discuss and explore examples of a few kinds of such "**command-and-control**" regulations.

6.6.4.1 Ambient Standard

Some policies have targets for the quality of some element of the environment that results from human behavior and natural processes. An **ambient standard** establishes a level of environmental quality that must be met. The Clean Air Act directs the U.S. Environmental Protection Agency (EPA) to establish National Ambient Air Quality Standards (NAAQSs) for a range of air pollutants such as ozone and fine particles. The Clean Water Act directs state offices of the EPA to set ambient water quality standards for rivers and streams in their boundaries. In practice, however, such standards are binding only on state regulators. State EPA offices are responsible for developing plans to ensure that air and surface water bodies meet these ambient quality standards, but they cannot do the clean up on their own. They need to use a different set of tools to induce private agents to actually reduce or clean up pollution such that the ambient standards can be met.

Some ambient standards (such as the NAAQSs) have provoked criticism from economists for being uniform across space. Every county in the country has to meet the same air quality goals, even though the efficient levels of air quality might vary from one county to the next with variation in the marginal benefits and marginal costs of cleaning the air. However, uniform ambient standards grant all people in the U.S. the same access to clean air—a goal that has powerful appeal on the grounds of equity.

6.6.4.2 Individual Standards

First, we discuss a kind of policy applied to individual people or companies called a **technology standard**. Pollution and resource degradation result from a combination of human activity and the characteristics of the technology that humans employ in that activity. Behavior can be difficult to monitor and control. Hence, lawmakers have often drafted rules to control our tools rather than our behaviors. For example, automakers are required to install catalytic converters on new automobiles so that cars have lower pollution rates, and people in some parts of the country must use low-flow showerheads and water-efficient toilets to try to reduce water usage.

Technology standards have the great advantage of being easy to monitor and enforce; it is easy for a regulator to check what pollution controls are in the design of a car. Under some circumstances technology standards can reduce pollution and the rate of natural resource destruction, but they have several serious limitations. First, they provide no incentives for people to alter elements of their behavior other than technology choice. Cars may have to have catalytic converters to reduce emissions per mile, but people are given no reason to reduce the number of miles they drive. Indeed, these policies can sometimes have perverse effects on behavior. Early generations of water-efficient toilets performed very poorly; they used fewer gallons of water per flush, but people found themselves flushing multiple times in order to get waste down the pipes. Thus, these standards are neither always efficient nor cost effective. Second, technology standards are the worst policy in the toolkit for promoting technological innovation. Firms are actively forbidden from using any technology other than the one specified in the standards. Automakers might think of a better and cheaper way to reduce air pollution from cars, but the standard says they have to use catalytic converters.

A second type of policy applied to individual agents is called a **performance standard**. Performance standards set strict limits on an outcome of human activity. For example, in order to meet the NAAQSs, state EPA offices set emission standards for air pollution sources in their states. Those standards limit the amount of pollution a factory or power plant can release into the air, though each source can control its pollution in any way it sees fit. The limits on pollution are the same for all sources of a given type (e.g., power plant, cement factory, etc.). Performance standards are also used in natural resource regulation. For example, because stormwater runoff causes flooding and harms aquatic habitat, the city of Chicago requires all new development to be designed handle the first inch of rainfall in a storm onsite before runoff begins.

To enforce a performance standard the regulator must be able to observe the outcome of the agents' activities (e.g. measure the pollution, estimate the runoff). If that is possible, these policies have some advantages over technology standards. Performance standards do give people and firms some incentive to innovate and find cheaper ways to reduce pollution because they are free to use any technology they like to meet the stated requirements. Performance standards are also more efficient because they give people and firms incentives to change multiple things about their activity to reduce the total cost of pollution abatement; a power plant can reduce sulfur dioxide emissions by some combination of installing scrubber technology, switching to low-sulfur coal, and reducing total energy generation.

Performance standards also have some drawbacks and limitations, however. It is difficult for a regulator to figure out the cost effective allocation of total pollution reduction between sources and then set different performance standards for each source to reach that cost effective allocation. Hence, performance standards tend to be uniform across individual pollution sources, and so pollution reduction is not done in the cheapest way possible for the industry and society overall. This problem is particularly severe where there is great variation among sources in their abatement costs, and thus the cost-effective allocation of cleanup among sources is far from uniform.

6.6.5 Incentive Policies

Other approaches to environmental policy give firms and individuals incentives to change their behavior rather than mandating specific changes. These incentive policies try to make use of market forces for what they do best—allocating resources cost-effectively within an economy—while correcting the market failures associated with externalities, public goods, and common pool resources.

6.6.5.1 Tax/Subsidy

Environmental taxes are based on a simple premise: if someone is not bearing the full social costs of their actions, then we should charge them an **externality tax** per unit of harmful activity (e.g. ton of pollution, gallon of stormwater runoff) that is equal to the marginal cost that is not borne by the individual. In this way, that person must internalize the externality, and will have the incentive to choose a level of activity that is socially optimal. Thus, if we think the social marginal cost of ton of carbon dioxide (because of its contribution to climate change) is \$20, then we could charge a tax of \$20 per ton of carbon dioxide emitted. The easiest way to do this would be to have a tax on fossil fuels according to the amount of carbon dioxide that will be emitted when they are burned.

If a price is placed on carbon dioxide, all agents would have an incentive to reduce their carbon dioxide emissions to the point where the cost to them of reducing one more unit (their marginal abatement cost) is equal to the per unit tax. Therefore, several good things happen. All carbon dioxide sources are abating to the same marginal abatement cost, so the total abatement is accomplished in the most cost-effective way possible. Furthermore, total emissions in the economy overall will go down to the socially efficient level. Firms and individuals have very broad incentives to change things to reduce carbon dioxide emissions— reduce output and consumption, increase energy efficiency, switch to low carbon fuels—and strong incentives to figure out how to innovate so those changes are less costly. Finally, the government could use the revenue it collects from the tax to correct any inequities in the distribution of the program's cost among people in the economy or to reduce other taxes on things like income.

While taxes on externality-generating activities have many good features, they also have several drawbacks and limitations. First, while an externality tax can yield the efficient outcome (where costs and benefits are balanced for the economy as a whole), that only happens if policy makers know enough about the value of the externality to set the tax at the right level. If the tax is too low, we will have too much of the harmful activity; if the tax is too high, the activity will be excessively suppressed.

Second, even if we are able to design a perfect externality tax in theory, such a policy can be difficult to enforce. The enforcement agency needs to be able to measure the total quantity of the thing being taxed. In some cases that is easy—in the case of carbon dioxide for example, the particular fixed link between carbon dioxide emissions and quantities of fossil fuels burned means that through the easy task of measuring fossil fuel consumption we can measure the vast majority of carbon dioxide emissions. However, many externality-causing activities or materials are difficult to measure in total. Nitrogen pollution flows into streams as a result of fertilizer applications on suburban lawns, but it is impossible actually to measure the total flow of nitrogen from a single lawn over the course of a year so that one could tax the homeowner for that flow.

Third, externality taxes face strong political opposition from companies and individuals who don't want to pay the tax. Even if the government uses the tax revenues to do good things or to reduce other tax rates, the group that disproportionately pays the tax has an incentive to lobby heavily against such a policy. This phenomenon is at least partly responsible for the fact that there are no examples of pollution taxes in the U.S. Instead, U.S. policy makers have implemented mirror-image subsidy policies, giving subsidies for activities that reduce negative externalities rather than taxing activities that cause those externalities. Environmental policy in the case of U.S. agriculture is a prime example of this, with programs that pay farmers to take lands out of production or to adopt environmentally friendly farming practices. A subsidy is equivalent to the mirror-image tax in most ways. However, a subsidy tends to make the relevant industry more profitable (in contrast to a tax, which reduces profits), which in turn can stimulate greater output and have a slight perverse effect on total pollution or environmental degradation; degradation per unit output might go down, but total output goes up.

6.6.5.2 Tradable Permits

Another major type of incentive policy is a **tradable permits** scheme. Tradable permits are actually very similar to externality taxes, but they can have important differences. These policies are colloquially known as "cap and trade". If we know the efficient amount of the activity to have (e.g., number of tons of pollution, amount of timber to be logged) the policy maker can set a cap on the total amount of the activity equal to the efficient amount. Permits are created such that each permit grants the holder permission for one unit of the activity. The government distributes these permits to the affected individuals or firms, and gives them permission to sell (trade) them to one another. In order to be in compliance with the policy (and avoid punishment, such as heavy fines) all agents must hold enough permits to cover their total activity for the time period. The government doesn't set a price for the activity in question, but the permit market yields a price for the permits that gives all the market participants strong incentives to reduce their externality-generating activities, to make cost-effective trades with other participants, and to innovate to find cheaper ways to be in compliance. Tradable permit policies are similar to externality taxes in terms of efficiency, cost-effectiveness, and incentives to innovate.

Tradable permit policies have been used in several environmental and natural resource policies. The U.S. used tradable permits (where the annual cap declined to zero over a fixed number of years) in two separate policy applications to reduce the total cost to society of (a) phasing out the use of lead in gasoline and (b) eliminating production of ozone-depleting chlorofluorocarbons. The Clean Air Act amendments of 1990 put in place a nationwide tradable permit program for emissions of acid-rain precursor sulfur dioxide from electric power plants. The European Union used a tradable permit market as part of its policy to reduce carbon dioxide emissions under the Kyoto protocol. Individual tradable quotas for fish in fisheries of Alaska and New Zealand have been used to rationalize fishing activity and keep total catches down to efficient and sustainable levels (see Case Study: Marine Fisheries (Section 6.3)).

Tradable permits have been adopted more widely than externality taxes. Two factors may contribute to that difference. First, tradable permit policies can have different distributional effects from taxes depending on how the permits are given out. If the government auctions the permits to participants in a competitive marketplace, then the tradable permit scheme is the same as the tax; the industry pays the government an amount equal to the number of permits multiplied by the permit price. However, policy makers more commonly design policies where the permits are initially given for free to participants in the market, and then participants sell the permits to each other. This eliminates the transfer of wealth from the regulated sector (the electric utilities, the fishing boats, etc.) to the government, a feature that has been popular with industry. Second, taxes and tradable permits behave differently in the face of uncertainty. A tax policy fixes the marginal cost to the industry, but might yield more or less of the harmful activity than expected if market conditions fluctuate. A cap and trade program fixes the total amount of the harmful activity, but can yield costs to industry that are wildly variable. Environmentalists have liked the outcome certainty of tradable permits.

6.6.5.3 Liability

A third type of environmental policy was not designed by economists, but still functions to give agents incentives to take efficient actions to reduce environmental degradation: **liability**. Liability provisions can make people or firms pay for the damages caused by their actions. If the expected payment is equal to the total externality cost, then liability makes the agent internalize the externality and take efficient precautions to avoid harming the environment.

Two kinds of liability exist in the U.S.: statutory and common law. Common law derives from a long tradition of legal history in the U.S.—people have sued companies for damages from pollution under tort law under doctrines such as nuisance, negligence, or trespass. This approach has been highly problematic for a number of reasons. For example, tort law places a high burden of proof on the plaintiff to show that damages resulted directly from actions taken by the defendant. Plaintiffs have often struggled with that burden because pollution problems are often caused by many sources, and the harm caused by pollution can display large lags in space and time. If the defendant expects with high probability not to be held responsible by the courts, then liability does not function effectively to make agents internalize the externality costs of their actions.

Frustration with common law has led to several strong statutory liability laws in the U.S. which make explicit provisions for holding firms liable for damages from pollution with much more manageable burdens of proof. The Oil Pollution Act of 1990 holds companies like Exxon and British Petroleum strictly liable for the damages caused by oil spills from accidents such as the Valdez grounding in Prince William Sound or the Deepwater Horizon explosion in the Gulf of Mexico. Under a rule of strict liability, a party is liable for harm if the harm occurred as a result of their actions regardless of the presence (or absence) of negligence or intent. The Comprehensive Environmental Response, Compensation, and Liability Act (CERCLA, or "Superfund") holds companies strictly liable for damages from toxic waste "Superfund" sites.

These laws have surely increased the extent to which oil and chemical companies take precautions to avoid spills and other releases of hazardous materials into the environment. However, enforcement of these provisions is very costly. The legal proceedings for a big case like Deepwater Horizon entail court, lawyer, and expert witness activity (and high fees) for many years. The transaction costs are so burdensome to society that liability may not be a viable approach for all environmental problems.

6.6.6 Review questions

Question 6.6.1
What are some of the strengths and weaknesses of command and control regulation? When would these be the best policy tool to use?

Question 6.6.2
What are some of the strengths and weaknesses of incentive policies? When would these be the best policy tool to use?

Question 6.6.3

Did Coase think government policy was not necessary to solve externality problems? Briefly explain.

Question 6.6.4

How do liability laws function as incentive policies? What are some of their limitations?

6.6.7 References

Coase, R.H. 1960. The problem of social cost. *Journal of Law and Economics, 3,* 1-44.

Chapter 7

Modern Environmental Management

7.1 Modern Environmental Management – Chapter Introduction[1]

7.1.1 Introduction

In the Chapter **The Evolution of Environmental Policy in the United States** (Section 2.1), the ways in which our current environmental policy evolved were presented and discussed. Although the National Environmental Policy Act (Section 2.3.5: Risk Management as a Basis for Environmental Policy) (NEPA) provided lofty goals for our environmental policy, and most importantly a legal basis for action, the fact remains, then and today, that human actions produce very large quantities of waste, virtually all of it harmful to human and ecosystem health if not managed properly. This chapter is about how we currently manage these wastes (Module **Systems of Waste Management** (Section 7.2)), the laws and regulations that define our system of waste management (Module **Government and Laws on the Environment** (Section 7.4)), and how we determine the consequences, i.e. risks, associated with chemicals released into the environment (Module **Risk Assessment Methodology for Conventional and Alternative Sustainability Options** (Section 7.5)). Of course, environmental policies will continue to evolve, and although we may not know the exact pathway or form this will take, environmental policy of the future will most certainly build upon the laws and regulations that are used today to manage human interactions with the environment. Thus, it is important to develop an understanding of our current system, its legal and philosophical underpinnings, and the quantitative basis for setting risk-based priorities.

An interesting example of how our current system of environmental management has adapted to modern, and global, problems is the U.S. Supreme Court ruling, in April of 2007, in the case of Massachusetts vs. the Environmental Protection Agency[2] that the USEPA had misinterpreted the Clean Air Act in not classifying, and regulating, carbon dioxide, as a pollutant (the plaintiffs actually involved twelve states and several cities). Up until that time several administrations had said that the Act did not give the EPA legal authority to regulate CO_2 (and by inference all greenhouse gases). At the time the Clean Air Act (Section 7.4.4: Clean Air Act) was passed (most recently in 1990), "clean air" was thought to mean both visibly clean air, and also air free of pollutants exposure to which could cause harm to humans – harm being defined as an adverse outcome over a course of time that might extend to a human lifetime. And although there was concern about global climate change due to greenhouse gas emissions, the gases themselves were not thought of as "pollutants" in the classical sense. This ruling set the stage for the EPA to regulate greenhouse gases through a series of findings, hearings, rulings, and regulations in accord with terms set out in the Clean Air Act. This process is underway at the present time.

In addition to its significance for potentially mitigating the problem of global climate change, this case illustrates more generally how the environmental management system we have put in place today might

---

[1]This content is available online at <http://legacy.cnx.org/content/m41573/1.3/>.

[2]http://en.wikipedia.org/wiki/Massachusetts_v._Environmental_Protection_Agency%5D

adapt to problems of the future. Laws that are forward-thinking, not overly proscriptive, and administratively flexible may well accommodate unforeseen problems and needs. Of course, this does not preclude the passage of new laws or amendments, nor does it imply that all our laws on the environment will adapt in this way to future problems.

7.2 Systems of Waste Management[3]

7.2.1 Learning Objectives

After reading this module, students should be able to

- recognize various environmental regulations governing the management of solid and hazardous wastes, radioactive waste and medical waste
- understand the environmental concerns with the growing quantities and improper management of wastes being generated
- recognize **integrated waste management** strategies that consist of prevention, minimization, recycling and reuse, biological treatment, incineration, and landfill disposal

7.2.2 Introduction

Waste is an inevitable by-product of human life. Virtually every human activity generates some type of material side effect or by-product. When the materials that constitute these by-products are not useful or have been degraded such that they no longer fulfill their original or other obvious useful purpose, they are classified as a waste material.

Practically speaking, wastes are generated from a wide range of sources and are usually classified by their respective sources. Common generative activities include those associated with residences, commercial businesses and enterprises, institutions, construction and demolition activities, municipal services, and water/wastewater and air treatment plants, and municipal incinerator facilities. Further, wastes are generated from numerous industrial processes, including industrial construction and demolition, fabrication, manufacturing, refineries, chemical synthesis, and nuclear power/nuclear defense sources (often generating low- to high-level **radioactive wastes**).

Population growth and urbanization (with increased industrial, commercial and institutional establishments) contribute to increased waste production, as do the rapid economic growth and industrialization throughout the developing world. These social and economic changes have led to an ever-expanding consumption of raw materials, processed goods, and services. While these trends have, in many ways, improved the quality of life for hundreds of millions of people, it has not come without drastic costs to the environment. Proper management of a range of wastes has become necessary in order to protect public health and the environment as well as ensure sustained economic growth.

It is commonly believed that incineration and landfill disposal represent preferred options in dealing with waste products; however, many wastes have the potential to be recycled or re-used for some purpose or in some manner. Some waste materials may be reclaimed or re-generated and used again for their original or similar purpose, or they may be physically or chemically changed and employed for alternative uses. As natural resources continue to be depleted, and as incineration and landfill disposal options become more costly and unsustainable, numerous economic and social incentives are being promoted by government agencies to prevent or reduce waste generation and develop new methods and technologies for **recycling** and reusing wastes. Such efforts can have broader implications for energy conservation and the reduction of greenhouse gas emissions that contribute to global climate change, while concurrently fostering sustainable waste management practices.

---

[3]This content is available online at <http://legacy.cnx.org/content/m41572/1.5/>.

This section provides an overview of the existing regulatory framework mandating the management of wastes, environmental concerns associated with waste generation and management, and various alternatives for the proper management of wastes. Recent developments towards the development of sustainable waste management systems are also highlighted. It should be mentioned here that although the content of this section reflects the regulatory framework and practices within the United States, similar developments and actions have occurred in other developed countries and are increasingly being initiated in numerous developing countries.

7.2.3 Regulatory Framework

During the course of the 20th century, especially following World War II, the United States experienced unprecedented economic growth. Much of the growth was fueled by rapid and increasingly complex industrialization. With advances in manufacturing and chemical applications also came increases in the volume, and in many cases the **toxicity**, of generated wastes. Furthermore, few if any controls or regulations were in place with respect to the handling of toxic materials or the disposal of waste products. Continued industrial activity led to several high-profile examples of detrimental consequences to the environment resulting from these uncontrolled activities. Finally, several forms of intervention, both in the form of government regulation and citizen action, occurred in the early 1970s.

Ultimately, several regulations were promulgated on the state and federal levels to ensure the safety of public health and the environment (see Module **Government and Laws on the Environment** (Section 7.4)). With respect to waste materials, the Resource Conservation and Recovery Act[4] (RCRA), enacted by the United States Congress, first in 1976 and then amended in 1984, provides a comprehensive framework for the proper management of hazardous and non-hazardous **solid wastes** in the United States. RCRA stipulates broad and general legal objectives while mandating the United States Environmental Protection Agency[5] (USEPA) to develop specific regulations to implement and enforce the law. The RCRA regulations are contained in Title 40 of the Code of Federal Regulations (CFR), Parts 239 to 299. States and local governments can either adopt the federal regulations, or they may develop and enforce more stringent regulations than those specified in RCRA. Similar regulations have been developed or are being developed worldwide to manage wastes in a similar manner in other countries.

The broad goals of RCRA include: (1) the protection of public health and the environment from the hazards of waste disposal; (2) the conservation of energy and natural resources; (3) the reduction or elimination of waste; and (4) the assurance that wastes are managed in an environmentally-sound manner (e.g. the remediation of waste which may have spilled, leaked, or been improperly disposed). It should be noted here that the RCRA focuses only on active and future facilities and does not address abandoned or historical sites. These types of environmentally impacted sites are managed under a different regulatory framework, known as the Comprehensive Environmental Response, Compensation, and Liability Act[6] (CERCLA), or more commonly known as "Superfund."

7.2.3.1 Solid Waste Regulations

RCRA defines solid waste as any garbage or refuse, sludge from a wastewater treatment plant, water supply treatment plant, or air pollution control facility and other discarded material, including solid, liquid, semi-solid, or contained gaseous material resulting from industrial, commercial, mining, and agricultural operations, and from community activities. In general, solid waste can be categorized as either *non-hazardous waste* or *hazardous waste*.

Non-hazardous solid waste can be trash or garbage generated from residential households, offices and other sources. Generally, these materials are classified as **municipal solid waste** (MSW). Alternatively, non-hazardous materials that result from the production of goods and products by various industries (e.g. coal combustion residues, mining wastes, cement kiln dust), are collectively known as industrial solid waste.

[4]http://www.epa.gov/regulations/laws/rcra.html
[5]http://www.epa.gov/regulations/laws/rcra.html
[6]http://www.epa.gov/superfund/policy/cercla.htm

The regulations pertaining to non-hazardous solid waste are contained in 40 CFR Parts 239 to 259 (known as RCRA Subtitle D regulations[7]).These regulations prohibit the open dumping of solid waste, mandates the development of comprehensive plans to manage MSW and non-hazardous industrial waste, and establishes criteria for MSW **landfills** and other solid waste disposal facilities. Because they are classified as non-hazardous material, many components of MSW and industrial waste have potential for recycling and re-use. Significant efforts are underway by both government agencies and industry to advance these objectives.

Hazardous waste, generated by many industries and businesses (e.g. dry cleaners and auto repair shops), is constituted of materials that are dangerous or potentially harmful to human health and the environment. The regulatory framework with respect to hazardous waste, specifically hazardous waste identification, classification, generation, management, and disposal, is described in 40 CFR Parts 260 through 279 (collectively known as RCRA Subtitle C regulations[8]). These regulations control hazardous waste from the time they are generated until their ultimate disposal (a timeline often referred to as "cradle to grave").

According to the RCRA Subtitle C regulations, solid waste is defined as hazardous if it appears in one of the four hazardous waste classifications:

- F-List (non-specific source wastes as specified in 40 CFR 261.31), which includes wastes from common manufacturing and industrial processes, such as solvents used in cleaning and degreasing operations.
- K-list (source-specific waste as specified in 40 CFR 261.32), which includes certain wastes from specific industries such as petroleum or pesticide manufacturing.
- P-list and U-list (discarded commercial chemical products as specified in 40 CFR 261.33), which include commercial chemicals products in their unused form.

Additionally, a waste is classified as hazardous if it exhibits at least one of these four characteristics:

- **Ignitability** (as defined in 40 CFR 261.21), which refers to creation of fires under certain conditions; including materials that are spontaneously combustible or those that have a flash point less than 140 ^{0}F.
- **Corrosivity** (as defined in 40 CFR 261.22), which refers to capability to corrode metal containers; including materials with a pH less than or equal to 2 or greater than or equal to 12.5.
- **Reactivity** (as defined in 40 CFR 261.23), which refers to materials susceptible to unstable conditions such as explosions, toxic fumes, gases, or vapors when heated, compressed, or mixed with water under normal conditions.
- Toxicity (as defined in 40 CFR 261.24), which refers to substances that can induce harmful or fatal effects when ingested or absorbed, or inhaled.

7.2.3.2 Radioactive Waste Regulations

Although non-hazardous waste (MSW and industrial non-hazardous waste) and hazardous waste are regulated by RCRA, nuclear or radioactive waste is regulated in accordance with the Atomic Energy Act of 1954[9] by the Nuclear Regulatory Commission (NRC)[10] in the United States.

Radioactive wastes are characterized according to four categories: (1) **High-level waste** (HLW), (2) **Transuranic waste** (TRU), (3) **Low-level waste** (LLW), and (4) **Mill tailings**. Various radioactive wastes decay at different rates, but health and environmental dangers due to radiation may persist for hundreds or thousands of years.

HLW is typically liquid or solid waste that results from government defense related activities or from nuclear power plants and spent fuel assemblies. These wastes are extremely dangerous due to their heavy concentrations of radionuclides, and humans must not come into contact with them.

---

[7]http://en.wikipedia.org/wiki/Resource_Conservation_and_Recovery_Act#Subtitle_D:_Non-hazardous_Solid_Wastes
[8]http://en.wikipedia.org/wiki/Resource_Conservation_and_Recovery_Act#Subtitle_C:_.22Cradle_to_Grave.22_requirements
[9]http://en.wikipedia.org/wiki/Atomic_Energy_Act_of_1954
[10]http://www.nrc.gov/

TRU mainly results from the reprocessing of spent nuclear fuels and from the fabrication of nuclear weapons for defense projects. They are characterized by moderately penetrating radiation and a decay time of approximately twenty years until safe radionuclide levels are achieved. Following the passage of a reprocessing ban in 1977, most of this waste generation ended. Even though the ban was lifted in 1981, TRU continues to be rare because reprocessing of nuclear fuel is expensive. Further, because the extracted plutonium may be used to manufacture nuclear weapons, political and social pressures minimize these activities.

LLW wastes include much of the remainder of radioactive waste materials. They constitute over 80 percent of the volume of all nuclear wastes, but only about two percent of total radioactivity. Sources of LLW include all of the previously cited sources of HLW and TRU, plus wastes generated by hospitals, industrial plants, universities, and commercial laboratories. LLW is much less dangerous than HLW, and NRC regulations allow some very low-level wastes to be released to the environment. LLW may also be stored or buried until the isotopes decay to levels low enough such that it may be disposed of as non-hazardous waste. LLW disposal is managed at the state level, but requirements for operation and disposal are established by the USEPA and NRC. The Occupational Health and Safety Administration (OSHA)[11] is the agency in charge of setting the standards for workers that are exposed to radioactive materials.

Mill tailings generally consist of residues from the mining and extraction of uranium from its ore. There are more than 200 million tons of radioactive mill-tailings in the United States, and all of it is stored in sparsely populated areas within the western states, such as Arizona, New Mexico, Utah, and Wyoming. These wastes emit low-level radiation, and much of it is buried to reduce dangerous emissions.

7.2.3.3 Medical Waste Regulations

Another type of waste that is of environmental concern is **medical waste**. Medical waste is regulated by several federal agencies, including the USEPA, OSHA, the Center for Disease Control and Prevention (CDC)[12] of the U.S. Department of Health and Human Services, and the Agency for Toxic Substances and Disease Registry (ATSDR)[13] of the Public Health Service, U.S. Department of Health and Human Services[14] . During 1987-88, medical wastes and raw garbage washed up on beaches along the New Jersey Shore of the United States on several occasions (called, "Syringe Tide[15] ") which required closure of beaches. The U.S. Congress subsequently enacted the Medical Waste Tracking Act (MWTA)[16] to evaluate management issues and potential risks related to medical waste disposal. The seven types of wastes listed under MWTA include: (1) microbiological wastes (cultures and stocks of infectious wastes and associated biological media that can cause disease in humans); (2) human blood and blood products, including serum, plasma, and other blood components; (3) pathological wastes of human origin, including tissues, organs, and other body masses removed during surgeries or autopsies); (4) contaminated animal wastes (i.e. animal carcasses, body masses, and bedding exposed to infectious agents during medical research, pharmaceutical testing, or production of biological media); (5) isolation wastes (wastes associated with animals or humans known to be infected with highly communicable diseases); (6) contaminated sharps (including hypodermic needles, scalpels, and broken glass); and (7) uncontaminated sharps. In addition, the USEPA considered including any other wastes that had been in contact with infectious agents or blood (e.g. sponges, soiled dressings, drapes, surgical gloves, laboratory coats, slides).

LLW nuclear wastes are produced in hospitals by pharmaceutical laboratories and in performing nuclear medicine procedures (e.g. medical imaging to detect cancers and heart disease); however, the danger posed by these wastes is relatively low. A variety of hazardous substances have also been identified in medical wastes, including metals such as lead, cadmium, chromium, and mercury; and toxic organics such as dioxins and furans. All medical wastes represent a small fraction of total waste stream, estimated to constitute a maximum of approximately two percent. Medical wastes are commonly disposed of through incineration: as

---

[11]http://www.osha.gov/
[12]http://www.cdc.gov/
[13]http://www.atsdr.cdc.gov/
[14]http://www.hhs.gov/
[15]http://en.wikipedia.org/wiki/Syringe_Tide
[16]http://www.epa.gov/osw/nonhaz/industrial/medical/tracking.htm

with most wastes, the resulting volume is greatly reduced, and it assures the destruction and sterilization of infectious pathogens. Disadvantages include the potential of air pollution risks from dioxins and furans as well as the necessary disposal of potentially hazardous ash wastes. New options for disposal of medical wastes (including infectious wastes) are still being explored. Some other technologies include irradiation, microwaving, autoclaving, mechanical alternatives, and chemical disinfection, among others.

7.2.4 Environmental Concerns with Wastes

7.2.4.1 Managing Growing Waste Generation

An enormous quantity of wastes are generated and disposed of annually. Alarmingly, this quantity continues to increase on an annual basis. Industries generate and dispose over 7.6 billion tons of industrial solid wastes each year, and it is estimated that over 40 million tons of this waste is hazardous. Nuclear wastes as well as medical wastes are also increasing in quantity every year.

Generally speaking, developed nations generate more waste than developing nations due to higher rates of consumption. Not surprisingly, the United States generates more waste per capita than any other country. High waste per capita rates are also very common throughout Europe and developed nations in Asia and Oceania. In the United States, about 243 million tons (243 trillion kg) of MSW is generated per year, which is equal to about 4.3 pounds (1.95 kg) of waste per person per day. Nearly 34 percent of MSW is recovered and recycled or composted, approximately 12 percent is burned a combustion facilities, and the remaining 54 percent is disposed of in landfills. Waste stream percentages also vary widely by region. As an example, San Francisco, California captures and recycles nearly 75 percent of its waste material, whereas Houston, Texas recycles less than three percent.

With respect to waste mitigation options, landfilling is quickly evolving into a less desirable or feasible option. Landfill capacity in the United States has been declining primarily due to (a) older existing landfills that are increasingly reaching their authorized capacity, (b) the promulgation of stricter environmental regulations has made the permitting and siting of new landfills increasingly difficult, (c) public opposition (e.g. "Not In My Backyard" or NIMBYism[17]) delays or, in many cases, prevents the approval of new landfills or expansion of existing facilities. Ironically, much of this public opposition arises from misconceptions about landfilling and waste disposal practices that are derived from environmentally detrimental historic activities and practices that are no longer in existence. Regardless of the degree or extent of justification, NIMBYism is a potent opposition phenomenon, whether it is associated with landfills or other land use activities, such as airports, prisons, and wastewater treatment facilities.

7.2.4.2 Effects of Improper Waste Disposal and Unauthorized Releases

Prior to the passage of environmental regulations, wastes were disposed improperly without due consideration of potential effects on the public health and the environment. This practice has led to numerous contaminated sites where soils and groundwater have been contaminated and pose risk to the public safety. Of more than 36,000 environmentally impacted candidate sites, there are more than 1,400 sites listed under the Superfund program National Priority List (NPL) which require immediate cleanup resulting from acute, imminent threats to environmental and human health. The USEPA identified about 2,500 additional contaminated sites that eventually require remediation. The United States Department of Defense maintains 19,000 sites, many of which have been extensively contaminated from a variety of uses and disposal practices. Further, approximately 400,000 underground storage tanks have been confirmed or are suspected to be leaking, contaminating underlying soils and groundwater. Over $10 billion (more than $25 billion in current dollars) were specifically allocated by CERCLA and subsequent amendments to mitigate impacted sites. However, the USEPA has estimated that the value of environmental remediation exceeds $100 billion. Alarmingly, if past expenditures on NPL sites are extrapolated across remaining and proposed NPL sites, this total may be significantly higher – well into the trillions of dollars.

---

[17]http://en.wikipedia.org/wiki/NIMBY

It is estimated that more than 4,700 facilities in the United States currently treat, store or dispose of hazardous wastes. Of these, about 3,700 facilities that house approximately 64,000 solid waste management units (SWMUs) may require corrective action. Accidental spillage of hazardous wastes and nuclear materials due to anthropogenic operations or natural disasters has also caused enormous environmental damage as evidenced by the events such as the facility failure in Chernobyl, Ukraine[18] (formerly USSR) in 1986, the effects of Hurricane Katrina[19] that devastated New Orleans, Louisiana in 2005, and the 2011 Tōhoku earthquake and tsunami in Fukushima, Japan[20] .

7.2.4.3 Adverse Impacts on Public Health

A wide variety of chemicals are present within waste materials, many of which pose a significant environmental concern. Though the **leachate** generated from the wastes may contain toxic chemicals, the concentrations and variety of toxic chemicals are quite small compared to hazardous waste sites. For example, explosives and radioactive wastes are primarily located at Department of Energy (DOE) sites because many of these facilities have been historically used for weapons research, fabrication, testing, and training. Organic contaminants are largely found at oil refineries, or petroleum storage sites, and inorganic and pesticide contamination usually is the result of a variety of industrial activities as well as agricultural activities. Yet, soil and groundwater contamination are not the only direct adverse effects of improper waste management activities – recent studies have also shown that greenhouse gas emissions from the wastes are significant, exacerbating global climate change.

A wide range of toxic chemicals, with an equally wide distribution of respective concentrations, is found in waste streams. These compounds may be present in concentrations that alone may pose a threat to human health or may have a synergistic/cumulative effect due to the presence of other compounds. Exposure to hazardous wastes has been linked to many types of cancer, chronic illnesses, and abnormal reproductive outcomes such as birth defects, low birth weights, and spontaneous abortions. Many studies have been performed on major toxic chemicals found at hazardous waste sites incorporating epidemiological or animal tests to determine their toxic effects.

As an example, the effects of radioactive materials are classified as somatic or genetic. The **somatic effects** may be immediate or occur over a long period of time. Immediate effects from large radiation doses often produce nausea and vomiting, and may be followed by severe blood changes, hemorrhage, infection, and death. Delayed effects include leukemia, and many types of cancer including bone, lung, and breast cancer. **Genetic effects** have been observed in which gene mutations or chromosome abnormalities result in measurable harmful effects, such as decreases in life expectancy, increased susceptibility to sickness or disease, infertility, or even death during embryonic stages of life. Because of these studies, occupational dosage limits have been recommended by the National Council on Radiation Protection. Similar studies have been completed for a wide range of potentially hazardous materials. These studies have, in turn, been used to determine safe exposure levels for numerous exposure scenarios, including those that consider occupational safety and remediation standards for a variety of land use scenarios, including residential, commercial, and industrial land uses.

7.2.4.4 Adverse Impacts on the Environment

The chemicals found in wastes not only pose a threat to human health, but they also have profound effects on entire eco-systems. Contaminants may change the chemistry of waters and destroy aquatic life and underwater eco-systems that are depended upon by more complex species. Contaminants may also enter the food chain through plants or microbiological organisms, and higher, more evolved organisms bioaccumulate the wastes through subsequent ingestion. As the contaminants move farther up the food chain, the continued **bioaccumulation** results in increased contaminant mass and concentration. In many cases, toxic concentrations are reached, resulting in increased mortality of one or more species. As the populations of these

---

[18]http://en.wikipedia.org/wiki/Chernobyl_disaster
[19]http://en.wikipedia.org/wiki/Hurricane_Katrina
[20]http://en.wikipedia.org/wiki/2011_Tōhoku_earthquake_and_tsunami

species decrease, the natural inter-species balance is affected. With decreased numbers of predators or food sources, other species may be drastically affected, leading to a chain reaction that can affect a wide range of flora and fauna within a specific eco-system. As the eco-system continues to deviate from equilibrium, disastrous consequences may occur. Examples include the near extinction of the bald eagle due to persistent ingestion of DDT-impacted fish, and the depletion of oysters, crabs, and fish in Chesapeake Bay due to excessive quantities of fertilizers, toxic chemicals, farm manure wastes, and power plant emissions.

7.2.5 Waste Management Strategies

The long-recognized hierarchy of management of wastes, in order of preference consists of prevention, minimization, recycling and **reuse**, **biological treatment**, incineration, and landfill disposal (see Figure **Hierarchy of Waste Management** (Figure 7.1)).

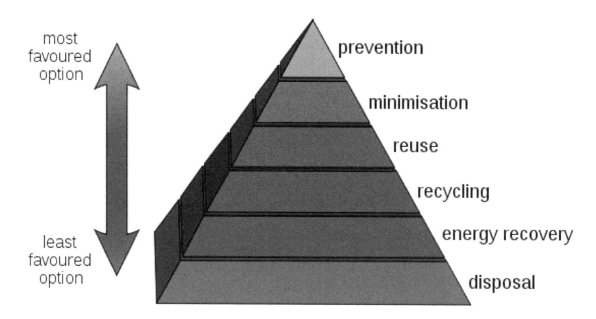

Figure 7.1: Hierarchy of Waste Management Figure shows the hierarchy of management of wastes in order or preference, starting with prevention as the most favorable to disposal as the least favorable option. *Source: Drstuey via Wikimedia Commons*[21]

7.2.5.1 Waste Prevention

The ideal waste management alternative is to prevent waste generation in the first place. Hence, **waste prevention** is a basic goal of all the waste management strategies. Numerous technologies can be employed throughout the manufacturing, use, or post-use portions of product life cycles to eliminate waste and, in turn, reduce or **prevent pollution**. Some representative strategies include environmentally conscious manufacturing methods that incorporate less hazardous or harmful materials, the use of modern leakage detection systems for material storage, innovative chemical neutralization techniques to reduce reactivity, or water saving technologies that reduce the need for fresh water inputs.

---

[21]http://commons.wikimedia.org/wiki/File:Waste_hierarchy.svg

7.2.5.2 Waste Minimization

In many cases, wastes cannot be outright eliminated from a variety of processes. However, numerous strategies can be implemented to reduce or minimize waste generation. **Waste minimization**, or source reduction, refers to the collective strategies of design and fabrication of products or services that minimize the amount of generated waste and/or reduce the toxicity of the resultant waste. Often these efforts come about from identified trends or specific products that may be causing problems in the waste stream and the subsequent steps taken to halt these problems. In industry, waste can be reduced by reusing materials, using less hazardous substitute materials, or by modifying components of design and processing. Many benefits can be realized by waste minimization or source reduction, including reduced use of natural resources and the reduction of toxicity of wastes.

Waste minimization strategies are extremely common in manufacturing applications; the savings of material use preserves resources but also saves significant manufacturing related costs. Advancements in streamlined packaging reduces material use, increased distribution efficiency reduces fuel consumption and resulting air emissions. Further, engineered building materials can often be designed with specific favorable properties that, when accounted for in overall structural design, can greatly reduce the overall mass and weight of material needed for a given structure. This reduces the need for excess material and reduces the waste associated with component fabrication.

The dry cleaning industry provides an excellent example of product substitution to reduce toxic waste generation. For decades, dry cleaners used tetrachloroethylene, or "perc" as a dry cleaning solvent. Although effective, tetrachloroethylene is a relatively toxic compound. Additionally, it is easily introduced into the environment, where it is highly recalcitrant due to its physical properties. Further, when its degradation occurs, the intermediate daughter products generated are more toxic to human health and the environment.

Because of its toxicity and impact on the environment, the dry cleaning industry has adopted new practices and increasingly utilizes less toxic replacement products, including petroleum-based compounds. Further, new emerging technologies are incorporating carbon dioxide and other relatively harmless compounds. While these substitute products have in many cases been mandated by government regulation, they have also been adopted in response to consumer demands and other market-based forces.

7.2.5.3 Recycling and Reuse

Recycling refers to recovery of useful materials such as glass, paper, plastics, wood, and metals from the waste stream so they may be incorporated into the fabrication of new products. With greater incorporation of recycled materials, the required use of raw materials for identical applications is reduced. Recycling reduces the need of natural resource exploitation for raw materials, but it also allows waste materials to be recovered and utilized as valuable resource materials. Recycling of wastes directly conserves natural resources, reduces energy consumption and emissions generated by extraction of virgin materials and their subsequent manufacture into finished products, reduces overall energy consumption and greenhouse gas emissions that contribute to the global climate change, and reduces the incineration or landfilling of the materials that have been recycled. Moreover, recycling creates several economic benefits, including the potential to create job markets and drive growth.

Common recycled materials include paper, plastics, glass, aluminum, steel, and wood. Additionally, many construction materials can be reused, including concrete, asphalt materials, masonry, and reinforcing steel. "Green" plant-based wastes are often recovered and immediately reused for mulch or fertilizer applications. Many industries also recover various by-products and/or refine and "re-generate" solvents for reuse. Examples include copper and nickel recovery from metal finishing processes; the recovery of oils, fats, and plasticizers by solvent extraction from filter media such as activated carbon and clays; and acid recovery by spray roasting, ion exchange, or crystallization. Further, a range of used food-based oils are being recovered and utilized in "biodiesel" applications.

Numerous examples of successful recycling and reuse efforts are encountered every day. In some cases, the recycled materials are used as input materials and are heavily processed into end products. Common examples include the use of scrap paper for new paper manufacturing, or the processing of old aluminum cans into new aluminum products. In other cases, reclaimed materials undergo little or no processing prior to their re-use. Some common examples include the use of tree waste as wood chips, or the use of brick and other fixtures into new structural construction. In any case, the success of recycling depends on effective collection and processing of recyclables, markets for reuse (e.g. manufacturing and/or applications that utilize recycled materials), and public acceptance and promotion of recycled products and applications utilizing recycled materials.

7.2.5.4 Biological Treatment

Landfill disposal of wastes containing significant organic fractions is increasingly discouraged in many countries, including the United States. Such disposal practices are even prohibited in several European countries. Since landfilling does not provide an attractive management option, other techniques have been identified. One option is to treat waste so that biodegradable materials are degraded and the remaining inorganic waste fraction (known as residuals) can be subsequently disposed or used for a beneficial purpose.

Biodegradation of wastes can be accomplished by using **aerobic** composting, **anaerobicdigestion**, or **mechanical biological treatment** (MBT) methods. If the organic fraction can be separated from inorganic material, aerobic composting or anaerobic digestion can be used to degrade the waste and convert it into usable **compost**. For example, organic wastes such as food waste, yard waste, and animal manure that consist of naturally degrading bacteria can be converted under controlled conditions into compost, which can then be utilized as natural fertilizer. Aerobic composting is accomplished by placing selected proportions of organic waste into piles, rows or vessels, either in open conditions or within closed buildings fitted with gas collection and treatment systems. During the process, bulking agents such as wood chips are added to the waste material to enhance the aerobic degradation of organic materials. Finally, the material is allowed to stabilize and mature during a curing process where pathogens are concurrently destroyed. The end-products of the composting process include carbon dioxide, water, and the usable compost material.

Compost material may be used in a variety of applications. In addition to its use as a soil amendment for plant cultivation, compost can be used remediate soils, groundwater, and stormwater. Composting can be labor-intensive, and the quality of the compost is heavily dependent on proper control of the composting process. Inadequate control of the operating conditions can result in compost that is unsuitable for beneficial applications. Nevertheless, composting is becoming increasingly popular; composting diverted 82 million tons of waste material away the landfill waste stream in 2009, increased from 15 million tons in 1980. This diversion also prevented the release of approximately 178 million metric tons of carbon dioxide in 2009 – an amount equivalent to the yearly carbon dioxide emissions of 33 million automobiles.

In some cases, aerobic processes are not feasible. As an alternative, anaerobic processes may be utilized. Anaerobic digestion consists of degrading mixed or sorted organic wastes in vessels under anaerobic conditions. The anaerobic degradation process produces a combination of methane and carbon dioxide (biogas) and residuals (biosolids). Biogas can be used for heating and electricity production, while residuals can be used as fertilizers and soil amendments. Anaerobic digestion is a preferred degradation for wet wastes as compared to the preference of composting for dry wastes. The advantage of anaerobic digestion is biogas collection; this collection and subsequent beneficial utilization makes it a preferred alternative to landfill disposal of wastes. Also, waste is degraded faster through anaerobic digestion as compared to landfill disposal.

Another waste treatment alternative, mechanical biological treatment (MBT), is not common in the United States. However, this alternative is widely used in Europe. During implementation of this method, waste material is subjected to a combination of mechanical and biological operations that reduce volume through the degradation of organic fractions in the waste. Mechanical operations such as sorting, shredding, and crushing prepare the waste for subsequent biological treatment, consisting of either aerobic composting or anaerobic digestion. Following the biological processes, the reduced waste mass may be subjected to incineration.

7.2.5.5 Incineration

Waste degradation not only produces useful solid end-products (such as compost), degradation by-products can also be used as a beneficial energy source. As discussed above, anaerobic digestion of waste can generate biogas, which can be captured and incorporated into electricity generation. Alternatively, waste can be directly incinerated to produce energy. Incineration consists of waste combustion at very high temperatures to produce electrical energy. The byproduct of incineration is ash, which requires proper characterization prior to disposal, or in some cases, beneficial re-use. While public perception of incineration can be negative, this is often based reactions to older, less efficient technologies. New incinerators are cleaner, more flexible and efficient, and are an excellent means to convert **waste to energy** while reducing the volume of waste. Incineration can also offset fossil fuel use and reduce greenhouse gas (GHG) emissions (Bogner et al., 2007 (p. 278)). It is widely used in developed countries due to landfill space limitations. It is estimated that about 130 million tons of waste are annually combusted in more than 600 plants in 35 countries. Further, incineration is often used to effectively mitigate hazardous wastes such as chlorinated hydrocarbons, oils, solvents, medical wastes, and pesticides.

Despite all these advantages, incineration is often viewed negatively because of the resulting air emissions, the creation of daughter chemical compounds, and production of ash, which is commonly toxic. Currently, many 'next generation" systems are being researched and developed, and the USEPA is developing new regulations to carefully monitor incinerator air emissions under the Clean Air Act[22] .

7.2.5.6 Landfill Disposal

Despite advances in reuse and recycling, landfill disposal remains the primary waste disposal method in the United States. As previously mentioned, the rate of MSW generation continues to increase, but overall landfill capacity is decreasing. New regulations concerning proper waste disposal and the use of innovative liner systems to minimize the potential of groundwater contamination from leachate infiltration and migration have resulted in a substantial increase in the costs of landfill disposal. Also, public opposition to landfills continues to grow, partially inspired by memories of historic uncontrolled dumping practices the resulting undesirable side effects of uncontrolled vectors, contaminated groundwater, unmitigated odors, and subsequent diminished property values.

Landfills can be designed and permitted to accept hazardous wastes in accordance with RCRA Subtitle C regulations, or they may be designed and permitted to accept municipal solid waste in accordance with RCRA Subtitle D regulations. Regardless of their waste designation, landfills are engineered structures consisting of bottom and side liner systems, leachate collection and removal systems, final cover systems, gas collection and removal systems, and groundwater monitoring systems (Sharma and Reddy, 2004 (p. 278)). An extensive permitting process is required for siting, designing and operating landfills. Post-closure monitoring of landfills is also typically required for at least 30 years. Because of their design, wastes within landfills are degraded anaerobically. During degradation, biogas is produced and collected. The collection systems prevent uncontrolled subsurface gas migration and reduce the potential for an explosive condition. The captured gas is often used in cogeneration facilities for heating or electricity generation. Further, upon closure, many landfills undergo "land recycling" and redeveloped as golf courses, recreational parks, and other beneficial uses.

Wastes commonly exist in a dry condition within landfills, and as a result, the rate of waste degradation is commonly very slow. These slow degradation rates are coupled with slow rates of degradation-induced settlement, which can in turn complicate or reduce the potential for beneficial land re-use at the surface. Recently, the concept of bioreactor landfills has emerged, which involves recirculation of leachate and/or injection of selected liquids to increase the moisture in the waste, which in turn induces rapid degradation. The increased rates of degradation increase the rate of biogas production, which increases the potential of beneficial energy production from biogas capture and utilization.

---

[22]http://www.epa.gov/air/caa/

7.2.6 Summary

Many wastes, such as high-level radioactive wastes, will remain dangerous for thousands of years, and even MSW can produce dangerous leachate that could devastate an entire eco-system if allowed infiltrate into and migrate within groundwater. In order to protect human health and the environment, environmental professionals must deal with problems associated with increased generation of waste materials. The solution must focus on both reducing the sources of wastes as well as the safe disposal of wastes. It is, therefore, extremely important to know the sources, classifications, chemical compositions, and physical characteristics of wastes, and to understand the strategies for managing them.

Waste management practices vary not only from country to country, but they also vary based on the type and composition of waste. Regardless of the geographical setting of the type of waste that needs to be managed, the governing principle in the development of any waste management plan is resource conservation. Natural resource and energy conservation is achieved by managing materials more efficiently. Reduction, reuse, and recycling are primary strategies for effective reduction of waste quantities. Further, proper waste management decisions have increasing importance, as the consequences of these decisions have broader implications with respect to greenhouse gas emissions and global climate change. As a result, several public and private partnership programs are under development with the goal of waste reduction through the adoption of new and innovative waste management technologies. Because waste is an inevitable by-product of civilization, the successful implementation of these initiatives will have a direct effect on the enhanced quality of life for societies worldwide.

7.2.7 Review Questions

Question 7.2.1
How is hazardous waste defined according to the Resource Conservation and Recovery Act (RCRA)? In your opinion, is this definition appropriate? Explain.

Question 7.2.2
Explain specific characteristics of radioactive and medical wastes that make their management more problematic than MSW.

Question 7.2.3
Compare and contrast environmental concerns with wastes in a rural versus urban setting.

Question 7.2.4
What are the pros and cons of various waste management strategies? Do you agree or disagree with the general waste management hierarchy?

Question 7.2.5
Explain the advantages and disadvantages of biological treatment and incineration of wastes.

7.2.8 References

Bogner, J., Ahmed, M.A., Diaz, C. Faaij, A., Gao, Q., Hashimoto,S., et al. (2007). Waste Management, In B. Metz, O.R. Davidson, P.R. Bosch, R. Dave, L.A. Meyer (Eds.), *Climate Change 2007: Mitigation. Contribution of Working Group III to the Fourth Assessment Report of the Intergovernmental Panel on Climate Change* (pp. 585-618). Cambridge University Press, Cambridge, United Kingdom and New York, NY, USA. Retrieved August 19, 2010 from http://www.ipcc.ch/pdf/assessment-report/ar4/wg3/ar4-wg3-chapter10.pdf[23]

Sharma, H.D. & Reddy, K.R. (2004). *Geoenvironmental Engineering: Site Remediation, Waste Containment, and Emerging Waste Management Technologies.* Hoboken, NJ: John Wiley.

---

[23]http://www.ipcc.ch/pdf/assessment-report/ar4/wg3/ar4-wg3-chapter10.pdf

7.3 Case Study: Electronic Waste and Extended Producer Responsibility[24]

Electronic waste, commonly known as e-waste, refers to discarded electronic products such as televisions, computers and computer peripherals (e.g. monitors, keyboards, disk drives, and printers), telephones and cellular phones, audio and video equipment, video cameras, fax and copy machines, video game consoles, and others (see Figure **Electronic Waste** (Figure 7.2)).

Figure 7.2: Electronic Waste Photograph shows many computers piled up in a parking lot as waste. *Source: Bluedisk via Wikimedia Commons*[25]

In the United States, it is estimated that about 3 million tons of e-waste are generated each year. This waste quantity includes approximately 27 million units of televisions, 205 million units of computer products, and 140 million units of cell phones. Less than 15 to 20 percent of the e-waste is recycled or refurbished; the remaining percentage is commonly disposed of in landfills and/or incinerated. It should be noted that e-waste constitutes less than 4 percent of total solid waste generated in the United States. However, with tremendous growth in technological advancements in the electronics industry, many electronic products are becoming obsolete quickly, thus increasing the production of e-waste at a very rapid rate. The quantities of e-waste generated are also increasing rapidly in other countries such as India and China due to high demand for computers and cell phones.

---

[24]This content is available online at <http://legacy.cnx.org/content/m41571/1.3/>.

[25]http://commons.wikimedia.org/wiki/File:Computer_Recycling.JPG

In addition to the growing quantity of e-waste, the hazardous content of e-waste is a major environmental concern and poses risks to the environment if these wastes are improperly managed once they have reached the end of their useful life. Many e-waste components consist of toxic substances, including heavy metals such as lead, copper, zinc, cadmium, and mercury as well as organic contaminants, such as flame retardants (polybrominated biphenyls and polybrominated diphenylethers). The release of these substances into the environment and subsequent human exposure can lead to serious health and pollution issues. Concerns have also been raised with regards to the release of toxic constituents of e-waste into the environment if landfilling and/or incineration options are used to manage the e-waste.

Various regulatory and voluntary programs have been instituted to promote reuse, recycling and safe disposal of bulk e-waste. Reuse and refurbishing has been promoted to reduce raw material use energy consumption, and water consumption associated with the manufacture of new products. Recycling and recovery of elements such as lead, copper, gold, silver and platinum can yield valuable resources which otherwise may cause pollution if improperly released into the environment. The recycling and recovery operations have to be conducted with extreme care, as the exposure of e-waste components can result in adverse health impacts to the workers performing these operations. For economic reasons, recycled e-waste is often exported to other countries for recovery operations. However, lax regulatory environments in many of these countries can lead to unsafe practices or improper disposal of bulk residual e-waste, which in turn can adversely affect vulnerable populations.

In the United States, there are no specific federal laws dealing with e-waste, but many states have recently developed e-waste regulations that promote environmentally sound management. For example, the State of California passed the Electronic Waste Recycling Act[26] in 2003 to foster recycling, reuse, and environmentally sound disposal of residual bulk e-waste. Yet, in spite of recent regulations and advances in reuse, recycling and proper disposal practices, additional sustainable strategies to manage e-waste are urgently needed.

One sustainable strategy used to manage e-waste is extended producer responsibility (EPR), also known as product stewardship. This concept holds manufacturers liable for the entire life-cycle costs associated with the electronic products, including disposal costs, and encourages the use of environmental-friendly manufacturing processes and products. Manufacturers can pursue EPR in multiple ways, including reuse/refurbishing, buy-back, recycling, and energy production or beneficial reuse applications. Life-cycle assessment and life-cycle cost methodologies may be used to compare the environmental impacts of these different waste management options. Incentives or financial support is also provided by some government and/or regulatory agencies to promote EPR. The use of non-toxic and easily recyclable materials in product fabrication is a major component of any EPR strategy. A growing number of companies (e.g. Dell, Sony, HP) are embracing EPR with various initiatives towards achieving sustainable e-waste management.

EPR is a preferred strategy because the manufacturer bears a financial and legal responsibility for their products; hence, they have an incentive to incorporate green design and manufacturing practices that incorporate easily recyclable and less toxic material components while producing electronics with longer product lives. One obvious disadvantage of EPR is the higher manufacturing cost, which leads to increased cost of electronics to consumers.

There is no specific federal law requiring EPR for electronics, but the United States Environmental Protection Agency (USEPA) undertook several initiatives to promote EPR to achieve the following goals: (1) foster environmentally conscious design and manufacturing, (2) increase purchasing and use of more environmentally sustainable electronics, and (3) increase safe, environmentally sound reuse and recycling of used electronics. To achieve these goals, USEPA has been engaged in various activities, including the promotion of environmental considerations in product design, the development of evaluation tools for environmental attributes of electronic products, the encouragement of recycling (or e-cycling), and the support of programs to reduce e-waste, among others. More than 20 states in the United States and various organizations worldwide have already developed laws and/or policies requiring EPR in some form when dealing with electronic products. For instance, the New York State Wireless Recycling Act[27] emphasizes that authorized retailers and service providers should be compelled to participate in take-back programs, thus allowing increased

---

[26]http://www.calrecycle.ca.gov/electronics/act2003/
[27]http://www.dec.ny.gov/chemical/8818.html

recycling and reuse of e-waste. Similarly, Maine is the first U.S. state to adopt a household e-waste law with EPR.

In Illinois, Electronic Products Recycling & Reuse Act[28] requires the electronic manufacturers to participate in the management of discarded and unwanted electronic products from residences. The Illinois EPA has also compiled e-waste collection site locations[29] where the residents can give away their discarded electronic products at no charge. Furthermore, USEPA compiled a list of local programs and manufacturers/retailers[30] that can help consumers to properly donate or recycle e-waste.

Overall, the growing quantities and environmental hazards associated with electronic waste are of major concern to waste management professionals worldwide. Current management strategies, including recycling and refurbishing, have not been successful. As a result, EPR regulations are rapidly evolving throughout the world to promote sustainable management of e-waste. However, neither a consistent framework nor assessment tools to evaluate EPR have been fully developed.

7.4 Government and Laws on the Environment[31]

7.4.1 Learning Objectives

After reading this section, students should be able to

- understand the purpose of government regulations set for the protection of human health and the environment
- distinguish the current environmental laws and regulations for various types of pollutants present in different media or phases of the environment
- discern the need for future environmental laws as related to the sustainability of industrial activity and the economy

7.4.2 Introduction

In the United States, the laws and regulations pertaining to the protection of the environment have been enacted by the U.S. Congress. The U.S. Environmental Protection Agency (EPA) is authorized to enforce the environmental laws and to implement the environmental regulations. The United States environmental laws cover various phases of the environment such as water, air, and hazardous waste, where most of the regulations have been based on the risk assessment of the pollutants. The major environmental laws and regulations are briefly listed in the Table **Summary of Major Environmental Laws** (Table 7.1).

Environmental Issue	Description	Acronym	Year Enacted
Water	Federal Water Pollution Control Act Amendment Clean Water Act	FWPC ACWA	1956 1972 1972
			continued on next page

[28]http://www.epa.state.il.us/land/electronic-waste-recycling/index.html

[29]http://www.epa.state.il.us/land/electronic-waste-recycling/consumer-education.html

[30]http://www.epa.gov/osw/conserve/materials/ecycling/donate.htm

[31]This content is available online at <http://legacy.cnx.org/content/m41570/1.3/>.

Drinking Water	Safe Drinking Water Act Amendments	SDWA	1974 1986, 1996
Air	Clean Air Act Amendments	CAA	1955 1990
Hazardous Wastes	Resource Conservation and Recovery Act Hazardous and Solid Wastes Amendment Comprehensive Environmental Response, Compensation and Liability Act (Superfund) Superfund Amendments and Reauthorization Act	RCRA HSWA CERCLA SARA	1976 1984 1980 1986
Oil Spills	Oil Pollution Act	OPA	1990
Toxic Substances	Toxic Substances Control Act	TSCA	1976
Pesticides	Federal Insecticide, Fungicide, and Rodenticide Act	FIRFA	1972
Pollution Prevention	Pollution Prevention Act	PPA	1990
Workplace Health and Safety	Occupational Safety and Health Act Amendment	OSHA	1970 1990

Table 7.1: **Summary of Major Environmental Laws** Table lists major environmental laws enacted from the 1950s onward.

7.4.3 Water

7.4.3.1 Clean Water Act

To protect the surface waters of the United States such as lakes, rivers, streams, shorelines and estuaries, the Federal Water Pollution Control Act was established in 1956. The amendment to the Federal Water Pollution Control Act (FWPCA) of 1972 focused on surface water quality goals, effluent limits based on available technology, and a national discharge permit system. The FWPCA (1972) introduced effluent limits for chemical substances in surface waters in conjunction with a National Pollutant Discharge Elimination System (NPDES) allowing for enforceable control over permits obtained by industry for discharge of effluents containing pollutants into natural water systems. The Clean Water Act (CWA) of 1977 placed emphasis on the control of waterborne toxic substances released into natural surface waters. The CWA introduced a Priority List of Pollutants which includes 127 toxic chemical substances including synthetic organic compounds and heavy metals. In accordance with the CWA, the EPA must establish effluent limitations for chemical substances on the List of Priority Pollutants for discharge by industrial facilities and municipal wastewater treatment plants.

The CWA aims to provide a system of national effluent standards for each industry, a set of water quality standards, an enforceable discharge permit program, provisions for special wastes such as toxic chemicals and oil spills, and a construction program for publicly owned treatment works (POTWs). Municipal wastewater treatment plants are examples of POTWs. The NPDES permits are issued according to the effluent limitations required by the Federal Water Pollution Control Act and the Clean Water Act. Because of higher costs associated with treatment of industrial effluents before discharge into natural waters which requires an NPDES permit, many industries discharge to a municipal sewer and have their wastes treated at the POTW following pretreatment regulations overseen by the POTW. In addition, the CWA provides permits for stormwater and other non-point source (see definition in Module "Sustainable Stormwater Management") pollution to prevent stormwater runoff over contaminated land and paved areas from polluting surface waters such as rivers and lakes. Stormwater pollution prevention plans and stormwater treatment facilities have to be implemented to avoid contamination of clean water.

7.4.3.2 Safe Drinking Water Act (SDWA)

The Safe Drinking Water Act (SDWA) of 1974 was established to prevent potential contamination of groundwater, which may serve as a source of drinking water. The SDWA amendments of 1986 and 1996 established standards for water quality, which apply to drinking water as supplied by the public water supply systems. The groundwater standards are also used to determine groundwater protection regulations under a number of other statutes. The EPA has established a set of standards for unhealthful contaminants in drinking water referred to as the National Primary Drinking Water Regulations (NPDWRs) as required by the SDWA amendment of 1986. The list of regulated contaminants includes synthetic organic compounds, inorganic species such as heavy metals, radionuclides, and pathogenic microorganisms. The NPDWR standards include both enforceable Maximum Contaminant Levels (MCLs) and nonenforceable Maximum Contaminant Level Goals (MCLGs) used as health goals. The MCLs are achieved in the drinking water treatment plant using the Best Available Technology (BAT) for removal of the contaminants from water. Many of the drinking water MCLGs have also become the working standards for organic and inorganic chemical contaminants as "Superfund" regulations for hazardous waste site cleanups; Superfund regulations deal with the cleanup of abandoned sites containing hazardous wastes. Table **Example Drinking Water Standards** (Table 7.2) lists the MCLs and MCLGs for several chemical contaminants. The Safe Drinking Water Act amendment of 1986 also introduced Secondary Maximum Contaminant Levels (SMCLs) that act as recommended maximum levels for contaminants, which do not have an adverse health effect but are mostly related to esthetics of water (such as color and odor). The use of sound science and risk-based standard setting for the NPDWRs is included in the SDWA amendment of 1996; new contaminants may be added in the future using a list of candidate contaminants. In addition, the SDWA amendment of 1996 provides guidance to individual states and industry toward protection of source water and well-head areas used for public water supply.

Organic Contaminant	MCL (mg/L)	MCLG (mg/L)	Potential Health Effect		Inorganic Contaminant	MCL (mg/L)	MCLG (mg/L)	Potential Health Effect
Benzene	0.005	Zero	Cancer		Arsenic	0.010	Zero	Nervous system, cancer
continued on next page								

Atrazine	0.003	0.003	Liver, kidney, lung		Chromium (total)	0.1	0.1	Liver, kidney, circulatory system
Pentachlorophenol 0.001		Zero	Cancer		Cyanide	0.2	0.2	Central nervous system
Polychlorinated 0.0005 biphenyls (PCBs)		Zero	Cancer		Nitrate	10	10	Blue baby syndrome
Benzo(a)pyrene 0.0002		Zero	Cancer		Mercury	0.002	0.002	Kidney, central nervous system

Table 7.2: **Example Drinking Water Standards (NPDWRs)** Table lists the drinking water maximum contaminant levels and the maximum contaminant level goals for a variety of chemical contaminants, along with the potential health effects that accompany these chemicals. *Source: A. Khodadoust using data from U.S. EPA, 2011*[32]

7.4.4 Clean Air Act

The Clean Air Act (CAA) of 1955 and subsequent amendments were established to improve the quality of the air resources in the United States. The CAA amendments of 1990 have provisions for maintenance of ambient air quality to promote and improve public health. Enforcement of regulations is carried out through the use of emission standards on stationary and mobile sources of air pollution that are directed at decreasing the production of air contaminants from various sources. A National Ambient Air Quality Standard (NAAQS) is the maximum permissible concentration of a contaminant in ambient air. Seven classes of air pollutants for which the NAAQS has been established are referred to as criteria pollutants: lead, nitrogen oxides, sulfur oxides, ozone, particulate matter smaller than 10 μm (PM_{10}), hydrocarbons and carbon monoxide. Some pollutants have short-term and long-term standards designed to protect against acute and chronic health effects, respectively. In addition to criteria pollutants, Hazardous Air Pollutants (HAPs) are those pollutants that are known or suspect carcinogens, or may lead to other serious health effects over a longer period of exposure. The main sources of HAPs are industrial and automotive emissions. The CAA amendments of 1990 have provisions for the reduction in emission of HAPs that lead to lower concentrations of HAPs in ambient air.

The CAA amendments of 1990 established a permit program for larger sources of air emissions, where permits are issued by states or by the EPA. Information on the types of pollutants that are emitted, the emission levels, the monitoring of the emissions, and the plans to decrease the emissions is included in the permit. All applicable information on the emissions and legal responsibilities of the business are conveyed by the permit system. The 1990 CAA amendments provide several market-based approaches to businesses to reach their pollution cleanup thresholds such as pollution allowances that can be traded. In addition, economic incentives are provided to businesses to trade the extra credit for operations requiring less cleanup in exchange with the lesser credit given for operations requiring more cleanup.

The CAA aims to reduce emissions from mobile sources such as cars and other vehicles, and to develop cleaner fuels. To maintain higher octane ranking in unleaded gasoline, the refiners have used more volatile

---

[32]http://water.epa.gov/drink/contaminants/

fractions in unleaded gasoline formulas, leading to release of volatile organic compounds (VOCs). Under the CAA amendments of 1990, gasoline fuels are required to contain less volatile fractions, to contain oxyfuel compounds (such as alcohol-based oxygenated compounds) for reduced production of carbon monoxide in cold weather, to contain detergents for smoother running of engines, and to contain less sulfur in diesel fuel. The production of cars capable of burning cleaner fuels such as natural gas or alcohol is mandated by the CAA amendments of 1990.

Emission of sulfur dioxide (SO_2) and nitrogen oxides (NO_x) from combustion processes contribute to the formation of acid rain. Most of the sulfur dioxide emitted annually in the United States is produced from the burning of high sulfur coal by electric utilities, resulting in acid rain with adverse impacts on the environment and public health. Reduction of sulfur dioxide emissions is mandated by the CAA. Pollution allowances (up to prescribed thresholds by EPA) for sulfur dioxide have been established by the EPA for each utility, where allowances may be traded between utilities or within a company. Companies with emissions less than the EPA allowance may trade their excess allowance with companies with allowance deficits, preventing severe hardships to those utilities that that are dependent on high-sulfur coal. The CAA has also set provisions for reduction of NO_x emissions. A market-based approach is employed by the 1990 CAA amendments to eliminate ozone-destroying chemical substances (such as chlorofluorocarbons) that deplete the ozone layer using a phasing-out schedule by terminating the production of these chemicals in accordance with the Montreal Protocol (1989). The recycling of chlorofluorocarbons (CFCs) and the labeling of ozone-friendly substitute chemicals are mandated by the CAA.

7.4.5 Hazardous Wastes

Hazardous wastes are wastes that pose a health and safety risk to humans and to the environment. The EPA designates hazardous wastes as wastes which contain components that have one of the four general characteristics of reactivity, corrosivity, ignitability and toxicity, in addition to other EPA classifications of hazardous wastes. The laws and regulations governing the management of hazardous wastes and materials may be divided into two categories: present and future hazardous materials and wastes are regulated under the Resource Conservation and Recovery Act (RCRA), while past and usually abandoned hazardous waste sites are managed under the Comprehensive Environmental Response, Compensation and Liability Act (CERCLA).

7.4.5.1 Resource Conservation and Recovery Act (RCRA)

The RCRA (1976) aims to achieve environmentally sound management of both hazardous and nonhazardous wastes. As required by RCRA, the EPA established a cradle-to-grave (see Module **Life Cycle Assessment** (Section 9.2)) hazardous material management system in an attempt to track hazardous material or waste from its point of generation to its ultimate point of disposal, where the generators of hazardous materials have to attach a "manifest" form to their hazardous materials shipments. The management of hazardous wastes including the transport, treatment, storage and disposal of hazardous wastes is regulated under the RCRA. For hazardous wastes disposal, this procedure will result in the shipment and arrival of those wastes at a permitted disposal site. The RCRA also promotes the concept of resource recovery to decrease the generation of waste materials. The RCRA, as amended, contains 10 subtitles. Subtitle C, for example, authorizes regulations for management of hazardous wastes and Subtitle I deals with regulation of Underground Storage Tanks (USTs).

Hazardous waste management facilities receiving hazardous wastes for treatment, storage or disposal are referred to as treatment, storage and disposal facilities (TSDFs). The EPA closely regulates the TSDFs so that they operate properly for protection of human health and the environment. TSDFs may be owned and operated by independent companies that receive wastes from a number of waste generators, or by the generators of waste themselves. TSDFs include landfills, incinerators, impoundments, holding tanks, and many other treatment units designed for safe and efficient management of hazardous waste. The EPA closely regulates the construction and operation of these TSDFs, where the operators of TSDFs must obtain a permit from the EPA delineating the procedures for the operation of these facilities. The operators must also provide insurance and adequate financial backing. The shipping of wastes to a TSDF or recycler is frequently less expensive than obtaining and meeting all the requirements for a storage permit.

The major amendment to Resource Conservation and Recovery Act was instituted in 1984 as the Hazardous and Solid Waste Amendments (HSWA). The HSWA provides regulation for leaking underground storage tanks (leaking USTs) affecting groundwater pollution. The RCRA regulates USTs containing hazardous wastes. The HSWA added Subtitle I to RCRA to provide for regulation of new and existing UST systems, including corrosion protection for all USTs to prevent the leaking of hazardous waste from corroded USTs. As part of the Superfund Amendments Reauthorization Act (SARA, 1986), Subtitle I to RCRA was modified to provide for remedies and compensation due to petroleum releases from UST systems. In addition, the HSWA provides for regulation to prevent the contamination of groundwater by hazardous wastes, where the EPA restricts the disposal of hazardous wastes in landfills due to the migration of hazardous constituents from the waste placed in landfills.

7.4.5.2 Comprehensive Environmental Response, Composition, and Liability Act (CERCLA)

The CERCLA (1980) also known as 'Superfund" aims to provide for liability, compensation and the cleanup of inactive or abandoned hazardous waste disposal sites, and for emergency response to releases of hazardous materials into the environment. CERCLA gives the EPA the power and the funding to clean up abandoned hazardous waste sites and to respond to emergencies related to hazardous waste releases. The Superfund Amendments and Reauthorization Act (SARA) of 1986 solidified many of the provisions of CERCLA such as increasing the authority of the EPA to respond to remediation of hazardous waste sites with a faster startup for cleanup of contaminated sites, and greatly increased the available trust fund for cleanup.

The EPA uses the National Priority List (NPL) to identify contaminated sites that present a risk to public health or the environment and that may be eligible for Superfund money. A numeric ranking system known as the Hazard Ranking System (HRS) has been established to determine the eligibility of contaminated sites for Superfund money, where sites with high HRS scores are most likely to be added to the NPL. The National Contingency Plan (NCP) provides guidance for the initial assessment and the HRS ranking of contaminated sites. After the initial assessment of a contaminated site, a remedial investigation is carried out where the NCP provides for a detailed evaluation of the risks associated with that site. A remedial investigation results in a work plan, which leads to the selection of an appropriate remedy referred to as a feasibility study. The feasibility study assesses several remedial alternatives, resulting in Record of Decision (ROD) as the basis for the design of the selected alternative. The degree of cleanup is specified by the NCP in accordance with several criteria such as the degree of hazard to the public health and the environment, where the degree of cleanup varies for different contaminated sites.

A separate addition to the provisions of CERCLA is Title III of SARA known as the Emergency Planning and Community Right-to-Know Act (EPCRA). The State Emergency Response Commission must be notified by a regulated facility that has extremely hazardous substances exceeding the EPA specified Threshold Planning Quantities. The community is responsible for establishing Local Emergency Planning Committees to develop a chemical emergency response plan which provides information on the regulated facilities, emergency response procedures, training and evacuation plans. The awareness of a community about the specific chemicals present in the community is an integral part of the Community's Right-to-Know, in addition to public information about potential hazards from those chemicals. The EPCRA also stipulates that each year those facilities that release chemicals above specified threshold levels should submit a Toxics Release Inventory (TRI) according to EPA specifications. The TRI includes information on both accidental and routine releases in addition to off-site transfers of waste. The availability of the TRI data to the public has led to serious consideration by industry to control their previously unregulated and uncontrolled emissions due to the heightened public concern about the presence and the releases of chemicals in their community.

7.4.6 Oil Pollution Act

The Oil Pollution Act (1990), or OPA, was established in response to the Exxon Valdez oil spill incident[33] . The Exxon Valdez oil spill (see Figure **Exxon Valdez Oil Spill** (Figure 7.3)), which occurred in Alaska in 1989, was the largest ever oil spill in the United States, causing major environmental and economic damage in Alaska.

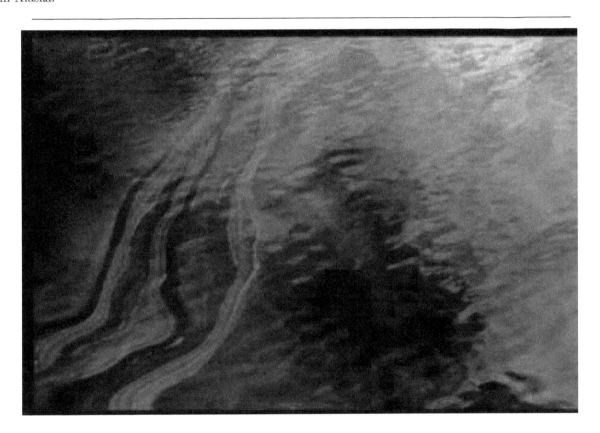

Figure 7.3: Exxon Valdez Oil Spill Heavy sheens of oil covering large areas of the Prince William Sound, Alaska a few days after the Exxon Valdez oil spill. *Source: U.S. National Oceanic and Atmospheric Administration via Wikimedia Commons*[34]

The prevention of oil spills in navigable waters and shorelines of the United States is stipulated through the OPA statute. The OPA encompasses oil spill prevention, preparedness, and response performance of industry and the federal government. Incentives are provided to owners and operators for oil spill prevention, enforced by the EPA through the oil spill liability and penalty provisions of the OPA. Oil companies in the United States engage in oil exploration, both offshore and onshore, resulting in accidental releases of crude petroleum into the environment from wells, drilling rigs, offshore platforms and oil tankers. With the exception of the 2010 BP Deepwater Horizon oil spill[35] in the Gulf of Mexico, the number and amount of oil spills have decreased over the past twenty years in the United States despite the increasing demand for oil. This decline has been attributed to the OPA after the Exxon Valdez oil spill incident. The Exxon Valdez oil

[33]http://en.wikipedia.org/wiki/Exxon_Valdez_oil_spill
[34]http://commons.wikimedia.org/wiki/File:OilSheenFromValdezSpill.jpg
[35]http://en.wikipedia.org/wiki/Deepwater_Horizon_oil_spill

spill was the largest ever in United States waters until the 2010 BP Deepwater Horizon oil spill (see Figure **Deepwater Horizon Oil Spill** (p. 288)). BP has been held to be responsible for the Deepwater Horizon oil spill, and has been made accountable for all cleanup costs and other damages by the federal government.

Figure 7.4: BP Deepwater Horizon Oil Spill The Deep Horizon oil spill in the Gulf of Mexico as seen from space. *Source: NASA/GSFC, MODIS Rapid Response AND demis.nl AND FT2, via Wikimedia Commons*[36]

7.4.7 Toxic Substances Control Act (TSCA)

Information on all chemical substances and the control of any of these substances which may have an unreasonable health risk has been granted to the EPA through the Toxic Substances Control Act (1976). The manufacturer or the importer of a new chemical must provide information on the identity and hazard, use, production volume and disposal characteristics of the chemical to the EPA. Toxicological tests and unpublished health and safety studies on listed chemicals may be required by the EPA. The EPA may approve, prohibit, or limit the manufacture and sale of the listed chemicals, or may require special labeling. Since some chemical substances such as pesticides, tobacco products, nuclear materials, pharmaceuticals and cosmetics substances are regulated under other acts, they are exempted from TSCA regulations.

---

[36]http://commons.wikimedia.org/wiki/File:Deepwater_Horizon_oil_spill_-_May_24,_2010_-_with_locator.jpg

The production and distribution of polychlorinated biphenyls (PCBs) are prohibited through TSCA. PCBs are synthetic organic compounds that were manufactured to be used as electrical transformer oil; exposure to PCBs increases the risk of cancer, and may affect the reproductive and nervous systems. The EPA enforces the handling and disposal of PCBs based on established regulations on PCBs, in addition to management of PCBs found at hazardous waste sites. After the amendments of 1986 and 1990, TSCA through the Asbestos Hazard Emergency Response Act requires that all public and commercial buildings identify, control and mitigate the asbestos hazard in these buildings.

7.4.8 Federal Insecticide, Fungicide, and Rodenticide Act (FIFRA)

Insecticides, fungicides and rodenticides are compounds that are employed to control or eliminate pest populations (pesticides). The Federal Insecticide, Fungicide, and Rodenticide Act (FIFRA) of 1972 with several subsequent amendments set guidelines for the use of pesticides in the United States. All manufacturers or importers must register their pesticide products with the EPA, where registration is allowed for a pesticide whose application does not have unreasonable adverse effects on the environment. Industries such as the agricultural sector employ pesticides to control vermin and other pests in industrial processes and in the workplace.

7.4.9 Pollution Prevention Act (PPA)

A pollution management system with a focus on generating less pollution at the source was established through the Pollution Prevention Act (PPA) of 1990. The pollution prevention hierarchy stipulates that the first step in reducing pollution is to minimize the amount of waste that is generated by all activities and processes, which is referred to as source reduction. When the generation of waste cannot be reduced at the source, then the waste should be recycled in order to decrease pollution. A waste that cannot be reduced at the source or recycled should go through treatment and disposal in an environmentally safe manner. A Pollution Prevention Office has been established by the EPA to promote source reduction as the preferred option in the pollution prevention hierarchy. Pollution prevention is a voluntary measure on the part of the polluting industry rather than a mandatory regulatory control enforced by the EPA and the individual states; industry is only required to file a toxic chemical source reduction and recycling report with EPA every year. Industry is given incentives to institute pollution prevention programs with the aim of realizing the economic benefits of pollution prevention to industry after the implementation of pollution prevention programs.

7.4.10 Occupational Safety and Health Act (OSHA)

The Occupational Safety and Hazard Act (OSHA) of 1970 and its amendment of 1990 aim to ensure safe and healthful working conditions for workers through enforcement of standards developed under OSHA, and to provide for research, training and education in the field of occupational safety and health. The standards for occupational health and safety are established by the Occupational Safety and Health Administration and its state partners, which are enforced through inspections of industry and providing guidance on better operating practices. The National Institute for Occupational Safety and Health (NIOSH) was established to recommend occupational safety and health standards based on extensive scientific testing, which are afterwards enforced by OSHA. Those industries which have followed OSHA standards have experienced a decline in overall injury and illness rates, where the costs due to worker injuries, illnesses and compensation associated with occupational safety are a major loss for industry. The OSHA standards for worker health and safety are recommended to be used in conjunction with various industrial pollution prevention programs.

7.4.11 Summary

Environmental laws and regulations serve the purpose of limiting the amount of pollution in the environment from anthropogenic sources due to industrial and other economic activities. Environmental regulations are specific to different phases of the environment such as water and air. Government regulations help industry to curtail the environmental impact of pollution, leading to the protection of human health and the environment. Future environmental laws and policy should convey and work in tandem with the efforts of the public and industry for a more sustainable economy and society.

7.4.12 Resources

1) For more information on environmental engineering, read Chapter 1 of:

Davis, M.L. & Cornwell, D.A. (2008). *Introduction to Environmental Engineering* (4th ed.). New York: McGraw-Hill.

2) For more information about managing environmental resources, read:

LaGrega, M.D., Buckingham, P.L., Evans, J.C., & Environmental Resources Management (2001). *Hazardous Waste Management* (2nd ed.). New York: McGraw-Hill.

3) For more information on the U.S. Environmental Protection Agency's laws and regulations, visit: http://www.epa.gov/lawsregs/[37]

7.5 Risk Assessment Methodology for Conventional and Alternative Sustainability Options[38]

7.5.1 Learning Objectives

After reading this module, students should be able to

- understand the content and the goals of four-step of risk assessment process
- know how to estimate dose received via each exposure pathway
- know how to integrate exposure and toxicity information to characterize health risks
- understand how to quantitatively estimate cumulative cancer and noncancer risks
- understand how to identify/evaluate uncertainties in risk assessment

7.5.2 Introduction

Risk assessment is a scientific process used by federal agencies and risk management decision-makers to make informed decisions about actions that may be taken to protect human health by ascertaining potential human health risks or health hazard associated with exposure to chemicals in the environment.

---

[37]http://www.epa.gov/lawsregs/
[38]This content is available online at <http://legacy.cnx.org/content/m41566/1.4/>.

Figure 7.5: Smoke Stack Emissions into the Atmosphere Figure shows emissions billowing from a smoke stack into the atmosphere. Risk assessment helps federal agencies and risk management decision-makers arrive at informed decisions about actions to take to protect human health from hazards such as air pollution, pictured here. *Source: Alfred Palmer via Wikipedia*[39]

Some of the real-world examples of risk assessment includes: establishment of national ambient air quality and drinking water standards for protection of public health (e.g. ozone, particulate matter in outdoor air; chromium, chloroform or benzene in water); establishment of clean-up levels for hazardous waste site remediation; development of fish consumption advisories for pregnant women and general population (e.g. PCBs, mercury); assessment of risks and benefits of different alternative fuels for sound energy policy development (e.g. oxygenated gasoline, biodiesel); and estimation of health risks associated with pesticide residues in food. The estimated risk is a function of exposure and toxicity, as described in detail in NAS (1983 (p. 301)) and EPA (1989 (p. 300)). The regulatory risk assessment follows a four-step paradigm using qualitative and/or quantitative approaches. In quantitative risk assessment using either **deterministic** or **probabilistic** approaches, the risk estimates pertaining to an exposure scenario is particularly useful when comparing a number of exposure or risk reduction measures among one another as an optimization protocol to determine the best economically viable option for protection of public health and the environment. With environmental sustainability and life-cycle analysis in the forefront of green technological innovation, energy, and economic savings in the 21st Century, risk assessment will pay a pivotal role in discerning the option(s) with the most benefit in health protection and, thus, will be an integral part of any environmentally sustainability analysis. Such comparative risk assessment can be performed for traditional approaches vs. environmentally

[39]http://en.wikipedia.org/wiki/File:AlfedPalmersmokestacks.jpg

sustainable approaches. They can also be performed among different environmentally sustainable options for an environmental pollution problem such hazardous waste site remediation and redevelopment, air quality management in urban areas, pest management practices, agricultural health and safety, alternative energy sources for transportation sources and among others.

The four steps of risk assessment are i) hazard identification (Section 7.5.3: Hazard Identification); ii) toxicity (Section 7.5.4: Toxicity (Dose-Response Assessment)) (or dose-response) assessment; iii) exposure assessment (Section 7.5.5: Exposure Assessment); and iv) risk characterization (Section 7.5.6: Risk Characterization), which are described below in detail. The emphasis is given in documenting the resources necessary to successfully perform each step.

7.5.3 Hazard Identification

In the hazard identification step, a scientific weight of evidence analysis is performed to determine whether a particular substance or chemical is or is not causally linked to any particular health effect at environmentally relevant concentrations. Hazard identification is performed to determine whether, and to what degree, toxic effects in one setting will occur in other settings. For example, is a chemical that is shown to cause **carcinogenicity** in animal test species (e.g. rat, mouse) likely to be a carcinogen in exposed humans? In order to assess the weight of evidence for adverse health effects, risk analysts follow the following steps (EPA, 1993 (p. 300)): (1) Compile and analyze all the available toxicology data on the substance of interest; (2) Weigh the evidence that the substance causes a toxic effect (cancer of non-cancer health end-points); and (3) Assess whether adverse health effect (or toxicity) could occur from human exposure in a real-life setting.

In the first task of hazard identification, risk analyst examines the toxicity literature using the following analytical tools in the order of importance:

- Epidemiological studies
- Controlled human exposure chamber experiments
- In-vivo animal **bioassays**
- In-vitro cell and tissue culture bioassays
- Quantitative Structure –Activity Relationship Analysis (QSAR)

Among these, in-vivo animal bioassays are, by far, the most utilized source of information for hazard identification for chemicals and, on rare instances, for chemical mixtures (e.g. diesel). When available, well-conducted epidemiological studies are regarded as the most valuable source of human health hazard identification information since they provide direct human evidence for potential health effects. **Epidemiology** is the study of the occurrence and distribution of a disease or physiological condition in human populations and of the factors that influence this distribution (Lilienfeld and Lilienfeld, 1980 (p. 301)). The advantages of epidemiological studies for hazard identification are (EPA, 1989 (p. 300); EPA, 1993 (p. 300)): animal-to-human extrapolation is not necessary, real exposure conditions, and a wide range of subjects with different genetic and life-style patterns. However, epidemiological studies have a number of shortcomings, which limit their usefulness in hazard identification. Some of these disadvantages include difficulty in recruiting and maintaining a control group; having no control over some of the non-statistical variables related to exposures, lifestyles, co-exposure to other chemicals, etc.; absence of actual exposure measurements along with memory bias for retrospective studies; lengthy latency periods for chronic health effects such as cancer; and poor sensitivity and inability to determine cause-effect relationships conclusively.

Animal bioassays remedy some of the weaknesses of epidemiological studies by allowing for greater control over the experiment and are deemed to be reliable measurement of toxic effects, although they require "high dose in animals-to low dose in humans" extrapolation. The selection of design parameters of animal bioassays is critically important in observing or missing an actual hazard. These parameters include: animal species selected for the experiment (rat, mouse); strain of the test species; age/sex of the test species; magnitude of exposure concentrations/doses applied or administered; number of dose levels studied; duration of exposure; controls selected; and route of exposure. Animal studies are characterized as acute (a single dose or exposures of short duration), chronic (exposures for full lifetimes of test species – about two years in rats/mice) and sub-chronic (usually 90 days) based on the exposure duration. In the hazard identification step, the following measures of toxicity are commonly compiled:

- **LD50/LC50/EC50**: The dose or concentration in a toxicity study at which causing 50 percent mortality in test species was observed. The EC_{50} is the effective concentration causing adverse effects or impairment in 50% of the test species.
- **NOAEL** (No Observable Adverse Effect Level): The highest dose or concentration in a toxicity study at which no adverse effect was observed.
- **LOAEL** (Lowest Observable Adverse Effect Level): The lowest dose or concentration in a toxicity study at which an adverse effect was observed.
- **MTD** (Maximum Tolerated Dose): The largest dose a test animal can receive for most of its lifetime without demonstrating adverse health effects other than carcinogenicity.

Risk scientists rely on a number of reputable sources to gather, compile, and analyze hazard identification information to be able to perform weight of evidence analysis and to conclude whether a chemical may cause a health effect in humans. Some of these sources are:

- **Hazardous Substances Data Bank** (HSDB) maintained by the National Library of Medicine: This scientifically peer-reviewed data bank provides human and animal toxicity data for about 5,000 chemicals and can be accessed via http://toxnet.nlm.nih.gov/cgi-bin/sis/htmlgen?HSDB[40]
- ChemicIDplus Advanced database maintained by the National Library of Medicine: This database allows users to search the NLM ChemIDplus database of over 370,000 chemicals. Compound identifiers such as Chemical Name, CAS Registry Number, Molecular Formula, Classification Code, Locator Code, and Structure or Substructure can be entered to display toxicity data via http://chem.sis.nlm.nih.gov/chemidplus/[41]
- National Toxicology Program (NTP) of the Department of Health and Human Services:
  - Report of Carcinogens (RoC): The RoC is an informational scientific and public health document that identifies and discusses agents, substances, mixtures, or exposure circumstances that may pose a hazard to human health by virtue of their carcinogenicity. The RoC is published biennially and serves as a meaningful and useful compilation of data on: a) the carcinogenicity (ability to cause cancer), genotoxicity (ability to damage genes), and biologic mechanisms (modes of action in the body) of the listed substance in humans and/or animals; b) the potential for human exposure to these substances; and c) Federal regulations to limit exposures. The link to the most recent version of the RoC can be accessed via http://ntp.niehs.nih.gov/?objectid=BD1A20B5-F1F6-975E-7CF8CBFACF0FC7EF[42]
  - NTP Toxicity Testing Study Results and Research Areas: NTP tests chemicals for their toxicity in human and animal systems. The results of these toxicity testing studies along with current research areas can be obtained at: http://ntp.niehs.nih.gov/index.cfm?objectid=720160DB-BDB7-CEBA-F7CC2DE0A230C920[43]
- National Institute of Occupational and Safety Health (NIOSH) Hazard Identification Databases: The following NIOSH website houses a multitude of databases and information for chemicals and their hazards under a single umbrella, including NIOSH's "Pocket Guide to Chemical Hazards": http://www.cdc.gov/niosh/database.html[44]
- Agency for Toxic Substances and Disease Registry (ATSDR) Toxicological Profiles and Public Health Statements: ATSDR produces **"toxicological profiles"** for hazardous substances found at National Priorities List (NPL) Superfund sites. About 300 toxicological profiles have so far been pub-

---

[40]http://toxnet.nlm.nih.gov/cgi-bin/sis/htmlgen?HSDB
[41]http://chem.sis.nlm.nih.gov/chemidplus/
[42]http://ntp.niehs.nih.gov/?objectid=BD1A20B5-F1F6-975E-7CF8CBFACF0FC7EF
[43]http://ntp.niehs.nih.gov/index.cfm?objectid=720160DB-BDB7-CEBA-F7CC2DE0A230C920
[44]http://www.cdc.gov/niosh/database.html

lished or are under development. The chemical-specific toxicological profiles can be accessed via http://www.atsdr.cdc.gov/toxprofiles/index.asp[45]

- **World Health Organization (WHO) International Programme of Chemical Safety (IPCS):** ICPS publishes "Environmental Health Criteria" (EHC) for chemical substances, which provide critical reviews on the effects of chemicals or combinations of chemicals and physical and biological agents on human health and the environment. The IPCS site can be accessed via http://www.who.int/ipcs/assessment/en/[46]

- **Material Safety Data Sheets (MSDS):** MSDS are invaluable resource to obtain compositional data for products and mixtures.

7.5.4 Toxicity (Dose-Response Assessment)

Dose-response assessment takes the toxicity data gathered in the hazard identification step from animal studies and exposed human population studies and describes the quantitative relationship between the amount of exposure to a chemical (or dose) and the extent of toxic injury or disease (or response). Generally, as the dose of a chemical increases, the toxic response increases either in the severity of the injury or in the incidence of response in the affected population (EPA, 1989 (p. 300); EPA, 1993 (p. 300)). In toxicity-assessment step, the relationship between the magnitude of the administered, applied, or absorbed dose and the probability of occurrence and magnitude of health effect(s) (e.g. tumor incidence in the case of cancer) is determined.

Dose-response assessment for carcinogens and non-carcinogens differ in toxicity values use and how these toxicity values are derived. In general, toxicity values provide a measure of toxic potency of the chemical in question. These toxicity values are:

- **Reference Dose (RfD) for oral/dermal pathways or Reference Concentration (RfC) for inhalation pathway – Noncarcinogens: A chronic RfD** is defined as an estimate (with uncertainty spanning perhaps an order of magnitude or greater) of a daily exposure level for the human population, including sensitive subpopulations, that is likely to be without an appreciable risk of deleterious effects during a lifetime. It has the unit of mg of pollutant per kg of body weight per day (mg/kg-day). Chronic RfDs are specifically developed to be protective for long-term exposure to a chemical, usually, for exposure periods between seven years (approximately 10 percent of a human lifetime) and a lifetime. After selection of a critical health effect study and a critical health effect through review of toxicity literature in the hazard identification step, the RfD is derived by dividing the NOAEL (or LOAEL) for the critical toxic effect by uncertainty factors (UFs) and a modifying factor (MF). The uncertainty factors generally consist of multiples of 10, with each factor representing a specific area of uncertainty inherent in the extrapolation from the available data (e.g. 10 for extrapolation from animals to humans; 10 for interhuman variability; 10 when LOAEL is used instead of NOAEL in deriving RfD; 10 when NOAEL is obtained from a subchronic study rather than a chronic study). A modifying factor ranging from >0 to 10 is included to account for additional uncertainties in the critical study and in the entire data based on a qualitative professional assessment. The default value for the MF is 1.The NOAEL is selected based on the assumption that if the critical toxic effect is prevented, then all toxic effects are prevented (EPA, 1989). The derivation of toxicity value, RfD/RfC, for noncarcinogens assumes that they are threshold chemicals, meaning there is a threshold below which no adverse effects are observed in test species. This dose level (i.e. NOAEL) in animals is simply adjusted by a number of factors (UFs and MF) to determine the safe dose level in humans (i.e. RfD) as shown by the following equation:

$$\text{RfD} = \frac{\text{NOAEL}}{\text{UF}_1 \text{xUF}_2 \text{xUF}_3 ... \text{xMF}} \qquad (7.1)$$

---

[45]http://www.atsdr.cdc.gov/toxprofiles/index.asp
[46]http://www.who.int/ipcs/assessment/en/

- **Cancer Slope Factor (CSF) for oral/dermal pathway or Unit Risk Factor (URF) for inhalation pathway – Carcinogens:** Unlike the noncarcinogens, carcinogens assumed to be non-threshold chemicals based on the Environmental Protection Agency (EPA) assumption that a small number of molecular events can evoke changes in a single cell that can lead to uncontrolled cellular proliferation and eventually to cancer. In deriving slope factors, firstly, an appropriate dose-response data set is selected. In this exercise, whenever available, human data of high quality are preferable to animal data. However, if only animal data are available, dose-response data from species that responds most similarly to humans with respect to metabolism, physiology, and pharmacokinetics is preferred. When no clear choice is possible, the most sensitive species is chosen. Secondly, a model to the available data set is applied and extrapolation from the relatively high doses administered to test species in animal bioassay (or the exposures recorded in epidemiologic studies) to the lower environmental exposure levels expected for humans is performed using the model. Although various models have been developed for this purpose (e.g. probit, logit, Weibull), the linearized multistage model has commonly been used by the EPA. After the data are fit to the appropriate model, the upper 95th percent confidence limit of the slope of the resulting dose-response curve is calculated, which is known as the Cancer Slope Factor (CSF). It represents an upper 95th percent confidence limit on the probability of a response per unit intake of a chemical over a lifetime (i.e. dose). Thus, its units are $(mg/kg-day)^{-1}$. This indicates that there is only a five percent chance that the probability of a response could be greater than the estimated value of CSF. Because the dose-response curve generally is linear only in the low-dose region, the slope factor estimate only holds true for low doses. Toxicity values for carcinogenic effects also can be expressed in terms of risk per unit concentration of the chemical, which are called unit risk factors (URFs). They are calculated by dividing the CSF by adult body weight (70 kg) and multiplying by the adult inhalation rate (20 m^3/day), for risk associated with unit concentration in air (EPA, 1989 (p. 300)).

A number of regulatory agencies responsible for environmental and public health protection have devoted resources in developing and documenting toxicity values for noncarcinogens (RfDs/RfCs) and carcinogens (CSFs/URFs). The following hierarchy of sources is recommended by the EPA in evaluating chemical toxicity for Superfund sites (EPA, 2003 (p. 301)):

- Integrated Risk Information System (IRIS) and cited references, which is the prime source for the chemical-specific toxicity value information and can be accessed via: http://cfpub.epa.gov/ncea/iris/index.cfm[47]
- The Provisional Peer Reviewed Toxicity Values (PPRTV) and cited references developed for the EPA Office of Solid Waste and Emergency Response (OSWER) Office of Superfund Remediation and Technology Innovation (OSRTI) programs (not publicly available).
- Other toxicity values, which includes the following sources of toxicity values that are commonly consulted by the EPA Superfund Program[48] when a relevant toxicity value is not available from either IRIS or the PPRTV database:
  - California Environmental Protection Agency (Cal EPA) Toxicity Criteria Database, available at: http://www.oehha.ca.gov/risk/chemicalDB/index.asp[49] ;
  - The Agency for Toxic Substances and Disease Registry (ATSDR) Minimal Risk Levels (MRLs, addressing noncancer effects only). MRL is an estimate of the daily human exposure to a hazardous substance that is likely to be without appreciable risk of adverse noncancer health effects over a specified duration of exposure. These substance-specific estimates, which are intended to serve as screening levels, are used by ATSDR health assessors and other responders to identify contaminants and potential health effects that may be of concern at hazardous waste sites. To date, 137 inhalation MRLs, 226 oral MRLs and 8 external radiation MRLs have been derived and can be found at: http://www.atsdr.cdc.gov/mrls/index.html[50] ;

[47]http://cfpub.epa.gov/ncea/iris/index.cfm
[48]http://www.epa.gov/superfund/policy/cercla.htm
[49]http://www.oehha.ca.gov/risk/chemicalDB/index.asp
[50]http://www.atsdr.cdc.gov/mrls/index.html

- · The EPA Superfund Health Effects Assessment Summary Tables (HEAST) database and cited references; and
- · Additional sources of toxicity values.

There are a number of other valuable sources for toxicity values (RfDs/RfCs for non-carcinogens and URFs/CSFs for carcinogens), which can be compiled via the following sources:

- **EPA Region 9** tabulated "**Preliminary Remediation Goals (PRGs)**" or "Regional Screening Levels (RSL)" for Chemical Contaminants at Superfund Sites," which also lists toxicity values (oral/inhalation RfD and oral/inhalation CSF) used in the medium-specific PRG/RSL calculation for each chemical. This table can be accessed via http://www.epa.gov/region09/waste/sfund/prg/index.html[51]
- The **Hot Spot Guidelines** published by California EPA for Air Toxics Program includes technical background documentation for toxicity criteria/values for chemicals (i.e. **Cancer Potency Factors (CPFs)**, which is equivalent to EPA's CSFs and **Chronic Recommended Exposure Limits (RELs)**, which are similar to USEPA's RfCs). The most recent version of REL Table is located at: http://www.oehha.org/air/allrels.html[52] . The Technical Support Document for CPFs that contains cancer unit risks and potency factors for 121 of the 201 carcinogenic substances or groups of substances can be accessed via http://www.oehha.ca.gov/air/cancer_guide/TSD2.html[53] .
- The Department of Energy's **Oak Ridge National Laboratory (ORNL)** maintains **Risk Assessment Information System (RAIS)** website, which contains useful information for risk assessment, including chemical-specific toxicity values. The RAIS information can be accessed via http://rais.ornl.gov/[54] .
- **Toxicology Excellence in Risk Assessment (TERA)**, a non-profit organization, manages and distributes a free Internet database of human health risk values and cancer classifications for over 600 chemicals of environmental concern from multiple organizations worldwide. This database, **Integrated Toxicity Estimates for Risk (ITER)**, can be accessed via: http://www.tera.org/iter/[55] or via NLM's TOXNET database at: http://toxnet.nlm.nih.gov[56] .

The dermal RfDs and CSFs can be derived from oral RfDs and CSFs, adjusted for chemical-specific gastrointestinal absorption efficiency, based on the recommended methodology in EPA's *Guidance for Dermal Risk Assessment* (EPA, 2004a (p. 301)).

7.5.5 Exposure Assessment

In the third step of risk assessment, the magnitude of exposure is determined by measuring or estimating the amount of an agent to which humans are exposed (i.e. exposure concentration) and the magnitude of dose (or intake) is estimated by taking the magnitude, frequency, duration, and route of exposure into account. Exposure assessments may consider past, present, and future exposures.

---

[51] http://www.epa.gov/region09/waste/sfund/prg/index.html
[52] http://www.oehha.org/air/allrels.html
[53] http://www.oehha.ca.gov/air/cancer_guide/TSD2.html
[54] http://rais.ornl.gov/
[55] http://www.tera.org/iter/
[56] http://toxnet.nlm.nih.gov/

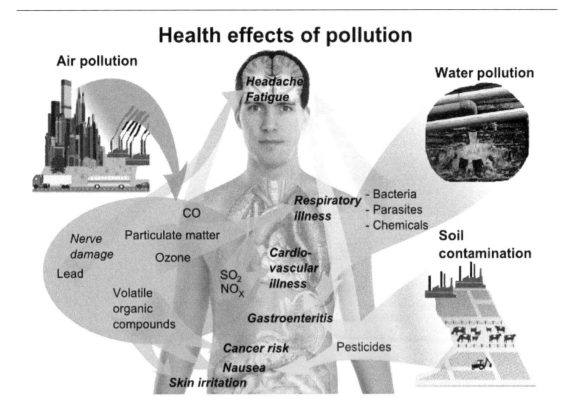

Figure 7.6: Human Health Effects of Environmental Pollution from Pollution Source to Receptor Figure shows the human health effects of environmental pollution from pollution source to receptor. *Source: Mikael Häggström via Wikimedia Commons*[57]

While estimates of past or current exposure concentration/dose can be based on measurements or models of existing conditions, estimates of future exposure concentration/dose can be based on models of future conditions. In the case of inhalation exposures, personal or area monitoring to sample for contaminants in the air can be employed. The sampling data can be augmented with modeling efforts using default and/or site-specific input parameters. The model application can begin with simple screening level dispersion models and/or can utilize higher-level 2-D or 3-D models depending on the complexity of the environmental pollution problem in hand.

In any exposure assessment, the risk scientists ask a number of questions to hypothesize the exposure scenario pertaining to environmental pollution affecting the population or a sub-group. Some of these are:

- What is the source of pollution at the site? (e.g. underground storage tank leak, emissions from an industrial plant, surface water run-off from agricultural fields)
- Which environmental compartments are likely to be contaminated? (i.e. air, water, sediment, soil, plants, animals, fish)
- What are the chemicals of concern (COC) originating from the pollution source?
- What are the fate and transport properties of these chemicals that may inform the aging of the pollution in the environment over time and resultant chemical signature in each environmental medium?
- Who is exposed? (e.g. children, elderly, asthmatics, general population, workers)

---

[57]http://commons.wikimedia.org/wiki/File:Health_effects_of_pollution.png

- How many people are exposed?
- Where are people exposed? (e.g. home, workplace, outside environment, retirement communities, schools)
- How are people exposed? (i.e. exposure pathway – inhalation, dermal contact or ingestion)
- How often are people exposed? (i.e. exposure frequency)
- How long are people exposed? (i.e. exposure duration)

Answers to these questions frame the problem at hand. In the next step, a number of exposure parameters are integrated into an estimate of daily dose received by an exposed individual via each exposure route (ingestion, dermal contact or skin absorption, and inhalation). The magnitude of human exposures, in general, is dependent on COC concentration in soil, exposure parameters describing human physiology (e.g. soil ingestion rate, body weight), and population-specific parameters describing exposure behavior (exposure frequency, duration). When evaluating subchronic or chronic exposures to noncarcinogenic chemicals, dose is averaged over the period of exposure, termed "Average Daily Dose" (ADD). However, for carcinogens, dose is averaged over an entire lifetime (i.e. 70 years), thus referred to as "Lifetime Average Daily Dose" (LADD). Both ADD and LADD represent normalized exposure rate in the units of mg of chemical per kg body weight per day (mg/kg-day). The ADD for noncarcinogenic COCs and LADD for carcinogenic COCs are estimated for four most commonly studied exposure pathways in EPA risk assessments, particularly for hazardous waste sites, as shown below (Erdal, 2007 (p. 301)):

Soil Ingestion: $L\,(\mathrm{ADD})_o = \frac{C_s \mathrm{xIR}_o \mathrm{xEFxEDxCF}}{\mathrm{BWxAT}}$

Dermal Contact: $L\,(\mathrm{ADD})_d = \frac{C_s \mathrm{xSAxAFxABSxEVxEFxEDxCF}}{\mathrm{BWxAT}}$

Inhalation of Particulates: $L\,(\mathrm{ADD})_{\mathrm{ip}} = \frac{C_s \mathrm{xIR}_i \mathrm{xEFxEDx}\left(\frac{1}{\mathrm{PEF}}\right)}{\mathrm{BWxAT}}$

Inhalation of Volatiles: $L\,(\mathrm{ADD})_{\mathrm{iv}} = \frac{C_s \mathrm{xIR}_i \mathrm{xEFxEDx}\left(\frac{1}{\mathrm{VF}}\right)}{\mathrm{BWxAT}}$

Where:

C_s: *Exposure Concentration (i.e., 95th Upper Confidence Limit on the Mean) of COC in soil (mg/kg) – (chemical-specific; can be estimated using EPA 2004b (p. 301))*

IR_o: *Ingestion rate of soil (mg/d)*

IR_i: *Inhalation rate (m^3/d)*

SA: Skin surface area (cm^2)

AF: Soil-to-skin adherence factor (mg/cm^2)

ABS: Dermal absorption fraction (unitless – chemical-specific)

EV: Event frequency (events/d)

EF: Exposure frequency (d/y)

ED: Exposure duration (y)

PEF: Particulate emission factor (m^3/kg) – 1.36 x 10^9 m^3/kg per (EPA 2002a (p. 301))

VF: Soil-to-air volatilization factor (m^3/kg – chemical-specific)

BW: Body weight (kg)

*AT: Averaging time (days) – (ED*365 d/y for noncarcinogens; 70 y*365 d/y for carcinogens)*

CF: Conversion factor – 10^{-6} kg/mg

In deterministic risk assessment, ADD and LADD estimates are performed for a reasonable maximum exposure scenario (RME) and a central tendency exposure scenario (CTE), resulting in a range. EPA's reliance on the concept of RME for estimating risks is based on a conservative but plausible exposure scenario (which is defined to be the 90th to 95th percentile exposure, signifying that fewer than five percent to 10 percent of the population would be expected to experience higher risk levels), and has been scientifically challenged over the years. For example, Burmaster and Harris (1993 (p. 300)) showed that the use of EPA recommended default exposure parameter values resulted in exposure and risk estimates well in excess of the 99th percentile due to multiplication of three upper-bound values (i.e. 95th percentiles) for IR, EF, and ED. The authors argued that this leads to hazardous waste site cleanup decisions based on health risks that virtually no one in the surrounding population would be expected to experience. They advised the EPA to endorse and promote the use of probabilistic methods (e.g. **Monte-Carlo simulations**) as a way to supplement or replace current risk assessment methods, in order to overcome the problem of "compounded conservatism" and enable calculation of risks using a more statistically defensible estimate of the RME. In probabilistic risk assessment, the input parameters are characterized by their unique probability distribution. The EPA's Exposure Factors Program provides information on development of exposure parameter distributions in support of probabilistic distributions and can be accessed via: http://cfpub.epa.gov/ncea/cfm/recordisplay.cfm?deid=20563[58] .

The values of the exposure parameters corresponding to RME or CTE scenarios are often compiled from EPA's Exposure Factors Handbook (EFH):

- General Exposure Factors Handbook (EPA, 1997 (p. 301)) provides exposure assessors with data needed on standard factors to calculate human exposure to toxic chemicals as part of risk assessments. These factors include: drinking water consumption, soil ingestion, inhalation rates, dermal factors including skin area and soil adherence factors, consumption of fruits and vegetables, fish, meats, dairy products, homegrown foods, breast milk intake, human activity factors, consumer product use, and residential characteristics. Recommended values are for the general population and also for various segments of the population who may have characteristics different from the general population. The most recent version of the EFH can be accessed via http://cfpub.epa.gov/ncea/cfm/recordisplay.cfm?deid=209866[59] .
- The **Children-Specific** EFH (EPA, 2002b (p. 301)) provides a summary of the available and up-to-date statistical data on various factors assessing child exposures, which can be accessed via http://cfpub.epa.gov/ncea/cfm/recordisplay.cfm?deid=56747[60] .

7.5.6 Risk Characterization

In the last step, a hazard quotient (HQ) as an indicator of risks associated with health effects other than cancer and excess cancer risk (ECR) as the incremental probability of an exposed person developing cancer over a lifetime, are calculated by integrating toxicity and exposure information, as shown below. If HQ $>$ 1, there may be concern for potential adverse systemic health effects in the exposed individuals. If HQ $\leq$ 1, there may be no concern. It should be noted that HQs are scaling factors and they are not statistically based. The EPA's acceptable criterion for carcinogenic risks is based on public policy as described in the National Contingency Plan (NCP) and is the exposure concentration that represent an ECR in the range of $10^{-4} - 10^{-6}$, i.e. 1 in 10,000 to 1 in 1,000,000 excess cancer cases (EPA, 1990 (p. 300)).

Noncancer Risk: HazardQuotient (HQ) $= \frac{\text{ADD}}{\text{RfD}}$

Excess Cancer Risk (ECR): ECR $= L (\text{ADD}) \text{xCSF}$

To account for exposures to multiple COCs via multiple pathways, individual HQs are summed to provide an overall Hazard Index (HI). If HI >1, COCs are segregated based on their critical health end-point and separate target organ-specific HIs are calculated. Only if target organ-specific HI > 1, is there concern for potential health effects for that end-point (e.g. liver, kidney, respiratory system).

Cumulative Noncancer Risk: HazardIndex $= \text{HI} = \sum_{\text{COC}_{\text{NC}}=1}^{n} (\text{HQ}_o + \text{HQ}_d + \text{HQ}_i)$

Cumulative Excess Cancer Risk: $\sum_{\text{COC}_C=1}^{n} \text{ECR} = \sum_{\text{COC}_C=1}^{n} (\text{ECR}_o + \text{ECR}_d + \text{ECR}_i)$

Here, o, d and i subscripts express oral (ingestion), dermal contact and inhalation pathways.

As discussed above, the HQ, HI, and ECR estimates are performed for RME and CTE scenarios separately in the case of deterministic risk assessment. Although EPA published the probabilistic risk assessment guidelines in 2001 (EPA, 2001 (p. 301)), its application has so far been limited. Proper evaluation of uncertainties, which are associated with compounded conservatism and potential underestimation of quantitative risk estimates (e.g. due to the presence of COCs without established toxicity values), is intrinsic to any risk-based scientific assessment. In general, uncertainties and limitations are associated with sampling and analysis, chemical fate and transport, exposure parameters, exposure modeling, and human dose-response or toxicity assessment (derivation of CSFs/RfDs, extrapolation from high animal doses to low human doses), and site-specific uncertainties.

---

[58]http://cfpub.epa.gov/ncea/cfm/recordisplay.cfm?deid=20563
[59]http://cfpub.epa.gov/ncea/cfm/recordisplay.cfm?deid=209866
[60]http://cfpub.epa.gov/ncea/cfm/recordisplay.cfm?deid=56747

7.5.7 Conclusion

The improvement in the scientific quality and validity of health risk estimates depends on advancements in our understanding of human exposure to, and toxic effects associated with, chemicals present in environmental and occupational settings. For example, life-cycle of and health risks associated with pharmaceuticals in the environment is poorly understood due to lack of environmental concentration and human exposure data despite extensive toxicological data on drugs. There are many other examples for which either data on exposure or toxicity or both have not yet been developed, preventing quantitative assessment of health risks and development of policies that protect the environment and public health at the same time. Therefore, it is important to continue to develop research data to refine future risk assessments for informed regulatory decision-making in environmental sustainability and to ensure that costs associated with different technological and/or engineering alternatives are scientifically justified and public health-protective. One area that, particularly, requires advancement is the assessment of health risks of chemical mixtures. Current risk assessment approaches consider one chemical at a time. However, chemicals are present in mixtures in the environment. Furthermore, physical, chemical and biological transformations in the environment and interactions among chemicals in the environment may change the toxic potential of the mixture over time. Thus, risk assessment is an evolving scientific discipline that has many uncertainties in all of the four steps. These uncertainties should be thoroughly documented and discussed and the risk assessment results should be interpreted within the context of these uncertainties.

7.5.8 Review Questions

Question 7.5.1
What are the human health hazards of vinyl chloride?

Question 7.5.2
What are the human toxicity values (RfD, CSF) of vinyl chloride and how are these values estimated?

Question 7.5.3
How do you calculate the dose received by children and adults via ingestion of vinyl chloride-contaminated drinking water under the RME scenario? Please document and explain your assumptions along with your references for the exposure parameters for each receptor of concern

Question 7.5.4
How do you calculate RME cancer and noncancer risks to children and adults for the above exposure scenario?

Question 7.5.5
What does excess cancer risk of three cases out of ten thousand exposed ($3x10^{-4}$) signify?

Question 7.5.6
If drinking water were also contaminated with benzene, how would you estimate cumulative cancer and noncancer risks associated with exposure to drinking water contaminated with vinyl chloride and benzene for children and adults under the RME scenario?

7.5.9 References

Burmaster, D.E. & Harris, R.H. (1993). The magnitude of compounding conservatisms in Superfund risk assessments. *Risk Analysis, 13*, 131-34.

EPA (U.S. Environmental Protection Agency). (1989). *Risk assessment guidance for Superfund, volume I: Human health evaluation manual (Part A) (Interim Final)* (EPA/540/1-89002). Office of Emergency and Remedial Response, Washington, DC

EPA (U.S. Environmental Protection Agency). (1990, March 8). National contingency plan. *Federal Register, 55*, 8848. Washington, DC.

EPA (U.S. Environmental Protection Agency). (1993, September). *SI 400: Introduction to risk assessment and risk management for hazardous air pollutants.* Air Pollution Training Institute. Environmental Research Center, Research Triangle Park, NC.

EPA (U.S. Environmental Protection Agency). (1997, August). *Exposure factors handbook, volume I – General factors* (EPA/600/P-95/002Fa). National Center for Environmental Assessment, Office of Research and Development, Washington, DC.

EPA (U.S. Environmental Protection Agency). (2001, December). *Risk assessment guidance for Superfund, volume III – Part A: Process for conducting probabilistic risk assessment* (EPA540-R-02-002). Office of Emergency and Remedial Response, Washington, DC.

EPA (U.S. Environmental Protection Agency). (2002a, December). *Supplemental guidance for developing soil screening levels for Superfund sites* (OSWER 9355.4-24). Office of Emergency and Remedial Response, Washington, DC.

EPA (U.S. Environmental Protection Agency). (2002b, September). *Child-specific exposure factors handbook* (EPA-600-P-00-002B). Interim Report. National Center for Environmental Assessment, Office of Research and Development, Washington, DC.

EPA (U.S. Environmental Protection Agency). (2003, December 5). *Human health toxicity values in Superfund risk assessments* (OSWER Directive 9285.7-53). Memorandum from Michael B. Cook, Director of Office of Superfund Remediation and Technology Innovation to Superfund National Policy Managers, Regions 1 – 10. Office of Emergency and Remedial Response, Washington, DC.

EPA (U.S. Environmental Protection Agency). (2004a, July). *Risk assessment guidance for Superfund, volume I: Human health evaluation manual (Part E, supplemental guidance for dermal risk assessment)* (EPA/540/R/99/005). Final. Office of Superfund Remediation and Technology Innovation, Washington, DC.

EPA (U.S. Environmental Protection Agency). (2004b, April). *ProUCL Version 3.00.02 user's guide and software* (EPA/600/R04/079). Prepared by Anita Singh and Robert Maichle with Lockheed Martin Environmental Services and Ashok K. Singh of University of Nevada for the U.S. Environmental Protection Agency.

Erdal, S. (2007). Case study: Multi-pathway risk assessment for adults and children living near a hazardous waste site. In M.G. Robson & W.A. Toscano (Eds.), *Environmental Health Risk Assessment for Public Health* (pp. 523-530). Association of Schools of Public Health.

Lilienfeld A.M. & Lilienfeld, D.E. (1980). The French influence on the development of epidemiology. *Henry E Sigerist Suppl Bull Hist Med, 4,* 28-42.

NAS (National Academy of Sciences). (1983). *Risk assessment in the federal government: Managing the process.* National Academy Press, Washington, DC.

Chapter 8

Sustainable Energy Systems

8.1 Sustainable Energy Systems - Chapter Introduction[1]

8.1.1 Learning Objectives

After reading this module, students should be able to

- outline the history of human energy use
- understand the challenges to continued reliance on fossil energy
- understand the motivations and time scale for transitions in energy use

8.1.2 Introduction and History

Energy is a pervasive human need, as basic as food or shelter to human existence. World energy use has grown dramatically since the rise of civilization lured humans from their long hunter-gatherer existence to more energy intensive lifestyles in settlements. Energy use has progressed from providing only basic individual needs such as cooking and heating to satisfying our needs for permanent housing, farming and animal husbandry, transportation, and ultimately manufacturing, city-building, entertainment, information processing and communication. Our present lifestyle is enabled by readily available inexpensive fossil energy, concentrated by nature over tens or hundreds of millions of years into convenient, high energy density deposits of **fossil fuels** that are easily recovered from mines or wells in the earth's crust.

8.1.3 Sustainability Challenges

Eighty five percent of world energy is supplied by combustion of fossil fuels. The use of these fuels (coal since the middle ages for heating; and coal, oil and gas since the **Industrial Revolution** for mechanical energy) grew naturally from their high energy density, abundance and low cost. For approximately 200 years following the Industrial Revolution, these energy sources fueled enormous advances in quality of life and economic growth. Beginning in the mid-20th Century, however, fundamental challenges began to emerge suggesting that the happy state of fossil energy use could not last forever.

8.1.3.1 Environmental Pollution

The first sustainability challenge to be addressed was environmental pollution, long noticed in industrial regions but often ignored. Developed countries passed legislation limiting the pollutants that could be emitted, and gradually over a period of more than two decades air and water quality improved until many of the most visible and harmful effects were no longer evident.

---

[1]This content is available online at <http://legacy.cnx.org/content/m41724/1.3/>.

8.1.3.2 Limited Energy Resources

The second sustainability issue to be addressed has been limited energy resources. The earth and its fossil resources are finite, a simple fact with the obvious implication that we cannot continue using fossil fuels indefinitely. The question is not when the resources will run out, rather when they will become too expensive or technically challenging to extract. Resources are distributed throughout the earth's crust – some easily accessible, others buried in remote locations or under impenetrable barriers. There are oil and gas deposits in the Arctic, for example, that have not been explored or documented, because until recently they were buried under heavy covers of ice on land and sea. We recover the easy and inexpensive resources first, leaving the difficult ones for future development. The cost-benefit balance is usually framed in terms of **peaking** – when will production reach a peak and thereafter decline, failing to satisfy rising demand, and thus create shortages? Peaks in energy production are notoriously hard to predict because rising prices, in response to rising demand and the fear of shortages, provide increasing financial resources to develop more expensive and technically challenging production opportunities.

Oil is a prime example of peaking. Although the peak in United States oil production was famously predicted by **M. King Hubbert** 20 years before it occurred, successful predictions of peaks in world oil production depend on unknown factors and are notoriously difficult (Owen, Inderwildi, & King, 2010 (p. 308); Hirsch, Bezdek, &Wendling, 2006 (p. 308)). The fundamental challenges are the unknown remaining resources at each level of recovery cost and the unknown technology breakthroughs that may lower the recovery cost. Receding Arctic ice and the growing ability to drill deeper undersea wells promise to bring more oil resources within financial and technical reach, but quantitative estimates of their impact are, at best, tentative.

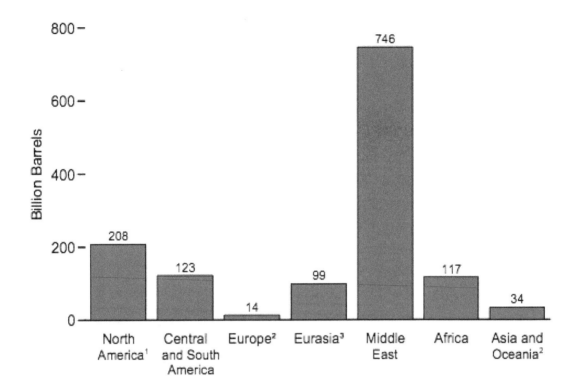

Figure 8.1: Crude Oil Reserves The global distribution of crude oil resources. [1] Includes 172.7 billion barrels of bitumen in oil sands in Alberta, Canada. [2] Excludes countries that were part of the former U.S.S.R. See " Union of Soviet Socialist Republics (U.S.S.R.)" in Glossary. [3] Includes only countries that were part of the former U.S.S.R.*Source: U.S.* [2]*Energy Information Administration, Annual Review, 2009, p. 312 (Aug. 2010)*[3]

8.1.3.3 Uneven Geographical Distribution of Energy

The third sustainability challenge is the uneven geographical distribution of energy resources. Figure **Crude Oil Reserves** (Figure 8.1) shows the distribution of crude oil reserves, with the Middle East having far more oil than any other region and Europe and Asia, two high population and high demand regions, with hardly any by comparison. This geographical imbalance between energy resources and energy use creates uncertainty and instability of supply. Weather events, natural disasters, terrorist activity or geopolitical decisions can all interrupt supply, with little recourse for the affected regions. Even if global reserves were abundant, their uneven geographical distribution creates an energy security issue for much of the world.

8.1.3.4 CO_2 Emissions and Climate Change

The final and most recent concern is carbon dioxide emissions and climate change (see Chapter **Climate and Global Change** (Section 3.1)). Since the Intergovernmental Panel on Climate Change was established by the United Nations in 1988, awareness of the links among human carbon dioxide emissions, global warming

---

[2]http://205.254.135.24/totalenergy/data/annual/pdf/aer.pdf

[3]http://205.254.135.24/totalenergy/data/annual/pdf/aer.pdf

and the potential for climate change has grown. Climate scientists worldwide have documented the evidence of global warming in surface air, land and sea temperatures, the rise of sea level, glacier ice and snow coverage, and ocean heat content (Arndt, Baringer, & Johnson, 2010 (p. 308)). Figure **Temperature, Sea Level, and Snow Cover 1850-2000** (Figure 8.2) shows three often quoted measures of global warming, the average surface temperature, the rise of sea level and the northern hemisphere snow cover.

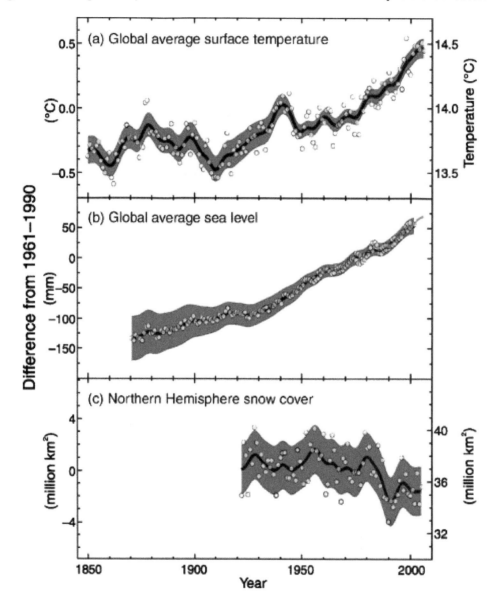

Figure 8.2:   Temperature, Sea Level, and Snow Cover 1850-2000 Three graphs show trends in average surface temperature, average sea level and northern hemisphere snow cover from 1850-2000. *Source: Climate Change 2007: Synthesis Report:* [4]*Contribution of Working Groups I, II and III to the Fourth Assessment Report of the Intergovernmental Panel on Climate Change, Cambridge University Press, figure 1.1, page 31*[5]

There can be no doubt of the rising trends, and there are disturbing signs of systematic change in other indicators as well (Arndt, et al., 2010 (p. 308)). The short-term extension of these trends can be estimated by extrapolation. Prediction beyond thirty or so years requires developing scenarios based on assumptions about the population, social behavior, economy, energy use and technology advances that will take place during this time. Because trends in these quantities are frequently punctuated by unexpected developments such as the recession of 2008 or the Fukushima nuclear disaster of 2011, the pace of carbon emissions, global warming and climate change over a century or more cannot be accurately predicted. To compensate for this uncertainty, predictions are normally based on a range of scenarios with aggressive and conservative assumptions about the degrees of population and economic growth, energy use patterns and technology advances. Although the hundred year predictions of such models differ in magnitude, the common theme is clear: continued reliance on fossil fuel combustion for 85 percent of global energy will accelerate global warming and increase the threat of climate change.

The present reliance on fossil fuels developed over time scales of decades to centuries. Figure **Primary Energy Consumption by Source, 1775-2009** (Figure 8.3) shows the pattern of fuel use in the United States since 1775.

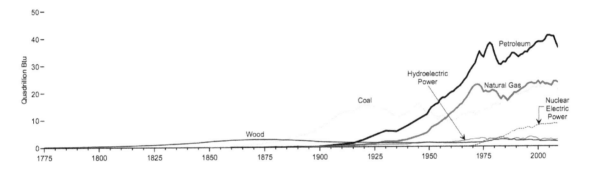

Figure 8.3: Primary Energy Consumption by Source, 1775-2009 Graph shows the pattern of fuel use in the United States since 1775. *Source: U.S. [6]Energy Information Administration, Annual Review, 2009, p. xx (Aug. 2010)*[7]

Wood was dominant for a century until the 1880s, when more plentiful, higher energy density and less expensive coal became king. It dominated until the 1950s when oil for transportation became the leading fuel, with natural gas for heating a close second. Coal is now in its second growth phase, spurred by the popularity of electricity as an energy carrier in the second half of the 20th Century. These long time scales are built into the energy system. Uses such as oil and its gasoline derivative for personal transportation in cars or the widespread use of electricity take time to establish themselves, and once established provide social and infrastructural inertia against change.

The historical changes to the energy system have been driven by several factors, including price and supply challenges of wood, the easy availability and drop-in replaceability of coal for wood, the discovery of abundant supplies of oil that enabled widespread use of the **internal combustion engine**, and the discovery of abundant natural gas that is cleaner and more transportable in pipelines than coal. These drivers of change are based on economics, convenience or new functionality; the resulting changes in our energy system provided new value to our energy mix.

The energy motivations we face now are of a different character. Instead of adding value, the motivation

[4]http://www.ipcc.ch/pdf/assessment-report/ar4/syr/ar4_syr.pdf
[5]http://www.ipcc.ch/pdf/assessment-report/ar4/syr/ar4_syr.pdf
[6]http://205.254.135.24/totalenergy/data/annual/pdf/aer.pdf
[7]http://205.254.135.24/totalenergy/data/annual/pdf/aer.pdf

is to avert "doomsday" scenarios of diminishing value: increasing environmental degradation, fuel shortages, insecure supplies and climate change. The alternatives to fossil fuel are more expensive and harder to implement, not cheaper and easier than the status quo. The historical motivations for change leading to greater value and functionality are reversed. We now face the prospect that changing the energy system to reduce our dependence on fossil fuels will increase the cost and reduce the convenience of energy.

8.1.4 Summary

Continued use of fossil fuels that now supply 85 percent of our energy needs leads to challenges of environmental degradation, diminishing energy resources, insecure energy supply, and accelerated global warming. Changing to alternate sources of energy requires decades, to develop new technologies and, once developed, to replace the existing energy infrastructure. Unlike the historical change to fossil fuel that provided increased supply, convenience and functionality, the transition to alternative energy sources is likely to be more expensive and less convenient. In this chapter you will learn about the environmental challenges of energy use, strategies for mitigating greenhouse gas emissions and climate change, electricity as a clean, efficient and versatile energy carrier, the new challenges that electricity faces in capacity, reliability and communication, the challenge of transitioning from traditional fossil to nuclear and renewable fuels for electricity production. You will also learn about the promise of biofuels from cellulose and algae as alternatives to oil, heating buildings and water with solar thermal and geothermal energy, and the efficiency advantages of combining heat and power in a single generation system. Lastly, you will learn about the benefits, challenges and outlook for electric vehicles, and the sustainable energy practices that will reduce the negative impact of energy production and use on the environment and human health.

8.1.5 Review Questions

Question 8.1.1
Fossil fuels have become a mainstay of global energy supply over the last 150 years. Why is the use of fossil fuels so widespread?

Question 8.1.2
Fossil fuels present four challenges for long-term sustainability. What are they, and how do they compare in the severity of their impact and cost of their mitigation strategies?

Question 8.1.3
The dominant global energy supply has changed from wood to coal to oil since the 1700s. How long did each of these energy transitions take to occur, and how long might a transition to alternate energy supplies require?

8.1.6 References

Arndt, D. S., Baringer, M. O., & Johnson, M. R. (eds.). (2010). State of the Climate in 2009. *Bull. Amer. Meteor. Soc.*, *91*, S1–S224, http://www.ncdc.noaa.gov/bams-state-of-the-climate/2009.php[8]

Hirsch, R.L., Bezdek, R., & Wendling, R. (2006). Peaking of World Oil Production and Its Mitigation. *AIChE Journal*, *52*, 2 – 8. doi: 10.1002/aic.10747

Owen, N.A., Inderwildi, O.R., & King, D.A. (2010). The status of conventional world oil reserves – Hype or cause for concern? *Energy Policy*,*38*, 4743 – 4749. doi: 10.1016/j.enpol.2010.02.026

---

[8]http://www.ncdc.noaa.gov/bams-state-of-the-climate/2009.php

8.2 Environmental Challenges in Energy, Carbon Dioxide, Air, Water and Land Use[9]

8.2.1 Learning Objectives

After reading this module, students should be able to

- outline environmental impacts of energy use
- evaluate the different energy sources based on their environmental impact
- understand the global capacity for each non-renewable energy source

8.2.2 Introduction

Energy to illuminate, heat and cool our homes, businesses and institutions, manufacture products, and drive our transportation systems comes from a variety of sources that are originate from our planet and solar system. This provides a social and economic benefit to society. The earth's core provides **geothermal energy**. The gravitational pull of moon and sun create tides. The sun makes power in multiple ways. By itself, the sun generates direct solar power. The sun's radiation in combination with the hydrologic cycle can make wind power and hydroelectric power. Through photosynthesis, plants grow making wood and **biomass** that decay after they die into organic matter. Over the course of thousands of years, this decay results in fossil fuels[10] that have concentrated or stored energy. To learn more about measuring different kinds of energy, known as emergy, see Chapter **Problem-Solving, Metrics and Tools for Sustainability** (Section 9.1). Each of these types of energy can be defined as **renewable** or **non-renewable** fuels and they each have some environmental and health cost.

Fossil fuel reserves are not distributed equally around the planet, nor are consumption and demand. We will see in this chapter that fuel distribution is critical to the sustainability of fossil fuel resources for a given geographic area. Access to renewable resources and their viability is greatly dependent on geography and climate. Making energy requires an input of energy so it is important to look at the net energy generated – the difference of the energy produced less the energy invested.

8.2.3 Environmental and Health Challenges of Energy Use

The environmental impacts of energy use on humans and the planet can happen anywhere during the life cycle of the energy source. The impacts begin with the extraction of the resource. They continue with the processing, purification or manufacture of the source, its transportation to place of energy generation, effects from the generation of energy including use of water, air, and land, and end with the disposal of waste generated during the process. Extraction of fossil fuels, especially as the more conventional sources are depleted, takes a high toll on the natural environment. As we mine deeper into mountains, further out at sea, or further into pristine habitats, we risk damaging fragile environments, and the results of accidents or natural disasters during extraction processes can be devastating. Fossils fuels are often located far from where they are utilized so they need to be transported by pipeline, tankers, rail or trucks. These all present the potential for accidents, leakage and spills. When transported by rail or truck energy must be expended and pollutants are generated. Processing of petroleum, gas and coal generates various types of emissions and wastes, as well as utilizes water resources. Production of energy at power plants results in air, water, and, often, waste emissions. Power plants are highly regulated by federal and state law under the Clean Air[11] and Clean Water Acts[12] , while nuclear power plants are regulated by the Nuclear Regulatory Commission[13] . As long as the facilities are complying, much of the environmental impact is mitigated by

---

[9]This content is available online at <http://legacy.cnx.org/content/m41725/1.4/>.

[10]http://www.epa.gov/cleanenergy/energy-and-you/glossary.html#F

[11]http://www.epa.gov/air/caa/

[12]http://www.epa.gov/regulations/laws/cwa.html

[13]http://www.nrc.gov/

treating the emissions and using proper waste disposal methods. However, from a sustainability perspective these still present environmental threats over the long run and have a complex variety of issues around them. Figure **Environmental Impacts of Nonrenewable and Renewable Electricity Sources** (Figure 8.4) summarizes these challenges. Later in the module, they are described more fully for each source of energy and examples are given.

SOURCE	Air Emissions lbs/MWh*				Water Resources			IMPACT		Land Resources			
	CO₂	NOx	SO₂	Other	Qty	Use	Aquatic Life	Water Discharges	Solid Waste	Extraction	Plant building	Aesthetics	Other
Coal	2,249	6	13	Mercury	Large	Mining	Yes	Pollutants & heat	Ash from plant, mining & clean stack gas	Yes	Yes	Yes	
Oil	1,672	4	12	PM, lead, VOCs	Large	Cooling at plants; Steam & cooling; Drilling water; Refineries	Yes	Rain run-off from coal piles - lead & arsenic; Treated wastewater from refineries; Drilling can contaminate underground water; Spills during shipping	Sludge from refining & other solid waste with toxics & metals	Yes	Yes	Yes	
Natural gas	1,135	1.7	0.1	Methane when not flared	Little; Large	Combustion; Hydraulic fracturing; Remove impurities while mining	Yes	Pollutants & heat; Haz chemicals from fracturing flow into surrounding area	Not much	Yes			
Nuclear	0	0	0	0	Large	Plants, steam production, cooling	Yes	Heavy metals & salts in system; Waste from mining contaminates water	Radioactive waste is problematic 2000 me-tons/yr in US	Yes	Yes	Yes	Waste storage
Hydroelectric				Methane from vegetation build up	Large	Dam affects flow of rivers	Yes	None	None			Yes	Salmon in turbines
Municipal Solid waste	3,685 (1/2 from fossil fuels)	6.7	1.2		Large	Steam & cooling	Yes	Pollutants & heat	Reduces waste to landfills but makes possibly toxic ash	Yes	Yes	Yes	Competes w/food crops
Biomass	Recycles carbon, less than fossil fuel				Large	Steam & cooling	Yes	Pollutants & heat	Ash				
Solar	Negligible				None unless making steam		No	None	Minimal haz waste from cell production	Yes			Possibly wildlife
Geothermal	Negligible				Small	Contamination from drilling & extraction							

Figure 8.4: Environmental Impacts of Nonrenewable and Renewable Electricity Sources
Source: C. Klein-Banai using data from U.S. Energy Information Administration and U.S. Environmental Protection Agency

8.2.4 Geopolitical Challenges of Fossil Fuels

The use of fossil fuels has allowed much of the global population to reach a higher standard of living. However, this dependence on fossil fuels results in many significant impacts on society. Our modern technologies and services, such as transportation, landscaping, and plastics production depend in many ways on fossil fuels. Meaning, if supplies become limited or extremely costly, our economies are vulnerable. If countries do not have fossil fuel reserves of their own, they incur even more risk. The United States has become more and more dependent on foreign oil since 1970 when our own oil production peaked. We imported over half of the crude oil and refined petroleum products that we consumed during 2009. Just over half of these imports came from the Western Hemisphere (see Figure **Sources of United States Net Petroleum Imports, 2009** (Figure 8.5)).

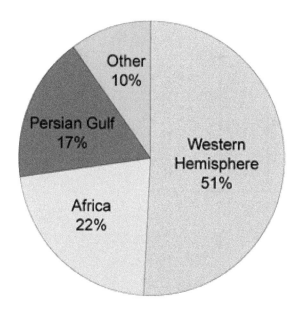

Figure 8.5: Sources of United States Net Petroleum Imports, 2009 Figure illustrates that the United States imported over half of the crude oil and refined petroleum products that it consumed during 2009. *Source: U.S. Energy Information Administration, Petroleum Supply Annual, 2009, preliminary data*[14]

The holder of oil reserves in the oil market is the Organization of Petroleum Exporting Countries[15] , (OPEC) (see Figure **Proven Oil Reserves Holders** (Figure 8.6)). As of January 2009, there were 12 member countries in OPEC: Algeria, Angola, Ecuador, Iran, Iraq, Kuwait, Libya, Nigeria, Qatar, Saudi Arabia, the United Arab Emirates, and Venezuela. OPEC attempts to influence the amount of oil available to the world by assigning a production quota to each member except Iraq, for which no quota is presently set. Overall compliance with these quotas is mixed since the individual countries make the actual production decisions. All of these countries have a national oil company but also allow international oil companies to operate within their borders. They can restrict the amounts of production by those oil companies. Therefore, the OPEC countries have a large influence on how much of world demand is met by OPEC and non-OPEC supply. A recent example of this is the price increases that occurred during the year 2011 after multiple popular uprisings in Arab countries, including Libya.

---

[14]http://www.eia.doe.gov/energy_in_brief/foreign_oil_dependence.cfm
[15]http://www.opec.org/

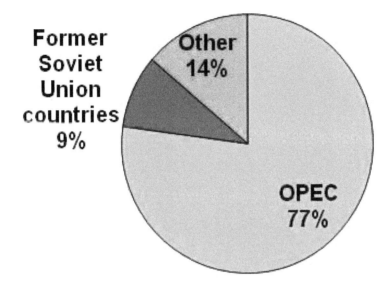

Figure 8.6: **Proven Oil Reserves Holders** Pie chart shows proven oil reserves holders. *Source: C. Klein-Banai*[16] *using data from BP Statistical Review of World Energy (2010)*[17]

This pressure has lead the United States to developing policies that would reduce reliance on foreign oil such as developing additional domestic sources and obtaining it from non-Middle Eastern countries such as Canada, Mexico, Venezuela, and Nigeria. However, since fossil fuel reserves create jobs and provide dividends to investors, a lot is at stake in a nation that has these reserves. Depending on whether that oil wealth is shared with the country's inhabitants or retained by the oil companies and dictatorships, as in Nigeria prior to the 1990s, a nation with fossil fuel reserves may benefit or come out even worse.

8.2.5 Nonrenewable Energy and the Environment

Fossil fuels are also known as non-renewable energy because it takes thousands of years for the earth to regenerate them. The three main fuel sources come in all phases – solid, liquid, and gas – and will be discussed in that order. One overriding concern is the carbon dioxide emissions that contribute to climate change. Figure **Fuel Type and Carbon Emissions** (Figure 8.7) displays the relationship between fuel type and carbon emissions.

---

[16]http://cnx.org/member_profile/cindykb
[17]http://www.bp.com/statisticalreview

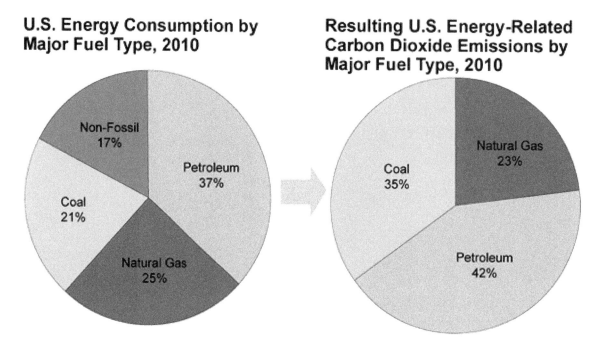

Figure 8.7: Fuel Type and Carbon Emissions The two charts show the relationship between fuel type and carbon emissions for U.S. energy consumption in 2010. *Source: U.S. Energy Information Administration*[18]

8.2.5.1 Solid Fossil Fuel: Coal

Coal comes from organic matter that was compressed under high pressure to become a dense, solid carbon structure over thousands to millions of years. Due to its relatively low cost and abundance, coal is used to generate about half of the electricity consumed in the United States. Coal is the largest domestically produced source of energy. Figure **Historic U.S. Coal Production** (Figure 8.8) shows how coal production has doubled in the United States over the last sixty year. Current world reserves are estimated at 826,000 million tonnes, with nearly 30 percent of that in the United States. It is a major fuel resource that the United States controls domestically.

---

[18]http://www.eia.gov/energy_in_brief/role_coal_us.cfm

Million Short Tons

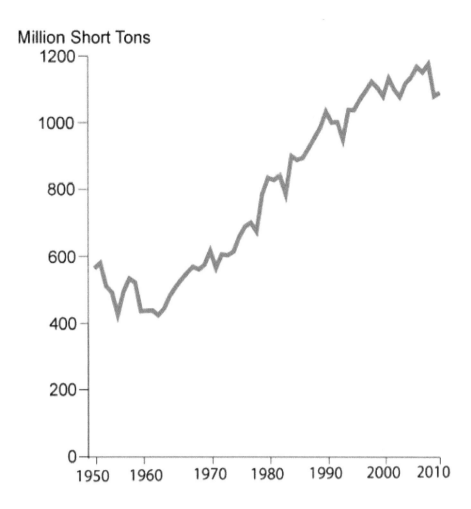

Figure 8.8: Historic U.S. Coal Production Graph shows U.S. Coal Production from 1950-2010. *Source: U.S. Energy Information Administration*[19]

Coal is plentiful and inexpensive, when looking only at the market cost relative to the cost of other sources of electricity, but its extraction, transportation, and use produces a multitude of environmental impacts that the market cost does not truly represent. Coal emits sulfur dioxide, nitrogen oxide, and mercury, which have been linked to acid rain, smog, and health issues. Burning of coal emits higher amounts of carbon dioxide per unit of energy than the use of oil or natural gas. Coal accounted for 35 percent of the total United States emissions of carbon dioxide released into the Earth's atmosphere in 2010 (see Figure **Fuel Type and Carbon Emissions** (Figure 8.7)). Ash generated from combustion contributes to water contamination. Some coal mining has a negative impact on ecosystems and water quality, and alters landscapes and scenic views. There are also significant health effects and risks to coal miners and those living in the vicinity of coal mines.

Traditional underground mining is risky to mine workers due to the risk of entrapment or death. Over the last 15 years, the U.S. Mine Safety and Health Administration has published the number of mine worker fatalities and it has varied from 18-48 per year (see Figure **U.S. Coal Mining Related Fatalities** (Figure 8.9)).

[19]http://www.eia.gov/energy_in_brief/images/charts/us_coal_production-large.jpg

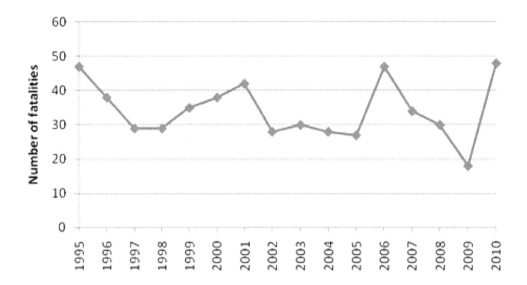

Figure 8.9:   U.S. Coal Mining Related Fatalities Graph shows U.S. coal mining related fatalities from 1995-2010. *Source: C. Klein-Banai*[20] *using data from the U.S. Department of Labor, Mine Safety and Health Administration*[21]

Twenty-nine miners died on April 6, 2010 in an explosion at the Upper Big Branch coal mine in West Virginia, contributing to the uptick in deaths between 2009 and 2010. In other countries, with less safety regulations, accidents occur more frequently. In May 2011, for example, three people died and 11 were trapped in a coalmine in Mexico for several days. There is also risk of getting black lung disease (pneumoconiosis)[22] This is a disease of the lungs caused by the inhalation of coal dust over a long period of time. It causes coughing and shortness of breath. If exposure is stopped the outcome is good. However, the complicated form may cause shortness of breath that gets increasingly worse.

Mountain Top Mining (MTM), while less hazardous to workers, has particularly detrimental effects on land resources. MTM is a surface mining practice involving the removal of mountaintops to expose coal seams, and disposing of the associated mining waste in adjacent valleys – "valley fills." The process of MTM[23] is described in more detail by the U.S. Environmental Protection Agency (U.S. EPA).

[20] http://cnx.org/member_profile/cindykb
[21] http://www.msha.gov/FATALS/FABC95.HTM
[22] http://www.cdc.gov/niosh/topics/pneumoconioses/
[23] http://www.epa.gov/region3/mtntop/process.htm

Figure 8.10: Mountaintop Removal Coal Mining in Martin County, Kentucky Photograph shows mountaintop coal removal mining in Martin County, Kentucky. *Source: Flashdark*[24].

The following are some examples of the impact of MTM:

- an increase of minerals in the water that negatively impact fish and macroinvertebrates, leading to less diverse and more pollutant-tolerant species
- streams are sometimes covered up by silt from mining
- the re-growth of trees and woody plants on regraded land may be slowed due to compacted soils
- affects the diversity of bird and amphibian species in the area since the ecosystem changes from wooded areas to other
- there may be social, economic and heritage issues created by the loss of wooded land that may have been important to traditions and economies of the area

A study by Epstein, et al. (2011) (p. 333) assigned a monetary value (full cost accounting) for the life cycle of coal in the United States, accounting for many environmental and health impacts of coal. The authors found the cost to be about \$0.178/kWh of electricity generated from coal (\$345.4 billion in 2008), doubling or tripling the price of coal-generated electricity. This study accounted for all of the impacts discussed above and more.

8.2.5.2 Liquid Fossil Fuel: Petroleum

Thirty seven percent of the world's energy consumption and 43 percent of the United States energy consumption comes from oil. As discussed above, most of the oil production is in the Gulf region. Scientists and policy-makers often discuss the question of when the world will reach peak oil production, and there are a lot of variables in that equation, but it is generally thought that peak oil will be reached by the middle of the 21st Century. Currently world reserves are 1.3 trillion barrels, or 45 years left at current level of production, but we may reduce production as supplies run low.

---

[24]http://en.wikipedia.org/wiki/File:Martin_County_home.jpg

8.2.5.2.1 Environmental Impacts of Oil Extraction and Refining

Oil is usually found one to two miles (1.6 – 3.2 km) below the surface. Oil refineries separate the mix of crude oil into the different types for gas, diesel fuel, tar, and asphalt. To find and extract oil workers must drill deep below ocean floor. As the United States tries to extract more oil from its own resources, we are drilling even deeper into the earth and increasing the environmental risks.

The largest United States oil spill to date[25] began in April 2010 when an explosion occurred on Deepwater Horizon Oil Rig killing 11 employees and spilling nearly 200 million gallons of oil before the resulting leak could be stopped. Wildlife, ecosystems, and people's livelihood were adversely affected. A lot of money and huge amounts of energy and waste were expended on immediate clean-up efforts. The long-term impacts are still not known. The National Commission on the Deepwater Horizon Oil Spill and Offshore Drilling[26] was set up to study what went wrong. This video[27] summarizes their findings.

Once oil is found and extracted it must be refined. Oil refining is one of top sources of air pollution in the United States for volatile organic hydrocarbons and toxic emissions, and the single largest source of carcinogenic benzene.

When petroleum is burned as gasoline or diesel, or to make electricity or to power boilers for heat, it produces a number of emissions that have a detrimental effect on the environment and human health:

- Carbon dioxide[28] (CO_2) is a greenhouse gas and a source of climate change.
- Sulfur dioxide[29] (SO_2) causes acid rain, which damages plants and animals that live in water, and it increases or causes respiratory illnesses and heart diseases, particularly in vulnerable populations like children and the elderly.
- Nitrous oxides[30] (NO_x) and Volatile Organic Carbons[31] (VOCs) contribute to ozone[32] at ground level, which is an irritatant and causes damage to the lungs.
- Particulate Matter[33] (PM) produces hazy conditions in cities and scenic areas, and combines with ozone to contribute to asthma and chronic bronchitis, especially in children and the elderly. Very small, or "fine PM," is also thought to penetrate the respiratory system more deeply and cause emphysema and lung cancer.
- Lead[34] can have severe health impacts, especially for children.
- Air toxins are known or probable carcinogens.

There are other domestic sources of liquid fossil fuel that are being considered as conventional resources and are being depleted. These include soil sands/tar sands – deposits of moist sand and clay with 1-2 percent bitumen (thick and heavy petroleum rich in carbon and poor in hydrogen). These are removed by strip mining (see section above on coal). Another source is oil shale in United States west which is sedimentary rock filled with organic matter that can be processed to produce liquid petroleum. Also, mined by strip mines or subsurface mines, oil shale can be burned directly like coal or baked in the presence of hydrogen to extract liquid petroleum. However, the net energy values are low and they are expensive to extract and process. Both of these resources have severe environmental impacts due to strip mining, carbon dioxide, methane and other air pollutants similar to other fossil fuels.

8.2.5.3 Gaseous Fossil Fuel: Natural Gas

Natural gas meets 20 percent of world energy needs and 25 percent of United States needs. Natural gas is mainly composed of methane, the shortest hydrocarbon (CH_4), and is a very potent greenhouse gas. There

[25]http://en.wikipedia.org/wiki/Deepwater_Horizon_oil_spill
[26]http://www.oilspillcommission.gov/
[27]http://www.oilspillcommission.gov/media/
[28]http://www.oilspillcommission.gov/media/
[29]http://www.epa.gov/cleanenergy/energy-and-you/glossary.html#S
[30]http://www.epa.gov/cleanenergy/energy-and-you/glossary.html#N
[31]http://www.epa.gov/air/emissions/voc.htm
[32]http://www.epa.gov/ozone/
[33]http://www.epa.gov/cleanenergy/energy-and-you/glossary.html#P
[34]http://www.epa.gov/iaq/lead.html

are two types of natural gas. Biogenic gas is found at shallow depths and arises from anaerobic decay of organic matter by bacteria, like landfill gas. Thermogenic gas comes from the compression of organic matter and deep heat underground. They are found with petroleum in reservoir rocks and with coal deposits, and these fossil fuels are extracted together.

Methane is released into the atmosphere from coal mines, oil and gas wells, and natural gas storage tanks, pipelines, and processing plants. These leaks are the source of about 25 percent of total U.S. methane emissions, which translates to three percent of total U.S. greenhouse gas emissions. When natural gas is produced but cannot be captured and transported economically, it is "flared," or burned at well sites. This is considered to be safer and better than releasing methane into the atmosphere because CO_2 is a less potent greenhouse gas than methane.

In the last few years a new reserve of natural gas has been identified - shale resources. The United States possesses 2,552 trillion cubic feet (Tcf) (72.27 trillion cubic meters) of potential natural gas resources, with shale resources accounting for 827 Tcf (23.42 tcm). As gas prices increased it has become more economical to extract the gas from shale. Figure **U.S. Natural Gas Supply, 1990-2035** (Figure 8.11) shows the past and forecasted U.S. natural gas production and the various sources. The current reserves are enough to last about 110 years at the 2009 rate of U.S. consumption (about 22.8 Tcf per year -645.7 bcm per year).

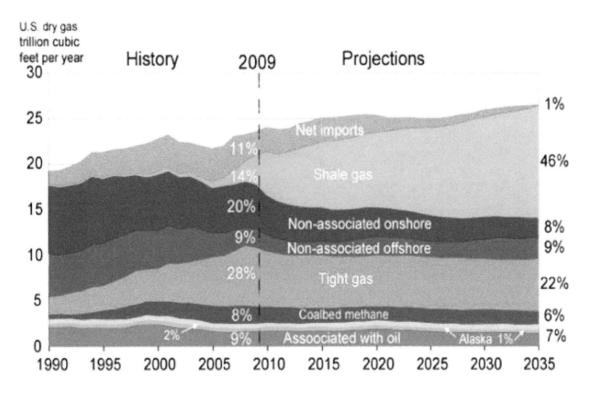

Figure 8.11: **U.S. Natural Gas Supply, 1990-2035** Graph shows U.S. historic and projected natural gas production from various sources. *Source: U.S. Energy Information Administration*[35]

Natural gas is a preferred energy source when considering its environmental impacts. Specifically, when burned, much less carbon dioxide (CO_2), nitrogen oxides, and sulfur dioxide are omitted than from the combustion of coal or oil (see Table **Environmental Impacts of Nonrenewable and Renewable Electricity Sources**). It also does not produce ash or toxic emissions.

---

[35]http://www.eia.gov/energy_in_brief/about_shale_gas.cfm

8.2.5.3.1 Environmental Impacts of Exploration, Drilling, and Production

Land resources are affected when geologists explore for natural gas deposits on land, as vehicles disturb vegetation and soils. Road clearing, pipeline and drill pad construction also affect natural habitats by clearing and digging. Natural gas production can also result in the production of large volumes of contaminated water. This water has to be properly handled, stored, and treated so that it does not pollute land and water supplies.

Extraction of shale gas is more problematic than traditional sources due to a process nicknamed "fracking," or fracturing of wells, since it requires large amounts of water (see Figure **Hydraulic Fracturing Process** (Figure 8.12)). The considerable use of water may affect the availability of water for other uses in some regions and this can affect aquatic habitats. If mismanaged, hydraulic fracturing fluid can be released by spills, leaks, or various other exposure pathways. The fluid contains potentially hazardous chemicals such as hydrochloric acid, glutaraldehyde, petroleum distillate, and ethylene glycol. The risks of fracking have been highlighted in popular culture in the documentary, Gasland[36] (2010).

Fracturing also produces large amounts of wastewater, which may contain dissolved chemicals from the hydraulic fluid and other contaminants that require treatment before disposal or reuse. Because of the quantities of water used and the complexities inherent in treating some of the wastewater components, treatment and disposal is an important and challenging issue.

The raw gas from a well may contain many other compounds besides the methane that is being sought, including hydrogen sulfide, a very toxic gas. Natural gas with high concentrations of hydrogen sulfide is usually flared which produces CO_2, carbon monoxide, sulfur dioxide, nitrogen oxides, and many other compounds. Natural gas wells and pipelines often have engines to run equipment and compressors, which produce additional air pollutants and noise.

---

[36]http://www.gaslandthemovie.com/

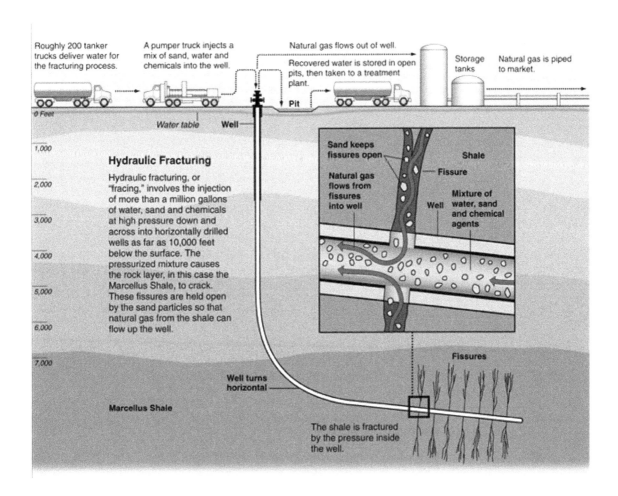

Figure 8.12: Hydraulic Fracturing Process Graphic illustrates the process of hydraulic fracturing. *Source: Al Granberg, ProPublica*[37]. *This graphic may not be relicensed for sale except by the copyright holder (ProPublica).*

8.2.6 Alternatives to Fossil Fuels

8.2.6.1 Nuclear Power

Nuclear power plants produce no carbon dioxide and, therefore, are often considered an alternative fuel, when the main concern is climate change. Currently, world production is about 19.1 trillion KWh, with the United States producing and consuming about 22 percent of that. Nuclear power provides about nine percent of our total consumption for electricity (see Figure **U.S. Energy Consumption by Energy Source, 2009** (Figure 8.13)).

However, there are environmental challenges with nuclear power. Mining and refining uranium ore and making reactor fuel demands a lot of energy. The plants themselves are made of metal and concrete which also requires energy to make. The main environmental challenge for nuclear power is the wastes including uranium mill tailings, spent (used) reactor fuel, and other radioactive wastes. These materials have long **radioactive half-lives** and thus remain a threat to human health for thousands of years. The U.S. Nuclear

---
[37]http://www.propublica.org/special/hydraulic-fracturing-national

Regulatory Commission[38] regulates the operation of nuclear power plants and the handling, transportation, storage, and disposal of radioactive materials to protect human health and the environment.

By volume, uranium mill tailings are the largest waste and they contain the radioactive element radium, which decays to produce radon, a radioactive gas. This waste is placed near the processing facility or mill where they come from, and are covered with a barrier of a material such as clay to prevent radon from escaping into the atmosphere and then a layer of soil, rocks, or other materials to prevent erosion of the sealing barrier.

High-level radioactive waste consists of used nuclear reactor fuel. This fuel is in a solid form consisting of small fuel pellets in long metal tubes and must be stored and handled with multiple containment, first cooled by water and later in special outdoor concrete or steel containers that are cooled by air. There is no long-term storage facility for this fuel in the United States.

There are many other regulatory precautions governing permitting, construction, operation, and decommissioning of nuclear power plants due to risks from an uncontrolled nuclear reaction. The potential for contamination of air, water and food is high should an uncontrolled reaction occur. Even when planning for worst-case scenarios, there are always risks of unexpected events. For example, the March 2011 earthquake and subsequent tsunami that hit Japan resulted in reactor meltdowns at the Fukushima Daiichi Nuclear Power Station causing massive damage to the surrounding area.

NOTE: Fukushima Daiichi Nuclear Power Station[39]

- March 11, 2011: Magnitude 9.0 earthquake 231 miles northeast of Tokyo. Less than 1 hour later a 14m tsunami hit
- 50 power station employees worked around the clock to try to stabilize the situation

United States' nuclear reactors have containment vessels that are designed to withstand extreme weather events and earthquakes. However, in the aftermath of the Japan incident, they are reviewing their facilities, policies, and procedures.

---

[38]http://www.nrc.gov/
[39]http://www.iaea.org/newscenter/focus/fukushima/index.html

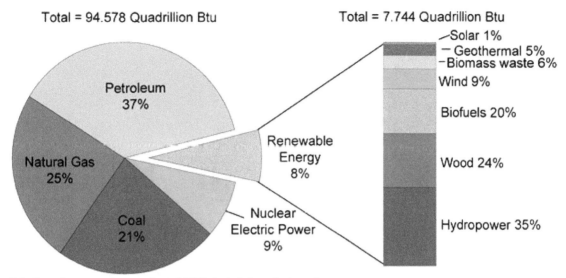

Figure 8.13: U.S. Energy Consumption by Energy Source, 2009 Renewable energy makes up 8% of U.S. energy consumption. *Source: U.S. Energy Information Administration*[40]

8.2.6.2 Hydropower

Hydropower (hydro-electric) is considered a clean and renewable source of energy since it does not directly produce emissions of air pollutants and the source of power is regenerated. However, hydropower dams, reservoirs, and the operation of generators can have environmental impacts. Figure **Hoover Power Plant** (Figure 8.14) shows the Hoover Power Plant located on the Colorado River. Hydropower provides 35 percent of the United States' renewable energy consumption (see Figure **U.S. Energy Consumption by Energy Source, 2009** (Figure 8.13)). In 2003 capacity was at 96,000 MW and it was estimated that 30,000 MW capacity is undeveloped.

---

[40]http://www.eia.gov/energy_in_brief/renewable_energy.cfm

Figure 8.14: Hoover Power Plant View of Hoover Power Plant on the Colorado River as seen from above. *Source: U.S. Department of the Interior*[41]

Migration of fish to their upstream spawning areas can be obstructed by a dam that is used to create a reservoir or to divert water to a run-of-river hydropower plant. A reservoir and operation of the dam can affect the natural water habitat due to changes in water temperatures, chemistry, flow characteristics, and silt loads, all of which can lead to significant changes in the ecology and physical characteristics of the river upstream and downstream. Construction of reservoirs may cause natural areas, farms, and archeological sites to be covered and force populations to relocate. Hydro turbines kill and injure some of the fish that pass through the turbine although there are ways to reduce that effect. In areas where salmon must travel upstream to spawn, such as along the Columbia River in Washington and Oregon, the dams get in the way. This problem can be partially alleviated by using "fish ladders" that help the salmon get up the dams.

Carbon dioxide and methane may also form in reservoirs where water is more stagnant and be emitted to the atmosphere. The exact amount of greenhouse gases produced from hydropower plant reservoirs is uncertain. If the reservoirs are located in tropical and temperate regions, including the United States, those emissions may be equal to or greater than the greenhouse effect of the carbon dioxide emissions from an equivalent amount of electricity generated with fossil fuels (EIA, 2011 (p. 333)).

---

[41]http://www.usbr.gov/lc/hooverdam/gallery/pwrplant.html

8.2.6.3 Municipal Solid Waste

Waste to energy processes are gaining renewed interest as they can solve two problems at once – disposal of waste as landfill capacity decreases and production of energy from a renewable resource. Many of the environmental impacts are similar to those of a coal plant – air pollution, ash generation, etc. Since the fuel source is less standardized than coal and hazardous materials may be present in municipal solid waste (MSW), or garbage, incinerators and waste-to-energy power plants need to clean the stack gases of harmful materials. The U.S. EPA regulates these plants very strictly and requires anti-pollution devices to be installed. Also, while incinerating at high temperature many of the toxic chemicals may break down into less harmful compounds.

The ash from these plants may contain high concentrations of various metals that were present in the original waste. If ash is clean enough it can be "recycled" as an MSW landfill cover or to build roads, cement block and artificial reefs.

8.2.6.4 Biomass

Biomass is derived from plants. Examples include lumber mill sawdust, paper mill sludge, yard waste, or oat hulls from an oatmeal processing plant. A major challenge of biomass is determining if it is really a more sustainable option. It often takes energy to make energy and biomass is one example where the processing to make it may not be offset by the energy it produces. For example, biomass combustion may increase or decrease emission of air pollutants depending on the type of biomass and the types of fuels or energy sources that it replaces. Biomass reduces the demand for fossil fuels, but when the plants that are the sources of biomass are grown, a nearly equivalent amount of CO_2 is captured through photosynthesis, thus it recycles the carbon. If these materials are grown and harvested in a sustainable way there can be no net increase in CO_2 emissions. Each type of biomass must be evaluated for its full life-cycle impact in order to determine if it is really advancing sustainability and reducing environmental impacts.

Figure 8.15: Woodchips Photograph shows a pile of woodchips, which are a type of biomass. *Source: Ulrichulrich*[42]

8.2.6.4.1 Solid Biomass: Burning Wood

Using wood, and charcoal made from wood, for heating and cooking can replace fossil fuels and may result in lower CO_2 emissions. If wood is harvested from forests or woodlots that have to be thinned or from urban trees that fall down or needed be cut down anyway, then using it for biomass does not impact those ecosystems. However, wood smoke contains harmful pollutants like carbon monoxide and particulate matter. For home heating, it is most efficient and least polluting when using a modern wood stove or fireplace insert that are designed to release small amounts of particulates. However, in places where wood and charcoal are major cooking and heating fuels such as in undeveloped countries, the wood may be harvested faster than trees can grow resulting in deforestation.

Biomass is also being used on a larger scale, where there are small power plants. For instance, Colgate College has had a wood-burning boiler since the mid-1980's and in one year it processed approximately 20,000 tons of locally and sustainably harvested wood chips, the equivalent of 1.17 million gallons (4.43 million liters) of fuel oil, avoiding 13,757 tons of emissions, and saving the university over $1.8 million in heating costs. The University's steam-generating wood-burning facility now satisfies more than 75 percent of the campus's heat and domestic hot water needs. For more information about this, click here[43]

---

[42]http://en.wikipedia.org/wiki/File:Raumaustragung_Hackschnitzel.JPG
[43]http://www.nwf.org/campusEcology/docs/Colgate%20University%202010%20Case%20Study%20Energy%20FINAL.pdf

8.2.6.4.2 Gaseous Biomass: Landfill Gas or Biogas

Landfill gas[44] and biogas is a sort of man-made "biogenic" gas as discussed above. Methane and carbon dioxide are formed as a result of biological processes in sewage treatment plants, waste landfills, anaerobic composting, and livestock manure management systems. This gas is captured, and burned to produce heat or electricity usually for on-site generation. The electricity may replace electricity produced by burning fossil fuels and result in a net reduction in CO_2 emissions. The only environmental impacts are from the construction of the plant itself, similar to that of a natural gas plant.

8.2.6.4.3 Liquid Biofuels: Ethanol and Biodiesel

Biofuels may be considered to be carbon-neutral because the plants that are used to make them (such as corn and sugarcane for ethanol, and soy beans and palm oil trees for biodiesel) absorb CO_2 as they grow and may offset the CO_2 produced when biofuels are made and burned. Calculating the net energy or CO_2 generated or reduced in the process of producing the biofuel is crucial to determining its environmental impact.

Even if the environmental impact is net positive, the economic and social effects of growing plants for fuels need to be considered, since the land, fertilizers, and energy used to grow biofuel crops could be used to grow food crops instead. The competition of land for fuel vs. food can increase the price of food, which has a negative effect on society. It could also decrease the food supply increasing malnutrition and starvation globally. Biofuels may be derived from parts of plants not used for food (cellulosic biomass) thus reducing that impact. Cellulosic ethanol feedstock includes native prairie grasses, fast growing trees, sawdust, and even waste paper. Also, in some parts of the world, large areas of natural vegetation and forests have been cut down to grow sugar cane for ethanol and soybeans and palm-oil trees to make biodiesel. This is not sustainable land use.

Biofuels typically replace petroleum and are used to power vehicles. Although ethanol has higher octane and ethanol-gasoline mixtures burn cleaner than pure gasoline, they also are more volatile and thus have higher "evaporative emissions" from fuel tanks and dispensing equipment. These emissions contribute to the formation of harmful, ground level ozone and smog. Gasoline requires extra processing to reduce evaporative emissions before it is blended with ethanol.

Biodiesel can be made from used vegetable oil and has been produced on a very local basis. Compared to petroleum diesel, biodiesel combustion produces less sulfur oxides, particulate matter, carbon monoxide, and unburned and other hydrocarbons, but more nitrogen oxide.

8.2.6.5 Endless Sources of Energy: Earth, Wind, and Sun

8.2.6.5.1 Geothermal Energy

Five percent of the United States' renewable energy portfolio is from geothermal energy (see Figure **U.S. Energy Consumption by Energy Source, 2009** (Figure 8.13)). The subsurface temperature of the earth provides an endless energy resource. The environmental impact of geothermal energy depends on how it is being used. Direct use and heating applications have almost no negative impact on the environment.

---

[44]http://www.eia.gov/tools/glossary/index.cfm?id=L

Figure 8.16: Installing a Geothermal Pipe System Drilling to install geothermal ground source pipe system. *Source: Office of Sustainability, UIC*[45]

Geothermal power plants do not burn fuel to generate electricity so their emission levels are very low. They release less than one percent of the carbon dioxide emissions of a fossil fuel plant. **Geothermal plants** use scrubber systems to clean the air of hydrogen sulfide that is naturally found in the steam and hot water. They emit 97 percent less acid rain-causing sulfur compounds than are emitted by fossil fuel plants. After the steam and water from a geothermal reservoir have been used, they are injected back into the earth.

Geothermal ground source systems utilize a heat-exchange system that runs in the subsurface about 20

---

[45]http://www.uic.edu/sustainability/

feet (5 meters) below the surface where the ground is at a constant temperature. The system uses the earth as a heat source (in the winter) or a heat sink[46] (in the summer). This reduces the energy consumption requires to generate heat from gas, steam, hot water, and chiller and conventional electric air-conditioning systems. See more in Chapter **Sustainable Energy Systems** (Section 8.1).

8.2.6.5.2 Solar Energy

Solar power has minimal impact on the environment, depending on where it is placed. In 2009, one percent of the renewable energy generated in the United States was from solar power (1646 MW) out of the eight percent of the total electricity generation that was from renewable sources. The manufacturing of **photovoltaic (PV) cells** generates some hazardous waste from the chemicals and solvents used in processing. Often solar arrays are placed on roofs of buildings or over parking lots or integrated into construction in other ways. However, large systems may be placed on land and particularly in deserts where those fragile ecosystems could be damaged if care is not taken. Some solar thermal systems use potentially hazardous fluids (to transfer heat) that require proper handling and disposal. Concentrated solar systems may need to be cleaned regularly with water, which is also needed for cooling the turbine-generator. Using water from underground wells may affect the ecosystem in some arid locations.

---

[46]http://en.wikipedia.org/wiki/Heat_sink

Figure 8.17: Rooftop Solar Installations Rooftop solar installation on Douglas Hall at the University of Illinois at Chicago has no effect on land resources, while producing electricity with zero emissions. *Source: Office of Sustainability, UIC*[47]

[47]http://www.uic.edu/sustainability/

8.2.6.5.3 Wind

Wind is a renewable energy source that is clean and has very few environmental challenges. Wind turbines are becoming a more prominent sight across the United States, even in regions that are considered to have less wind potential. Wind turbines (often called windmills) do not release emissions that pollute the air or water (with rare exceptions), and they do not require water for cooling. The U.S. wind industry had 40,181 MW of wind power capacity installed at the end of 2010, with 5,116 MW installed in 2010 alone, providing more than 20 percent of installed wind power around the globe. According to the American Wind Energy Association[48] , over 35 percent of all new electrical generating capacity in the United States since 2006 was due to wind, surpassed only by natural gas.

Figure 8.18: Twin Groves Wind Farm, Illinois Wind power is becoming a more popular source of energy in the United States. *Source: Office of Sustainability, UIC*[49]

Since a wind turbine has a small physical footprint relative to the amount of electricity it produces, many wind farms are located on crop, pasture, and forest land. They contribute to economic sustainability by providing extra income to farmers and ranchers, allowing them to stay in business and keep their property from being developed for other uses. For example, energy can be produced by installing wind turbines in the Appalachian mountains of the United States instead of engaging in mountain top removal for coal mining.

---

[48]http://www.awea.org/learnabout/industry_stats/index.cfm

[49]http://www.uic.edu/sustainability/

Off shore wind turbines on lakes or the ocean may have smaller environmental impacts than turbines on land.

Wind turbines do have a few environmental challenges. There are aesthetic concerns to some people when they see them on the landscape. A few wind turbines have caught on fire, and some have leaked lubricating fluids, though this is relatively rare. Some people do not like the sound that wind turbine blades make. Listen to one here[50] and see what you think.

Turbines have been found to cause bird and bat deaths particularly if they are located along their migratory path. This is of particular concern if these are threatened or endangered species. There are ways to mitigate that impact and it is currently being researched.

There are some small impacts from the construction of wind projects or farms, such as the construction of service roads, the production of the turbines themselves, and the concrete for the foundations. However, overall life cycle analysis has found that turbines make much more energy than the amount used to make and install them.

8.2.7 Summary

We derive our energy from a multitude of resources that have varying environmental challenges related to air and water pollution, land use, carbon dioxide emissions, resource extraction and supply, as well as related safety and health issues. A diversity of resources can help maintain political and economic independence for the United States. Renewable energy sources have lower environmental impact and can provide local energy resources. Each resource needs to be evaluated within the sustainability paradigm. In the near future, we can expect the interim use of more difficult and environmentally-challenging extraction methods to provide fossil fuels until the growth and development of renewable and clean energy sources will be able to meet our energy demands.

8.2.8 Review Questions

Question 8.2.1
Describe three major environmental challenges for fossil fuels in general or one in particular.

Question 8.2.2
What are the compelling reasons to continue using coal in spite of its challenges?

Question 8.2.3
Rate the following electricity sources for their contribution to climate change from most to least: biomass, coal, solar, wind, nuclear, natural gas, oil, geothermal, hydroelectric, MSW. Is there any compelling reason not to use any of the carbon neutral (no net carbon emissions) sources?

Question 8.2.4
Describe the environmental and social concerns with regard to biofuels.

8.2.9 Resources

To learn more about global energy issues, visit the International Energy Agency website[51] .

To learn more about United States and international energy issues, visit the U.S. Energy Information Administration website[52] .

To learn more about the U.S. Nuclear Regulatory Commission, please click here[53] .

Learn about your clean energy options here[54] .

---

[50]http://www.youtube.com/v/VuAiEOhMyMI&hl=en_US&feature=player_embedded&version=
[51]http://www.iea.org/
[52]http://www.eia.gov/tools/glossary/index.cfm?id=L
[53]http://www.eia.gov/tools/glossary/index.cfm?id=L
[54]http://www.epa.gov/cleanenergy/energy-and-you/index.html

8.2.10 References

American Wind Energy Association. (2011). *Industry Statistics.* Retrieved September 6, 2011 from http://www.awea.org/learnabout/industry_stats/index.cfm[55]

Epstein, P.R., Buonocare, J.J, Eckerle, K., Hendryx, M., Stout III, B.M., Heinberg, R., et al. (2011). Full cost accounting for the life cycle of coal. *Annals of the New York Academy of Sciences, 1219,* 73-98. Retrieved May 17, 2011 from http://mlui.org/downloads/CoalExternalitiesHarvard02-17-11.pdf[56]

U.S. Energy Information Administration. (2011). *Hydropower generators produce clean electricity, but hydropower does have environmental impacts.* Retrieved September 6, 2011 from http://www.eia.gov/energyexplained/index.cfm?page=hydropower_environment[57]

Wood, J.H., Long, G.R, & Morehouse, D.F. (2004). *Long-term world oil supply scenarios:The future is neither as bleak or rosy as some assert.* Energy Information Administration. Retrieved May 17, 2011 from http://www.eia.doe.gov/pub/oil_gas/petroleum/feature_articles/2004/worldoilsupply/oilsupply04.html[58]

8.3 Case Study: Greenhouse Gases and Climate Change[59]

8.3.1 Introduction

If increased greenhouse gas emissions from human activity are causing climate change, then how do we reduce those emissions? Whether dictated by an international, national, or local regulation or a voluntary agreement, plans are needed to move to a low-carbon economy. In the absence of federal regulation, cities, states, government institutions, and colleges and universities, have all taken climate action initiatives. This case study provides two examples of climate action plans – one for a city (Chicago) and one for an institution (the University of Illinois at Chicago).

8.3.2 Chicago's Climate Action Plan

Urban areas produce a lot of waste. In fact, 75 percent of all greenhouse gas emissions are generated in urban areas. Therefore, it is important for cities to develop plans to address environmental issues. The Chicago Climate Action Plan[60] (Chicago CAP) is one such example. The mid-term goal of this plan is a 25 percent reduction in greenhouse gas emissions by 2020 and final goal is 80 percent reduction below 1990 GHG levels by the year 2050.

The Chicago CAP outlines several benefits of a climate action plan. The first would obviously be the reduction of the effects of climate change. Under a higher emissions scenario as per the Intergovernmental Panel on Climate Change[61] (IPCC), it is predicted that the number of 100 degree Fahrenheit days per year would increase to 31, under the lower emissions scenario it would only be eight. Established by the United Nations Environment Programme[62] (UNEP), the IPCC is the leading international body that assesses climate change through the contributions of thousands of scientists.

Second, there is an economic benefit derived from increased efficiencies that reduce energy and water consumption. Third, local governments and agencies have great influence over their city's greenhouse gas emissions and can enhance energy efficiency of buildings through codes and ordinances so they play a key role in climate action at all governmental levels. Finally, reducing our dependence on fossil fuels helps the United States achieve energy independence.

---

[55]http://www.awea.org/learnabout/industry_stats/index.cfm
[56]http://mlui.org/downloads/CoalExternalitiesHarvard02-17-11.pdf
[57]http://www.eia.gov/energyexplained/index.cfm?page=hydropower_environment
[58]http://www.eia.doe.gov/pub/oil_gas/petroleum/feature_articles/2004/worldoilsupply/oilsupply04.html
[59]This content is available online at <http://legacy.cnx.org/content/m41726/1.3/>.
[60]http://www.chicagoclimateaction.org/
[61]http://www.ipcc.ch/
[62]http://www.unep.org/

8.3.3 Designing a Climate Action Plan

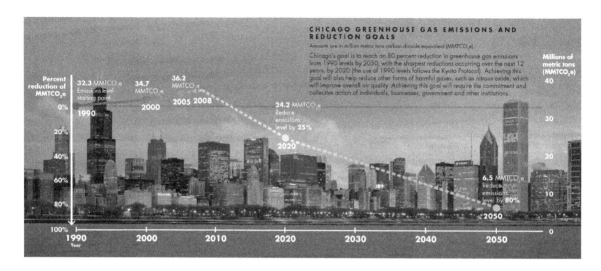

Figure 8.19: Chicago Greenhouse Gas Emissions and Reduction Goals Figure illustrates the emissions calculated for Chicago through 2005. *Source: City of Chicago, Chicago Climate Action Plan*[63]

A good climate action plan includes reporting of greenhouse gas emissions, as far back as there is data, preferably to 1990. Figure **Chicago Greenhouse Gas Emissions and Reduction Goals** (Figure 8.19) depicts the emissions calculated for Chicago through 2005. From that point there is an estimate (the dotted line) of a further increase before the reductions become evident and the goals portrayed can be obtained. The plan was released in September 2008 and provides a roadmap of five strategies with 35 actions to reduce greenhouse gas emissions (GHG) and adapt to climate change. The strategies are shown in Table **Alignment of the Chicago and UIC Climate Action Plans** (Table 8.1). Figure **Sources of the Chicago CAP Emission Reductions by Strategy** (Figure 8.20) identifies the proportion of emissions reductions from the various strategies.

---

[63]http://www.chicagoclimateaction.org/filebin/pdf/finalreport/CCAPREPORTFINALv2.pdf

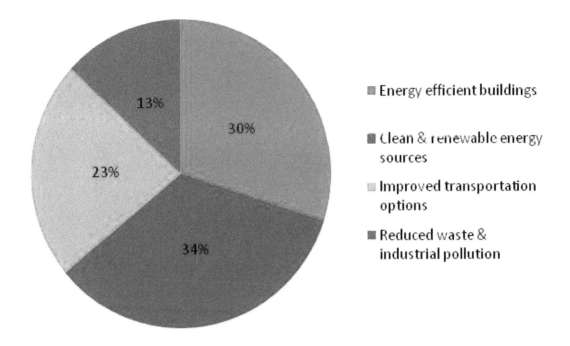

Figure 8.20: Graph shows the sources of the Chicago CAP emission reductions by strategy. *Source: C. Klein-Banai*[64] *using data from City of Chicago, Chicago Climate Action Plan*[65].

In 2010 CCAP put out a progress report[66] wherein progress is measured by the many small steps that are being taken to implement the plan. It is not translated exactly to emissions reductions but reports on progress for each step such as the number of residential units that have been retrofitted for energy efficiency, the number of appliances traded in, the increase in the number of rides on public transit, and the amount of water conserved daily.

8.3.4 University Climate Action Plan

Several factors caused a major Chicago university to develop a climate action plan. As part of the American College and University Presidents' Climate Commitment[67] (ACUPCC), nearly 670 presidents have signed a commitment to inventory their greenhouse gases, publicly report it, and to develop a climate action plan. Part of the Chicago CAP is to engage businesses and organizations within the city in climate action planning. In order to be a better steward of the environment, the University of Illinois at Chicago (UIC) developed a climate action plan[68] . The goals are similar to Chicago's: a 40 percent GHG emissions reduction by 2030 and at least 80 percent by 2050, using a 2004 baseline. The strategies align with those of the city in which the campus resides (see Table **Alignment of the Chicago and UIC Climate Action Plans** (Table 8.1)). UIC's greenhouse gas reports are also made publically available on the ACUPCC reporting site[69] . Figure **UIC's Projected Emissions Reductions** (Figure 8.21:) displays UIC's calculated emissions inventory

---

[64]http://cnx.org/member_profile/cindykb
[65]http://www.chicagoclimateaction.org/filebin/pdf/finalreport/CCAPREPORTFINALv2.pdf
[66]http://www.chicagoclimateaction.org/filebin/pdf/CCAPProgressReportv3.pdf
[67]http://www.presidentsclimatecommitment.org/
[68]http://www.uic.edu/sustainability/climateactionplan/
[69]http://rs.acupcc.org/

(in red) and then the predicted increases for growth if activities continue in a "business as usual (BAU)" approach. The triangular wedges below represent emissions reductions through a variety of strategies, similar to those of the wedge approach[70] that Professors Sokolow and Pacala proposed. Those strategies are displayed in Table **Alignment of the Chicago and UIC Climate Action Plans** (Table 8.1), alongside Chicago's for comparative purposes.

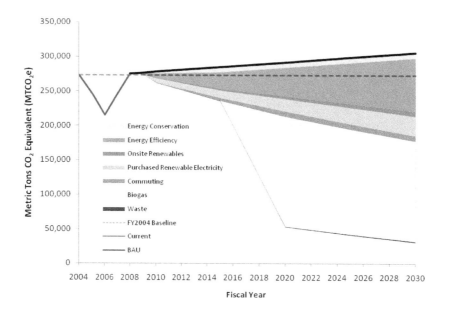

Figure 8.21: UIC's Projected Emissions Reductions Projected emissions reductions from 2004 to 2030. Where BAU stands for Business as Usual, what would happen if no action were taken? *Source: UIC Climate Action Plan, figure 6[71].*

The UIC CAP also has major strategy categories that are similar to Chicago's and within each strategy there are a number of recommended actions. Progress on this plan will be monitored both by reporting emissions at least every two years to the ACUPCC and by tracking individual actions and reporting to the campus community.

CHICAGO CAP	UIC CAP
Energy Efficient Buildings	**Energy Efficiency and Conservation**
Retrofit commercial and industrial buildings	Retrofit buildings
Retrofit residential buildings	Energy performance contracting
Trade in appliances	Monitoring and maintenance
	continued on next page

---

[70]http://www.wri.org/stories/2006/12/wedge-approach-climate-change
[71]http://www.uic.edu/sustainability/climateactionplan/drafts/UIC.CAP.FINALdft.pdf

Conserve water	Water conservation
Update City energy code	Establish green building standards
Establish new guidelines for renovations	
Cool with trees and green roofs	Green roofs/reflective roofs
Take easy steps	Energy conservation by campus community
Clean & Renewable Energy Sources	**Clean and Renewable Energy**
Upgrade power plants	Modify power plants
Improve power plant efficiency	Purchase electricity from a renewable electricity provider
Build renewable electricity	Build renewable electricity
Increase distributed generation	
Promote household renewable power	Geothermal heating and cooling
Improved Transportation Options	**Improved Transportation Options**
Invest more in transit	
Expand transit incentives	Expand transit incentives
Promote transit-oriented development	
Make walking and biking easier	Make walking and biking easier
Car share and car pool	Car sharing/car pool program
Improve fleet efficiency	Continue to improve fleet efficiency
Achieve higher fuel efficiency standards	
Switch to cleaner fuels	
Support intercity rail	Reduce business travel (web conferencing)
Improve freight movement	Anti-Idling regulations/guidelines
Reduced Waste & Industrial Pollution	**Recycling and Waste Management**
Reduce, reuse and recycle	Establishing recycling goals
Shift to alternative refrigerants	Composting
Capture stormwater on site	Sustainable food purchases & use of biodegradable packaging
	continued on next page

	Collecting and converting vegetable oil
	Develop a user-friendly property management system
	Expand the waste minimization program
	Recycle construction debris
	Purchasing policies
Preparation (Adaptation)	**Improved Grounds Operations**
Manage heat	Capture stormwater on site
Protect air quality	Use native species
Manage stormwater	Reduce/eliminate irrigation
Implement green urban design	Integrated pest management
Preserve plants and trees	Tree care plan
Pursue innovative cooling	
Engage the public	**Education, Research and Public Engagement**
Engage businesses	**Employment Strategies**
Plan for the future	Telecommuting
	Flextime
	Childcare center
	Public Engagement

Table 8.1: **Alignment of the Chicago and UIC Climate Action Plans** *Source: C. Klein-Banai using data from Chicago Climate Action Plant and UIC Climate Action Plan*

8.3.5 Conclusion

There is no one approach that will effectively reduce greenhouse gas emissions. Climate action plans are helpful tools to represent strategies to reduce emissions. Governmental entities such as nations, states, and cities can develop plans, as can institutions and businesses. It is important that there be an alignment of plans when they intersect, such as a city and a university that resides within it.

8.4 Energy Sources and Carriers

8.4.1 Electricity

8.4.1.1 Electricity[72]

8.4.1.1.1 Learning Objectives

After reading this module, students should be able to

- outline the growth of electricity as a clean, versatile, switchable energy carrier
- understand the components of the electricity grid – generation, delivery, use
- understand the challenges to the modern electricity grid – capacity, reliability, accommodating renewables

---

[72]This content is available online at <http://legacy.cnx.org/content/m41728/1.3/>.

8.4.1.1.2 Introduction

Over the past century and a half electricity has emerged as a popular and versatile energy carrier. Communication was an early widespread use for electricity following the introduction of the telegraph in the 1840s. In the 1870s and 1880s electric motors and lights joined the telegraph as practical electrical devices, and in the 1890s electricity distribution systems, the forerunners of today's **electricity grid**, began to appear. The telegraph became wireless with the invention of radio, demonstrated in the laboratory in the 1880s and for transatlantic communication in 1901. Today, electricity is exploited not only for its diverse end uses such as lighting, motion, refrigeration, communication and computation, but also as a primary carrier of energy. Electricity is one of two backbones of the modern energy system (liquid transportation fuels are the other), carrying high density energy over short and long distances for diverse uses. In 2009, electricity consumed the largest share of the United States' **primary energy**, 38 percent, with transportation a close second at 37 percent (EIA Annual Energy Review, 2009 (p. 347)). These two sectors also accounted for the largest shares of U.S. carbon emissions, 38 percent for electricity and 33 percent for transportation (EIA Annual Energy Review, 2009 (p. 347)). Figure **United States Electricity Net Generation Since 1949 and Uses** (Figure 8.22) shows the growth of electricity as an energy carrier since 1949 and the growing range of its uses.

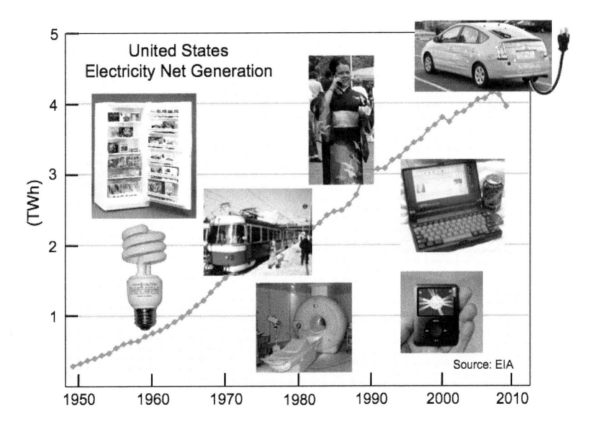

Figure 8.22: United States Electricity Net Generation Since 1949 and Uses The growth of United States electricity generation since 1949 and some of its uses. *Source: G. Crabtree*[73] *using data from EIA Annual Energy Review 2009, Table 8.2a, p 230.*[74]*; Felix O*[75]*, U.S. CPSC*[76]*, Joe Mabel,*[77] *Marcin Wichary*[78]*, Samboy*[79]*, Andrew*[80]*, Jan Ainali*[81]*, Lovelac7*[82]

Figure **Electricity Energy Chain** (Figure 8.23) shows the electricity energy chain from generation to use. By far most electricity is generated by combustion of fossil fuels to turn steam or gas turbines. This is the least efficient step in the energy chain, converting only 36 percent of the chemical energy in the fuel to electric energy, when averaged over the present gas and coal generation mix. It also produces all the carbon emissions of the electricity chain. Beyond production, electricity is a remarkably clean and efficient carrier. Conversion from rotary motion of the turbine and generator to electricity, the delivery of electricity through the power grid, and the conversion to motion in motors for use in industry, transportation and refrigeration can be more than 90 percent efficient. None of these steps produces greenhouse gas emissions. It is the post-production versatility, cleanliness, and **efficiency** of electricity that make it a prime energy carrier for the future. Electricity generation, based on relatively plentiful domestic coal and gas, is free of immediate fuel security concerns. The advent of electric cars promises to increase electricity demand and reduce dependency on foreign oil, while the growth of renewable wind and solar generation reduces carbon emissions. The primary sustainability challenges for electricity as an energy carrier are at the production step: efficiency and emission of carbon dioxide and toxins.

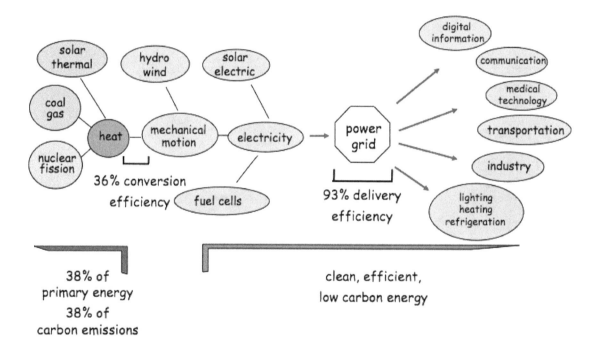

Figure 8.23: Electricity Energy Chain Graph shows the electricity energy chain from generation to use. *Source: G. Crabtree*[83]

[73]http://cnx.org/member_profile/crabtree
[74]http://205.254.135.24/totalenergy/data/annual/pdf/aer.pdf
[75]http://commons.wikimedia.org/wiki/File:Eletkriká_jednotka_420.95,_Štrbské_Pleso.jpg
[76]http://www.cpsc.gov/cpscpub/prerel/prhtml05/05279.html
[77]http://commons.wikimedia.org/wiki/File:Seattle_Bon_Odori_2007_114A.jpg
[78]http://commons.wikimedia.org/wiki/File:Prius_RechargeIT_03_2008_trim.jpg
[79]http://commons.wikimedia.org/wiki/File:Hb486_dillo_big.jpg
[80]http://commons.wikimedia.org/wiki/File:Ipod_nano_in_palm.jpg
[81]http://en.wikipedia.org/wiki/File:MRI-Philips.JPG
[82]http://en.wikipedia.org/wiki/File:Compact_fluorescent_transpa.png
[83]http://cnx.org/member_profile/crabtree

8.4.1.1.3 The Electricity Grid: Capacity and Reliability

Beyond production, electricity faces challenges of capacity, reliability, and implementing storage and transmission required to accommodate the remoteness and variability of renewables. The largest capacity challenges are in urban areas, where 79 percent of the United States and 50 percent of the world population live. The high population density of urban areas requires a correspondingly high energy and electric power density. In the United States, 33 percent of electric power is used in the top 22 metro areas, and electricity demand is projected to grow 31 percent by 2035 (Annual Energy Outlook, 2011 (p. 347)). This creates an "urban power bottleneck" where underground cables become saturated, hampering economic growth and the efficiencies of scale in transportation, energy use and greenhouse gas emission that come with high population density (Owen, 2009 (p. 347)). Saturation of existing cable infrastructure requires installation of substantial new capacity, an expensive proposition for digging new underground cable tunnels.

Superconducting underground cables with five times the power delivery capacity of conventional copper offer an innovative alternative (see Figure **Superconducting Underground Cables** (Figure 8.24)). Unlike conventional cables, superconducting cables emit no heat or electromagnetic radiation, eliminating interference with other underground energy and communication infrastructure. Replacing conventional with superconducting cables in urban areas dramatically increases capacity while avoiding the construction expense of additional underground infrastructure.

Figure 8.24: Superconducting Underground Cables The superconducting wires on the right carry the same current as the conventional copper wires on the left. Superconducting cable wound from these wires carries up to five times the current of conventional copper cables. *Source: Courtesy, American Superconductor Corporation*

The reliability of the electricity grid presents a second challenge. The United States' grid has grown continuously from origins in the early 20th Century; much of its infrastructure is based on technology and design philosophy dating from the 1950s and 1960s, when the major challenge was extending electrification to new rural and urban areas. Outside urban areas, the grid is mainly above ground, exposing it to weather and temperature extremes that cause most power outages. The response to outages is frustratingly slow and traditional – utilities are often first alerted to outages by telephoned customer complaints, and response requires sending crews to identify and repair damage, much the same as we did 50 years ago. The United States' grid reliability is significantly lower than for newer grids in Europe and Japan, where the typical customer experiences ten to 20 times less outage time than in the United States. Reliability is especially important in the digital age, when an interruption of even a fraction of a cycle can shut down a digitally controlled data center or fabrication line, requiring hours or days to restart.

Reliability issues can be addressed by implementing a **smart grid** with two-way communication between utility companies and customers that continuously monitors power delivery, the operational state of the delivery system, and implements demand response measures adjusting power delivered to individual customers in accordance with a previously established unique customer protocol. Such a system requires installing digital sensors that monitor power flows in the delivery system, digital decision and control technology and digital communication capability like that already standard for communication via the Internet. For customers with on-site solar generation capability, the smart grid would monitor and control selling excess power from the customer to the utility.

Figure **Smart Grid** (Figure 8.25) illustrates the two-way communication features of the smart grid. The conventional grid in the upper panel sends power one way, from the generating station to the customer, recording how much power leaves the generator and arrives at the customer. In the smart grid, the power flow is continuously monitored, not only at the generator and the customer, but also at each connection point in between. Information on the real time power flow is sent over the Internet or another special network to the utility and to the customer, allowing real time decisions on adding generation to meet changes in load, opening circuit breakers to reroute power in case of an outage, reducing power delivered to the customer during peak periods to avoid outages (often called "demand response"), and tracking reverse power flows for customers with their own solar or other generation capacity. The conventional power grid was designed in the middle of the last century to meet the simple need of delivering power in one direction. Incorporating modern Internet-style communications and control features could bring the electricity grid to a qualitatively new level of capability and performance required to accommodate local generation and deliver higher reliability.

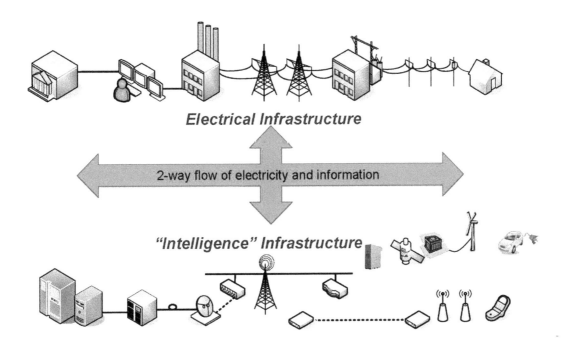

Figure 8.25: Smart Grid The addition of real-time monitoring and communicating capability like that used on the Internet would add 'smart' operation of the electricity grid. *Source: National Institute of Standards and Technology*[84]

Smart components incorporated throughout the grid would be able to detect overload currents and open breakers to interrupt them quickly and automatically to avoid unnecessary damage and triggering a domino effect cascade of outages over wide areas as happened in the Northeast Blackout of 2003. For maximum effectiveness, such smart systems require fast automatic response on millisecond time scales commensurate with the cycle time of the grid. Even simple digital communication meets this requirement, but many of the grid components themselves cannot respond so quickly. Conventional mechanical circuit breakers, for example, take many seconds to open and much longer to close. Such long times increase the risk of dangerous overload currents damaging the grid or propagating cascades. Along with digital communications, new breaker technology, such as that based on fast, self-healing superconducting fault current limiters, is needed to bring power grid operation into the modern era.

8.4.1.1.4 Integrating Renewable Electricity on the Grid

Accommodating renewable electricity generation by wind and solar plants is among the most urgent challenges facing the grid. Leadership in promoting renewable electricity has moved from the federal to the state governments, many of which have legislated Renewable Portfolio Standards (RPS) that require 20 percent of state electricity generation to be renewable by 2020. 30 states and the District of Columbia have such requirements, the most aggressive being California with 33 percent renewable electricity required by 2020 and New York with 30 percent by 2015. To put this legal requirement in perspective, wind and solar now account for about 1.6 percent of U.S. electricity production; approximately a factor of ten short of the RPS requirements. (Crabtree & Misewich, 2010 (p. 347)).

---

[84]http://www.nist.gov/itl/antd/emntg/smartgrid.cfm

8.4.1.1.4.1 Renewable Variability

The grid faces major challenges to accommodate the variability of wind and solar electricity. Without significant storage capacity, the grid must precisely balance generation to demand in real time. At present, the variability of demand controls the balancing process: demand varies by as much as a factor of two from night to day as people go through their daily routines. This predictable variability is accommodated by switching reserve generation sources in and out in response to demand variations. With **renewable generation**, variation can be up to 70 percent for solar electricity due to passing clouds and 100 percent for wind due to calm days, much larger than the variability of demand. At the present level of 1.6 percent wind and solar penetration, the relatively small variation in generation can be accommodated by switching in and out conventional resources to make up for wind and solar fluctuations. At the 20 percent penetration required by state Renewable Portfolio Standards, accommodating the variation in generation requires a significant increase in the conventional reserve capacity. At high penetration levels, each addition of wind or solar capacity requires a nearly equal addition of conventional capacity to provide generation when the renewables are quiescent. This double installation to insure reliability increases the cost of renewable electricity and reduces its effectiveness in lowering greenhouse gas emissions.

A major complication of renewable variation is its unpredictability. Unlike demand variability, which is reliably high in the afternoon and low at night, renewable generation depends on weather and does not follow any pattern. Anticipating weather-driven wind and solar generation variability requires more sophisticated forecasts with higher accuracy and greater confidence levels than are now available. Because today's forecasts often miss the actual performance target, additional conventional reserves must be held at the ready to cover the risk of inaccuracies, adding another increase to the cost of renewable electricity.

8.4.1.1.4.2 Storing Electricity

Storage of renewable electricity offers a viable route to meeting the variable generation challenge. Grid electricity storage encompasses many more options than portable electricity storage required for electric cars. Unlike vehicle storage, grid storage can occupy a large footprint with little or no restriction on weight or volume. Grid storage can be housed in a controlled environment, eliminating large temperature and humidity variations that affect performance. Grid storage must have much higher capacity than vehicle storage, of order 150 **MWh** for a wind farm versus 20-50 **kWh** for a vehicle. Because of these differences, the research strategy for grid and vehicle energy storage is very different. To date, much more attention has been paid to meeting vehicle electricity storage requirements than grid storage requirements.

There are many options for grid storage. Pumped hydroelectric storage, illustrated in Figure **Pumped Hydroelectric Storage** (Figure 8.26), is an established technology appropriate for regions with high and low elevation water resources. Compressed Air Energy Storage (CAES) is a compressed air equivalent of pumped hydro that uses excess electricity to pump air under pressure into underground geologic formations for later release to drive generators. This option has been demonstrated in Huntorf, Germany and in Mcintosh, Alabama. High temperature sodium-sulfur batteries operating at 300 °C have high energy density, projected long cycle life, and high round trip efficiency; they are the most mature of the battery technologies suggested for the grid. Flow batteries are an attractive and relatively unexplored option, where energy is stored in the high charge state of a liquid electrolyte and removed by electrochemical conversion to a low charge state. Each flow battery requires an electrolyte with a high and low charge state and chemical reaction that takes one into the other. There are many such electrolytes and chemical reactions, of which only a few have been explored, leaving a host of promising opportunities for the future. The energy storage capacity depends only on the size of the storage tank, which can be designed fully independently of the power capacity that depends on the size of the electrochemical reactor. Sodium sulfur and flow batteries store electric charge and can be used at any place in the electricity grid. In contrast, thermal storage applies only to concentrating solar power technologies, where mirrors focus solar radiation to heat a working fluid that drives a conventional turbine and generator. In these systems, heat energy can be stored as a molten salt in a highly insulated enclosure for hours or days, allowing solar electricity to be generated on demand after sunset or on cloudy days. All of these options are promising and require research and development to explore innovations, performance and cost limits.

Figure 8.26: **Pumped Hydroelectric Storage** Upper storage reservoir for pumped hydroelectric storage, an established technology for storing large amounts of grid electricity. *Source: Ongrys via Wikimedia Commons*[85]

8.4.1.1.4.3 How to Transmit Electricity Over Long Distances

The final challenge for accommodating renewables is long distance transmission. As Figure **Renewable Resource Location vs. Demand Location** (Figure 8.27) shows, the largest wind resources, located at mid-continent, and the largest solar resources, in the southwest, are far from the population centers east of Mississippi and on the West Coast. If these resources are to be used, higher capacity long distance transmission must be developed to bring the renewable electricity to market. Although such long distance delivery is possible where special high voltage transmission lines have been located, the capacity and number of such lines is limited. The situation is much like automobile transportation before the interstate highway system was built in the 1950s. It was possible to drive coast to coast, but the driving time was long and uncertain and the route indirect. To use renewable electricity resources effectively, we must create a kind of interstate highway system for electricity.

---

[85]http://commons.wikimedia.org/wiki/File:Zar_zbiornik.jpg

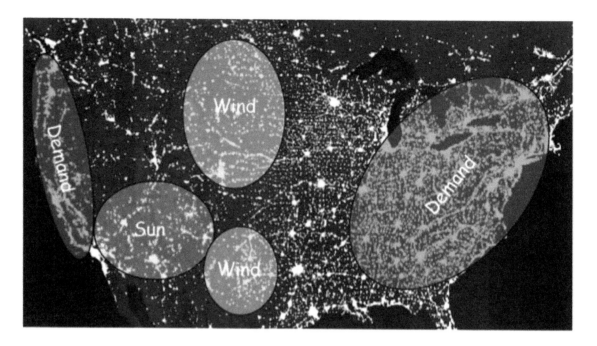

Figure 8.27: Renewable Resource Location vs. Demand Location Wind and solar electricity resources are located far from population centers, requiring a dramatic improvement in long-distance electricity transmission – an "interstate highway system for electricity." *Source: Integrating Renewable Electricity on the Grid, Report of the Panel on Pubic Affairs, American Physical Society (2010)* (p. 347).

8.4.1.1.5 Summary

Electricity and liquid petroleum are the two primary energy carriers in the United States, and in the world. Once produced, electricity is clean and versatile making it an appealing energy carrier for the future. The challenges facing the electricity grid are capacity, reliability, and accommodating renewable sources such as solar and wind whose output is variable and whose location is remote from population centers. Electricity storage and long distance transmission are needed to accommodate these renewable resources.

8.4.1.1.6 Review Questions

Question 8.4.1.1.1
Electricity is the fastest growing energy carrier in the world, trailed by liquid fuels for transportation. Why is electricity more appealing than liquid fuels?

Question 8.4.1.1.2
A primary challenge for the electricity grid is capacity to handle the "urban power bottleneck" in cities and suburbs. How can superconducting cables address urban capacity issues?

Question 8.4.1.1.3
Renewable wind and solar electricity is plentiful in the United States, but they are located remotely from high population centers and their output is variable in time. How can these two issues be addressed?

8.4.1.1.7 References

Crabtree, G. & Misewich, J. (Co-Chairs). (2010). *Integrating Renewable Electricity on the Grid, American Physical Society*. American Physical Society, Washington D.C. Retrieved August 12, 2011 from http://www.aps.org/policy/reports/popa-reports/upload/integratingelec.pdf[86]

Owen, D. (2009). *Green Metropolis: Why Living Smaller, Living Closer, And Driving Less Are the Keys to Sustainability*. New York: Riverhead Books.

U.S. Energy Information Administration. (2010). *Annual Energy Review 2009*. Retrieved August 12, 2011 from http://www.eia.gov/totalenergy/data/annual/pdf/aer.pdf[87]

8.4.1.2 Fossil Fuels (Coal and Gas)[88]

8.4.1.2.1 Learning Objectives

After reading this module, students should be able to

- outline the relative contributions of coal and gas to electricity generation and to carbon emissions
- understand the link between electricity generation and carbon emissions
- understand the challenges of sequestering carbon in geologic formations – chemical transformation, migration, and longevity

8.4.1.2.2 Introduction

At present the fossil fuels used for electricity generation are predominantly coal (45 percent) and gas (23 percent); petroleum accounts for approximately 1 percent (see Figure **Electricity Generation by Source (Figure 8.28)**). Coal electricity traces its origins to the early 20th Century, when it was the natural fuel for steam engines given its abundance, high energy density and low cost. Gas is a later addition to the fossil electricity mix, arriving in significant quantities after World War II and with its greatest growth since 1990 as shown in Figure **Growth of Fuels Used to Produce Electricity in the United States** (Figure 8.29) (EIA Annual Energy Review, 2009 (p. 352)). Of the two fuels, coal emits almost twice the carbon dioxide as gas for the same heat output, making it significantly greater contributor to global warming and climate change.

---

[86] http://www.aps.org/policy/reports/popa-reports/upload/integratingelec.pdf
[87] http://www.eia.gov/totalenergy/data/annual/pdf/aer.pdf
[88] This content is available online at <http://legacy.cnx.org/content/m41727/1.3/>.

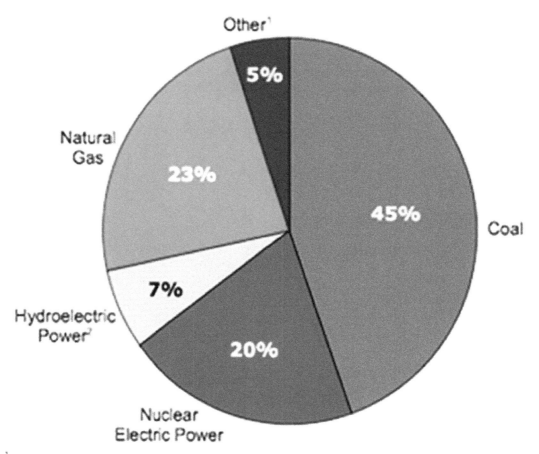

[1] Wind, petroleum, wood, waste, geothermal, other gases, solar thermal and photovoltaic, batteries, chemicals, hydrogen, pitch, purchased steam, sulfur, miscellaneous technologies, and non-renewable waste (municipal solid waste from non-biogenic sources, and tire-derived fuels

[2] Conventional hydroelectric power and pumped storage

Note: Sum of components may not equal 100 percent due to independent rounding.

Figure 8.28: Electricity Generation by Source Chart shows U.S. electricity generation by source. *Source: U.S.* [89] *Energy Information Administration, Annual Review, 2009, p. 228 (Aug. 2010)* [90]

[89] http://205.254.135.24/totalenergy/data/annual/pdf/aer.pdf
[90] http://205.254.135.24/totalenergy/data/annual/pdf/aer.pdf

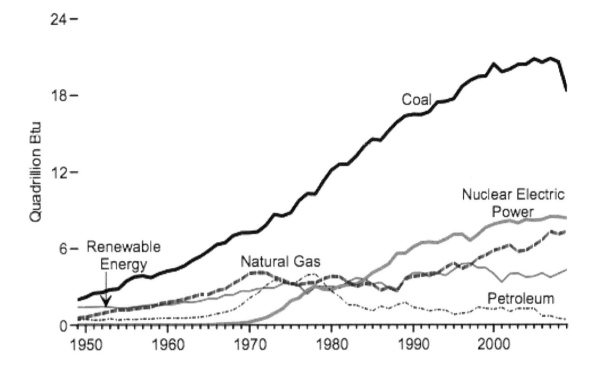

Figure 8.29: Growth of Fuels Used to Produce Electricity in the United States Graph shows the growth of fuels used to produce electricity in the United States from 1950 to 2009. *Source: U.S. Energy Information Administration, Annual Energy Review 2009, p. 238 (Aug. 2010)*[91]

8.4.1.2.3 The Future of Gas and Coal

The future development of coal and gas depend on the degree of public and regulatory concern for carbon emissions, and the relative price and supply of the two fuels. Supplies of coal are abundant in the United States, and the transportation chain from mines to power plants is well established by long experience. The primary unknown factor is the degree of public and regulatory pressure that will be placed on carbon emissions. Strong regulatory pressure on carbon emissions would favor retirement of coal and addition of gas power plants. This trend is reinforced by the recent dramatic expansion of shale gas reserves in the United States due to technology advances in horizontal drilling and hydraulic fracturing ("fracking") of shale gas fields. Shale gas production has increased 48 percent annually in the years 2006 – 2010, with more increases expected (EIA Annual Energy Outlook, 2011 (p. 352)). Greater United States production of shale gas will gradually reduce imports and could eventually make the United States a net exporter of natural gas.

The technique of hydraulic fracturing of shale uses high-pressure fluids to fracture the normally hard shale deposits and release gas and oil trapped inside the rock. To promote the flow of gas out of the rock, small particles of solids are included in the fracturing liquids to lodge in the shale cracks and keep them open after the liquids are depressurized. Although hydraulic fracturing has been used since the 1940s, is technologically feasible, economic, and proven to enhance gas an oil recovery, it faces considerable environmental challenges. In aquifers overlying the Marcellus and Utica shale formations of northeastern Pennsylvania and upstate New York, methane contamination of drinking water associated with shale gas extraction has been reported (Osborn, (p. 352)Vengosh, Warner, & Jackson, 2011 (p. 352)). The public reaction to these reports has

---

[91]http://205.254.135.24/totalenergy/data/annual/pdf/aer.pdf

been strong and negative, prompting calls for greater transparency, scientific investigation and regulatory control to clearly establish the safety, sustainability and public confidence in the technique. See Module **Environmental Challenges in Energy, Carbon Dioxide, Air and Water** (Section 8.2) for more on the process of hydraulic fracturing and its associated risks.

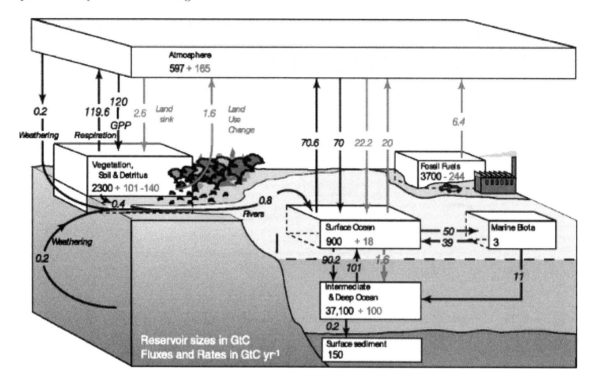

Figure 8.30: Global Carbon Cycle, 1990s The global carbon cycle for the 1990s, showing the main annual fluxes in GtC yr–1: pre-industrial 'natural' fluxes in black and 'anthropogenic' fluxes in red. *Source: Climate Change 2007: The Physical Science Basis:* [92]*Contribution of Working Group I to the Fourth Assessment Report of the Intergovernmental Panel on Climate Change, Cambridge University Press, figure 7.3*[93]

Beyond a trend from coal to gas for electricity generation, there is a need to deal with the carbon emissions from the fossil production of electricity. Figure **Global Carbon Cycle, 1990s** (Figure 8.30) shows the size of these emissions compared to natural fluxes between ocean and atmosphere and from vegetation and land use. The anthropogenic fluxes are small by comparison, yet have a large effect on the concentration of carbon dioxide in the atmosphere. The reason is the step-wise dynamics of the carbon cycle. The ultimate storage repository for carbon emissions is the deep ocean, with abundant capacity to absorb the relatively small flux from fossil fuel combustion. Transfer to the deep ocean, however, occurs in three steps: first to the atmosphere, then to the shallow ocean, and finally to the deep ocean. The bottleneck is the slow transfer of carbon dioxide from the shallow ocean to the deep ocean, governed by the **great ocean conveyor belt** or **thermohaline circulation** illustrated in Figure **Great Ocean Conveyor Belt** (Figure 8.31). The great ocean conveyor belt takes 400 – 1000 years to complete one cycle. While carbon dioxide waits to be transported to the deep ocean, it saturates the shallow ocean and "backs up" in the atmosphere causing global warming and threatening climate change. If carbon emissions are to be captured and stored (or

---

[92]http://www.ipcc.ch/publications_and_data/ar4/wg1/en/ch7s7-3.html
[93]http://www.ipcc.ch/publications_and_data/ar4/wg1/en/ch7s7-3.html

"sequestered") they must be trapped for thousands of years while the atmosphere adjusts to past and future carbon emissions (Lenton, 2006 (p. 352)).

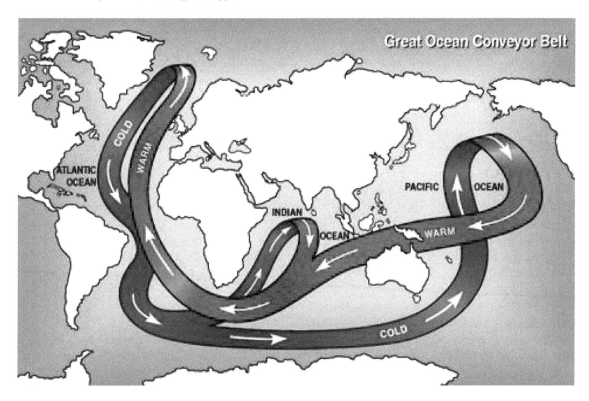

Figure 8.31: Great Ocean Conveyor Belt The great ocean conveyor belt (or thermohaline current) sends warm surface currents from the Pacific to Atlantic oceans and cold deep currents in the opposite direction. The conveyor belt is responsible for transporting dissolved carbon dioxide from the relatively small reservoir of the shallow ocean to much larger reservoir of the deep ocean. It takes 400 - 1000 years to complete one cycle. *Source: Argonne National Laboratory*[94]

Sequestration of carbon dioxide in underground geologic formations is one process that, in principle, has the capacity to handle fossil fuel carbon emissions (Olajire, 2010 (p. 352)); chemical reaction of carbon dioxide to a stable solid form is another (Stephens & Keith, 2008 (p. 352)). For sequestration, there are fundamental challenges that must be understood and resolved before the process can be implemented on a wide scale.

The chemical reactions and migration routes through the porous rocks in which carbon dioxide is stored underground are largely unknown. Depending on the rock environment, stable solid compounds could form that would effectively remove the sequestered carbon dioxide from the environment. Alternatively, it could remain as carbon dioxide or transform to a mobile species and migrate long distances, finally finding an escape route to the atmosphere where it could resume its contribution to greenhouse warming or cause new environmental damage. The requirement on long term sequestration is severe: a leak rate of 1 percent means that all the carbon dioxide sequestered in the first year escapes in a century, a blink of the eye on the timescale of climate change.

---

[94]http://www.anl.gov/Media_Center/Frontiers/2003/d8ee.html

8.4.1.2.4 Summary

Coal (45 percent) and gas (23 percent) are the two primary fossil fuels for electricity production in the United States. Coal combustion produces nearly twice the carbon emissions of gas combustion. Increasing public opinion and regulatory pressure to lower carbon emissions are shifting electricity generation toward gas and away from coal. The domestic supply of gas is increasing rapidly due to shale gas released by hydraulic fracturing, a technology with significant potential for harmful environmental impact. Reducing the greenhouse gas impact of electricity production requires capturing and sequestering the carbon dioxide emitted from power plants. Storing carbon dioxide in underground geologic formations faces challenges of chemical transformation, migration, and longevity.

8.4.1.2.5 Review Questions

Question 8.4.1.2.1

The United States' electricity supply is provided primarily by coal, natural gas, nuclear, and hydropower. How safe are these fuel supplies from interruption by international disasters, weather events or geopolitical tension?

Question 8.4.1.2.2

Natural gas reserves from shale are increasing rapidly due to increased use of hydrofracturing technology ("fracking"). The increased domestic resource of shale gas has the potential to provide greater energy security at the expense of greater environmental impact. What are the long-term costs, benefits, and outlook for tapping into domestic shale gas reserves?

Question 8.4.1.2.3

Anthropogenic carbon emissions are small compared to natural exchange between ocean and atmosphere and fluxes from vegetation and land use. Why do anthropogenic emissions have such a large effect on the concentration of carbon dioxide in the atmosphere?

Question 8.4.1.2.4

One proposal for mitigating carbon emissions is capturing and storing them in underground geologic formations (sequestration). What scientific, technological and policy challenges must be overcome before sequestration can be deployed widely?

8.4.1.2.6 References

Lenton, T.M. (2006). Climate change to the end of the millennium. *Climatic Change*, 76, 7-29. doi: 10.1007/s10584-005-9022-1

Olajire, A. (2010). CO2 capture and separation technologies for end-of-pipe applications: A review, *Energy* 35, pp. 2610-2628. doi: 10.1016/j.energy.2010.02.030

Osborn, S.G., Vengosh, A., Warner, N.R., & Jackson, R.B. (2011). Methane contamination of drinking water accompanying gas-well drilling and hydraulic fracturing. *PNAS*, 108, pp. 8172-1876. doi: 10.1073/pnas.1100682108

Stephens, J.C. & Keith, D.W. (2008). Assessing geochemical carbon management. *Climatic Change*, 90, 217-242. doi: 10.1007/s10584-008-9440-y

U.S. Energy Information Administration. (2010). *Annual Energy Review 2009*. Retrieved August 12, 2011 from http://www.eia.gov/totalenergy/data/annual/pdf/aer.pdf[95]

U.S. Energy Information Administration. (2011). *Annual Energy Outlook 2011*. Retrieved September 2, 2011 from http://www.eia.gov/forecasts/aeo/pdf/0383(2011).pdf[96]

---

[95]http://www.eia.gov/totalenergy/data/annual/pdf/aer.pdf
[96]http://www.eia.gov/forecasts/aeo/pdf/0383(2011).pdf

8.4.1.3 Nuclear Energy[97]

8.4.1.3.1 Learning Objectives

After reading this module, students should be able to

- outline the rapid development of nuclear electricity and its plateau due to public concerns about safety
- understand the dilemma nuclear electricity presents for sustainability – reduced carbon emissions and long term storage of spent fuel
- understand the sustainable benefits and proliferation threats of reprocessing spent nuclear fuel

8.4.1.3.2 Introduction

From a sustainability perspective, nuclear electricity presents an interesting dilemma. On the one hand, nuclear electricity produces no carbon emissions, a major sustainable advantage in a world facing human induced global warming and potential climate change. On the other hand, nuclear electricity produces spent fuel that must be stored out of the environment for tens or hundreds of thousands of years, it produces bomb-grade plutonium and uranium that could be diverted by terrorists or others to destroy cities and poison the environment, and it threatens the natural and built environment through accidental leaks of long lived radiation. Thoughtful scientists, policy makers and citizens must weigh the benefit of this source of carbon free electricity against the environmental risk of storing spent fuel for thousands or hundreds of thousands of years, the societal risk of nuclear proliferation, and the impact of accidental releases of radiation from operating reactors. There are very few examples of humans having the power to permanently change the dynamics of the earth. Global warming and climate change from carbon emissions is one example, and radiation from the explosion of a sufficient number of nuclear weapons is another. Nuclear electricity touches both of these opportunities, on the positive side for reducing carbon emissions and on the negative side for the risk of nuclear proliferation.

8.4.1.3.3 Debating Nuclear Energy

Nuclear electricity came on the energy scene remarkably quickly. Following the development of nuclear technology at the end of World War II for military ends, nuclear energy quickly acquired a new peacetime path for inexpensive production of electricity. Eleven years after the end of World War II, in 1956, a very short time in energy terms, the first commercial nuclear reactor produced electricity at Calder Hall in Sellafield, England. The number of nuclear reactors grew steadily to more than 400 by 1990, four years after the Chernobyl disaster[98] in 1986 and eleven years following Three Mile Island[99] in 1979. Since 1990, the number of operating reactors has remained approximately flat, with new construction balancing decommissioning, due to public and government reluctance to proceed with nuclear electricity expansion plans. Figure **Growth of Fuels Used to Produce Electricity in the United States** (Figure 8.29) and Figure **Nuclear Share of United States Electricity Generation** (Figure 8.32) show the development and status of nuclear power in the United States, a reflection of its worldwide growth.

---

[97]This content is available online at <http://legacy.cnx.org/content/m41729/1.3/>.
[98]http://en.wikipedia.org/wiki/Chernobyl_disaster
[99]http://en.wikipedia.org/wiki/Three_Mile_Island_accident

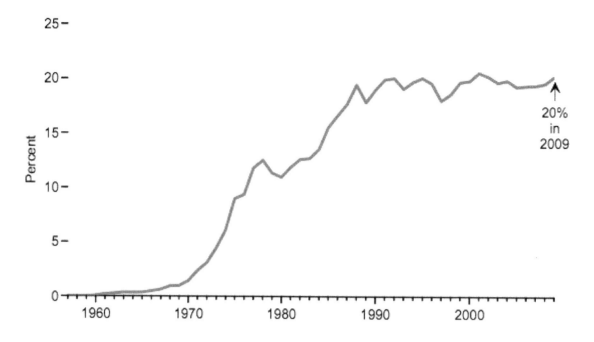

Figure 8.32: Nuclear Share of United States Electricity Generation The percentage of electricity generated by nuclear power in the United States, 1957-2009. *Source: U.S. Energy Information Agency, Annual Energy Review 2009, p. 276 (Aug. 2010)*[100]

The outcome of this debate (Ferguson, Marburger, & Farmer, 2010 (p. 356)) will determine whether the world experiences a nuclear renaissance that has been in the making for several years (Grimes & Nuttall, 2010 (p. 356)). The global discussion has been strongly impacted by the unlikely nuclear accident in Fukushima, Japan[101] in March 2011. The Fukushima nuclear disaster was caused by an earthquake and tsunami that disabled the cooling system for a nuclear energy complex consisting of operating nuclear reactors and storage pools for underwater storage of spent nuclear fuel ultimately causing a partial meltdown of some of the reactor cores and release of significant radiation. This event, 25 years after Chernobyl, reminds us that safety and public confidence are especially important in nuclear energy; without them expansion of nuclear energy will not happen.

---

[100]http://205.254.135.24/totalenergy/data/annual/pdf/aer.pdf
[101]http://en.wikipedia.org/wiki/Fukushima_Daiichi_nuclear_disaster

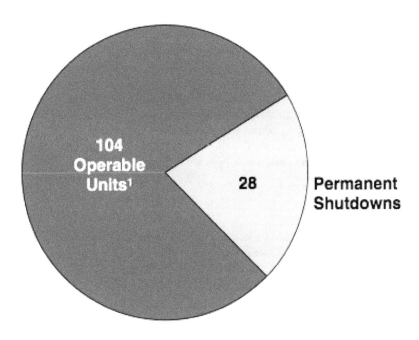

' Units holding full-power operating licenses, or equivalent permission to operate, at the end of the year.

Figure 8.33: Operating and Decommissioned Nuclear Power Plants in the United States
Graph shows the number of operating versus decommissioned nuclear power plants in the United States. *Source: U.S. Energy Information Agency, Annual Energy Review 2009, p. 274 (Aug. 2010)*[102]

There are two basic routes for handling the spent fuel of nuclear reactors: **once through** and **reprocessing** (World Nuclear Association; Kazimi, Moniz, & Forsberg, 2010 (p. 356)). Once through stores spent fuel following a single pass through the reactor, first in pools at the reactor site while it cools radioactively and thermally, then in a long-term geologic storage site, where it must remain for hundreds of thousands of years. Reprocessing separates the useable fraction of spent fuel and recycles it through the reactor, using a greater fraction of its energy content for electricity production, and sends the remaining high-level waste to permanent geologic storage. The primary motivation for recycling is greater use of fuel resources, extracting ~ 25 percent more energy than the once through cycle. A secondary motivation for recycling is a significant reduction of the permanent geologic storage space (by a factor of ~ 5 or more) and time (from hundreds of thousands of years to thousands of years). While these advantages seem natural and appealing from a sustainability perspective, they are complicated by the risk of theft of nuclear material from the reprocessing cycle for use in illicit weapons production or other non-sustainable ends. At present, France, the United Kingdom, Russia, Japan and China engage in some form of reprocessing; the United States, Sweden and Finland do not reprocess.

---

[102]http://205.254.135.24/totalenergy/data/annual/pdf/aer.pdf

8.4.1.3.4 Summary

Nuclear electricity offers the sustainable benefit of low carbon electricity at the cost of storing spent fuel out of the environment for up to hundreds of thousands of years. Nuclear energy developed in only 11 years, unusually quickly for a major energy technology, and slowed equally quickly due to public concerns about safety following Three Mile Island and Chernobyl. The Fukushima reactor accident in March 2011 has raised further serious concerns about safety; its impact on public opinion could dramatically affect the future course of nuclear electricity. Reprocessing spent fuel offers the advantages of higher energy efficiency and reduced spent fuel storage requirements with the disadvantage of higher risk of weapons proliferation through diversion of the reprocessed fuel stream.

8.4.1.3.5 Review Questions

Question 8.4.1.3.1
Nuclear electricity came on the scene remarkably quickly following the end of World War II, and its development stagnated quickly following the Three Mile Island and Chernobyl accidents. The Fukushima disaster of 2011 adds a third cautionary note. What conditions must be fulfilled if the world is to experience an expansion of nuclear electricity, often called a nuclear renaissance?

Question 8.4.1.3.2
Nuclear fuel can be used once and committed to storage or reprocessed after its initial use to recover unused nuclear fuel for re-use. What are the arguments for and against reprocessing?

Question 8.4.1.3.3
Storage of spent nuclear fuel for tens to hundreds of thousands of years is a major sustainability challenge for nuclear electricity. Further development of the Yucca Mountain storage facility has been halted. What are some of the alternatives for storing spent nuclear fuel going forward?

8.4.1.3.6 Resources

Ferguson, C.D.,Marburger, L.E. & Farmer, J.D. (2010) A US nuclear future? *Nature*, *467*, 391-393. doi: 10.1038/467391a

Grimes, R.J. & Nuttall, W.J. (2010). Generating the Option of a two-stage nuclear renaissance. *Science*, *329*, 799-803. doi: 10.1126/science.1188928

Kazimi, M., Moniz, E.J., & Forsberg, C. (2010) *The Future of the Nuclear Fuel Cycle*. MIT Energy Initiative. Retrieved May 30, 2011 from http://web.mit.edu/mitei/research/studies/nuclear-fuel-cycle.shtml[103]
.

World Nuclear Association (2011). *Processing of Used Nuclear Fuel*. Retrieved May 30, 2011 from http://www.world-nuclear.org/info/inf69.html[104] .

8.4.1.4 Renewable Energy: Solar, Wind, Hydro and Biomass[105]

8.4.1.4.1 Learning Objectives

After reading this module, students should be able to

- outline the societal motivations for renewable energy
- understand the ultimate sources of renewable energy
- appreciate the geographical distribution of renewable energy
- understand cost and public opinion as two key barriers to the widespread deployment of renewable energy

---

[103]http://web.mit.edu/mitei/research/studies/nuclear-fuel-cycle.shtml
[104]http://www.world-nuclear.org/info/inf69.html
[105]This content is available online at <http://legacy.cnx.org/content/m41731/1.3/>.

8.4.1.4.2 Introduction

Strong interest in renewable energy in the modern era arose in response to the **oil shocks** of the 1970s, when the Organization of Petroleum Exporting Countries[106] (OPEC) imposed oil embargos and raised prices in pursuit of geopolitical objectives. The shortages of oil, especially gasoline for transportation, and the eventual rise in the price of oil by a factor of approximately 10 from 1973 to 1981 disrupted the social and economic operation of many developed countries and emphasized their precarious dependence on foreign energy supplies The reaction in the United States was a shift away from oil and gas to plentiful domestic coal for electricity production and the imposition of fuel economy standards for vehicles to reduce consumption of oil for transportation. Other developed countries without large fossil reserves, such as France and Japan, chose to emphasize nuclear (France to the 80 percent level and Japan to 30 percent) or to develop domestic renewable resources such as hydropower and wind (Scandinavia), geothermal (Iceland), solar, biomass and for electricity and heat. As oil prices collapsed in the late 1980s interest in renewables, such as wind and solar that faced significant technical and cost barriers, declined in many countries, while other renewables, such as hydro and biomass, continued to experience growth.

The increasing price and volatility of oil since 1998, and the increasing dependence of many developed countries on foreign oil (60 percent of United States and 97 percent of Japanese oil was imported in 2008) spurred renewed interest in renewable alternatives to ensure energy security. A new concern, not known in previous oil crises, added further motivation: our knowledge of the emission of greenhouse gases and their growing contribution to global warming, and the threat of climate change. An additional economic motivation, the high cost of foreign oil payments to supplier countries (approximately \$350 billion/year for the United States at 2011 prices), grew increasingly important as developed countries struggled to recover from the economic recession of 2008. These energy security, carbon emission, and climate change concerns drive significant increases in fuel economy standards, fuel switching of transportation from uncertain and volatile foreign oil to domestic electricity and biofuels, and production of electricity from low carbon sources.

8.4.1.4.3 Physical Origin of Renewable Energy

Although renewable energy is often classified as hydro, solar, wind, biomass, geothermal, wave and tide, all forms of renewable energy arise from only three sources: the light of the sun, the heat of the earth's crust, and the gravitational attraction of the moon and sun. Sunlight provides by far the largest contribution to renewable energy, illustrated in Figure **Forms of Renewable Energy Provided by the Sun** (Figure 8.34). The sun provides the heat that drives the weather, including the formation of high- and low-pressure areas in the atmosphere that make wind. The sun also generates the heat required for vaporization of ocean water that ultimately falls over land creating rivers that drive hydropower, and the sun is the energy source for photosynthesis, which creates biomass. Solar energy can be directly captured for water and space heating, for driving conventional turbines that generate electricity, and as excitation energy for electrons in semiconductors that drive photovoltaics. The sun is also responsible for the energy of fossil fuels, created from the organic remains of plants and sea organisms compressed and heated in the absence of oxygen in the earth's crust for tens to hundreds of millions of years. The time scale for fossil fuel regeneration, however, is too long to consider them renewable in human terms.

Geothermal energy originates from heat rising to the surface from earth's molten iron core created during the formation and compression of the early earth as well as from heat produced continuously by radioactive decay of uranium, thorium and potassium in the earth's crust. Tidal energy arises from the gravitational attraction of the moon and the more distant sun on the earth's oceans, combined with rotation of the earth. These three sources – sunlight, the heat trapped in earth's core and continuously generated in its crust, and gravitational force of the moon and sun on the oceans – account for all renewable energy.

---

[106]http://www.opec.org/opec_web/en/

Figure 8.34: Forms of Renewable Energy Provided by the Sun The sun is the ultimate source for many forms of renewable energy: wind and running water that can be used for power generation without heat or combustion, and photosynthesis of green plants (biomass) for combustion to provide heat and power generation and for conversion to biofuels (upper panels). Solar energy can be directly captured for water and space heating in buildings, after concentration by mirrors in large plants for utility-scale power generation by conventional turbines, and without concentration in photovoltaic cells that produce power without heat or combustion (lower panels). *Source: G. Crabtree using images from Linuxerist*[107], *Mor plus*[108], *Richard Dorrell*[109], *Hernantron*[110], *BSMPS*[111], *Cachogaray*[112], *and Andy F*[113].

As relative newcomers to energy production, renewable energy typically operates at lower efficiency than its conventional counterparts. For example, the best commercial solar photovoltaic modules operate at about 20 percent efficiency, compared to nearly 60 percent efficiency for the best combined cycle natural gas turbines. Photovoltaic modules in the laboratory operate above 40 percent efficiency but are too expensive for general use, showing that there is ample headroom for performance improvements and cost reductions. Wind turbines are closer to their theoretical limit of 59 percent (known as **Betz's law**) often achieving 35 – 40 percent efficiency. Biomass is notoriously inefficient, typically converting less than one percent of incident sunlight to energy stored in the chemical bonds of its roots, stalks and leaves. Breeding and genetic

[107]http://commons.wikimedia.org/wiki/File:Sun.lxset.svg
[108]http://commons.wikimedia.org/wiki/File:Sonnenschirm-im-Wind.JPG
[109]http://commons.wikimedia.org/wiki/File:River_Roskhill_after_rain_-_geograph.org.uk_-_1018110.jpg
[110]http://commons.wikimedia.org/wiki/File:Panel_Solar_en_La_Llosa.JPG
[111]http://commons.wikimedia.org/wiki/File:12-05-08_AS1.JPG
[112]http://commons.wikimedia.org/wiki/File:Calefon_solar_termosifonico_compacto.jpg
[113]http://commons.wikimedia.org/wiki/File:Biomass_crop_west_of_Staverton_-_geograph.org.uk_-_1498992.jpg

modification may improve this poor energy efficiency, though hundreds of millions of years of evolution since the appearance of multicelled organisms have not produced a significant advance. Geothermal energy is already in the form of heat and temperature gradients, so that standard techniques of thermal engineering can be applied to improve efficiency. Wave and tidal energy, though demonstrated in several working plants, are at early stages of development and their technological development remains largely unexplored.

8.4.1.4.4 Capacity and Geographical Distribution

Although renewable energies such as wind and solar have experienced strong growth in recent years, they still make up a small fraction of the world's total energy needs. Figure **Renewable Energy Share of Global Final Energy Consumption, 2008** (Figure 8.35) shows the contribution of fossil, nuclear and renewable energy to final global energy consumption in 2008. The largest share comes from traditional biomass, mostly fuel wood gathered in traditional societies for household cooking and heating, often without regard for sustainable replacement. Hydropower is the next largest contributor, an established technology that experienced significant growth in the 20th Century. The other contributors are more recent and smaller in contribution: water and space heating by biomass combustion or harvesting solar and geothermal heat, biofuels derived from corn or sugar cane, and electricity generated from wind, solar and geothermal energy. Wind and solar electricity, despite their large capacity and significant recent growth, still contributed less than one percent of total energy in 2008.

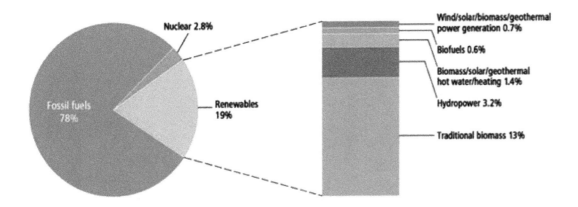

Figure 8.35: Renewable Energy Share of Global Final Energy Consumption, 2008 The contribution of fossil, nuclear and renewable energy to global final energy consumption in 2008. *Source: REN21. 2010. Renewables 2010 Global Status Report (Paris: REN21 Secretariat), p. 15*[114]

The potential of renewable energy resources varies dramatically. Solar energy is by far the most plentiful, delivered to the surface of the earth at a rate of 120,000 Terawatts (TW), compared to the global human use of 15 TW. To put this in perspective, covering 100x100 km^2 of desert with 10 percent efficient solar cells would produce 0.29 TW of power, about 12 percent of the global human demand for electricity. To supply all of the earth's electricity needs (2.4 TW in 2007) would require 7.5 such squares, an area about the size of Panama (0.05 percent of the earth's total land area). The world's conventional oil reserves are estimated at three trillion barrels, including all the oil that has already been recovered and that remain for future recovery. The solar energy equivalent of these oil reserves is delivered to the earth by the sun in 1.5 days.

The global potential for producing electricity and transportation fuels from solar, wind and biomass is limited by geographical availability of land suitable for generating each kind of energy (described as

[114]http://www.ren21.net/Portals/97/documents/GSR/REN21_GSR_2010_full_revised%20Sept2010.pdf

the **geographical potential**), the technical efficiency of the conversion process (reducing the geographical potential to the **technical potential**), and the economic cost of construction and operation of the conversion technology (reducing the technical potential to the **economic potential**). The degree to which the global potential of renewable resources is actually developed depends on many unknown factors such as the future extent of economic and technological advancement in the developing and developed worlds, the degree of globalization through business, intellectual and social links among countries and regions, and the relative importance of environmental and social agendas compared to economic and material objectives. **Scenarios** evaluating the development of renewable energy resources under various assumptions about the world's economic, technological and social trajectories show that solar energy has 20-50 times the potential of wind or biomass for producing electricity, and that each separately has sufficient potential to provide the world's electricity needs in 2050 (de Vries, 2007 (p. 366))

The geographical distribution of useable renewable energy is quite uneven. Sunlight, often thought to be relatively evenly distributed, is concentrated in deserts where cloud cover is rare. Winds are up to 50 percent stronger and steadier offshore than on land. Hydroelectric potential is concentrated in mountainous regions with high rainfall and snowmelt. Biomass requires available land that does not compete with food production, and adequate sun and rain to support growth. Figure **Renewable Electricity Opportunities** (Figure 8.36) shows the geographical distribution of renewable electricity opportunities that are likely to be economically attractive in 2050 under an aggressive world development scenario.

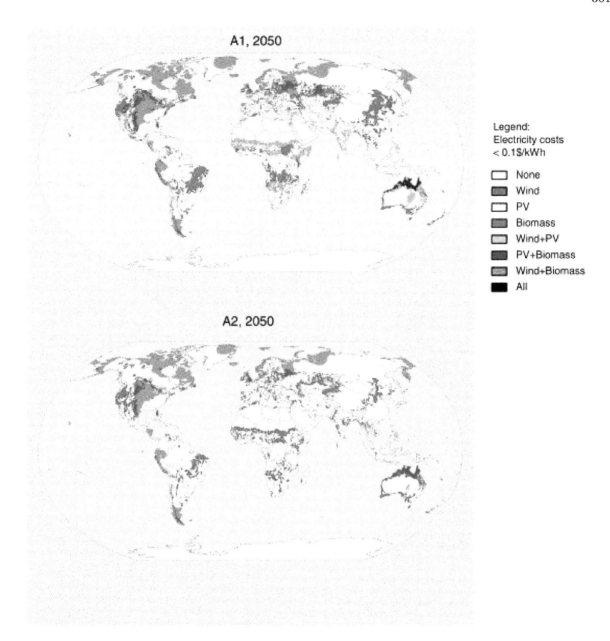

Figure 8.36: Renewable Electricity Opportunities Map shows areas where one or more of the wind, solar, and biomass options of renewable electricity is estimated to be able to produce electricity in 2050 at costs below 10 b kWh. *Source: de Vries, B.J.M., van Vuuren, D.P., & Hoogwijk, M.M. (2007) (p. 366). A hyper-text must be included to the Homepage of the journal from which you are licensing at http://www.sciencedirect.com/science/journal/03014215/35/4*[115]. *Permission for reuse must be obtained from Elsevier.*

---

[115]http://www.sciencedirect.com/science/journal/03014215/35/4

8.4.1.4.5 Wind and Solar Resources in the United States

The United States has abundant renewable resources. The solar resources of the United States, Germany and Spain are compared in Figure **Solar Resources of the United States, Spain and Germany** (Figure 8.37). The solar irradiation in the southwestern United States is exceptional, equivalent to that of Africa and Australia, which contain the best solar resources in the world. Much of the United States has solar irradiation as good or better than Spain, considered the best in Europe, and much higher than Germany. The variation in irradiation over the United States is about a factor two, quite homogeneous compared to other renewable resources. The size of the United States adds to its resource, making it a prime opportunity for solar development.

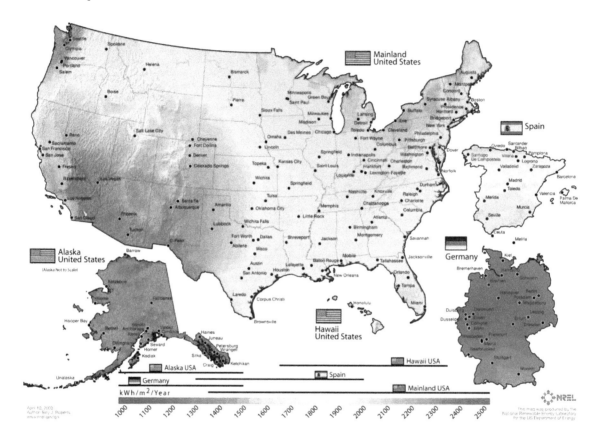

Figure 8.37: Solar Resources of the United States, Spain and Germany The solar resources of the United States, Spain and Germany, expressed as solar insolation averaged over the year. The geographic variation of solar irradiation in the United States is only a factor of two, much less than for other renewable energy sources. *Source: U.S. Department of Energy, Energy Efficiency and Renewable Energy, 2008 Solar Technologies Market Report, DOE/GO-102010-2867 (January, 2010), p52.*[116]

The wind resource of the United States, while abundant, is less homogeneous. Strong winds require steady gradients of temperature and pressure to drive and sustain them, and these are frequently associated with topological features such as mountain ranges or coastlines. The onshore wind map of the United States shows this pattern, with the best wind along a north-south corridor roughly at mid-continent (Figure **80 Meter Wind Resource Map** (Figure 8.38)). Offshore winds over the Great Lakes and the east and west

---

[116]http://www1.eere.energy.gov/solar/pdfs/46025.pdf

coasts are stronger and steadier though they cover smaller areas. The technical potential for onshore wind is over 8000 GW of capacity (Lu, 2009 (p. 366); Black & Veatch, 2007 (p. 366)) and offshore is 800 – 3000 GW (Lu, 2009 (p. 366); Schwartz, Heimiller, Haymes, & Musial, 2010 (p. 366)). For comparison, the United States used electricity in 2009 at the rate of 450 GW averaged over the day-night and summer-winter peaks and valleys.

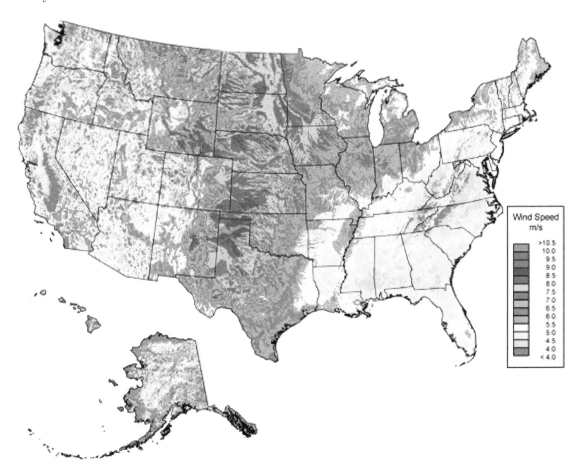

Figure 8.38: 80 Meter Wind Resource Map Figure shows the average wind speeds in the United States at 80 meters. Also see offshore wind resource maps[117]. *Source: U.S. Department of Energy, National Renewable Energy Laboratory and AWS Truepower LLC*[118]

8.4.1.4.6 Barriers to Deployment

Renewable energy faces several barriers to its widespread deployment. Cost is one of the most serious, illustrated in Figure **Production Cost of Electricity - 2020 Projection** (Figure 8.39). Although the cost of renewables has declined significantly in recent years, most are still higher in cost than traditional fossil alternatives. Fossil energy technologies have a longer experience in streamlining manufacturing, incorporating new materials, taking advantage of economies of scale and understanding the underlying physical and

---

[117]http://www.windpoweringamerica.gov/windmaps/offshore.asp
[118]http://www.windpoweringamerica.gov/wind_maps.asp

chemical phenomena of the energy conversion process. As Figure **Production Cost of Electricity - 2020 Projection** (Figure 8.39) shows, the lowest cost electricity is generated by natural gas and coal, with hydro and wind among the renewable challengers. Cost, however, is not an isolated metric; it must be compared with the alternatives. One of the uncertainties of the present business environment is the ultimate cost of carbon emissions. If governments put a price on carbon emission to compensate the social cost of global warming and the threat of climate change, the relative cost of renewables will become more appealing even if their absolute cost does not change. This policy uncertainty in the eventual cost of carbon-based power generation is a major factor in the future economic appeal of renewable energy.

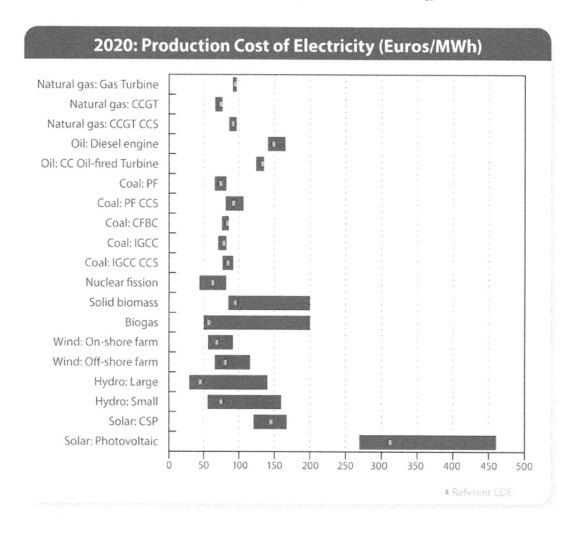

Figure 8.39: Production Cost of Electricity - 2020 Projection Estimates of the cost of electricity in 2020 by fossil, nuclear and renewable generation. *Source: European Commission, Strategic Energy Technologies Information System*[119]

A second barrier to widespread deployment of renewable energy is public opinion. In the consumer market, sales directly sample public opinion and the connection between deployment and public acceptance

---

[119]http://setis.ec.europa.eu/newsroom-items-folder/production-cost-of-electricity-2020-projection

is immediate. Renewable energy is not a choice that individual consumers make. Instead, energy choices are made by government policy makers at city, state and federal levels, who balance concerns for the common good, for "fairness" to stakeholders, and for economic cost. Nevertheless, public acceptance is a major factor in balancing these concerns: a strongly favored or disfavored energy option will be reflected in government decisions through representatives elected by or responding to the public. Figure **Acceptance of Different Sources of Energy** (Figure 8.40) shows the public acceptance of renewable and fossil electricity options. The range of acceptance goes from strongly positive for solar to strongly negative for nuclear. The disparity in the public acceptance and economic cost of these two energy alternatives is striking: solar is at once the most expensive alternative and the most acceptable to the public.

The importance of public opinion is illustrated by the Fukushima nuclear disaster of 2011[120] . The earthquake and tsunami that ultimately caused meltdown of fuel in several reactors of the Fukushima complex and release of radiation in a populated area caused many of the public in many countries to question the safety of reactors and of the nuclear electricity enterprise generally. The response was rapid, with some countries registering public consensus for drastic action such as shutting down nuclear electricity when the licenses for the presently operating reactors expire. Although its ultimate resolution is uncertain, the sudden and serious impact of the Fukushima event on public opinion shows the key role that social acceptance plays in determining our energy trajectory.

QD4 **Are you in favour or opposed to the use of these different sources of energy in (OUR COUNTRY)?**

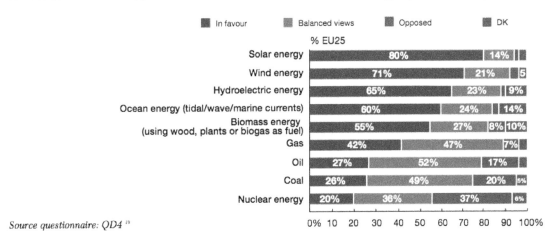

Source questionnaire: QD4 [19]

Figure 8.40: **Acceptance of Different Sources of Energy** Figure shows the European Union citizens' public acceptance of renewable and fossil electricity generation technologies. *Source: European Commission, Eurobarameter on Energy Technologies: Knowledge-Perception-Measures, p. 33*[121]

8.4.1.4.7 Summary

Strong interest in renewable energy arose in the 1970s as a response to the shortage and high price of imported oil, which disrupted the orderly operation of the economies and societies of many developed countries. Today there are new motivations, including the realization that growing greenhouse gas emission accelerates global warming and threatens climate change, the growing dependence of many countries on foreign oil, and the economic drain of foreign oil payments that slow economic growth and job creation. There are three

---

[120]http://en.wikipedia.org/wiki/Fukushima_Daiichi_nuclear_disaster
[121]http://ec.europa.eu/research/energy/pdf/energy_tech_eurobarometer_en.pdf

ultimate sources of all renewable and fossil energies: sunlight, the heat in the earth's core and crust, and the gravitational pull of the moon and sun on the oceans. Renewable energies are relatively recently developed and typically operate at lower efficiencies than mature fossil technologies. Like early fossil technologies, however, renewables can be expected to improve their efficiency and lower their cost over time, promoting their economic competitiveness and widespread deployment.

The future deployment of renewable energies depends on many factors, including the availability of suitable land, the technological cost of conversion to electricity or other uses, the costs of competing energy technologies, and the future need for energy. Scenario analyses indicate that renewable energies are likely to be technically and economically capable of supplying the world's electricity needs in 2050. In addition to cost, public acceptance is a key factor in the widespread deployment of renewable energy.

8.4.1.4.8 Review Questions

Question 8.4.1.4.1
What events in the 1970s and late 1990s motivated the modern interest in renewable energy?

Question 8.4.1.4.2
Renewable energy is often divided into solar, wind, hydropower, biomass, geothermal, wave and tide. What are the ultimate sources of each of these renewable energies? What is the ultimate source of fossil fuel and why is it not classified as renewable?

Question 8.4.1.4.3
Renewable energy has the technical potential to supply global electricity needs in 2050. What factors determine whether renewable energy will actually be deployed to meet this need? How can unknowns, such as the rate of technological and economic advances, the economic, intellectual and social connections among countries, and the relative importance of environmental and social agendas be taken into account in determining the course of deployment of renewable energy?

Question 8.4.1.4.4
Public acceptance is a key factor in the growth of renewable energy options. What is the public acceptance of various energy options, and how might these change over the next few decades?

8.4.1.4.9 References

Attari, S.Z., DeKay, M.L., Davidson, C.I., & de Bruin, W.B. (2010). Public perceptions of energy consumption and savings. *PNAS, 107*, 16054.

Black & Veatch (2007, October). *Twenty percent wind energy penetration in the United States: A technical analysis of the energy resource.* Walnut Creek, CA: Black & Veatch Corp. Retrieved December 9, 2011 from www.20percentwind.org/Black_Veatch_20_Percent_Report.pdf[122]

Clean Energy Progress Report, IEA (2011), http://www.iea.org/publications/free_new_Desc.asp?PUBS_ID=238[123]

de Vries, B.J.M., van Vuuren, D.P., & Hoogwijk, M.M. (2007). Renewable energy sources: Their global potential for the first-half of the 21st century at a global level: An integrated approach. *Energy Policy, 35*, 2590.

Jacobson, M.Z. & Delucchi, M.A. (2009). A plan for a sustainable future. *Scientific American, 301*, 58.

Kaldellis, J.K. & Zafirakis, D. (2011). The wind energy (r)evolution: A short review of a long history. *Renewable Energy, 36*, 1887-1901.

Lu, X., McElroy, M.B., & Kiviluoma, J. (2009). Global potential for wind-generated electricity. *PNAS, 106*, 10933.

Renewables 2010 Global Status Report, REN21, Renewable Energy Policy Network for the 21st Century, http://www.ren21.net/REN21Activities/Publications/GlobalStatusReport/GSR2010/tabid/5824/Default.aspx[124]

---

[122]http://www.20percentwind.org/Black_Veatch_20_Percent_Report.pdf
[123]http://www.iea.org/publications/free_new_Desc.asp?PUBS_ID=2384
[124]http://www.ren21.net/REN21Activities/Publications/GlobalStatusReport/GSR2010/tabid/5824/Default.aspx

Schwartz, M., Heimiller, D., Haymes, S., & Musial, W. (2010, June). *Assessment of offshore wind energy resources for the United States* (NREL-TP-500-45889). Golden, CO: National Renewable Energy Laboratory. Retrieved December 9, 2011 from www.nrel.gov/docs/fy10osti/45889.pdf[125]

8.4.2 Liquid Fuels

8.4.2.1 Fossil Fuel (Oil)[126]

8.4.2.1.1 Learning Objectives

After reading this module, the student should be able to

- outline the global dependence of transportation on oil
- understand the threat to energy security posed by concentration of oil in a few countries
- understand the challenge of capturing carbon emissions from transportation and the value of replacing oil with an alternate, such as biofuel or electricity

8.4.2.1.2 Introduction

Liquid petroleum fuels and electricity are the two dominant **energy carriers** in the United States, oil accounting for 37 percent of primary energy and electricity for 38 percent. These two energy carriers account for a similar fraction of carbon emissions, 36 percent and 38 percent, respectively. Two thirds of oil consumption is devoted to transportation, providing fuel for cars, trucks, trains and airplanes. For the United States and most developed societies, transportation is woven into the fabric of our lives, a necessity as central to daily operations as food or shelter. The concentration of oil reserves in a few regions or the world (Figure **Crude Oil Reserves** (Figure 8.1)) makes much of the world dependent on imported energy for transportation.

The rise in the price of oil in the last decade makes dependence on imported energy for transportation an economic as well as an energy issue. The United States, for example, now spends upwards of $350 billion annually on imported oil, a drain of economic resources that could be used to stimulate growth, create jobs, build infrastructure and promote social advances at home.

From a sustainability perspective, oil presents several challenges. First is the length of time over which the world's finite oil reserves can continue to supply rising demand. Second is the impact on global warming and climate change that carbon emissions from oil combustion will have, and third is the challenge of finding a sustainable replacement for oil for transportation. The first challenge, how much oil is left and when its production will peak, was discussed in Module **Sustainable Energy Systems - Chapter Introduction** (Section 8.1). The bottom line is that, as Yogi Berra famously said, making predictions is difficult, especially about the future. Although we know the general course of initial rise and ultimate fall that global oil production must take, we do not know with confidence the time scale over which it will play out.

The uncertainty of the timing of the peak in global oil production encourages us to find other issues and motivations for dealing with an inevitably unsustainable supply. A prime motivation is energy security, the threat that oil supplies could be interrupted by any of several events including weather, natural disaster, terrorism and geopolitics. Much of the world feels these threats are good reasons for concerted effort to find replacements for oil as our primary transportation fuel. A second motivation is the environmental damage and accumulation of greenhouse gases in the atmosphere due to transportation emissions. Unlike electricity generation, transportation emissions arise from millions of tiny sources, e.g. the tailpipes of cars and trucks and the exhaust of trains and airplanes. The challenge of capturing and sequestering carbon dioxide from these distributed and moving sources is dramatically greater than from the large fixed sources of power plants. A more achievable objective may be replacing oil as a transportation fuel with biofuel that recycles naturally each year from tailpipes of cars to biofuel crops that do not compete with food crops. Other

---

[125]http://www.nrel.gov/docs/fy10osti/45889.pdf
[126]This content is available online at <http://legacy.cnx.org/content/m41735/1.3/>.

options include replacing liquid fuels with electricity produced domestically, or increasing the efficiency of vehicles by reducing their weight, regeneratively capturing braking energy, and improving engine efficiency. Each of these options has promise and each must overcome challenges.

Changes in the energy system are inevitably slow, because of the time needed to develop new technologies and the operational inertia of phasing out the infrastructure of an existing technology to make room for a successor. The transportation system exhibits this operational inertia, governed by the turnover time for the fleet of vehicles, about 15 years. Although that time scale is long compared to economic cycles, the profit horizon of corporations and the political horizon of elected officials, it is important to begin now to identify and develop sustainable alternatives to oil as a transportation fuel. The timescale from innovation of new approaches and materials to market deployment is typically 20 years or more, well matched to the operational inertia of the transportation system. The challenge is to initiate innovative research and development for alternative transportation systems and sustain it continuously until the alternatives are established.

8.4.2.1.3 Summary

Oil for transportation and electricity generation are the two biggest users of primary energy and producers of carbon emissions in the United States. Transportation is almost completely dependent on oil and internal combustion engines for its energy. The concentration of oil in a few regions of the world creates a transportation energy security issue. Unlike electricity generation emissions, carbon emissions from transportation are difficult to capture because their sources, the tailpipes of vehicles, are many and moving. The challenges of oil energy security and capturing the carbon emissions of vehicles motivate the search for an oil replacement, such as biofuels, electricity or greater energy efficiency of vehicles.

8.4.2.1.4 Review Questions

Question 8.4.2.1.1
The almost exclusive dependence of the transportation system on liquid fuels makes oil an essential commodity for the orderly operation of many societies. What are some alternatives to oil as a transportation fuel?

Question 8.4.2.1.2
There are many reasons to reduce consumption of oil, including an ultimately finite supply, the high cost and lost economic stimulus of payments to foreign producers, the threat of interruption of supply due to weather, natural disaster, terrorism or geopolitical decisions, and the threat of climate change due to greenhouse gas emissions. Which of these reasons are the most important? Will their relative importance change with time?

Question 8.4.2.1.3
The transportation system changes slowly, governed by the lifetime of the fleet of vehicles. Compare the time required for change in the transportation system with the timescale of economic cycles, the profit horizon of business, the political horizon of elected officials and the time required to develop new transportation technologies such as electric cars or biofuels. What challenges do these time scales present for changing the transportation system?

8.4.2.1.5 References

Trench, C.J. (n.d.). *Oil Market Basics*. U.S.Energy Information Administration. Retrieved September 12, 2011 from http://205.254.135.24/pub/oil_gas/petroleum/analysis_publications/oil_market_basics/default.htm[127]

---

[127]http://205.254.135.24/pub/oil_gas/petroleum/analysis_publications/oil_market_basics/default.htm

8.4.2.2 The Conversion of Biomass into Biofuels[128]

8.4.2.2.1 Learning Objectives

After reading this module, students should be able to

- understand the social and environmental motivations for biofuels production
- learn the main types of catalytic and biocatalytic routes to produce biofuels and biochemicals
- compare alcohol (ethanol and butanol) biofuels to hydrocarbon biofuels (green gasoline, diesel, and jet fuel)

8.4.2.2.2 Introduction

Biofuels are fuels made from biomass. The best known example is ethanol, which can be easily fermented from sugar cane juice, as is done in Brazil. Ethanol can also be fermented from broken down (saccarified) corn starch, as is mainly done in the United States. Most recently, efforts have been devoted to making drop-in replacement hydrocarbon biofuels called green gasoline, green diesel, or green jet fuel. This chapter discusses the need for biofuels, the types of biofuels that can be produced from the various available biomass feedstocks, and the advantages and disadvantages of each fuel and feedstock. The various ways of producing biofuels are also reviewed.

8.4.2.2.3 The Need for Renewable Transportation Fuels

In crude oil, coal, and natural gas, (collectively called fossil fuels) our planet has provided us with sources of energy that have been easy to obtain and convert into useful fuels and chemicals. That situation will soon change, however, in a few decades for petroleum crude and in a few centuries for coal and natural gas. **Peak oil** refers to the peak in oil production that must occur as petroleum crude runs out. As shown in Figure **Peak Oil – The Growing Gap** (Figure 8.41), the main discoveries of crude oil occurred prior to 1980.

[128]This content is available online at <http://legacy.cnx.org/content/m41736/1.3/>.

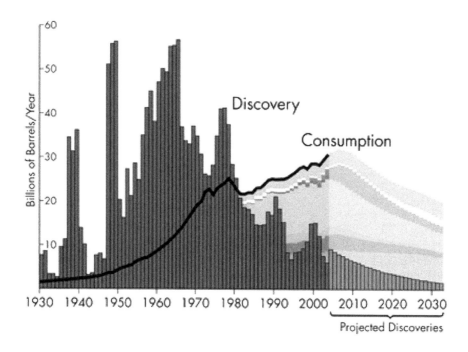

Figure 8.41: Peak Oil – The Growing Gap Petroleum crude oil discoveries versus refined oil
production. *Source: Rep. Roscoe Bartlett, Maryland*[129]

Since oil is getting harder and harder to find, we now have to obtain it from less accessible places such
as far under the ocean, which has led to hard-to-repair accidents such as the Deepwater Horizon oil spill[130]
in May, 2010. An additional effect is the higher cost of refining the petroleum since it comes from more
remote locations or in less desirable forms such as thick, rocky "tar sand" or "oil sand" found in Canada
or Venezuela. Overall, the use of petroleum crude cannot exceed the amount of petroleum that has been
discovered, and assuming that no major oil discoveries lie ahead, the production of oil from crude must start
to decrease. Some analysts think that this peak has already happened.

An additional aspect of oil scarcity is energy independence. The United States currently imports about
two thirds of its petroleum, making it dependent on the beneficence of countries that possess large amounts of
oil. These countries are shown in Figure **The World According to Oil** (Figure 8.42), a world map rescaled
with the area of each country proportional to its oil reserves. Middle Eastern countries are among those with
the highest oil reserves. With its economy and standard of living so based on imported petroleum crude it is
easy to see why the United States is deeply involved in Middle East politics. It should be noted that Figure
Peak Oil – The Growing Gap (Figure 8.41) corresponds to the entire world and even currently oil-rich
countries such as Saudi Arabia will soon experience peak oil.

---

[129]http://www.bartlett.house.gov/uploadedfiles/PeakOilGapDiscoveryConsumption.pdf
[130]http://en.wikipedia.org/wiki/Deepwater_Horizon_oil_spill

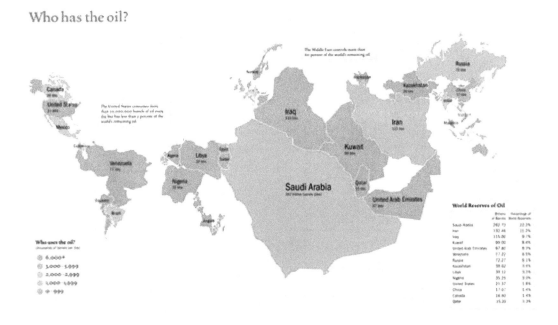

Who has the oil?

Figure 8.42: The World According to Oil World map redrawn with country area proportional to oil resources. *Source: Rep. Roscoe Bartlett, Maryland*[131]

A second major motivation to move away from petroleum crude is global climate change. While the correlation of carbon dioxide (CO_2) concentration in the atmosphere to average global temperature is presently being debated, the rise of CO_2 in our atmosphere that has come from burning fossil fuel since the industrial revolution is from about 280 ppm to about 390 ppm at present, and cannot be denied. Energy sources such as wind, solar, nuclear, and biomass are needed that minimize or eliminate the release of atmospheric CO_2. Biomass is included in this list since the carbon that makes up plant fiber is taken from the atmosphere in the process of photosynthesis. Burning fuel derived from biomass releases the CO_2 back into the atmosphere, where it can again be incorporated into plant mass. The Energy Independence and Security Act (EISA) of 2007[132] defines an advanced biofuel as one that lowers lifecycle greenhouse gas emissions (emissions from all processes involved in obtaining, refining, and finally burning the fuel) by 60% relative to the baseline of 2005 petroleum crude.

8.4.2.2.4 First Generation Biofuels

First generation biofuels are commonly considered to be ethanol, as has been produced in Brazil for over 30 years from sugar cane, and biodiesel produced by breaking down, in a process called **transesterification**, vegetable oil. Brazil can efficiently harvest the juice from its sugar cane and make ethanol, which is price-competitive with gasoline at cost per mile.

[131]http://www.bartlett.house.gov/uploadedfiles/PeakChartWhoHastheOil.pdf
[132]http://en.wikipedia.org/wiki/Energy_Independence_and_Security_Act_of_2007

Figure 8.43: Gas/Ethanol Fuel Pump A fuel pump in Brazil offering either ethanol alcohol (A) or gasoline (G). *Source: Natecull*[133]

There, if the cost of alcohol (as it is known colloquially) is less than 70% than the cost of gasoline, tanks are filled with ethanol. If the cost of alcohol is more than 70% of the cost of gasoline, people fill up with gasoline since there is about a 30% penalty in gas mileage with ethanol. This comes about simply because the chemical structure of ethanol has less energy per volume (about 76,000 Btu/gallon or 5,100 kcal/liter) than gasoline (115 Btu/gallon or 7,600 kcal/liter) or diesel (132,000 Btu/gallon or 8,800 kcal/liter). Cane ethanol qualifies, per EISA 2007, as an advanced biofuel.

In the United States, for a cost of about twice that of cane-derived ethanol, corn starch is saccharified and fermented into ethanol. Ethanol is used predominantly as a high octane, oxygenated blend at 10% to improve the combustion in gasoline engines. The distribution of ethanol as E85 flex fuel[134] (85% ethanol and 15% gasoline) has faltered probably because the price, even with a 50 cents/gallon federal subsidy, does not make up for the 25 – 30% decrease in gas mileage (see Figure **Mileage Comparisons** (Figure 8.44)).

---

[133]http://www.flickr.com/photos/natecull/3515757/
[134]http://en.wikipedia.org/wiki/E85

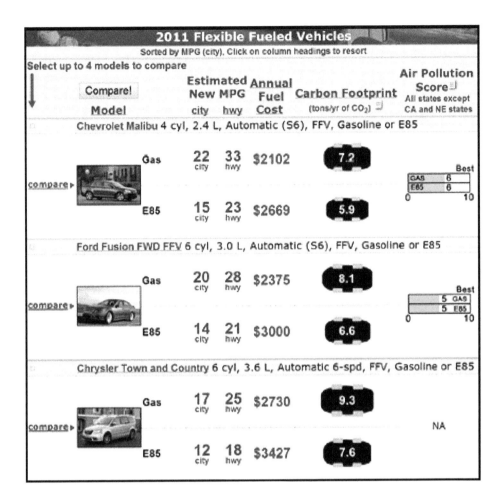

Figure 8.44: Mileage Comparisons Mileage comparison of gasoline and E85 flex fuel. *Source: U.S. Department of Energy, Energy Efficiency and Renewable Energy. Image created at http://www.fueleconomy.gov/feg/byfueltype.htm*[135]

First generation biodiesel is made via the base catalyzed **transesterification** of plant oils such as soy and palm. The main disadvantage with plant oil-based biofuels is the high cost of the plant oil, owing to the relatively little oil that can be produced per acre of farmland compared to other biofuel sources. The problem with transesterification is that it produces a fuel relatively high in oxygen, which a) causes the biodiesel to become cloudy (partially freeze) at relatively high temperature, and makes the biodiesel b) less stable, and c) less energy dense than petroleum-derived diesel.

Cane ethanol qualifies as an advanced biofuel, as its production lowers greenhouse gas emissions more than 60% relative to the 2005 petroleum baseline (per EISA 2007). Corn ethanol is far from this energy efficiency. However, ethanol made from **lignocellulose** – the non-food part of plants - comes close, at a 50% reduction. This brings us to the second generation of biofuels.

---

[135]http://www.fueleconomy.gov/feg/byfueltype.htm

8.4.2.2.5 Second Generation Biofuels

Second generation biofuels are shown in Figure **Second Generation Biofuels** (Figure 8.45). In anticipation of the "food versus fuel" debate, EISA 2007 placed a cap on the production of corn ethanol (at 15 billion gallons/year, close to what is now produced), with the bulk of biofuels to be derived from agricultural residues such as corn stover (the parts of the corn plant left over from the ears of corn – the stalk and leaves) and wheat straw, forest waste (wood trimmings) and energy crops such as switchgrass and short rotation poplar trees which can be grown on abandoned or marginal farmland with minimal irrigation and fertilization. A U.S. Department of Agriculture study commissioned in 2005 called the Billion Ton Study[136] estimated that approximately one billion tons per year of biomass could be sustainably produced in the United States each year; the energy in this biomass equals to the amount of oil we import. If the energy contained in this biomass can be recovered at an efficiency of 50 percent, we can replace half of our imported oil with domestically produced biofuels.

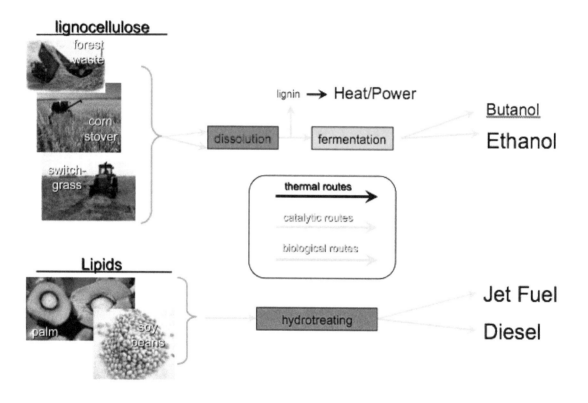

Figure 8.45: Second Generation Biofuels Cellulosic ethanol and green diesel. *Source: John Regalbuto*[137]

Collectively termed "lignocellulose," this material consists of three main components; cellulose, hemicellulose, and lignin. Chemical or biological pretreatments are required to separate the whole biomasss into these fractions. Hemicellulose and cellulose, with the appropriate enzymes or inorganic acids, can be deconstructed into simple sugars and the sugars fermented into ethanol, or with some newer strains of microbes, into butanol. Butanol has only 10% less energy density than gasoline. The lignin fraction of biomass is

---

[136]http://feedstockreview.ornl.gov/pdf/billion_ton_vision.pdf
[137]http://cnx.org/member_profile/jrr

the most resistant to deconstruction by biological or chemical means and is often burned for heat or power recovery.

At the same time attention turned toward cellulosic ethanol, petroleum refining companies set about to improve biodiesel. A petroleum refining process called **hydrotreating** was used to upgrade plant oil. In this process, the oil is reacted with hydrogen in the presence of inorganic catalysts, and the plant oil is converted into a much higher quality, oxygen-free "green diesel" and jet fuel. This type of biofuel is in fact a "drop in replacement" to petroleum-derived diesel and jet fuel and passes all of the stringent regulations demanded by the automobile and defense industries. It has been tested in a number of commercial and military aircraft.

8.4.2.2.6 "Advanced" Biofuels

Advanced biofuels are, in fact, characterized by their similarity to present day gasoline, diesel, and jet fuels. Advanced biofuels are **infrastructure compatible** and **energy dense**. The two disadvantages with even cellulosic ethanol are its low energy density (the energy content of ethanol being independent of whether it comes from corn, cellulose, etc.) and its incompatibility with existing car engines, oil pipelines, storage tanks, refineries, etc. For these two reasons the latest research and development efforts in the United States have been devoted to hydrocarbon biofuels, which have the same gas mileage as the gasoline and diesel fuels now used, and are completely compatible with the existing oil infrastructure.

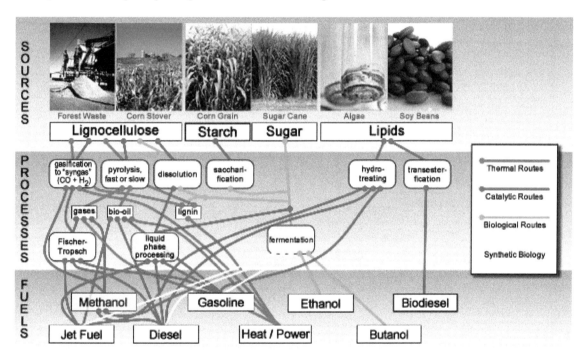

Figure 8.46: Routes to Advanced Biofuels Various routes to drop-in replacement hydrocarbon biofuels. *Source: John Regalbuto*[138]

The various routes to drop-in replacement hydrocarbon biofuels are shown in Figure **Routes to Advanced Biofuels** (Figure 8.46). On the left side of the figure, feedstocks are ordered relative to their abundance and cost. The most abundant and, therefore, cheapest feedstock is lignocellulose from sources such as agricultural residue, forest waste, and energy crops such as switch grass and short rotation poplar

---

[138]http://cnx.org/member_profile/jrr

trees. Of lesser abundance and higher expense are the sugars and starches – corn and sugar cane. The least abundant and most expensive biofuels, lipid-based feedstocks from plant oil or animal fat, are shown at the bottom. Efforts are underway to mass produce oil-laden algae. The oils harvested from algae are relatively easy to convert to hydrocarbon biofuels, by using processing similar to hydrotreating. The main set of problems associated with algae lie in its mass production. Algal feedstocks are easy to convert to hydrocarbons but algae itself is difficult to mass produce, whereas lignocellulose is very abundant but more difficult to convert into hydrocarbons.

Two of the routes to hydrocarbon biofuels compete directly with **fermentation** of sugars to ethanol. The same sugars can be treated with inorganic catalysts, via the blue liquid phase processing routes seen in the center of Figure **Routes to Advanced Biofuels** (Figure 8.46), or with microbial routes to yield hydrocarbons as the fermentation product (pink routes). Microbes are examples of biocatalysts; enzymes within the microbe act in basically the same way that inorganic catalysts act in inorganic solutions. The field of research in which enzymes are engineered to alter biological reaction pathways is called synthetic biology.

A flow sheet of an inorganic catalytic set of processes to hydrocarbon biofuels, from a leading biofuel startup company (Virent Energy Systems[139] of Madison, Wisconsin) is shown in Figure **Inorganic Catalytic Routes to Advanced Biofuels** (Figure 8.47). Both of the **biocatalytic** and the inorganic catalytic processes involve an intrinsic separation of the hydrocarbon product from water, which eliminates the energy intensive distillation step needed for alcohol fuels. For the microbial route the added benefit of this self-separation is that the microbes are not poisoned by the accumulation of product as occurs in fermentation to alcohol.

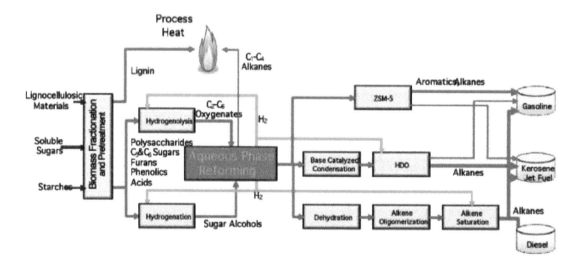

Figure 8.47: Inorganic Catalytic Routes to Advanced Biofuels A flow sheet of an inorganic catalytic set of processes to hydrocarbon biofuels, from a leading biofuel startup company, Virent Energy Systems. *Source: Virent Energy Systems, figure 1*[140]

Two other main routes to hydrocarbon biofuels are seen in the upper section of Figure **Routes to Advanced Biofuels** (Figure 8.46): **gasification** and **pyrolysis**. An advantage of both of these routes is that they process whole biomass, including the energy-rich lignin fraction of it. Gasification produces a mixture of carbon monoxide and hydrogen called synthesis gas, which can be converted to hydrocarbon

---

[139]http://www.virent.com/
[140]http://www.virent.com/News/in_the_media/catalytic_conversion_of_sugar.pdf

fuels by a number of currently commercialized catalytic routes including **Fischer-Tropsch synthesis** and methanol-to-gasoline. The challenge with biomass is to make these processes economically viable at small scale. The second process is pyrolysis, which yields a crude-like intermediate called pyrolysis oil or bio-oil. This intermediate must be further treated to remove oxygen; once this is done it can be inserted into an existing petroleum refinery for further processing.

8.4.2.2.7 Summary

The motivations for hydrocarbon biofuels are energy independence and a reduction in greenhouse gas emissions. The first renewable biofuels were biodiesel and bioethanol. With **inorganic catalysis** and **synthetic biology**, these have been supplanted with drop-in replacement gasoline, diesel, and jet fuels. These can be made in the United States in a number of ways from presently available, sustainably produced lignocellulosic feedstocks such as corn stover, wood chips, and switchgrass, and in the future, from mass-produced algae. It is too early to tell which production method will prevail, if in fact one does. Some processes might end up being particularly advantageous for a particular feedstock such as wood or switchgrass. What we do know is that something has to be done; our supply of inexpensive, easily accessible oil is running out. Biofuels will be a big part of the country's long-term energy independence. A great deal of scientific and engineering research is currently underway; it's an exciting time for biofuels.

8.4.2.2.8 Review Questions

Question 8.4.2.2.1
What are the potential advantages of hydrocarbon biofuels over alcohol biofuels?

Question 8.4.2.2.2
How could biofuels be used with other alternate energy forms to help the United States become energy independent?

8.4.3 Heat

8.4.3.1 Geothermal Heating and Cooling[141]

8.4.3.1.1 Learning Objectives

After reading this module, students should be able to

- understand the basic thermodynamic principles of a heat
- learn what makes geothermal heating and cooling more efficient than conventional systems
- compare different types of geothermal systems and the principles that govern their design

8.4.3.1.2 Introduction

With limited supplies of fossil fuels in the coming decades and increasing awareness of environmental concerns related to combustions of fossil fuels, alternate energy sources such as geothermal are becoming increasingly attractive. **Geothermal energy** is energy that comes from the earth. In this section we describe the basic principles of geothermal energy systems and the energy savings that can result from their use.

---

[141]This content is available online at <http://legacy.cnx.org/content/m41737/1.4/>.

8.4.3.1.3 The Heat Pump

The key to understanding a geothermal energy system is the heat pump. Normally heat goes from a hot area to a cold area, but a heat pump is a device that enables heat to be transferred from a lower temperature to a higher temperature with minimal consumption of energy (see Figure **A Simple Heat Pump** (Figure 8.48)). A home refrigerator is an example of a simple heat pump. A refrigerator removes heat from the inside of a refrigerator at approximately 3 °C, 38 °F (See *Heat In* in the Figure **A Simple Heat Pump** (Figure 8.48)) and then discards it to the kitchen (at approximately 27 °C, 80 °F (See *Heat Out* in Figure **A Simple Heat Pump** (Figure 8.48)). It is *pumping* heat from the inside of the refrigerator to the outside using a compressor, hence the name **heat pump**.

The fact the most fluids boil at different temperatures when pressure is changed[142] is crucial to the operation of the heat pump. Boiling removes heat from the environment, just like boiling water takes heat from the stove. In a heat pump, boiling takes place at a lower pressure and, consequently, at a lower temperature. Let's assume 40 °F, or 4 °C, so that it can effectively remove heat from the soil or the pond water (the heat source) in the geothermal unit at 50 °F, or 10 °C. The steam produced from the boiling can then be compressed (see *Compressor* in Figure **A Simple Heat Pump** (Figure 8.48)) to higher pressure so that it will condense (the opposite of boiling) at a much higher temperature. When a geothermal unit is incorporated into a building, it is the building that removes the heat, subsequently warming it up (See *Heat Out* in Figure **A Simple Heat Pump** (Figure 8.48)). The condensed steam in a geothermal heat pump will thus provide heat at a much higher temperature to the area being heated than the original heat source. Finally a throttle, similar to a water faucet at home, is used to lower the pressure (See *Expansion Valve* in Figure **A Simple Heat Pump** (Figure 8.48)) to complete the closed system cycle, which is then repeated. By switching the direction of the heat pump, the geothermal system can be used for cooling as well.

---

[142]This is the same reason why water boils at lower temperatures at higher elevations where pressure is lower, for example in Boulder, Colorado.

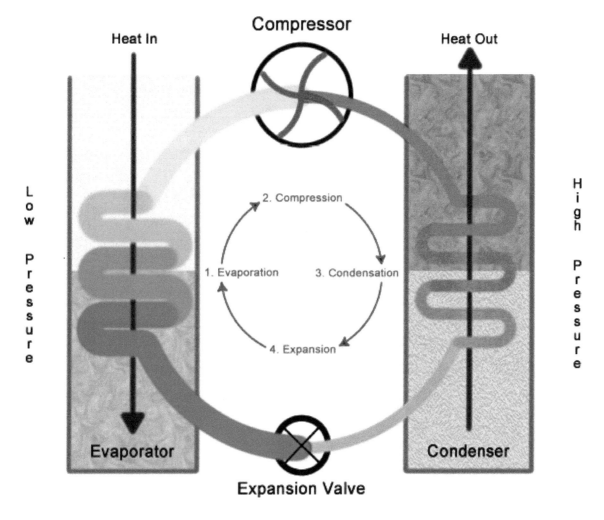

Figure 8.48: A Simple Heat Pump A typical vapor compression heat pump for cooling used with a Geothermal System. *Source: Sohail Murad*[143] *adapted from Ilmari Karonen*[144]

8.4.3.1.4 Geothermal Heating and Cooling

Geothermal systems are suited to locations with somewhat extreme temperature ranges. Areas with moderate temperature ranges (e.g. some areas of California) can use ordinary heat pumps with similar energy savings by adding or removing heat to/from the outside air directly. Areas that experience somewhat extreme temperatures (e.g. the Midwest and East Coast) are ideal target locations for geothermal systems. For regions with moderate climates, such as many parts of the South or the West Coast, conventional heat pumps, that exchange energy generally with the outside air, can still be used with similar energy savings. Geothermal heat pumps (GHPs) use the almost constant temperatures (7 °C to 8 °C, or 45 °F to 48 °F) of soil beneath the frost line as an energy source to provide efficient heating and cooling all year long. The installation cost of GHPs is higher than conventional systems due to additional drilling and excavation expenses, but the added cost is quickly offset by GHPs' higher efficiency. It is possible to gain up to 50

---

[143]http://cnx.org/member_profile/murad
[144]http://en.wikipedia.org/wiki/File:Heatpump.svg

percent savings over conventional heating and cooling systems (see Figure **Estimated Cooling Costs Comparison** (Figure 8.49)), which allows the additional capital costs from installation to be recovered, on average, in less than 5 years. GHP's have an average lifespan of over 30 years, leaving 25 years or more of heating/cooling savings for those willing to make the investment. In addition, GHPs are space efficient and, because they contain fewer moving components, they also have lower maintenance costs.

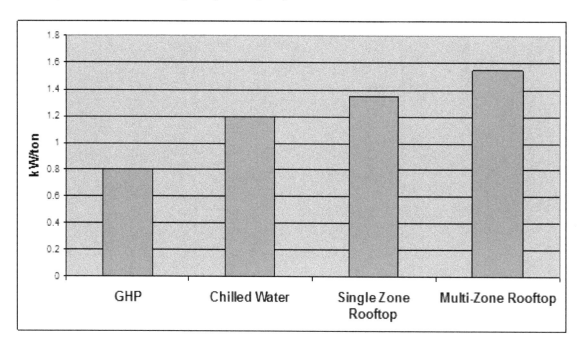

Figure 8.49: **Estimated Cooling Costs Comparison** Estimated cooling costs of geothermal systems compared with conventional systems. *Source: Sohail Murad*[145]

8.4.3.1.5 Types of Geothermal Systems

There are two major types of geothermal systems: *in ground* and *pond* systems. *In ground geothermal systems* can be vertical and horizontal as shown in Figure **In Ground Geothermal Systems** (Figure 8.50). The excavation cost of vertical systems is generally higher and they require more land area for installation, which is generally not an option in urban locations. Other than excavation costs, vertical and horizontal GHPs have similar efficiencies since the ground temperature below the frost line is essentially constant.

[145]http://cnx.org/member_profile/murad

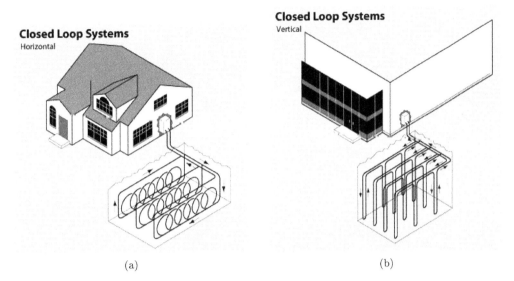

(a)   (b)

Figure 8.50: In Ground Geothermal Systems Examples of horizontal and vertical ground systems.
Source: U.S. Department of Energy, Energy Efficiency and Renewable Energy[146]

Pond geothermal systems are generally preferable if there is water available in the vicinity at almost constant temperature year round. These systems are especially suited to industrial units (e.g. oil refineries) with water treatment facilities to treat processed water before it is discharged. The temperature of treated water from these facilities is essentially constant throughout the year and is an ideal location for a pond system. Pond geothermal systems are constructed with either open loops or closed loops (see Figure **Pond Geothermal Systems** (Figure 8.51)). Open loop systems actually remove water from the pond, while the close loop systems only remove energy in the form of heat from the pond water. Of course, in open pond system this water is again returned to the pond, albeit at a lower temperature when used for heating.

[146]http://www.energysavers.gov/your_home/space_heating_cooling/index.cfm/mytopic=12650

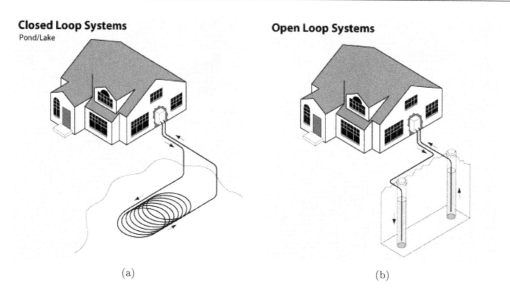

Figure 8.51: Pond Geothermal Systems Examples of closed and open loop pond systems. *Source: U.S. Department of Energy, Energy Efficiency and Renewable Energy*[147]

8.4.3.1.6 Economics of Geothermal Systems

As stated earlier, depending upon the type of system, the capital and installation cost of a geothermal system is about twice the cost of a traditional **heating, ventilation, air conditioning (HVAC)** system. However, both the operating and maintenance costs are much lower and switching from heating to cooling is effortless. A typical return of investment (ROI) plot for a ground geothermal system for a multi-unit building is favorable (see Figure **Return of Investment in Geothermal System** (Figure 8.52)). A geothermal system that had an additional $500,000 in capital costs but lower operating and maintenance costs allowed the added cost to be recouped in 5 to 8 years. Since the average lifespan of a geothermal system is at least 30 years, the savings over the lifetime of the system can be substantial. The efficiency of ground geothermal systems is fairly constant since there are no large variations in ground temperature. The efficiency for pond systems would, in general, be much higher than those shown in Figure **Return of Investment in Geothermal System** (Figure 8.52) if, during the winter months, the pond water temperature is higher than typical ground temperatures below the frost line ($7\,^{\circ}$C - $8\,^{\circ}$C, or $44\,^{\circ}$F - $48\,^{\circ}$F) because the efficiency of heat pumps increases with higher heat source temperature. Another reason for higher efficiency of pond systems is the much higher heat transfer rate between a fluid and the outer surface of the geothermal pipes, especially if the water is flowing.

---

[147]http://www.energysavers.gov/your_home/space_heating_cooling/index.cfm/mytopic=12650

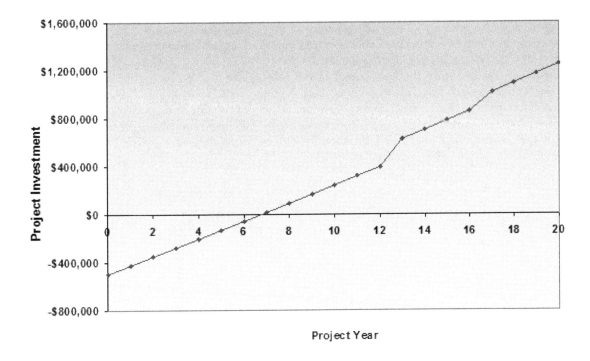

Figure 8.52: Return of Investment in Geothermal System Return of additional capital investment in a typical geothermal system. *Source: Murad, S., & Al-Hallaj, S. from Feasibility Study For a Hybrid Fuel Cell/Geothermal System, Final Report, HNTB Corporation, August 2009.*

8.4.3.1.7 Increasing Efficiency of Geothermal Systems

Several strategies are available to increase the efficiency of geothermal systems. One of the most promising possibilities is to use it in conjunction with **phase change materials (PCM)** (see also Module **Applications of Phase Change Materials for Sustainable Energy** (Section 8.6)), particularly to handle peak loads of energy consumptions. Phase change materials are materials that can absorb and deliver much larger amounts of energy compared to typical building materials. The cost of geothermal systems unlike other HVAC systems increases almost linearly with system size (approximately $1000/ton). Thus, building larger systems to account for peak loads can significantly add to both the capital and installation costs. PCM can be incorporated into all four geothermal systems described earlier. The best approach is to incorporate PCMs with geothermal systems for applications in systems with non-uniform energy requirements, or systems with short but significant swings and peaks in energy needs. For example, designers may include snow melting heating systems for train platforms or they may build a buffer energy reservoir using PCMs to satisfy peak needs of cooling on a hot summer afternoon. The advantages in the former application would be to avoid running the geothermal system for heat loads at low temperatures over prolonged periods, which would not be as energy efficient and would require specially designed systems.

Using phase change materials allows for the use of standard geothermal systems, which would then store energy in a PCM unit to supply heat at a constant temperature and at a uniform heat rate to, for example, melt the snow on train platforms. Once the energy in the PCM is nearly used the geothermal system would repower the PCM storage. The extra energy needs for peak periods could be stored in PCM Storage Tanks and then used to address such needs. For example, on a hot summer day, the PCM unit can be used to remove additional heat above the designed capacity of the geothermal system during temperature spikes, which generally last only a few hours. This then reduces the load on the geothermal system during peak hours when electricity cost is generally the highest.

PCM Storage Tanks reduce the overall cost of the geothermal heat pump system significantly since it does not have to be designed to address peak heating/cooling needs. In addition, it also shifts energy loads from peak hours to non-peak hours. Figure **Temperature Variation** (Figure 8.53) shows temperature variations for a typical summer day in July 2010 in Chicago. The high temperature of 90 degree lasted only for a short period of about 4 hours, and then returned to below 85 degrees rapidly. These relatively short temperature peaks can be easily managed by PCMs.

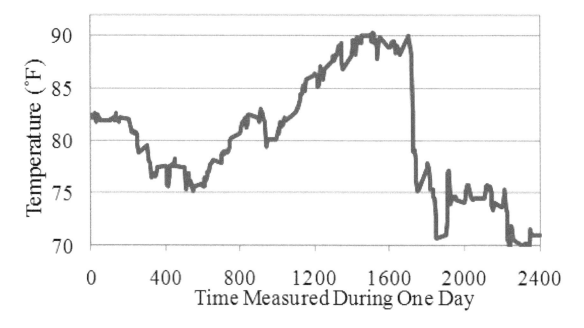

Figure 8.53: Temperature Variation Temperature variation during a typical July day in Chicago. *Source: Sohail Murad[148] produced figure using data from Great Lakes Environmental Research Laboratory[149]*

In conclusion, geothermal heat pumps are a very attractive, cost efficient sustainable energy source for both heating and cooling with a minimal carbon print. It is a well-developed technology that can be easily incorporated into both residential and commercial buildings at either the design stage or by retrofitting buildings.

8.4.3.1.8 Review Questions

Question 8.4.3.1.1
On what principle does a geothermal heat pump work?

Question 8.4.3.1.2
What makes it more cost efficient than electrical heating or conventional furnaces?

---

[148]http://cnx.org/member_profile/murad
[149]http://www.glerl.noaa.gov/metdata/chi/archive/

Question 8.4.3.1.3

Are geothermal heat pumps suitable for moderate climates (e.g. Miami, FL)? Are conventional electrical or gas furnaces the only choices in these areas?

8.5 Energy Uses

8.5.1 Electric and Plug-in Hybrids[150]

8.5.1.1 Learning Objectives

After reading this module, students should be able to

- outline the traditional dependence of transportation on oil and the internal combustion engine
- understand two alternatives to oil as a transportation fuel: hydrogen and electricity
- understand the dual use of oil and electricity in hybrid vehicles and their impact on energy efficiency and carbon emissions

8.5.1.2 Introduction

Since the early 20th Century, oil and the **internal combustion engine** have dominated transportation. The fortunes of oil and vehicles have been intertwined, with oil racing to meet the energy demands of the ever growing power and number of personal vehicles, vehicles driving farther in response to growing interstate highway opportunities for long distance personal travel and freight shipping, and greater personal mobility producing living patterns in far-flung suburbs that require oil and cars to function. In recent and future years, the greatest transportation growth will be in developing countries where the need and the market for transportation is growing rapidly. China has an emerging middle class that is larger than the entire population of the United States, a sign that developing countries will soon direct or strongly influence the emergence of new technologies designed to serve their needs. Beyond deploying new technologies, developing countries have a potentially large second advantage: they need not follow the same development path through outdated intermediate technologies taken by the developed world. Leapfrogging directly to the most advanced technologies avoids legacy infrastructures and long turnover times, allowing innovation and deployment on an accelerated scale.

The internal combustion engine and the vehicles it powers have made enormous engineering strides in the past half century, increasing efficiency, durability, comfort and adding such now-standard features as air conditioning, cruise control, hands-free cell phone use, and global positioning systems. Simultaneously, the automobile industry has become global, dramatically increasing competition, consumer choice and marketing reach. The most recent trend in transportation is dramatic swings in the price of oil, the lifeblood of traditional vehicles powered with internal combustion engines.

8.5.1.3 Hydrogen as an Alternative Fuel

The traditional synergy of oil with automobiles may now be showing signs of strain. The reliance of vehicles on one fuel whose price shows strong fluctuations and whose future course is ultimately unsustainable presents long-term business challenges. Motivated by these business and sustainability concerns, the automobile industry is beginning to diversify to other fuels. Hydrogen made its debut in the early 2000s, and showed that it has the potential to power vehicles using fuel cells to produce on-board electricity for electric motors (Eberle and von Helmholt, 2010 (p. 390), Crabtree, Dresselhaus, & Buchanan, 2004 (p. 390)). One advantage of hydrogen is efficiency, up to 50 percent or greater for fuel cells, up to 90 percent or greater for electric motors powering the car, compared with 25 percent efficiency for an internal combustion engine. A

---

[150]This content is available online at <http://legacy.cnx.org/content/m41738/1.2/>.

second advantage is reduced dependence on foreign oil – hydrogen can be produced from natural gas or from entirely renewable resources such as solar decomposition of water. A third potential advantage of hydrogen is environmental – the emissions from the hydrogen car are harmless: water and a small amount of heat, though the emissions from the hydrogen production chain may significantly offset this advantage.

The vision of hydrogen cars powered by fuel cells remains strong. It must overcome significant challenges, however, before becoming practical, such as storing hydrogen on board vehicles at high densities, finding inexpensive and earth-abundant catalysts to promote the reduction of oxygen to water in fuel cells, and producing enough hydrogen from renewable sources such as solar driven water splitting to fuel the automobile industry (Crabtree & Dresselhaus, 2008 (p. 390)). The hydrogen and electric energy chains for automobiles are illustrated in **Figure** Electric Transportation (Figure 8.54). Many scientists and automobile companies are exploring hydrogen as a long-term alternative to oil.

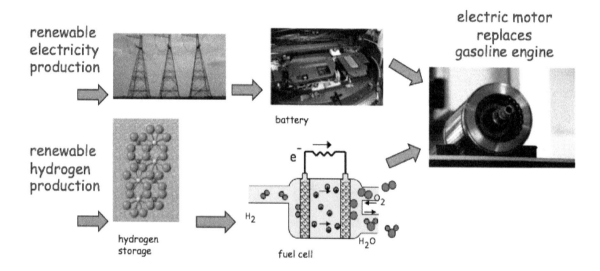

Figure 8.54: Electric Transportation Transportation is electrified by replacing the gasoline engine with an electric motor, powered by electricity from a battery on board the car (upper panel) or electricity from a fuel cell and hydrogen storage system on board the car (lower panel). For maximum effectiveness, both routes require renewable production of electricity or hydrogen. *Source: George Crabtree*[151] *using images from Rondol*[152], *skinnylawyer*[153], *Tinu Bao*[154], *U.S. Department of Energy, Office of Science*[155]

8.5.1.4 Electricity as an Alternative Fuel

Electric cars represent a second alternative to oil for transportation, with many similarities to hydrogen (see **Figure** Electric Transportation (Figure 8.54)). Electric vehicles are run by an electric motor, as in a fuel cell car, up to four times as efficient as a gasoline engine. The electric motor is far simpler than a gasoline engine, having only one moving part, a shaft rotating inside a stationary housing and surrounded by a coil of copper wire. Electricity comes from a battery, whose storage capacity, like that of hydrogen materials, is too small to enable long distance driving. Developing higher **energy density** batteries for vehicles is a

[151]http://cnx.org/member_profile/crabtree
[152]http://commons.wikimedia.org/wiki/File:Anker_power_lines_.JPG
[153]http://www.flickr.com/photos/skinnylawyer/5871298909/
[154]http://www.flickr.com/photos/tinou/393794108/#/
[155]http://science.energy.gov/~/media/bes/pdf/reports/files/nhe_rpt.pdf

major challenge for the electric car industry. The battery must be charged before driving, which can be done from the grid using excess capacity available at night, or during the day from special solar charging stations that do not add additional load to the grid. Because charging typically takes hours, a potentially attractive alternative is switching the battery out in a matter of minutes for a freshly charged one at special swapping stations. A large fleet of electric cars in the United States would require significant additional electricity, as much as 130 GW if the entire passenger and light truck fleet were converted to electricity, or 30 percent of average United States electricity usage in 2008.

The energy usage of electric cars is about a factor of four less than for gasoline cars, consistent with the higher efficiency of electric motors over internal combustion engines. Although gasoline cars vary significantly in their energy efficiency, a "typical" middle of the road value for a five-passenger car is 80kWh/100km. A typical electric car (such as the Think Ox from Norway, the Chevy Volt operating in its electric mode, or the Nissan Leaf) uses $\sim$ 20 kWh/100km. While the energy cost of electric cars at the **point of use** is significantly less, one must consider the cost at the **point of production**, the electricity generating plant. If the vehicle's electricity comes from coal with a conversion efficiency of 33 percent, the primary energy cost is 60 kWh/100km, approaching but still smaller than that of the gasoline car. If electricity is generated by combined cycle natural gas turbines with 60 percent efficiency, the primary energy cost is 33 kWh/100km, less than half the primary energy cost for gasoline cars. These comparisons are presented in **Table** Comparisons of Energy Use (Table 8.2: Comparisons of Energy Use).

Comparisons of Energy Use

	Gasoline Engine 5 passenger car	Battery Electric Nissan Leaf, Chevy Volt (battery mode), Think Ox
Energy use at point of use	80 kWh/100km	20 kWh/100km
Energy use at point of production: Coal at 33% efficiency		60 kWh/100km
Combined Cycle Natural Gas at 60% efficiency		33 kWh/100km

Table 8.2: Comparison of energy use for gasoline driven and battery driven cars, for the cases of inefficient coal generation (33%) and efficient combined cycle natural gas generation (60%) of electricity. *Source: George Crabtree[156]* .

Comparisons of Carbon Emissions

	Gasoline Engine 5 passenger car	Battery Electric Nissan Leaf, Chevy Volt (battery mode), Think Ox
CO2 Emissions at point of use	41 lbs	$\sim$ 0
		continued on next page

[156]http://cnx.org/member_profile/crabtree

CO2 Emissions at point of production Coal@2.1 lb CO2/kWh		42 lbs
Gas@1.3 lb CO2/kWh		25 lbs
Nuclear, hydro, wind or solar		< 1 lb

Table 8.3: Comparison of carbon emissions from gasoline driven and battery driven cars, for the cases of high emission coal generation (2.1 lb CO_2/kWh), lower emission natural gas (1.3 lb$CO2$/kWh) and very low emission nuclear, hydro, wind or solar electricity. *Source: George Crabtree*[157] .

The carbon footprint of electric cars requires a similar calculation. For coal-fired electricity producing 2.1 lb CO_2/kWh, driving 100km produces 42 lbs (19 kgs) of carbon dioxide; for gas-fired electricity producing 1.3 lb CO_2/kWh, 100km of driving produces 26 lbs (11.7 kgs) of carbon dioxide. If electricity is produced by nuclear or renewable energy such as wind, solar or hydroelectric, no carbon dioxide is produced. For a "typical" gasoline car, 100km of driving produces 41 lbs (18.5 kgs) of carbon dioxide. Thus the carbon footprint of a "typical" electric car is, at worst equal, to that of a gasoline car and, at best, zero. **Table Comparisons of Carbon Emissions (Table 8.3: Comparisons of Carbon Emissions) summarizes the carbon footprint comparisons.

8.5.1.5 The Hybrid Solutions

Unlike electric cars, **hybrid vehicles** rely only on gasoline for their power. Hybrids do, however, have a supplemental electric motor and drive system that operates only when the gasoline engine performance is weak or needs a boost: on starting from a stop, passing, or climbing hills. Conventional gasoline cars have only a single engine that must propel the car under all conditions; it must, therefore, be sized to the largest task. Under normal driving conditions the engine is larger and less efficient than it needs to be. The hybrid solves this dilemma by providing two drive trains, a gasoline engine for normal driving and an electric motor for high power needs when starting, climbing hills and passing. The engine and motor are tailored to their respective tasks, enabling each to be designed for maximum efficiency. As the electric motor is overall much more efficient, its use can raise fuel economy significantly.

The battery in hybrid cars has two functions: it drives the electric motor and also collects electrical energy from regenerative braking, converted from kinetic energy at the wheels by small generators. Regenerative braking is effective in start-stop driving, increasing efficiency up to 20 percent. Unlike gasoline engines, electric motors use no energy while standing still; hybrids therefore shut off the gasoline engine when the car comes to a stop to save the idling energy. Gasoline engines are notoriously inefficient at low speeds (hence the need for low gear ratios), so the electric motor accelerates the hybrid to ~15 mph (24 kph) before the gasoline engine restarts. Shutting the gasoline engine off while stopped increases efficiency as much as 17 percent.

The energy saving features of hybrids typically lower their energy requirements from 80 kWh/100km to 50-60 kWh/100km, a significant savings. It is important to note, however, that despite a supplementary electric motor drive system, all of a hybrid's energy comes from gasoline and none from the electricity grid.

The plug-in hybrid differs from conventional hybrids in tapping both gasoline and the electricity grid for its energy. Most plug-in hybrids are designed to run on electricity first and on gasoline second; the gasoline engine kicks in only when the battery runs out. The plug-in hybrid is thus an electric car with a supplemental gasoline engine, the opposite of the conventional hybrid cars described above. The value of the plug-in hybrid is that it solves the "driving range anxiety" of the consumer: there are no worries about getting home safely from a trip that turns out to be longer than expected. The disadvantage of the plug-in hybrid is the additional supplemental gasoline engine technology, which adds cost and complexity to the automobile.

---

[157]http://cnx.org/member_profile/crabtree

8.5.1.6 The Battery Challenge

To achieve reasonable driving range, electric cars and plug-in hybrids need large batteries, one of their greatest design challenges and a potentially significant consumer barrier to widespread sales. Even with the largest practical batteries, driving range on electricity is limited, perhaps to ~100km. Designing higher energy density batteries is currently a major focus of energy research, with advances in Li-ion battery technology expected to bring significant improvements. The second potential barrier to public acceptance of electric vehicles is charging time, up to eight hours from a standard household outlet. This may suit overnight charging at home, but could be a problem for trips beyond the battery's range – with a gasoline car the driver simply fills up in a few minutes and is on his way. Novel infrastructure solutions such as battery swapping stations for long trips are under consideration.

From a sustainability perspective, the comparison of gasoline, electric, hybrid and plug-in hybrid cars is interesting. Hybrid cars take all their energy from gasoline and represent the least difference from gasoline cars. Their supplementary electric drive systems reduce gasoline usage by 30-40 percent, thus promoting conservation of a finite resource and reducing reliance on foreign oil. Electric cars, however, get all of their energy from grid electricity, a domestic energy source, completely eliminating reliance on foreign oil and use of finite oil resources. Their sustainability value is therefore higher than hybrids. Plug-in hybrids have the same potential as all electric vehicles, provided their gasoline engines are used sparingly. In terms of carbon emissions, the sustainability value of electric vehicles depends entirely on the electricity source: neutral for coal, positive for gas and highly positive for nuclear or renewable hydro, wind or solar. From an energy perspective, electric cars use a factor of four less energy than gasoline cars at the point of use, but this advantage is partially compromised by inefficiencies at the point of electricity generation. Even inefficient coal-fired electricity leaves an advantage for electric cars, and efficient gas-fired combined cycle electricity leaves electric cars more than a factor of two more energy efficient than gasoline cars.

8.5.1.7 Summary

Electricity offers an attractive alternative to oil as a transportation fuel: it is domestically produced, uses energy more efficiently, and, depending on the mode of electricity generation, can emit much less carbon. Electric vehicles can be powered by fuel cells producing electricity from hydrogen, or from batteries charged from the electricity grid. The hydrogen option presents greater technological challenges of fuel cell cost and durability and high capacity on-board hydrogen storage. The battery option is ready for implementation in the nearer term but requires higher energy density batteries for extended driving range, and a fast charging or battery swapping alternative to long battery charging times.

8.5.1.8 Review Questions

Question 8.5.1.1
Transportation relies almost exclusively for its fuel on oil, whose price fluctuates significantly in response to global geopolitics and whose long-term availability is limited. What are the motivations for each of the stakeholders, including citizens, companies and governments, to find alternatives to oil as a transportation fuel?

Question 8.5.1.2
Electricity can replace oil as a transportation fuel in two ways: by on board production in a hydrogen fuel cell, and by on board storage in a battery. What research and development, infrastructure and production challenges must be overcome for each of these electrification options to be widely deployed?

Question 8.5.1.3
Electric- and gasoline-driven cars each use energy and emit carbon dioxide. Which is more sustainable?

Question 8.5.1.4

How do gasoline-driven, battery-driven and hybrid cars (like the Prius) compare for (i) energy efficiency, (ii) carbon emissions, and (iii) reducing dependence on foreign oil?

8.5.1.9 References

Crabtree, G.W., Dresselhaus, M.S., & Buchanan, M.V. (2004). The Hydrogen Economy, *Physics Today*, *57*, 39-45. Retrieved September 2, 2011 from http://tecnet.pte.enel.it/depositi/tecnet/articolisegnalati/1447/38648-hydrogen_economy.pdf[158]

Crabtree, G.W. & Dresselhaus, M.S. (2008). The Hydrogen Fuel Alternative. *MRS Bulletin,33*, 421-428. Retrieved September 2, 2011 from http://www.physics.ohio-state.edu/~wilkins/energy/Resources/harnessing-mtl-energy/hfuel.pdf[159]

Doucette, R.T. & McCulloch, M.D. (2011). Modeling the CO2 emissions from battery electric vehicles given the power generation mixes of different countries. *Energy Policy*, *39*, 803-811. doi: 10.1016/j.enpol.2010.10.054

Eberle, U. & Helmolt, R.V. (2010). Sustainable transportation based on electric vehicle concepts: a brief overview. *Energy and Environmental Science*, *3*, 689-699. doi: 10.1039/C001674H

8.5.2 Combined Heat and Power[160]

8.5.2.1 Learning Objectives

After reading this module, students should be able to

- define combined heat and power (CHP) as an alternative energy source
- provide CHP component characteristics and operational benefits
- outline the characteristics of good CHP applications

8.5.2.2 Introduction

Electricity in the United States is generated, for the most part, from central station power plants at a conversion efficiency of roughly 30 to 35 percent. Meaning, for every 100 units of fuel energy into a simple cycle central station electric power plant, we get only 30 to 35 units of electricity. The remainder of the energy in the fuel is lost to the atmosphere in the form of heat.

The thermal requirements of our buildings and facilities are generally provided on-site through the use of a boiler or furnace. The efficiencies of this equipment have improved over the years and now it is common to have boilers and furnaces in commercial and industrial facilities with efficiencies of 80 percent and higher. Meaning, for every 100 units of fuel energy into the boiler/furnace, we get about 80 units of useful thermal energy.

Commercial and industrial facilities that utilize the conventional energy system found in the United States (electricity supplied from the electric grid and thermal energy produced on-site through the use of a boiler/furnace) will often times experience overall fuel efficiencies of between 40 to 55 percent (actual efficiency depends on the facilities heat to power ratio).

Combined Heat and Power (CHP) is a form of distributed generation. It is an integrated system located at or near the building/facility that generates utility grade electricity which satisfies at least a portion of the electrical load of the facility, and captures and recycles the waste heat from the electric generating equipment to provide useful thermal energy to the facility.

---

[158]http://tecnet.pte.enel.it/depositi/tecnet/articolisegnalati/1447/38648-hydrogen_economy.pdf
[159]http://www.physics.ohio-state.edu/~wilkins/energy/Resources/harnessing-mtl-energy/hfuel.pdf
[160]This content is available online at <http://legacy.cnx.org/content/m41740/1.2/>.

Conventional CHP (also referred to as topping cycle CHP) utilizes a single dedicated fuel source to sequentially produce useful electric and thermal power. **Figure** Conventional (Topping Cycle) CHP (p. 391) provides a diagram of a typical topping cycle CHP system. A variety of fossil fuels, renewable fuels, and waste products are utilized as input fuel to power a **prime mover** that generates mechanical shaft power (exception is fuel cells). Prime movers might include **reciprocating engines, gas turbines, steam turbines** or **fuel cells**. The mechanical shaft power is converted into utility grade electricity through a highly efficient generator. Since the CHP system is located at or near the building/facility, the heat lost through the prime mover can be recycled through a heat exchanger and provide heating, cooling (**absorption chillers**), and/or **dehumidification (desiccants)** to meet the thermal load of the building. These systems can reach fuel use efficiencies of as high as 75 to 85 percent (versus the conventional energy system at approximately 40 to 55 percent).

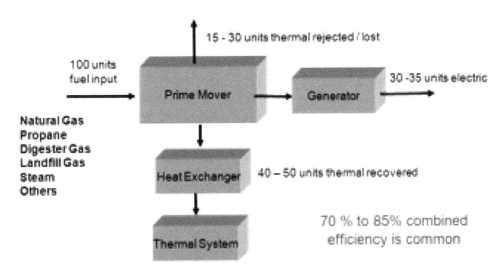

Figure 8.55: Conventional (Topping Cycle) CHP Diagram illustrates a typical topping cycle of CHP systems. *Source: John Cuttica*[161]

In our example of 100 units of fuel into the CHP system, only 30 to 35 units of electricity are generated, but another 40 to 50 units of the fuels energy can be recovered and utilized to produce thermal power. What this tells us is that for conventional CHP systems to reach the high efficiency level, there must be a use for the recovered thermal energy. Thus a key factor for conventional CHP systems is the coincidence of electric and thermal loads in the building. This is shown in **Figure** Importance of Waste Heat Recovery (p. 391). The "Y" axis represents the cost of generating electricity with a CHP system utilizing a 32 percent efficient reciprocating engine. The "X" axis represents the cost of natural gas utilized to operate the CHP system and also the value of the natural gas being displaced if the recycled heat from the engine can be utilized. The lines in the chart show various levels of recoverable heat available from the engine. If no heat is recovered (no use for the thermal energy), the cost of generating electricity with the CHP system is $0.08/kWhr. When the full amount of heat from the engine is recovered (full use of the thermal energy), the cost of generating electricity with the CHP system then drops to $0.03/kWhr.

---

[161]http://cnx.org/member_profile/cuttica

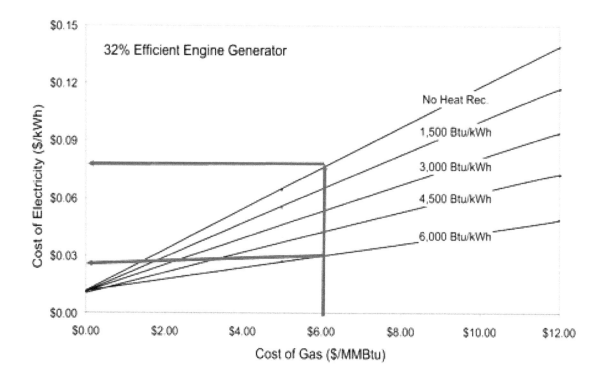

Figure 8.56: Importance of Waste Heat Recovery Graph shows the importance of waste heat recovery in CHP systems. *Source: John Cuttica*[162]

Since the high efficiency of a CHP system is dependent on the effective use of the recoverable heat, CHP systems are often times sized to meet the thermal load of the application and the amount of electricity produced is the by-product. The electricity is used to off set the electricity otherwise purchased from the local electric utility. When the CHP system does not produce enough electricity to satisfy the load, the utility supplies the difference from the grid. When the CHP system (sized from the thermal requirements) produces more electricity than the load requires, the excess electricity can be sold to the local utility (normally at the **avoided cost of power** to the utility).

There are three general modes of operation for CHP on-site generators relative to the electric utility grid:

- Stand Alone (totally isolated from the grid)
- Isolated from the grid with utility back-up (when needed)
- Parallel operation with the grid

The preferred mode of operation is parallel with the grid. Both the on-site CHP system and the utility grid power the facility simultaneously. With a proper sizing and configuration of the CHP system, the parallel mode of operation provides the most flexibility. Should the grid go down, the CHP system can keep operating (e.g. during the 2003 Northeast Blackout[163] and the 2005 Hurricane Katrina[164]), and should the CHP system go down, the utility grid can supply power to the load. Overall reliability of power to the load is increased.

The basic components of a conventional (topping cycle) CHP system are:

---

[162]http://cnx.org/member_profile/cuttica
[163]http://en.wikipedia.org/wiki/Northeast_Blackout_of_2003
[164]http://en.wikipedia.org/wiki/Hurricane_Katrina_effects_by_region

- Prime Mover that generates mechanical shaft energy
  - Reciprocating engine
  - Turbines (gas, micro, steam)
  - Fuel Cell (fuel cells ustilize an electrochemical process rather than a mechanical shaft process)
- Generator converts the mechanical shaft energy into electrical energy
  - **Synchronous generator** (provides most flexibility and independence from the grid)
  - **Induction generator** (grid goes down – the CHP system stops operating)
  - **Inverter** (used mainly on fuel cells – converts DC power to utility grade AC power)
- Waste Heat Recovery is one or more heat exchangers that capture and recycle the heat from the prime mover
- Thermal Utilization equipment converts the recycled heat into useful heating, cooling (absorption chillers) and/or dehumidification (deisiccant dehumidifiers)
- Operating Control Systems insure the CHP components function properly together

8.5.2.3 Reducing CO2 Emissions

In 2007, McKinsey & Company[165] published a study[166] on reducing United States greenhouse gas emissions. The report analyzed the cost and potential impact of over 250 technology options regarding contribution to reducing CO_2 emissions. Two conclusions stated in the report were:

- Abatement opportunities are highly fragmented and spread across the economy.
- Almost 40 percent of abatement could be achieved at negative marginal costs.

Figure Cost of CO (Figure 8.57)$_2$ Reduction Technologies (Figure 8.57) emphasizes both of these points. It is interesting to point out that CHP (both industrial and commercial applications), when sized and installed appropriately, delivers CO_2 reductions at a negative marginal cost. All the technologies that show a negative marginal cost on the chart generate positive economic returns over the technology's life cycle. The figure also shows that in terms of cost effectiveness of the wide range of abatement technologies, energy efficiency measures are by far more effective than renewable, nuclear and clean coal generating technologies. CHP technologies stand out as having negative marginal costs and overall positive cost effectiveness comparable to most of the energy efficiency measures.

---

[165] http://www.mckinsey.com/
[166] http://www.mckinsey.com/en/Client_Service/Sustainability/Latest_thinking/Reducing_US_greenhouse_gas_emissions.aspx

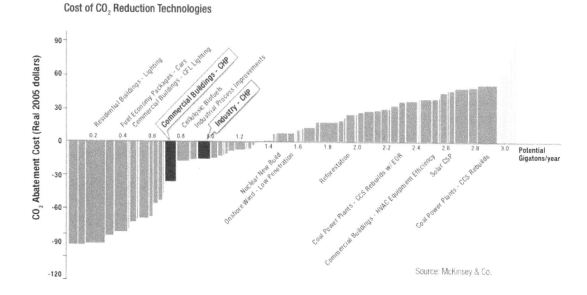

Figure 8.57: Cost of CO2 Reduction Technologies Figure shows the cost of CO_2 reduction technologies. *Source: Oak Ridge National Laboratory (2008) (p. 397), p. 13, and McKinsey & Company,* "[167]*Reducing U.S. Greenhouse Gas Emissions: How Much at What Cost?," December, 2007*[168]

8.5.2.4 CHP Applications

Today there are more than 3,500 CHP installations in the United States, totaling more than 85,000 MW of electric generation. That represents approximately 9 percent of the total electric generation capacity in the United States. The 85,000 MW of installed CHP reduces energy consumption by 1.9 Quads (10^{15} Btus) annually and eliminates approximately 248 million metric tons (MMT) of CO_2 annually.

CHP systems are generally more attractive for applications that have one or more of the following characteristics:

- Good coincidence between electric and thermal loads
- Maximum cost differential between electricity cost from the local utility and the cost of the fuel utilized in the CHP system (referred to as spark spread)
- Long operating hours (normally more than 3,000 hours annually)
- Need for good power quality and reliability

The following are just a few of the type applications where CHP makes sense:

- Hospitals
- Colleges and Universities
- High Schools
- Fitness Centers
- Office Buildings
- Hotels

---

[167]http://www.mckinsey.com/en/Client_Service/Sustainability/Latest_thinking/Reducing_US_greenhouse_gas_emissions.aspx
[168]http://www.mckinsey.com/en/Client_Service/Sustainability/Latest_thinking/Reducing_US_greenhouse_gas_emissions.aspx

- Data Centers
- Prisons
- Pulp and Paper Mills
- Chemical Manufacturing Plants
- Metal Fabrication Facilities
- Glass Manufacturers
- Ethanol Plants
- Food Processing Plants
- Waste Water Treatment Facilities
- Livestock Farms

8.5.2.5 CHP Benefits

CHP is not the only solution to our energy problems. In fact, CHP is not the most cost effective solution in all applications or in all areas of the country. There are many variables that determine the viability of CHP installations. However, when the technical and financial requirements of the application are met, a well designed, installed and operated CHP system provides benefits for the facility owner (end user), the electric utility, and society in general. The high efficiency attained by the CHP system provides the end user with lower overall energy costs, improved electric reliability, improved electric power quality, and improved energy security. In areas where the electric utility distribution grid is in need of expansion and/or upgrades, CHP systems can provide the electric utility with a means of deferring costly modifications to the grid. Although the electricity generated on-site by the end user displaces the electricity purchased from the local electric utility and is seen as lost revenue by many utilities, energy efficiency and lower utility costs are in the best interest of the utility customer and should be considered as a reasonable customer option by forward-looking customer oriented utilities. Finally, society in general benefits from the high efficiencies realized by CHP systems. The high efficiencies translate to less air pollutants (lower greenhouse gas and NOx emissions) than produced from central station electric power plants.

8.5.2.6 Waste Heat to Power

There is a second type of CHP system, referred to as **Waste Heat to Power** (Bottoming Cycle CHP). Unlike conventional CHP where a dedicated fuel is combusted in a prime mover, Waste Heat to Power CHP systems captures the heat otherwise wasted in an industrial or commercial process. The waste heat, rather than the process fuel, becomes the fuel source for the waste heat to power system. It is used to generate steam or hot water, which in turn is utilized to drive a steam turbine or (for lower temperatures) an **organic rankine cycle** heat engine. In this case, the waste heat from the industrial/commercial process is converted to electric power. **Figure** Waste Heat to Power (Bottoming Cycle) CHP (Figure 8.58) provides a diagram of a Waste Heat to Power CHP system.

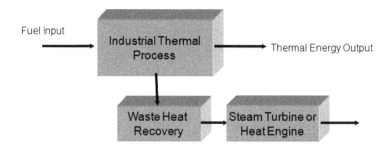

- No Additional Fuel Consumed
- No Additional On-Site Emissions
- May or May Not Generate Additional Thermal Energy

Figure 8.58: Waste Heat to Power (Bottoming Cycle) CHP Diagram illustrates a waste heat to power (bottoming cycle) CHP system. *Source: John Cuttica*[169]

8.5.2.7 Summary

Combined Heat and Power (CHP) represents a proven and effective near-term alternative energy option that can enhance energy efficiency, ensure environmental quality, and promote economic growth. The concept of generating electricity on-site allows one to capture and recycle the waste heat from the prime mover providing fuel use efficiencies as high as 75 to 85 percent. Like other forms of alternative energy, CHP should be considered and included in any portfolio of energy options.

8.5.2.8 Review Questions

Question 8.5.2.1
What drives the system efficiency in a conventional CHP system?

Question 8.5.2.2
To ensure high system efficiency, how would you size a conventional CHP system?

Question 8.5.2.3
What is the preferred method of operating a CHP system that provides the most flexibility with the utility grid?

Question 8.5.2.4
Why are CHP systems considered one of the most cost-effective CO_2 abatement practices?

Question 8.5.2.5
Name at least three application characteristics that make CHP an attractive choice.

---

[169]http://cnx.org/member_profile/cuttica

8.5.2.9 Resources

For more information on Combined Heat and Power and Waste Heat to Power, see www.midwestcleanenergy.org[170]

8.5.2.10 References

Oak Ridge National Laboratory. (2008). *Combined Heat and Power, Effective Energy Solutions for a Sustainable Future.* Retrieved September 26, 2011 from http://www1.eere.energy.gov/industry/distributedenergy/pdfs/chp_report_12-08.pdf[171]

8.6 Applications of Phase Change Materials for Sustainable Energy[172]

8.6.1 Learning Objectives

After reading this module, students should be able to

- learn the general concept of Phase Change Materials (PCM)
- understand the applications of PCMs in sustainable energy
- recognize the uses of PCM for heating and cooling systems
- recognize the uses of PCM in buildings
- recognize the uses of PCM in transportation

8.6.2 Introduction

The growing demand for sustainable energy from consumers and industry is constantly changing. The highest demand of energy consumption during a single day brings a continuous and unsolved problem: how to maintain a consistent desired temperature in a sustainable way. Periods of extreme cold or warm weather are the triggering factors for increasing the demand on heating or cooling. Working hours, industry processes, building construction, operating policies, and type and volume of energy production facilities are some of the main reasons for peak demand crises. Better power generation management and significant economic benefit can be achieved if some of the peak load could be shifted to the off peak load period. This can be achieved by thermal storage for space heating and cooling purposes.

Thermal energy can be stored as a change in the internal energy of certain materials as **sensible heat**, **latent heat** or both. The most commonly used method of thermal energy storage is the sensible heat method, although **phase change materials** (PCM), which effectively store and release latent heat energy, have been studied for more than 30 years. Latent heat storage can be more efficient than sensible heat storage because it requires a smaller temperature difference between the storage and releasing functions. Phase change materials are an important and underused option for developing new energy storage devices, which are as important as developing new sources of renewable energy. The use of phase change material in developing and constructing sustainable energy systems is crucial to the efficiency of these systems because of PCM's ability to harness heat and cooling energies in an effective and sustainable way.

8.6.3 Phase Change Materials for Energy Storage Devices

Thermal storage based on sensible heat works on the temperature rise on absorbing energy or heat, as shown in the solid and liquid phases in Figure **Temperature Profile of a PCM** (p. 398). When the stored heat is released, the temperature falls, providing two points of different temperature that define the storage and release functions. Phase change materials are conceptually different, however. They operate by storing

---

[170]http://www.midwestcleanenergy.org/
[171]http://www1.eere.energy.gov/industry/distributedenergy/pdfs/chp_report_12-08.pdf
[172]This content is available online at <http://legacy.cnx.org/content/m41734/1.4/>.

energy at a constant temperature while phase change occurs, for example from solid to a liquid, as illustrated in the center of Figure **Temperature Profile of a PCM** (p. 398). As heat is added to the material, the temperature does not rise; instead heat drives the change to a higher energy phase. The liquid, for example, has kinetic energy of the motion of atoms that is not present in the solid, so its energy is higher. The higher energy of the liquid compared to the solid is the *latent heat*. When the solid is fully transformed to liquid, added energy reverts to going into *sensible heat* and raising the temperature of the liquid.

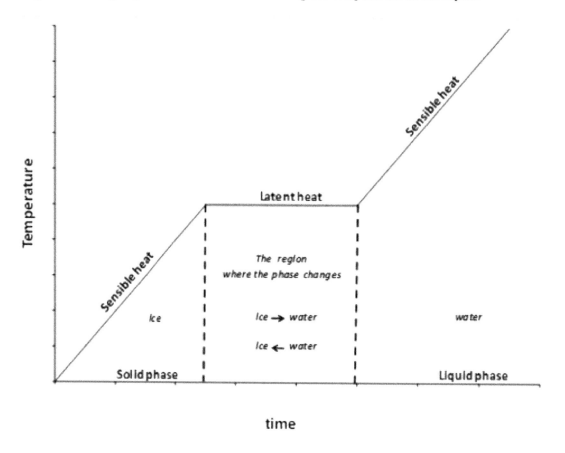

Figure 8.59:   Temperature Profile of a PCM. Figure shows the temperature profile of a PCM. In the region where latent heat is effective, the temperature keeps either constant or in a narrow range. The phase of the material turns from one to another and both phases appears in the medium. *Source: Said Al-Hallaj*[173] *& Riza Kizilel*[174]

A PCM is a substance with a high **latent heat** (also called the heat of fusion if the phase change is from solid to liquid) which is capable of storing and releasing large amounts of energy at a certain temperature. A PCM stores heat in the form of latent heat of fusion which is about 100 times more than the sensible heat. For example, latent heat of fusion of water is about 334kJ/kg whereas sensible heat at 25° Celsius (77°F) is about 4.18kJ/kg. PCM will then release thermal energy at a freezing point during solidification process (Figure **Phase Change of a PCM** (p. 399)). Two widely used PCMs by many of us are water and wax. Think how water requires significant amount of energy when it changes from solid phase to liquid

---

[173]http://cnx.org/member_profile/sah
[174]http://cnx.org/member_profile/rkizilel

phase at $0\,^\circ$C ($32\,^\circ$F) or how wax extends the burning time of a candle. Moreover, the cycle of the melting and solidification can be repeated many times.

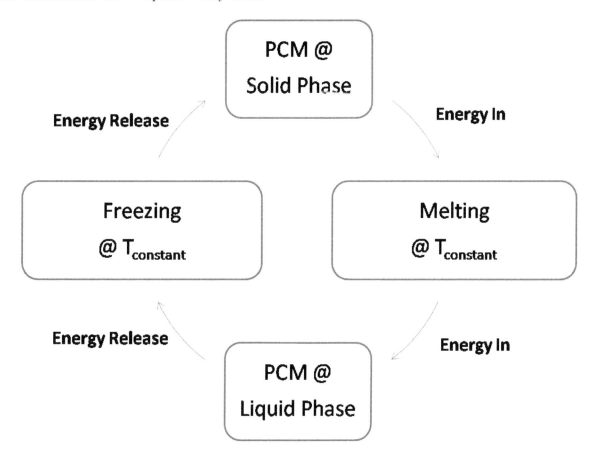

Figure 8.60: Phase Change of a PCM. Figure represents the phase change of a PCM when the heat is applied or removed. *Source: Said Al-Hallaj*[175] *& Riza Kizilel*[176]

There are large numbers of PCMs that melt and solidify at a wide range of temperatures, making them attractive in a number of applications in the development of the energy storage systems. Materials that have been studied during the last 40 years include **hydrated salts**, **paraffin waxes**, fatty acids and **eutectics** of organic and non-organic compounds (Figure **Energy Storage Systems** (p. 399)). Therefore, the selection of a PCM with a suitable phase transition temperature should be part of the design of a thermal storage system. It should be good at heat transfer and have high latent heat of transition. The melting temperature should lie in the range of the operation, be chemically stable, low in cost, non-corrosive and nontoxic.

---

[175]http://cnx.org/member_profile/sah

[176]http://cnx.org/member_profile/rkizilel

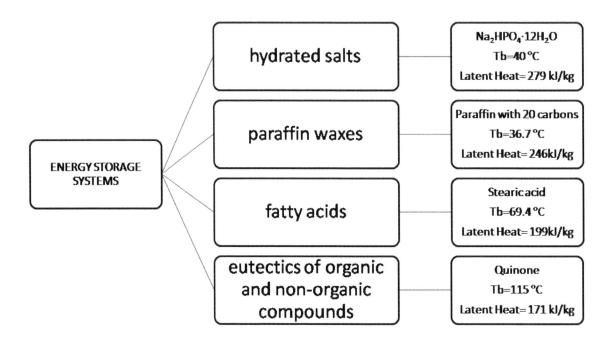

Figure 8.61: Energy Storage Systems. Figure shows materials commonly studied for use in PCMs due to their ability to melt and solidify at a wide range of temperatures. *Source: Said Al-Hallaj*[177] *& Riza Kizilel*[178]

Even though the list of the PCMs is quite long, only a limited number of the chemicals are possible candidates for energy applications due to the various limitations of the processes. **Paraffins** and **hydrated salts** are the two most promising PCMs. Generally, paraffins have lower fusion energy than salt hydrates but do not have the reversibility issue, i.e paraffin is only in physical changes and keeps its composition when heat is released or gained whereas hydrated salt is in chemical change when heat is released or gained. Therefore, a major problem with salt hydrates is incongruent melting, which reduces the reversibility of the phase change process. This also results in a reduction of the heat storage capacity of the salt hydrate. On the other hand, paraffins also have a major drawback compared to salt hydrates. The low thermal conductivity creates a major drawback which decreases the rates of heat stored and released during the melting and crystallization processes and hence results in limited applications. The thermal conductivity of paraffin used as PCM is slightly above 0.20 W/mK (compare with ice; $k_{ice} = \sim 2$ W/mK). Several methods such as **finned tubes** with different configurations and **metal matrices** filled with PCM have been investigated to enhance the heat transfer rate of PCM. Novel composite materials of PCM, which have superior properties, have also been proposed for various applications. For example, when PCM is embedded inside a **graphite matrix**, the heat conductivity can be considerably increased without much reduction in energy storage.

---

[177]http://cnx.org/member_profile/sah
[178]http://cnx.org/member_profile/rkizilel

8.6.4 Applications of PCMs

The three applications of PCMs listed below (solar energy, buildings, and vehicles) are only a small portion of the many areas where they can be used (catering, telecom shelters, electronics, etc.). The applications of PCMs in these areas have been widely studied in order to minimize the greenhouse effect and to minimize the need for foreign gasoline which costs U.S. economy millions of dollars every year.

Increasing concerns of the impact of fossil fuels on the environment and their increasing cost has led to studies on thermal energy storage for the space heating and cooling of buildings. Extreme cold or warm weather increases the demand on heating or cooling. If the thermal energy of heat or coolness is stored and then provided during the day or night, part of the peak loads can be shifted to off-peak hours. Therefore, an effective energy management and economic benefit can be achieved.

Solar energy is recognized as one of the most promising alternative energy resource options. However, it is intermittent by nature: there is no sun at night. The reliability of solar energy can be increased by storing it when in excess of the load and using the stored energy whenever needed.

The minimization of heat loss or gain through walls, ceilings, and floors has been studied for a long time and PCM applications have been considered for more than 30 years to minimize these losses/gains, and thus reduce the cost of electricity or natural gas use in buildings. Studies on viability of PCMs in vehicle applications are also growing widely. **Denaturation** of food during transport brings a major problem which is being partially solved by refrigerated trucks. However, this causes not only more expensive foods, but also irreversible environmental effects on living organisms.

8.6.4.1 Solar Energy Applications

Solar thermal energy is a technology for harnessing solar energy for thermal energy. The solar energy is absorbed by the earth and is dissipated throughout the ground at different rates that is dependent on the compositions of the ground and amount of water. Ground temperature is stable and solar energy can be transferred between the ground and space heating/cooling places. Water heaters that use solar energy play an important role for this purpose and they started to become popular in the late 1960s (Figure **Solar Heater** (p. 401)). In order to utilize the energy from the sun at all times, this precious energy should be stored and used when needed. Passive systems using PCMs have been good candidates for thermal energy storage and have been applied since 1980s. At first, the water heaters were supported by filling the bottom of the heaters with PCMs, which was a first step in storing energy in heating systems. However, the quantity of the available energy in the storage system was limited by low thermal conductivity of the PCM. Improvements on thermal storage systems and developments in the incorporation of PCMs that utilize the solar energy have been extensively studied since then.

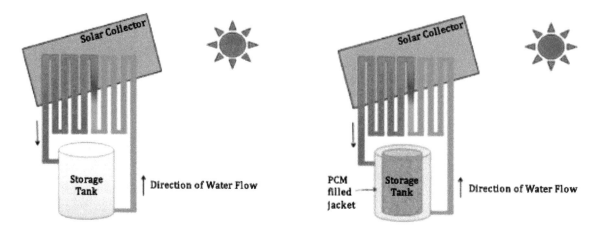

Figure 8.62: Solar Heater. Figure shows solar heating system with and without PCM. *Source: Said Al-Hallaj*[179] *& Riza Kizilel*[180]

Later studies have mainly concentrated on increasing thermal conductivity using composite materials. Adding PCM modules at the top of the water tank gives the system a higher storage density and compensate for heat loss in the top layer because of the latent heat of PCM. The configuration of the PCM storage unit can result in advantageous control of the water temperature rise and drop during both day and night time. Therefore, thermally stratified water tanks are widely used for short term thermal energy storage. Application of these tanks significantly increases not only the energy density with the number of PCM modules, but also the cooling period and keeps the water temperature higher compared to the ones without PCMs. Besides, solar water heating systems operate within a wide range of temperatures from **ambient temperatures** to 80 °C (176 °F). A PCM has much larger heat storage capacity relative to water over a narrow temperature range, close to its melting temperature.

A major component of total household energy consumption is cooking. Solar energy offers an economical option for cooking in households, especially in third world countries. A solar cooker is a device which uses the energy of sunlight to heat food or drink to cook or sterilize it (Figure **Solar Cooker** (p. 402)). It uses no fuel, costs nothing to operate, and reduces air pollution. A solar cooker's reflective surface concentrates the light into a small cooking area and turns the light into heat. It is important to trap the heat in the cooker because heat may be easily lost by convection and radiation. The feasibility of using a phase change material as the storage medium in solar cookers have been examined since 1995. A box-type solar cooker with stearic acid based PCM has been designed and fabricated by Buddhi and Sahoo (1997) (p. 407), showing that it is possible to cook food even in the evening with a solar cooker. The rate of heat transfer from the PCM to the cooking pot during the discharging mode of the PCM is quite slow and more time is required for cooking food in the evening. Fins that are welded at the inner wall of the PCM container were used to enhance the rate of heat transfer between the PCM and the inner wall of the PCM container. Since the PCM surrounds the cooking vessel, the rate of heat transfer between the PCM and the food is higher and the cooking time is shorter. It is remarkable that if food is loaded into the solar cooker before 3:30 p.m. during the winter season, it could be cooked. However, the melting temperature of the PCM should be selected carefully. The more the input solar radiation, the larger quantity of heat there is in a PCM. Few examples for PCMs for solar cooker applications are acetamide (melting point of 82 °C), acetanilide (melting point of 118 °C), erythritol (melting point of 118 °C) and magnesium nitrate hexahydrate (melting point of 89–90 °C).

[179]http://cnx.org/member_profile/sah
[180]http://cnx.org/member_profile/rkizilel

Figure 8.63: Solar Cooker. Photograph shows solar heating system. *Source: Atlascuisinesolaire via Wikimedia Commons*[181].

8.6.4.2 Building Applications

PCMs can be used for temperature regulation, heat or cold storage with high storage density, and thermal comfort in buildings that require a narrow range of temperature (Figure **Typical Application of PCM in Buildings** (p. 403)). Therefore, if the solar energy is stored effectively, it can be utilized for night cold. The use of PCMs brings an opportunity to meet the demand for heating. It helps to store the energy which is available during daytime and to keep the temperature of the building in the comfort level.

---

[181]http://en.wikipedia.org/wiki/File:ALSOL.jpg

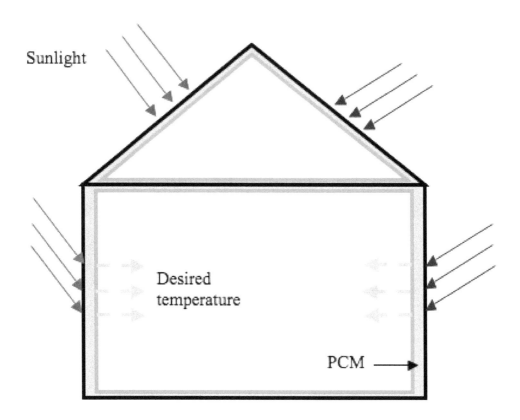

Figure 8.64: Typical Application of PCM in Buildings Figure illustrates a typical application of PCM in buildings. Heat storage and delivery occur over a fairly narrow temperature range. Wallboards containing PCM have a large heat transfer area that supports large heat transfer between the wall and the space. *Source: Said Al-Hallaj[182] & Riza Kizilel[183]*

Energy storage in the walls or other components of the building may be enhanced by encapsulating PCM within the surfaces of the building. The latent heat capacity of the PCM is used to capture solar energy or man-made heat or cold directly and decrease the temperature swings in the building. It also maintains the temperature closer to the desired temperature throughout the day. Researchers have proposed macro or micro level encapsulated PCM in concrete, gypsum wallboard, ceiling and floor in order to achieve a reasonably constant temperature range.

Today, it is possible to improve the thermal comfort and reduce the energy consumption of buildings without substantial increase in the weight of the construction materials by the application of micro and macro encapsulated PCM. The maximum and minimum peak temperatures can be reduced by the use of small quantities of PCM, either mixed with the construction material or attached as a thin layer to the walls and roofs of a building. In addition, the energy consumption can also be reduced by absorbing part of the incident solar energy and delaying/reducing the external heat load.

The absorption of heat gains and the release of heat at night by a paraffin wax-based PCMs encapsulated within a co-polymer and sandwiched between two metal sheets (PCM board) have been used in some building

[182]http://cnx.org/member_profile/sah
[183]http://cnx.org/member_profile/rkizilel

materials. The PCM boards on a wall reduce the interior wall surface temperature during the charging process, whereas the PCM wall surface temperature is higher than the other walls during the heat releasing process. The heat flux density of a PCM wall in the melting zone is almost twice as large as that of an ordinary wall. Also, the heat-insulation performance of a PCM wall is better than that of an ordinary wall during the charging process, while during the heat discharging process, the PCM wall releases more heat energy.

Unlike structural insulated panels, which exhibit fairly uniform thermal characteristics, a PCM's attributes vary depending upon environmental factors. The structural insulated panel works at all times, resisting thermal flow from hot temperatures to colder temperatures. The thermal flux is directly proportional to the temperature difference across the structural insulated panel insulation. The usefulness of PCM is seen when the in-wall temperatures are such that it causes the PCM to change state. It can be inferred that the greater the temperature difference between day and night, the better the PCM works to reduce heat flux. The use of a phase change material structural insulated panel wall would be excellent for geographic areas where there is typically a large temperature swing, warm during the day and cool at night.

8.6.4.3 Vehicle Applications

Studies on viability of PCM in vehicle applications are growing widely. For example, PCMs are studied with regard to refrigerated trucks, which are designed to carry perishable freight at specific temperatures. Refrigerated trucks are regulated by small refrigeration units that are placed outside the vehicle in order to keep the inside of the truck trailer at a constant temperature and relative humidity. They operate by burning gas, hence the cost of shipment is highly affected by the changes of temperature in the trailer. The use of PCM has helped in lowering peak heat transfer rates and total heat flows into a refrigerated trailer. Ahmed, Meade, and Medina (2010) (p. 407) modified the conventional method of insulation of the refrigerated truck trailer by using paraffin-based PCMs in the standard trailer walls as a heat transfer reduction technology. An average reduction in peak heat transfer rate of 29.1 percent was observed when all walls (south, east, north, west, and top) were considered, whereas the peak heat transfer rate was reduced in the range of 11.3 - 43.8 percent for individual walls. Overall average daily heat flow reductions into the refrigerated compartment of 16.3 percent were observed. These results could potentially translate into energy savings, pollution abatement from diesel-burning refrigeration units, refrigeration equipment size reduction, and extended equipment operational life.

Vehicles are mainly powered by **gasoline** (i.e gas or petrol). **Liquified petroleum gases** and **diesel** are other types of fluids used in vehicles. Lately, hybrid vehicles became popular among consumers as they significantly reduce the toxic exhaust gases if the vehicles run in electric mode. Li-ion batteries have been used in electronic devices for a long time (cell-phones, laptops, and portable devices). Many scientists, especially in the United States, have been working on the possibility of using Li-ion batteries for transportation applications in order to double the fuel efficiency and reduce emissions of hybrid vehicles. **Li-ion battery** modules can be connected in order to meet the **nominal voltage** of the vehicle to run the vehicle in the electric mode. However this brings a huge problem which keeps away the uses of Li-ion batteries in many applications: as a result of exothermic electrochemical reactions, Li-ion batteries release energy during discharge. The generated energy should be transferred from the body of the battery to environment. If the rate of the transfer is not sufficient, some of the gelled phase materials turn into **gas phase** and increase the internal pressure of the cell. Therefore the energy should be released from the cell as soon as possible or the temperature of the cell should not lead to an increase. Sveum, Kizilel, Khader, and Al-Hallaj (2007) (p. 407) have shown that Li-ion batteries with thermal management using PCM eliminate the need for additional cooling systems and improve available power (Figure **Application with PCM Technology** (p. 405)). The researchers maintained battery packs at an optimum temperature with proper thermal management and the PCM was capable of removing large quantities of heat due to its high latent heat of fusion.

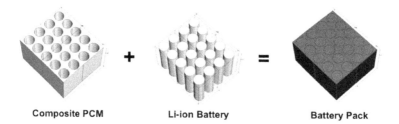

Figure 8.65: Application with PCM Technology. A pack of Li-ion batteries kept at a narrow temperature range with a proper use of passive thermal management system. *Source: AllCell's PCM Technology*©

8.6.5 Summary

There is a great interest in saving energy and in the use of renewable energies. PCMs provide an underused option for developing new energy storage devices in order to minimize greenhouse effects. They operate at constant temperature; as heat is added to the material, the temperature remains stable, but the heat drives the change to a higher energy phase. A PCM stores heat in the form of latent heat of fusion which is about 100 times more than the sensible heat. Hydrated salts, paraffin waxes, fatty acids and eutectics of organic and non-organic compounds are the major types of PCMs that melt at a wide range of temperatures. The specific melting point of the PCM determines the design of thermal storage system.

In this module, applications of PCM in solar energy, buildings, and vehicles were reviewed. Solar heaters have been popular since 1960s and PCMs have been used to store the precious energy from sun since 1980s. They have been used extensively in solar cookers, especially in the third world countries in order to decrease the thermal related costs. The cookers do not use fuel and hence reduce air pollution.

PCM can be used for temperature regulation in order to minimize the heat loss or gain through building walls. They have been used to capture solar heat and decrease the temperature fluctuations in buildings. Moreover, since a small amount of PCM is sufficient in order to store solar energy, thermal comfort is achieved without substantial increase in the weight of the construction materials.

Application of PCMs in transportation is growing widely. Today, refrigerated trucks are regulated by refrigeration units, but the use of PCMs is a viable option to prevent the denaturation of food during transportation. The transfer rate of heat can be reduced significantly with PCMs. Moreover, PCM makes Li-ion batteries, which have high energy density, viable for high-power applications. The generated energy during discharge or drive mode can be transferred from the body of the battery to environment with the help of PCMs. Battery packs can be maintained at an optimum temperature with proper thermal management and the PCM has been shown to be capable of removing large quantities of heat due to its high latent heat of fusion.

Even though there is a lot of on-going research on effective and efficient applications of PCMs in a variety of areas (e.g. solar cookers, buildings, vehicles), PCMs have yet to become a widely used technology for sustainable energy. The advantages of PCMs are hardly known by many people and, therefore, the applications of PCMs and their benefits should be offered to consumers. The sun is out there, continuously transferring its energy for free, but we need to do more to harness that sustainable energy for our own needs.

8.6.6 Review Questions

Question 8.6.1
Explain briefly how phase change materials work.

Question 8.6.2

What is the main disadvantage of the paraffin wax as a phase change material?

Question 8.6.3

Name three different areas in the sustainable energy field in which PCMs are a key element in balancing heating and cooling.

8.6.7 References

Ahmed, M., Meade, O., & Medina, M. A. (2010, March). Reducing heat transfer across the insulated walls of refrigerated truck trailers by the application of phase change materials. *Energy Conversion and Management, 51*, 383-392. doi: 10.1016/j.enconman.2009.09.003

Buddhi, D. & Sahoo, L. K. (1997, March). Solar cooker with latent heat storage: Design and experimental testing. *Energy Conversion and Management, 38*, 493-498. doi: 10.1016/S0196-8904(96)00066-0

Sveum, P., Kizilel, R., Khader, M., & Al-Hallaj, S. (2007, September). IIT Plug-in Conversion Project with the City of Chicago. Paper presented at the Vehicle Power and Propulsion Conference, Arlington, TX. doi: 10.1109/VPPC.2007.4544174

Chapter 9

Problem-Solving, Metrics, and Tools for Sustainability

9.1 Problem-Solving, Metrics, and Tools for Sustainability - Chapter Introduction[1]

9.1.1 Introduction

"What gets measured gets done" is an oft-quoted saying (attributed to many individuals) that attempts to capture the essential role of quantification in order to understand a system, solve a problem, advance a cause, or establish a policy. Throughout this text a wide variety of measurements are put forth, cited, and discussed in connection with particular concepts including climate change, economics, social well-being, engineering efficiency, and consumer habits. This chapter is devoted to a special collection of methods, measurements, tools, indicators, and indices that are used to assess the comparative sustainability among potential and often competing options, designs, or decisions, and to measure progress toward achieving the goals of sustainability over time.

The chapter begins in the Module **Life Cycle Assessment** (Section 9.2) with a brief discussion of industrial ecology, an emerging science that focuses on understanding material and energy flows to and through different kinds of human-created systems. This kind of understanding is essential for framing problems that need to be solved in a holistic way. Industrial ecologists study such topics as recycling and reuse of materials, energy efficiency, organizational structures, supply chains, the social impacts of decisions, and the economics of product development. It has been termed "the science of sustainability" (Graedel, 2000 (p. 410)).

One of the principal tools of industrial ecology which is discussed in this chapter is life cycle assessment (LCA), a comprehensive set of procedures for quantifying the impacts associated with the energy and resources needed to make and deliver a product or service. LCA's are carried out for two main reasons: (a) to analyze all the steps in a product chain and see which use the greatest amount of energy and materials or produce the most waste, and (b) to enable comparisons among alternative products or supply chains and to see which one create the least environmental impact. Inherent in the concept of LCA is the notion of trade-offs – the recognition that in a finite world choosing one product, pathway, or way of living has consequences for environmental and social well-being. Of course choices must be made, but the goal of quantifying the implications of our actions as holistically as possible is to avoid consequences that are "unintended."

Although life cycle assessment grew out of the needs of industry to better design products and understand the implications of their decisions, the systemic manner of framing problems upon which LCA is based has permeated a wide variety of fields, stimulating what might be termed "life cycle thinking" in each of them.

---

[1]This content is available online at <http://legacy.cnx.org/content/m38623/1.3/>.

The Subcollection **Derivative Life Cycle Concepts**[2] in this chapter contains modules devoted to presentations of a number of ways of expressing the impacts of humans on the environment. These are derived from life cycle principles and are drawn from the fields of ecology, thermodynamics, and environmental science. They include "**footprinting** (Section 9.3.2)" and several **sustainability indicators** (Section 9.3.1), all of which quantify human impacts in terms of resource consumption and waste production over an extended geographic range and/or over timeframes that go beyond the immediate. **A case study on the UN Millennium Development Goals Indicator** (Section 9.3.6) presents a comprehensive approach for assessing not only environmental sustainability, but also hunger and poverty, education, gender equity, infant mortality, maternal health, disease, and global partnerships – all elements of sustainable development made clear in the Brundtland report. Finally, this chapter concludes with a module about **sustainability and business** (Section 9.4).

9.1.2 References

Graedel, T.E. (2000). The Evolution of Industrial Ecology. *Environmental Science and Technology*, 34, 28A-31A. doi: 10.1021/es003039c

9.2 Life Cycle Assessment[3]

9.2.1 Learning Objectives

After reading this module, students should be able to

- learn to view problem solving in a systematic and holistic manner
- understand the basic elements of industrial ecology and life cycle analysis
- become aware of available tools for conducting life cycle analysis

9.2.2 Problem Solving for Sustainability

It should be clear by now that making decisions and solving problems in support of greater sustainability of human-created systems and their impact on the natural environment is a complex undertaking. Often in modern life our decisions and designs are driven by a single goal or objective (e.g. greater monetary profitability, use of less energy, design for shorter travel times, generation of less waste, or reduction of risk), but in most cases solving problems sustainably requires a more holistic approach in which the functioning of many parts of the system must be assessed simultaneously, and multiple objectives must be integrated when possible. Furthermore, as noted in the Brundtland Report[4] (or see Chapter **Introduction to Sustainability: Humanity and the Environment** (Section 1.1)), often our decisions require the recognition of tradeoffs – there are many kinds of impacts on the environment and most decisions that we make create more than one impact at the same time. Of course choices must be made, but it is better if they are made with fuller knowledge of the array of impacts that will occur. The history of environmental degradation is littered with decisions and solutions that resulted in unintended consequences.

An illustrative example of the role of sustainability in solving problems is the issue of biofuels – turning plant matter into usable energy (mostly liquid hydrocarbon-based fuels). When viewed from afar and with a single goal, "energy independence," using our considerable agricultural resources to turn solar energy, via photosynthesis, into usable fuels so that we can reduce our dependence on imported petroleum appears to be quite attractive. The United States is the largest producer of grain and forest products in the world. It has pioneered new technologies to maintain and even increase agricultural productivity, and it has vast processing capabilities to create artificial fertilizer and to convert biomass into agricultural products (see

---

[2]*Sustainability: A Comprehensive Foundation* <http://legacy.cnx.org/content/col11325/latest/>
[3]This content is available online at <http://legacy.cnx.org/content/m38643/1.12/>.
[4]http://en.wikipedia.org/wiki/Brundtland_Commission#Brundtland_Report

Module **Renewable Energy: Solar, Wind, Hydro and Biomass** (Section 8.4.1.4)). And, after all, such a venture is both "domestic" and "natural" – attributes that incline many, initially at least, to be favorably disposed. However upon closer examination this direction is not quite as unequivocally positive as we might have thought. Yes it is possible to convert grain into ethanol and plant oils into diesel fuel, but the great majority of these resources have historically been used to feed Americans and the animals that they consume (and not just Americans; the United States is the world's largest exporter of agricultural products). As demand has increased, the prices for many agricultural products have risen, meaning that some fraction of the world's poor can no longer afford as much food. More marginal lands (which are better used for other crops, grazing, or other uses) have been brought under cultivation for fermentable grains, and there have been parallel "indirect" consequences globally – as the world price of agricultural commodities has risen, other countries have begun diverting land from existing uses to crops as well. Furthermore, agricultural runoff from artificial fertilizers has contributed to over 400 regional episodes of **hypoxia** in estuaries around the world, including the U.S. Gulf Coast and Chesapeake Bay.

In response to such problems, U.S. Congress passed the Energy Independence and Security Act[5] in 2007, which limits the amount of grain that can be converted into biofuels in favor of using agriculturally-derived cellulose, the chief constituent of the cell walls of plants. This has given rise to a large scientific and technological research and development program to devise economical ways to process cellulosic materials into ethanol, and parallel efforts to investigate new cellulosic cropping systems that include, for example, native grasses[6]. Thus, the seemingly simple decision to grow our biofuels industry in response to a political objective has had unintended political, financial, dietary, social, land use, environmental quality, and technological consequences.

With hindsight, the multiple impacts of biofuels have become clear, and there is always the hope that we can learn from examples like this. But we might also ask if there is a way to foresee all or at least some of these impacts in advance, and adjust our designs, processes, and policies to take them into account and make more informed decisions, not just for biofuels but also for complex societal problems of a similar nature. This approach is the realm of the field of **industrial ecology**, and the basis for the tool of **life cycle assessment (LCA)**, a methodology that has been designed to perform holistic analyses of complex systems.

9.2.3 Industrial Ecology

Many systems designed by humans focus on maximizing profitability for the firm, business or corporation. In most cases this means increasing production to meet demand for the products or services being delivered. An unfortunate byproduct of this is the creation of large amounts of waste, many of which have significant impacts if they enter the environment. Figure **Human-Designed Industry** (Figure 9.1) is a general-purpose diagram of a typical manufacturing process, showing the inputs of materials and energy, the manufacturing of products, and the generation of wastes (the contents of the "manufacturing box" are generic and not meant to depict any particular industry—it could be a mine, a factory, a power plant, a city, or even a university). What many find surprising is the large disparity between the amounts of waste produced and the quantity of product delivered. Table **Waste-to-Product Ratios for Selected Industries** (Table 9.1) provides such information, in the form of waste-to-product ratios, for a few common industries.

---

[5]http://www.govtrack.us/congress/bill.xpd?bill=h110-6
[6]http://www.nsf.gov/news/news_summ.jsp?cntn_id=108206

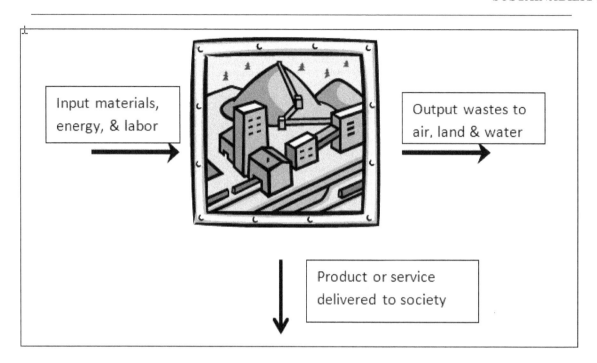

Figure 9.1: Human-Designed Industry Generic representation of a human-designed industry. *Source: Theis, T.*[7]

That industrial systems designed to maximize production and/or profits while ignoring wastes should be so materially inefficient is not surprising. As noted in the Module **Sustainability and Public Policy** (Section 2.4), the impacts of wastes on human health and the environment have historically been ignored, or steeply underpriced, so that little incentive has existed to limit waste production. More recently laws have been enacted that attempt to force those responsible for waste emissions into a more appropriate accounting (see Chapters **Environmental and Resource Economics** (Section 8.1) and **Modern Environmental Management** (Section 7.1) for a fuller treatment of the laws, regulations, and practices used to incorporate society's costs into the production chain). Once realistic costs are assigned to the waste sector, manufacturers are quick to innovate and investigate ways to eliminate them.

Industrial Sector	Waste-to-Product Ratio
Automobiles	2/1 (up to 10/1 if consumer use is included)
Paper	10/1
Basic Metals (e.g. Steel and Aluminum)	30-50/1
Chemicals	0.1-100/1
Nanostructured materials (e.g. computer chips)	700-1700/1
Modern Agriculture	~4/1

[7]http://cnx.org/member_profile/theist

Table 9.1: **Waste-to-Product Ratios for Selected Industries:** Table shows the waste to product ratios for six common industries. *Source: Theis, T.*[8]

In 1989, Robert Frosch & Nicholas Gallopoulos, who worked in the General Motors Research Laboratory, published an important analysis of this problem in Scientific American (Frosch and Gallopoulos, 1989 (p. 424)). Their paper was entitled "Strategies for Manufacturing"[9] ; in it they posed a critical question: Why is it that human-designed manufacturing systems are so wasteful, but systems in nature produce little, if any, waste? Although there had been many studies on ways to minimize or prevent wastes, this was the first to seek a systemic understanding of what was fundamentally different about human systems in distinction to natural systems. The paper is widely credited with spawning the new field of Industrial Ecology, an applied science that studies material and energy flows through industrial systems. Industrial Ecology[10] is concerned with such things as closing material loops (recycling and reuse), process and energy efficiency, organizational behavior, system costs, and social impacts of goods and services. A principle tool of Industrial Ecology is life cycle assessment.

9.2.4 Life Cycle Assessment Basics

LCA[11] is a systems methodology for compiling and evaluating information on materials and energy as they flow through a product or service manufacturing chain. It grew out of the needs of industry, in the early 1960s, to understand manufacturing systems, supply chains, and market behavior, and make choices among competing designs, processes, and products. It was also applied to the evaluation of the generation and emission of wastes from manufacturing activities. During the 1970s and 1980s general interest in LCA for environmental evaluation declined as the nation focused on the control of toxic substances and remediation of hazardous waste sites (see Chapters **The Evolution of Environmental Policy in the United States** (Section 2.1) and **Modern Environmental Management** (Section 7.1)), but increasing concern about global impacts, particularly those associated with greenhouse gas emissions, saw renewed interest in the development of the LCA methodology and more widespread applications.

LCA is a good way to understand the totality of the environmental impacts and benefits of a product or service. The method enables researchers and practitioners to see where along the product chain material and energy are most intensively consumed and waste produced. It allows for comparisons with conventional products that may be displaced in commerce by new products, and helps to identify economic and environmental tradeoffs.

LCA can facilitate communication of risks and benefits to stakeholders and consumers (e.g. the "carbon footprint"[12] of individual activities and life styles). Perhaps most importantly of all, LCA can help to prevent unintended consequences, such as creating solutions to problems that result in the transferal of environmental burdens from one area to another, or from one type of impact to another.

A complete LCA assessment defines a system as consisting of four general stages of the product or service chain, each of which can be further broken down into substages:

- Acquisition of materials (through resource extraction or recycled sources)
- Manufacturing, refining, and fabrication
- Use by consumers
- End-of-life disposition (incineration, landfilling, composting, recycling/reuse)

Each of these involves the transport of materials within or between stages, and transportation has its own set of impacts.

In most cases, the impacts contributed from each stage of the LCA are uneven, i.e. one or two of the stages may dominate the assessment. For example, in the manufacture of aluminum products it is acquisition

---

[8]http://cnx.org/member_profile/theist
[9]http://en.wikipedia.org/wiki/Industrial_ecology#History
[10]http://en.wikipedia.org/wiki/Industrial_ecology
[11]http://www.epa.gov/nrmrl/std/sab/lca/
[12]http://www.epa.gov/climatechange/emissions/ind_calculator.html

of materials (mining), purification of the ore, and chemical reduction of the aluminum into metal that create environmental impacts. Subsequent usage of aluminum products by consumers contributes very few impacts, although the facilitation of recycling of aluminum is an important step in avoiding the consumption of primary materials and energy. In contrast, for internal combustion-powered automobiles, usage by consumers creates 70-80% of the life cycle impacts. Thus, it is not always necessary that the LCA include all stages of analysis; in many cases it is only a portion of the product/service chain that is of interest, and often there is not enough information to include all stages anyway. For this reason there are certain characteristic terminologies for various "scopes" of LCAs that have emerged:

- *Cradle-to-grave*: includes the entire material/energy cycle of the product/material, but excludes recycling/reuse.
- *Cradle-to-cradle*: includes the entire material cycle, including recycling/reuse.
- *Cradle-to-gate*: includes material acquisition, manufacturing/refining/fabrication (factory gate), but excludes product uses and end-of-life.
- *Gate-to-gate*: a partial LCA looking at a single added process or material in the product chain.
- *Well-to-wheel*: a special type of LCA involving the application of fuel cycles to transportation vehicles.
- *Embodied energy*: A cradle-to-gate analysis of the life cycle energy of a product, inclusive of the latent energy in the materials, the energy used during material acquisition, and the energy used in manufacturing intermediate and final products. Embodied energy is sometimes referred to as "emergy", or the cumulative energy demand (CED) of a product or service.

9.2.5 LCA Methodology

Over time the methodology for conducting Life Cycle Analyses (LCAs) has been refined and standardized; it is generally described as taking place in four steps: scoping, inventory, impact assessment, and interpretation. The first three of these are consecutive, while the interpretation step is an ongoing process that takes place throughout the methodology. Figure **General Framework for Life Cycle Assessment** (Figure 9.2) illustrates these in a general way.

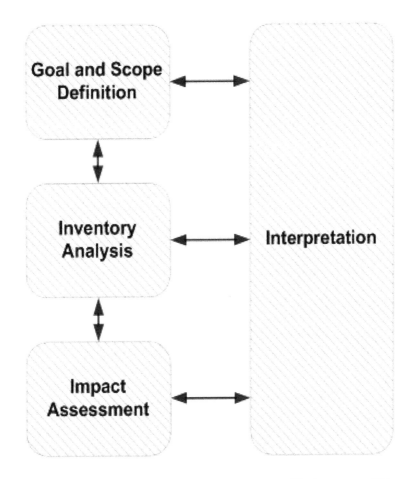

Figure 9.2: General Framework for Life Cycle Assessment The four steps of life cycle assessment and their relationship to one another. *Source: Mr3641 via Wikipedia*[13]

9.2.5.1 Scoping

Scoping is arguably the most important step for conducting an LCA. It is here that the rationale for carrying out the assessment is made explicit, where the boundaries of the system are defined, where the data quantity, quality, and sources are specified, and where any assumptions that underlie the LCA are stated. This is critically important both for the quality of the resultant analysis, and for comparison among LCAs for competing or alternative products.

9.2.5.2 Inventory Analysis

The inventory analysis step involves the collection of information on the use of energy and various materials used to make a product or service at each part of the manufacturing process. If it is true that scoping is the most important step in an LCA then the inventory is probably the most tedious since it involves locating, acquiring, and evaluating the quality of data and specifying the sources of uncertainties that may have arisen. For products that have been produced for a long time and for which manufacturing processes are well known, such as making steel, concrete, paper, most plastics, and many machines, data are readily

---

[13]http://en.wikipedia.org/wiki/File:PhasesOfLifeCycleAnalysis.png

available. But for newer products that are either under development or under patent protection, data are often considered proprietary and are generally not shared in open sources. Uncertainty can arise because of missing or poorly documented data, errors in measurement, or natural variations caused by external factors (e.g., weather patterns can cause considerable variation in the outputs of agricultural systems or the ways that consumers use products and services can cause variability in the emission of pollutants and the disposition of the product at end of life). Often the manufacturing chain of a process involves many steps resulting in a detailed inventory analysis. Figure **Detailed System Flow Diagram for Bar Soap** (Figure 9.3), for example, shows the manufacturing flow for a bar of soap (this diagram is for making bar soap using saponification—the hydrolysis of triglycerides using animal fats and lye). The inventory requires material and energy inputs and outputs for each of these steps, although it may turn out that some steps contribute little to the ultimate impact analysis. For example, the inventory associated with capital equipment for a manufacturing process, i.e. machines that are replaced at lengthy intervals such that their impacts in the short term are minimal, are often omitted from the analysis.

There are two additional aspects of LCA that should also be addressed during inventory analysis: the **functional unit** of comparison, and the **allocation** of inventory quantities among co-products or services. The functional unit is the basis for comparing two or more products, processes, or services that assure equality of the function delivered. This may seem like a straightforward task. For example, for the soap produced by the process of Figure **Detailed System Flow Diagram for Bar Soap** (Figure 9.3), one might choose "one bar of soap" as a functional unit of comparison. But then how would a LCA comparison be made with, say, liquid hand soap or a body wash product (which combines the functionality of soap and shampoo)? Perhaps "number of washings" would be a better choice, or maybe concentration of surfactant made available per average use (in the latter case an "average dose" would need to be defined). Furthermore, soaps have other additives and attributes such as scents, lotions, colors, and even the functionality of the shape – factors that may not affect cleaning effectiveness but certainly do have an impact on consumer preferences, and hence quantity sold. Since it is quite likely that essentially all soaps purchased by consumers will eventually be washed down the drain, such marketability factors may indeed have an environmental impact.

Inventory data are virtually always sought for a total supply-manufacturing-consumer-use chain rather than individual products, thus when that same chain produces multiple products it is necessary to allocate the materials, energy, and wastes among them. Again, referring to Figure **Detailed System Flow Diagram for Bar Soap** (Figure 9.3), there are potentially several co-products produced: tallow and other animal products, forest products, cardboard and paper, and salable scrap. There are generally three ways to allocate materials and energy among co-products: mass, volume, and economic value. Mass and volume allocations are the most straightforward, but may not capture market forces that are important in bringing materials into the environment. Allocation via economic valuation usually reflects the value of the energy and any "value added" to the raw materials, but may miss the impacts of the materials themselves. In addition, market values may fluctuate over time. In the final analysis the important aspect of any allocation procedure is that it be fully documented.

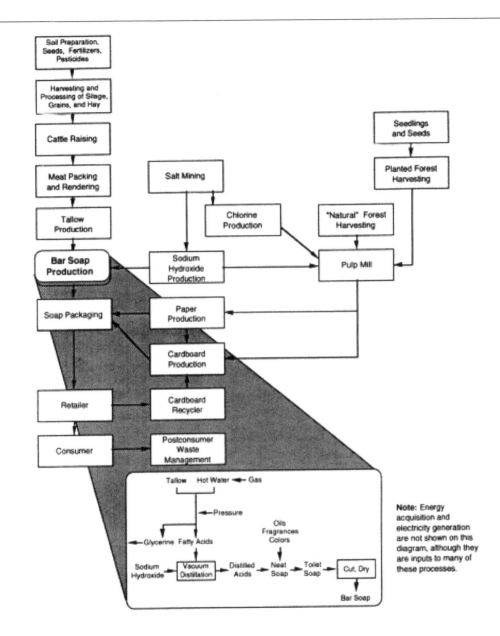

Figure 9.3: Detailed System Flow Diagram for Bar Soap The manufacturing flow for a bar of soap (this diagram is for making bar soap using saponification—the hydrolysis of triglycerides using animal fats and lye). *Source: (U.S. Environmental Protection Agency, 2006) (p. 424)*

9.2.5.3 Impact Assessment

The **life cycle impact assessment (LCIA)** takes the inventory data on material resources used, energy consumed, and wastes emitted by the system and estimates potential impacts on the environment. At first glance, given that an inventory may include thousands of substances, it may seem that the number of potential impacts is bewilderingly large, but the problem is made more tractable through the application of a system of impact classifications within which various inventory quantities can be grouped as having similar consequences on human health or the environment. Sometimes inventoried quantities in a common impact category originate in different parts of the life cycle and often possess very different chemical/biological/physical characteristics. The LCIA groups emissions based on their common impacts rather than on their chemical or physical properties, choosing a reference material for which health impacts are well known, as a basic unit of comparison. A key aspect is the conversion of impacts of various substances into the reference unit. This is done using characterization factors, some of which are well-known, such as global warming potential[14] and ozone depletion potential[15] , and LC_{50}[16] (the concentration of a substance at which fifty percent of an exposed population is killed), and others are still under development. Table **Common Impact Categories and Their References** (Table 9.2) presents several impact categories that are frequently used in the LCIA along with their references. The categories listed in Table **Common Impact Categories and Their References** (Table 9.2) are not exhaustive – new types of impact categories, such as land use and social impacts – and continue to be developed.

Human Health (cancer)	**Kg Benzene eq/unit**
Human Health (non-cancer)	LC_{50} eq from exposure modeling
Global Climate Change	Kg CO_2 eq/unit
Eutrophication	Kg Nitrogen eq/unit
EcotoxicityAquatic, Terrestrial Toxicity	Kg 2,4 D eq/unitLC_{50} eq from exposure modeling
Acidification	Kg H^+/unit
Smog Formation	Kg Ethane eq/unit
Stratospheric Ozone Depletion	Kg CFC-11 eq/unit

Table **9.2**: **Common Impact Categories and Their References:** Several impact categories that are frequently used in the LCIA along with their references. *Source: T. Theis*[17] *adapted from (U.S. Environmental Protection Agency, 2006) (p. 424)*

An example will help to illustrate the type of information that results from **life cycle inventory** and impact assessments. In this case, a system that produces a biologically-derived plastic, polylactide, is examined. (PLA)[18] . PLA has been proposed as a more sustainable alternative to plastics produced from petroleum because it is made from plant materials, in this case corn, yet has properties that are similar to plastics made from petroleum. Figure **Processing Diagram for Making Polylactide** (Figure 9.4) shows a schematic of the system, which is a cradle-to-gate assessment. As with any plastic, PLA can be turned into a variety of final products and each will have different cradle-to-grave LCA characteristics. The production of PLA involves growing corn, harvesting and processing the grain, and polymerizing the lactic acid molecules produced from fermentation. At each step a variety of chemicals and energy are used or produced. It is these production materials that contribute to the impact analysis. Inventory quantities were allocated among major bio-products on a mass basis.

---

[14]http://en.wikipedia.org/wiki/Global-warming_potential
[15]http://en.wikipedia.org/wiki/Ozone_depletion_potential
[16]http://en.wikipedia.org/wiki/Median_lethal_dose
[17]http://cnx.org/member_profile/theist
[18]http://en.wikipedia.org/wiki/Polylactic_acid

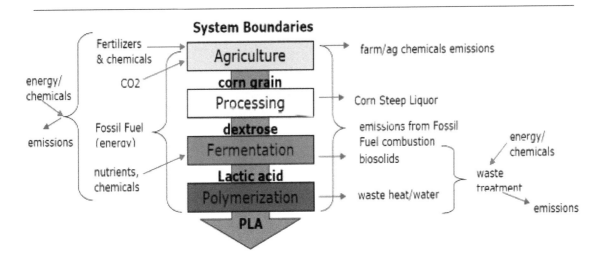

Figure 9.4: Processing Diagram for Making Polylactide (PLA) The production of PLA involves growing corn, harvesting and processing the grain, and polymerizing the lactic acid molecules produced from fermentation. At each step a variety of chemicals and energy are used or produced. It is these production materials that contribute to the impact analysis. *Source: Landis, A.E. (2007) (p. 424)*

Among the inventory data acquired in this case is life cycle fossil fuel used by the system, mostly to power farming equipment ("Agriculture"), wet-mill corn ("CWM"), heat fermentation vats ("Ferment"), and Polymerization ("Polym"). The transport of intermediate products from sources to the processing center is also included. Figure **Fossil Fuel Use to Make PLA vs. Petroleum-Based Plastics** (Figure 9.5) shows the fossil fuel used to make PLA compared with fossil fuel used for making several petroleum-based plastics. Figure **Global Warming Potential Impact Analysis** (Figure 9.6) shows the global warming potential impact analysis. As might have been expected, the fossil fuels used to make PLA are slightly less than for the petroleum-derived plastics on an

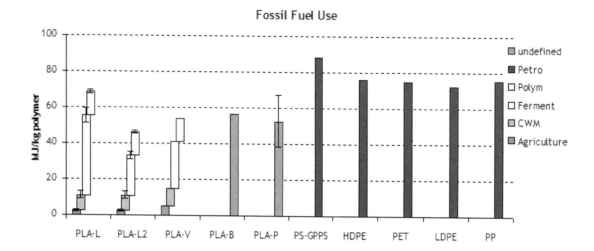

Figure 9.5: Fossil Fuel Use to Make PLA vs. Petroleum-Based Plastics The amount of fossil fuels used when making PLA is slightly less in comparison to making several petroleum-based products. (note: PS-GPPS – General Purpose Polystyrene; HDPE – High Density Polyethylene; PET – Polyethylene Terephthalate; LDPE – Low Density Polyethylene; PP – Polypropylene). *Source: Landis, A.E. using data from: PLA-L, PLA-L2, (Landis, A.E., 2007) (p. 424); PLA-V, (Vink, et al., 2003) (p. 424); PLA-B, (Bohlmann, 2004) (p. 424); PLA-P, (Patel, et al., 2006) (p. 424).*

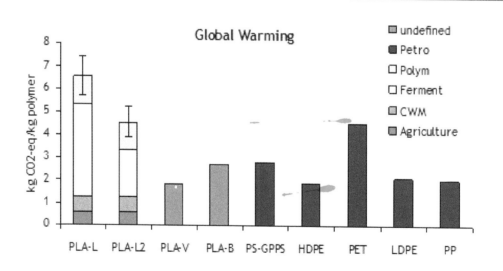

Figure 9.6: Global Warming Potential Impact Analysis Global warming impact for PLA compared with several other petroleum- derived plastics. *Source: Landis, A.E. (2007) (p. 424)*

equal mass basis (the functional unit is one kilogram of plastic). The PLA inventory also shows the sources of fossil fuel used for each step along the manufacturing chain, with the fermentation step being the most intense user. What may not be obvious is that the total greenhouse gases (GHG) emitted from the process, on an equivalent carbon dioxide (CO_2) basis, are generally higher for the biopolymer in comparison with the petroleum polymers in spite of the lower fossil fuel usage. When the data are examined closely this is due to the agricultural step, which consumes generates relatively little fossil fuel, but is responsible for a disproportionate amount of emissions of GHGs, mostly in the form of nitrous oxide, a powerful greenhouse gas (310 times the global warming potential of CO_2) that is a by-product of fertilizer application to fields. This example also illustrates counter-intuitive results that LCAs often generate, a principal reason why it is important to conduct them.

9.2.6 Interpretation of LCA

The interpretation step of LCA occurs throughout the analysis. As noted above, issues related to the rationale for conducting the LCA, defining the system and setting its boundaries, identifying data needs, sources, and quality, and choosing functional units, allocation procedures, and appropriate impact categories must all be addressed as the LCA unfolds. There are essentially two formal reasons for conducting an LCA: (a) identification of "hot spots" where material and/or energy use and waste emissions, both quantity and type, are greatest so that efforts can be focused on improving the product chain; and (b) comparison of results between and among other LCAs in order to gain insight into the preferable product, service, process, or pathway. In both cases, there are cautions that apply to the interpretation of results.

9.2.6.1 Assumptions

Typically a variety of assumption must be made in order to carry out the LCA. Sometimes these are minor, for example, exclusion of elements of the study that clearly have no appreciable impact on the results, and sometimes more critical, for example choosing one set of system boundaries over another. These must be explicitly stated, and final results should be interpreted in light of assumptions made

9.2.6.2 Data Quality, Uncertainty, and Sensitivity

In the course of conducting an LCA it is usually the case that a variety of data sources will be used. In some cases these may be from the full-scale operation of a process, in others the source is from a small scale or even laboratory scale, in still other cases it may be necessary to simulate information from literature sources. Such heterogeneity inevitably leads to uncertainty in the final results; there are several statistical methods that can be applied to take these into account. An important aspect of the completed LCA is the degree of sensitivity the results display when key variables are perturbed. Highly sensitive steps in the chain have a greater need to narrow uncertainties before drawing conclusions with confidence.

9.2.6.3 Incommensurability

Sometimes LCA impact categories, such as those shown in Table **Common Impact Categories and Their References** (Table 9.2), overlap in the sense that the same pollutant may contribute to more than one category. For instance, if a given assessment comes up with high scores for both aquatic toxicity and human toxicity from, say, pesticide use then one might be justified in using both of these categories to draw conclusions and make choices based on LCA results. However, more typically elevated scores are found for categories that are not directly comparable. For instance, the extraction, refining, and use of petroleum generate a high score for global warming (due to GHG release), while the product chain for the biofuel ethanol has a high score for eutrophication (due to nitrogen release during the farming stage). Which problem is worse – climate change or coastal hypoxia? Society may well choose a course of action that favors one direction over another, but in this case the main value of the LCA is to identify the tradeoffs and inform us of the consequences, not tell us which course is "correct."

9.2.6.4 Risk Evaluation and Regulation

One of the inherent limits to LCA is its use for assessing risk. Risk assessment and management, as described in the Modules **The Evolution of Environmental Policy in the United States** (Section 2.1) and **Modern Environmental Management** (Section 7.1), is a formal process that quantifies risks for a known population in a specific location exposed to a specific chemical for a defined period of time. It generates risk values in terms of the probability of a known consequence due to a sequence of events that are directly comparable, and upon which decisions on water, land, and air quality standards and their violation can be and are made. LCA is a method for evaluating the impacts of wastes on human health and the environment from the point of view of the product/service chain rather than a particular population. It can be used to identify the sources of contamination and general impacts on the environment – a sort of "where to look" guide for regulation, but its direct use in the environmental regulatory process has been, to date, rather limited. One application for LCA that has been suggested for regulatory use is for assessing the impacts of biofuel mandates on land use practices, in the United States and other regions, however no regulatory standards for land use have yet been proposed.

9.2.7 Tools for Conducting LCA

Fortunately a number of databases and tools, in the form of computer software, are available to assist in carrying out LCAs. This is an active area of development; in this section a few of the more well-known and widely used tools are described.

9.2.7.1 The Greenhouse Gases, Regulated Emissions, and Energy Use in Transportation Model (GREET)

GREET[19] is a spreadsheet-based database developed by Argonne National Laboratory that links energy use to emissions on a life cycle basis. Early versions were limited to greenhouse gases, but as the model has been refined many other types of contaminants have been added. Although it has been widely used for comparing transportation and fuel options (hence its title), GREET has been used for many other applications that have a significant energy component, including agriculture, material and product development, and strategies for recycling.

9.2.7.2 SimaPro

SimaPro[20] was developed by PRé Consultants in the Netherlands. It is a process-based tool for analyzing products and systems for their energy usage and environmental impacts over their life cycle. It contains a number of databases for simulating processes, performing inventories, assembling products and systems, analyzing results, and assessing life cycle impacts, and features modules for performing uncertainty and sensitivity analyses.

9.2.7.3 Tool for the Reduction and Assessment of Chemical and Other Environmental Impacts (TRACI)

TRACI[21] is a tool for performing life cycle impact analyses developed by the U.S. Environmental Protection Agency. It uses inventory data as input information to perform a "mid-point" impact analysis using categories such as those shown in Table **Common Impact Categories and Their References** (Table 9.2). A mid-point analysis assesses impact based upon results at a common point in the risk chain, for example, global warming potential, because subsequent end-point impact assessments require several assumptions and value choices that often differ from case to case. The values for the various impact categories given in Table **Common Impact Categories and Their References** (Table 9.2) are mid-point references.

---

[19]http://greet.es.anl.gov/
[20]http://www.pre.nl/content/simapro-lca-software
[21]http://www.epa.gov/nrmrl/std/sab/traci/

9.2.7.4 Economic Input Output Life Cycle Assessment (EIO-LCA)

EIO-LCA (http://www.eiolca.net/[22]) takes a different approach to the development of a life cycle assessment. In comparison with the somewhat complicated "bottom-up" approach described above, EIO-LCA uses a more aggregated, matrix-based approach in which the economy is composed of several hundred "sectors," each linked to the other through a series of factors. EIO was first developed in the 1950s by Wassily Leontief (1905-1999) who was awarded a Nobel Prize in economics for his work. EIO has proven to be a very useful tool for national and regional economic planning. The developers of EIO-LCA then linked the main economic model to a series of environmental impacts. EIO-LCA uses economic measures to perturb the system; for example, if a factory seeks to increase its output by ten percent, then the aggregated inputs across the economy will have to increase by ten percent. Of course some of the inputs from some sectors will increase very little if at all, while others will bear the major brunt of the increase in output by increasing input. In EIO-LCA, part of the new outputs will be increased contaminant loads to the environment.

EIO-LCA has several advantages in comparison with the "bottom-up" approach. There is no need to be concerned with defining system boundaries, i.e. the "boundary" is the entire economy of the United States (or a sub-region), which includes all material and energy inputs and outputs. The data used in EIO-LCA are, for the most part, already collected by the federal government thereby obviating the tedium of the inventory stage. Finally, software models are readily available to carry out the analysis. While a "bottom-up" LCA may take months or even years to complete, EIO-LCA typically takes a few hours.

Of course, at this level of aggregation much information is lost, especially on how the system actually functions. For example, the "energy" sector of the economy includes electricity generated, but doesn't distinguish among nuclear, fossil, or renewable sources. And if one is concerned with the functional reasons for a particular result, EIO-LCA will be of limited use. Often the "bottom-up" and EIO-LCA approaches are combined (a "hybrid" approach).

9.2.8 Conclusions

The life cycle approach is a useful way to come to an understanding of the material and energy needed to make a product or deliver a service, see where wastes are generated, and estimate the subsequent impacts that these wastes may have on the environment. It is a good way to improve a product chain, articulate tradeoffs, and make comparisons among alternative processes and products. In these contexts LCA facilitates decision making by managers, designers, and other stakeholders. Most importantly, LCA is a way of framing policy options in a comprehensive and systematic way.

9.2.9 Review Questions

Question 9.2.1
Using the information in Table **Waste-to-Product Ratios for Selected Industries** (Table 9.1), fill in numerical values, per unit of product, for the diagram in Figure **Human-Designed Industry** (Figure 9.1). One diagram for each industrial sector.

Question 9.2.2
What are some of the reasons to use Life Cycle Assessments?

Question 9.2.3
What are the basic stages of a product or service chain that serve as the basis for a life cycle assessment?

Question 9.2.4
What are the steps involved in performing a life cycle assessment?

Question 9.2.5
Name several characteristic scopes of life cycle assessments.

---

[22]http://www.eiolca.net/

Question 9.2.6

What is "embodied energy"?

Question 9.2.7

Name several impact assessment categories and the reference units typically used to express them.

Question 9.2.8

Name several life cycle impact analysis tools and their major characteristics.

Question 9.2.9

What are some of the limitations of life cycle assessments?

Question 9.2.10

Locate and read a completed Life Cycle Assessment online. Consider whether widespread adoption by society would result in measureable lowering of environmental impacts? If so what kind? What might the obstacles be? Are there any tradeoffs associated with adoption, i.e. some impacts may be reduced, but others might get worse?)

9.2.10 References

Bohlmann, G. M. (2004). Biodegradable packaging life cycle assessment. *Environmental Progress*, 23(4), 49-78. doi: 10.1002/ep.10053

Frosch, R. & Gallopoulos, N. (1989). Strategies for Manufacturing. *Scientific American*, 261(3), 144-152.

Landis, A. E. (2007). *Environmental and Economic Impacts of Biobased Production*. Unpublished doctoral dissertation, University of Illinois at Chicago.

Patel, M., Crank, M., Dornburg, V., Hermann, B., Roes, L., Huesling, B., et al. (2006, September). *Medium and long term opportunities and risks of the biotechnological production of bulk chemicals from renewable resources – The potential of white biotechnology: The BREW Project*. Utrecht University, Netherlands: European Commission's GROWTH Programme (DG Research).

U.S. Environmental Protection Agency. (2006). *Life cycle assessment: Principles and practice*. (EPA Publication No. EPA/600/R-06/060). Systems Analysis Branch, National Risk Management Research Laboratory. Cincinnati, Ohio. http://www.epa.gov/nrmrl/lcaccess/pdfs/600r06060.pdf[23] .

Vink, E. T. H., Rábagno, K.R., Glassner, D.A., & Gruber, P.R. (2003). Applications of life cycle assessment to NatureWorks polylactide (PLA) production. *Polymer Degradation and Stability* 80(3), 403-419. doi: 10.1016/S0141-3910(02)00372-5

9.3 Derivative Life Cycle Concepts

9.3.1 Sustainability Metrics and Rating Systems[24]

9.3.1.1 Learning Objectives

After reading this section, students should be able to

- understand what the challenges are when measuring sustainability
- be able to compare and contrast some commonly used measures for sustainability
- identify the different types of measures and their value within a measuring system

---

[23]http://www.epa.gov/nrmrl/lcaccess/pdfs/600r06060.pdf
[24]This content is available online at <http://legacy.cnx.org/content/m41616/1.7/>.

9.3.1.2 Introduction

The ideal method to measure sustainability would reflect the three-legged stool paradigm – environmental protection, social equity, and economic benefit. The metrics must make the connection between what the indicators measure and actual sustainability. A useful **indicator** will reflect changes over time that show whether a system is becoming more or less sustainable, and generally substitutes for something else or represents several measures (Sahely, 2005 (p. 435)). The challenge of studying sustainability as an objective science is that the work is value-loaded and socially charged. If we are aware of the purpose of the analysis we can use a multidisciplinary approach to the problem definition and the research methodology (Lele and Norgaard, 1996 (p. 435)).

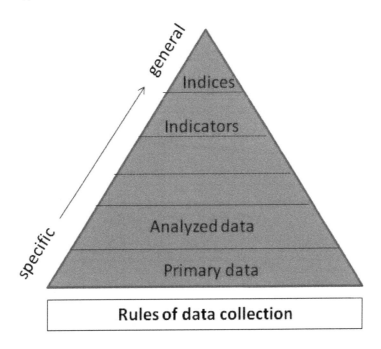

Figure 9.7: Information Pyramid The Information Pyramid shows ways of handling data when studying sustainability. *Source: C. Klein-Banai*[25].

In general, three approaches to sustainability measurement and reporting are commonly utilized: accounts that use **quantitative data** and convert them to a common unit such as money, area or energy; **narrative assessments** that include text, maps, graphics and tabular data; and **indicator-based systems** that may include the information that a narrative assessment has but they are organized around indicators or measurable parts of a system. Indicator-based systems are generally found to perform better and are easily measurable and comparable since they are more objective than narrative systems, or use only individual data points (Dalal-Clayton, 2002 (p. 435)). Decision-makers and stakeholders need to participate in the development of indicators to be sure that their values and concerns are addressed. However, the system does need to be technically and scientifically based.

In the next few modules we will briefly discuss existing sustainability metrics that are generally based within certain disciplines such as ecology, economics, and physics, and how they may reflect other disciplines (see Table **Common Sustainability Metrics** (Table 9.3: Common Sustainability Metrics)). Most of these metrics are described in greater details in the following modules: **The IPAT Equation** (Section 1.3),

---

[25]http://cnx.org/member_profile/cindykb

Biodiversity, Species Loss, and Ecosystem Function (Section 4.3), **Tragedy of the Commons** (Section 6.2), **Environmental Valuation** (Section 6.4), **Evaluating Projects and Policies** (Section 6.5), and **Life Cycle Assessment** (Section 9.2).

Common Sustainability Metrics

	Method	Brief Description	Use
Economic	Contingent valuation method (CVM)	Captures the preferences of the public regarding a good or service by measuring its willingness to pay	Good or service
	Ecosystem services valuation	Valuation of services provided by nature such as cleaning of water by microorganisms	Good or service
	Cost Benefit Analysis (CBA)	Valuation of cost and benefits for each year of project/policy; calculation of a net present value (NPV) by aggregating and comparing costs and benefits over the whole life of project policy.	Project or policy
	Index of Sustainable Economic Welfare (ISEW)	Weights personal expenditures with an index of income inequality	Regional welfare
	Net national product (NNP)	Total income of the people in an economy less capital consumption or depreciation	Regional welfare
	Green NNP	Modification of above to account for loss of natural resource capital	Regional welfare
Ecological	Resilience	Intensity of disturbance required to move system to a new regime	Ecosystem
		continued on next page	

	Carrying capacity: Maximum sustainable yield (MSY) & IPAT	The maximum amount of resource extraction while not depleting the resource from one harvest to the next	Ecosystem
	Ecological footprint (EF)	Total area of productive land and water ecosystems needed to produce resources and assimilate waste of a given population	Individual, institutional, regional
Physical	Emergy	The amount of solar energy that has been used directly or indirectly to make a good or service	Good or service
	Exergy	The maximum work that can be extracted from a system when it moves towards thermodynamic equilibrium with a reference state	Policy, evaluation of energy systems

Table 9.3: Table lists common sustainability metrics. *Source: C. Klein-Banai*[26]

9.3.1.3 Ecological Measures

Ecological measures of sustainability are used for natural systems. These measures include resilience and several constructs that are derivatives from carrying capacity. **Resilience** is the time needed for a system that provides desirable **ecosystem goods and services** to go back to a defined dynamic regime after disturbance. Resilience stresses the changing nature of **ecosystems**, rather than seeing them as static and providing a continuous and constant amount of natural resources. **Carrying capacity** estimates society's total use of the resource stocks and flows provided by an ecosystem relative to the remaining resources needed by the ecosystem for stability and regeneration. **Maximum sustainable yield (MSY)** is an outgrowth of carrying capacity and the goal is to reach the maximum amount of resource extraction while not depleting the resource from one harvest to the next. Sustainability, in this context, can be understood as the point when the rate of resource extraction or harvest (MSY) equals the amount produced by the ecosystem. Previously discussed methods are types of measures of sustainability such as IPAT (see Module **The IPAT Equation** (Section 1.3)) which accounts for the effect of society on the amount of resources used when looking at carrying capacity. This type of measure looks at whether the impact of a human society is increasing or decreasing over time and can be used to compare impacts between societies of difference sizes or affluence levels.

Footprinting (see Module **Footprinting: Carbon, Ecological and Water** (Section 9.3.2)) is often used as a measure of sustainability that can be understood intuitively and is, therefore, useful when talking to the general public. The ecological footprint, which also represents the carrying capacity of the earth, is defined as "the total area of productive land and water ecosystems required to produce the resources that the population consumes and assimilate the wastes that the population produces, wherever on Earth that land and water may be located" (Rees and Wackernagel, 1996 (p. 435)). This results in an evaluation of the demand and supply of natural capital of a given population (individual to planet) or a product/service.

[26] http://cnx.org/member_profile/cindykb

Life-cycle assessment (LCA), a structured methodology that can be utilized to evaluate the environmental impacts of products, processes, projects, or services throughout their life cycles from cradle to grave (see Module **Life Cycle Assessment** (Section 9.2)) may be considered an ecological metric. A greenhouse gas emissions inventory is an example of this methodology (see **Case Study: Greenhouse Gases and Climate Change** (Section 8.3)).

9.3.1.4 Economic Measures

Economic measures place a monetary value on sustainability. Economists use the following measures of sustainability: ecosystem valuation, contingent valuation, and net national product, which are discussed in Chapter **Environmental and Resource Economics** (Section 6.1). Standard economic methods can be used to evaluate environmental projects.

Indices that are used on a national and international level by organizations like the United Nations may be used to examine the economic and social welfare of a region. The Index of Sustainable Economic Welfare (ISEW)[27] and other related frameworks that account for sustainable development have been conceived to provide an alternative to the Gross Domestic Product[28] , which does not capture human welfare in its calculations. This system weights personal expenditures within a population with an index of income inequality and a set of factors are then added or subtracted to this monetary value. Monetary analysis of sustainability does not value the variety of sustainability issues especially those that cannot be measured as a product or service in today's markets (Gasparatos, et al., 2008 (p. 435)).

9.3.1.5 Physical Measures

Physical measures of sustainability use thermodynamic concepts in their calculations. Two physical approaches to measuring sustainability are **exergy** and emergy. These concepts are derived from the second law of thermodynamics which states that a closed system with constant mass and no energy inputs tends toward higher **entropy** or disorder. For instance, a piece of wood that is the product of many years of complex tree growth releases energy (light and heat in the flame) when burned, and becomes carbon ash, smoke, gases, and water vapor. This means that as properties within a system such as mass, energy, and chemical concentrations degrade (decompose) over time or burn, they also make available useful energy (exergy) for work. Ecosystems and human economies function under this second law, but they can use external energy (the sun) to maintain or increase energy supplies.

Emergy is the amount of energy of one kind (solar) that has been used directly or indirectly (through a transformation process) to make a service or a product of one type and it is expressed in units of (solar energy) **emjoule**. It can be thought of as a measure of all the entropy that has been produced over the whole process of creating a given product or service (Brown and Ulgiati, 2002 (p. 435)). An example is the process of fossil fuel creation: solar energy was used by plants to grow and is stored in the complex molecular structures that held the plants together, when those plants died they decomposed and were buried over time under the changing earth, and the energy was concentrated into fossil fuels. Emergy, thus, allows us to account for all the environmental support needed by human and eco-systems or inputs.

Measures of energy inputs are transformed to emergy by use of a factor that represents the amount of environmental work needed to produce a product or provide a service. The emergy flows within a system include renewable resources (sunlight, rain, wind, agricultural production, timber harvest, etc.), non-renewable production (fossil fuels, metals, minerals, soils), and imports/exports. A sustainable system would have a net positive (or zero) emergy flow across its boundary (Mayer, et al., 2004 (p. 435)). Emergy evaluations have been used, for instance, to quantitatively demonstrate that renewable energy plants had higher sustainability compared to thermal plants (Brown and Ugliati, 2002 (p. 435)).

Exergy can be defined as the maximum work that can be extracted from a system as it moves to thermodynamic equilibrium with a reference state, as in the example of burned wood above. It has been used to study efficiency of chemical and thermal processes. This represents an entropy-free form of energy

---

[27]http://en.wikipedia.org/wiki/Index_of_Sustainable_Economic_Welfare
[28]http://en.wikipedia.org/wiki/Gross_domestic_product

that is a measure of its usefulness, quality or potential to make change. Exergy accounting provides insights into the metabolism of a system and its effect on the environment using a common denominator. It can address energy utilization, be used for design and analysis of energy systems and to quantify waste and energy losses reflecting resource use. Exergy can account for an economic component, labor input, and impact of emissions on human health (Gasparatos, et al., 2008 (p. 435); Odum, 1996 (p. 435)).

9.3.1.6 Comparison of Measures

So far we highlighted three categories for measures of sustainability – ecological, economic, and physical – and provided a few examples. Sustainability measures is an evolving field of study and the metrics are innumerable. Ecological measures include indicators that try to measure the sustainability of the ecosystem as a whole. Economic metrics use monetary measures and try to put a price on the environment and its services. They are valued based on currency, which is an anthropocentric value, meaning it is significant only to humans. They account only for human welfare to the extent that it depends on nature to survive. They do not account for the effect on an ecosystem as a whole, including plants and animals. Physical metrics are closely tied to thermodynamics and energy, and are generally expressed in units of energy.

Sustainability indicators are needed to improve our understanding of the nature of human demands on ecosystems and the extent to which these can be modified. Society uses resources for physical and social infrastructure and continually increases its needs due to population growth which is made possible by changing the way we grow and produce food, thus manipulating the food web. Some of these economic metrics are closely tied to social sustainability metrics as well and try to account for the social welfare of a population. Overall, while physical tools can capture certain environmental and economic issues, too, they do not address economic issues from the same perspective as conventional economic analysis. Moreover, they do not capture most social issues.

Economic markets do not usually directly value goods and services that ecological systems provide to human economies and societies. These ecosystem services include the uptake of carbon dioxide by plants and trees, purification of water by microorganisms, enrichment of soil through degradation of plant and animal materials, and rainfall that provides irrigation (see Constanza, et al., 1997 (p. 435)). Also economists do not agree on the degree of substitutability between natural and man-made capital. This concept of substitutability means that natural capital such as 100 year old ("old forest") trees used to build homes and furniture can be replaced by replanting fast-growing trees and provide the same value (Pearce, 1993 (p. 435)). Technology also transforms the use of resources for instance by making them more readily available and more economic. An example of this is the use of "fracking" to produce natural gas from sources that were difficult to extract from a decade ago (see Module **Environmental Challenges in Energy, Carbon Dioxide, Air and Water** (Section 8.2)).

9.3.1.7 Sustainability Indicators and Composite Indices

There is no single **indicator** that can capture all aspects of sustainability within complex systems. When we speak of systems, we are referring to institutions, cities, regions, or nations. However, a group of indicators could be selected and analyzed under certain criteria that will better represent this type of system. An indicator represents a particular operational attribute of a system such as overall energy reduction, a GHG gas emissions inventory, what percentage of people commute by public transit, or percentage of people with a college degree. These are measured or observed at different times, locations, populations or combinations thereof. The Figure **Information Pyramid** (Figure 9.7) represents the relationship between all these measures.

A group of indicators can then be evaluated using a composite indicator/index (CI) or rating. CIs stand at the top of an information pyramid where primary data lies at the base, followed by analyzed data, then indicators, and topped by indices. A composite indicator is formed by the compilation of various individual indicators into one index based on an underlying model. (Nardo, et al., 2005 (p. 435)). An example is the Leadership in Energy and Environmental Design (LEED)[29] which is a green building certification system

---

[29] http://www.usgbc.org/DisplayPage.aspx?CMSPageID=1988

developed by the U.S. Green Building Council (USGBC)[30] . It accounts for a large variety of building attributes that contribute to a building being considered "sustainable" such as building materials, location, landscape, energy usage, access to alternative transportation and so on. The final result is a numerical rating for the building that is then associated with a certain certification level (Certified, Silver, Gold, Platinum). This kind of system is most widely accepted and valued when a peer-review is conducted to determine what weights should be given to each attribute. When the USGBC decided to update its rating system because it did not accurately reflect the values of its members, it underwent review through its various committees[31] .

Sometimes, when you have a lot of different measures that use different units you do not want to aggregate them together into one number. In this case, a multi-criteria assessment (MCA) can be used where constituent indicators are not aggregated into a single index. Multi-criteria analysis (similar name, different context) can be used as a tool to establish weights for several criteria, without requiring that all data be converted into the same units (Hermann, 2007 (p. 435)). There are several multi-criteria evaluation methods that can be used for this. These methods may either be data-driven (bottom-up) when high-quality data is available or theory driven (top-down) when data is available for only one of the aspects. A broader review of this can be found in Gasparatos, et al. (2008) (p. 435).

Many industry sectors are developing frameworks or rating systems that provide ways to report and measure sustainability. Two examples are discussed here.

The Global Reporting Initiative (GRI)[32] provides a system for organizations to publish their sustainability performance. Its purpose is to provide transparency and accountability for stakeholders and to be comparable among organizations. It is developed in an international, multi-stakeholder process and it is continuously improved. An organization determines which indicators from among those proposed it will report. However, no overall index or scores are reported. There is also usually a narrative portion to the report (Global Reporting Initiative). The indicators are broken down in environmental, economic and social performance indicators. Each area has core indicators with some additional indicators that may be used based on the organization's choice.

The American Association of Higher Education (AASHE)[33] , is the lead organization in North America for sustainability in colleges and universities. One of their major projects has been the development of the Sustainability Tracking, Assessment and Rating System (STARS)[34] . This is a voluntary, self-reporting framework that is to be used to measure relative progress of universities and colleges as they work toward sustainability. STARS was developed using a collaborative process that involved input from many institutions. In 2008, a pilot study of 66 institutions was conducted to test the viability of the system and STARS version 1.0 was released in January 2010 with many schools reporting by January 2011. The credits are given in three categories of equal weight – education and research; operations; planning, administration and engagement. Each credit is given a weight based on the extent to which the credit contributes to improved environmental, financial and social impacts, and whether there are educational benefits associated with the achievement of this credit and the breadth of that impact. The result is a composite indicator, with transparent individual scoring. Schools participating in STARS will use an on-line reporting tool which makes the results publicly available. Depending on the total points achieved, a level of achievement is be assigned. The STARS rating will be good for three years but a school may choose to update annually. See Case Study: Comparing Greenhouse Gas Emissions, Ecological Footprint and Sustainability Rating of a University (Section 9.3.3) for an example of this reporting.

9.3.1.8 Examples of How an Index is Developed

Krajnc and Glavic (2005) (p. 435) developed a composite sustainable development index (I_{CSD}) to track economic, environmental and social performance of company. Economic, environmental, and social sub-indices were calculated from normalized indicators within each sector. To calculate normalized indicators,

---

[30]http://www.usgbc.org/DisplayPage.aspx?CMSPageID=1988
[31]http://www.usgbc.org/DisplayPage.aspx?CMSPageID=1750
[32]http://www.globalreporting.org/ReportingFramework/ReportingFrameworkOverview/
[33]http://www.aashe.org/
[34]http://www.aashe.org/stars

the indicators for each sector, which typically have different units, were divided by the value in time (year) with its average value of all the time in the years measured. Alternatively, they can be normalized by using maximum and minimum values or target values. The Analytic Hierarchy Process[35] was used to determine the weights of the environmental indicators. This is a multi-attribute decision model. The steps are:

1. Setting the problem as a hierarchy with the top being the objective of the decision and lower levels consist of the criteria used at arriving at the decision.
2. Pair-wise comparisons between two indicators.
3. Use of a consistency ratio to check the consistency of each judgment.
4. Step-by-step procedure of grouping various basic indicators into the sustainability sub-index.
5. Sub-indices are combined into the composite sustainable development index.

The economic, environmental and social measures that were used in this model are as follows:

Economic	Environmental	Social
Sales	Total energy consumption	No. of occupational accidents
Operating profit	Water consumption	No. of non-profit projects
Investment capital & expenditures	Production mass	No. of odor complains
Net earnings	Carbon dioxide, nitrous oxides, sulfur dioxide & dust emissions	No. of noise complaints
Research & development costs	Wastewater	No. of dust complaints
Number of employees	Waste for disposal	No. of neighbor complaints
	Recycling	
	Hazardous waste	

Table 9.4

An analytical tool, called COMPLIMENT, was developed to provide detailed information on the overall environmental impact of a business (Hermann, 2007 (p. 435)). This tool integrates the concepts of life cycle assessment, multi-criteria analysis and environmental performance indicators. The combinations of environmental performance indicators used depend on the organization and reflect the relevant parts of the production train. The method includes setting system boundaries, data collection, calculation of potential environmental impacts and their normalization, aggregation of impacts using a multi-criteria analysis, the weights per impact category are multiplied by normalization potential impacts and the results can be added up for each perspective. The system boundary strives to be cradle-to-grave (from extraction of resources to disposal) although it may be a cradle-to-gate (from extraction of resources to completion of production) analysis.

Adoption of any single group of tools means that a certain perspective will be more highly represented in the sustainability assessment. "The need to address the multitude of environmental, social, economic issues, together with intergenerational and intragenerational equity concerns" (Gasparatos, et al., 2008 (p. 435), p. 306) produces problems that none of the disciplinary approaches can solve separately. Combining the outputs of biophysical and monetary tools will result in a more comprehensive sustainability perspective. The result is that the choice of metrics and tools must be made based on the context and characteristics that are desired by the analysts (Gasparatos, et al., 2008 (p. 435)). Using a composite indicator or a set of individual indicators presented together can overcome the problem of using a single metric to measure sustainability.

---

[35]http://www.boku.ac.at/mi/ahp/ahptutorial.pdf

Existing indicator-based sustainability assessments vary in the number of subsystems or assessment areas, the number of levels between subsystem and indicator, and whether they result in an index (compound indicator) of the state of the system and subsystems. These would include the ecosystem or environment, people or economy and society, and possibly institutions. The more subsystems assigned, the lower the weight given to the environmental portion. As more indicator systems are developed they become increasingly complex, yet there is a demand for a simple presentation that does not erase the complexity. A single indicator with true significance is not achievable, but by combining indicators into indices the results are more meaningful.

9.3.1.9 Representing Results for Multi-Criteria Assessment

Since measuring sustainability does not come down to a simple metric or few it is useful to use visualization techniques to display the results. One way to depict sustainability performance is to use a graphical view of progress, as shown in Figure **Visualizing Results of Sustainability** (p. 432) below for the GRI for universities. For each category a mapping of the scores was created. This appears as a hexagon indicating progress in each area for which points are achieved.

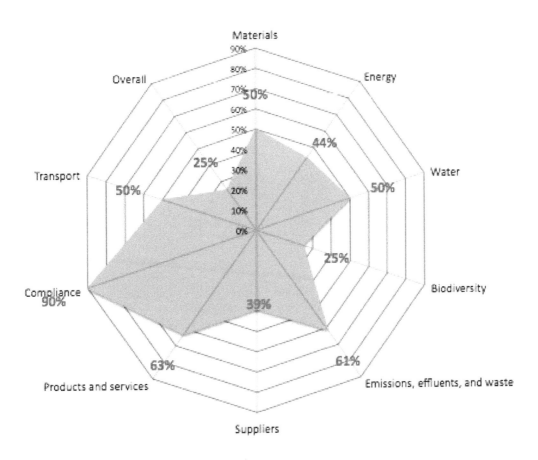

Environment

Figure 9.8: Visualizing Results of Sustainability Assessments Hypothetical graphical representation of the Environmental Dimension of the GRI for universities. The red numbers indicate the percentage of points achieved within each sub-category within the category of environment. *Source: D. Fredman adapted from Lozano (2006)* (p. 435).

Another example of visualizing sustainability is seen in a framework developed for universities to use (Troschinetz et al., 2007 (p. 435)). Again, multidimensional sustainability indicators, each having an economic, environmental and social component are used. The categories are listed in Figure **Sustainability Indicator Triangle** (Figure 9.9). Each indicator was examined using a sustainability indicator triangle where each corner is delineated as economic, environmental or social and the indicators are placed within to the triangle to reflect how well each measures those aspects.

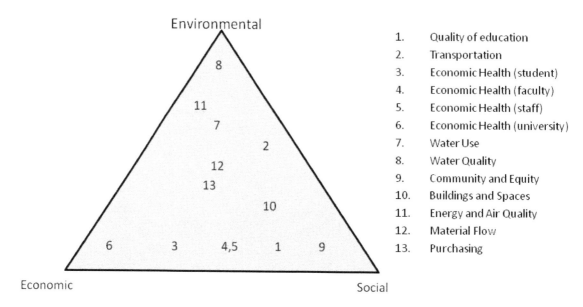

1. Quality of education
2. Transportation
3. Economic Health (student)
4. Economic Health (faculty)
5. Economic Health (staff)
6. Economic Health (university)
7. Water Use
8. Water Quality
9. Community and Equity
10. Buildings and Spaces
11. Energy and Air Quality
12. Material Flow
13. Purchasing

Figure 9.9: Sustainability Indicator Triangle The thirteen sustainability indicators are placed according to how well each measures a dimension of sustainability, i.e. environmental, societal and economic. *Source: C. Klein-Banai*[36] *adapted from Troschinetz, et al. (2007) (p. 435).*

9.3.1.10 Conclusion

Measuring sustainability is difficult because of the interdisciplinary nature and complexity of the issues that this concern represents. Methods have been developed out of the different disciplines that are based in the ecological, economic, physical and social sciences. When approaching a measure of sustainability it is important to understand what you will use the results of that measure for, what the major concerns you want to address are, and the limits of the system you choose. Often it is more meaningful to measure progress of the entity you are examining – is it more sustainable than it was before? It is difficult to compare similar entities (countries, companies, institutions, even products) due to the complexity and variability in the data. Using visualization to represent the data is a helpful way to show the state of sustainability rather than trying to express it in one number or in a table of numbers.

9.3.1.11 Review Questions

Question 9.3.1.1
What is the difference between data and an index?

Question 9.3.1.2
What is the major challenge in measuring sustainability?

Question 9.3.1.3
Give three general categories of indicators that are used for measuring sustainability and provide one example of each.

Question 9.3.1.4
Why is it important to have experts provide input to rating systems?

---

[36]http://cnx.org/member_profile/cindykb

9.3.1.12 References

Brown, M.T. & Ulgiati, S. (2002). Emergy evaluations and environmental loading of electricity production systems. *Journal of Cleaner Production, 10,* 321-334. doi:10.1016/S0959-6526(01)00043-9

Constanza, R., d'Arge, R., de Groot, R., Farber, S., Grasso, R., Hannon, B., et al. (1997). The value of the world's ecosystem services and natural capital. *Nature, 387,* 253–260.

Dalal-Clayton, B. & Bass, S. (2002). *Sustainable development strategies: A resource book.* London: Earthscan Publications Ltd.

Gasparatos, A., El-Haram, M., & Horner, M. (2008). A critical review of reductionist approaches for assessing the progress towards sustainability. *Environmental Impact Assessment Review, 28,* 286-311. doi:10.1016/j.eiar.2007.09.002[37]

Hammond, A., Adriaanse, A., Rodenburg, E., Bryant, D., & Woodward, R. (1995). Environmental indicators: a systematic approach to measuring and reporting on environmental policy performance in the context of sustainable development. *World Resources Institute.* Retrieved March 7, 2011, from http://pdf.wri.org/environmentalindicators_bw.pdf[38] .

Hermann, B.G., Kroeze, C., & Jawjit, W. (2007). Assessing environmental performance by combining life cycle assessment, multi-criteria analysis and environmental performance indicators. *Journal of Cleaner Production, 15,* 1878-1796. doi:10.1016/j.jclepro.2006.04.004[39]

Krajnc, D. & Glavic, P. (2005). A model for integrated assessment of sustainable development. *Resources Conservation & Recycling, 43,* 189-203.

Lele, S. & Norgaad, R.B. (1996, April). Sustainability and the scientist's burden. *Conservation Biology, 10,* 354-365. doi 10.1046/j.1523-1739.1996.10020354.x

Lozano, R. (2006). A tool for graphical assessment of sustainability in universities. *Journal of Cleaner Production, 14,* 963-972. doi: 10.1016/j.jclepro.2005.11.041

Mayer, A.L., Thurston, H.W. & Pawlowski, C.W. (2004). The multidisciplinary influence of common sustainability indices. *Ecological Environment, 2,* 419-426. doi:10.1890/1540-9295(2004)002[0419:TMIOCS]2.0.CO;2

Nardo, M., Saisana, M., Saltelli, A, Tarantola S., Hoffman, A. & Giovannini, E. (2005). Handbook on constructing composite indicators: Methodology and user guide (STD/DOC (2005)3). *Paris: OECD Statistics Directorate.* Retrieved February 26, 2011, from http://www.oecd.org/dataoecd/37/42/42495745.pdf[40]

Odum, H.T. (1996). *Environmental Accounting, Emergy, and Environmental Decision Making.* New York: John Wiley & Sons, Inc.

Pearce, D.W. & G.D. Atkinson (1993). Capital theory and the measurement of sustainable development: an indicator of "weak" sustainability. *Ecological economics, 8,* 103-108.

Rees, W.E. & Wackernagel, M. (1996). Urban ecological footprints: why cities cannot be sustainable and why they are a key to sustainability. *Enviromental Impact Assessment Review, 16,* 223-248.

Reporting Framework Overview. (n.d.). *Global Reporting Initiative.* Retrieved August 21, 2011, from http://www.globalreporting.org/ReportingFramework/ReportingFrameworkOverview/[41]

Sahely, H.R., Kennedy, C.A. & Adams, B.J. (2005). Developing sustainability criteria for urban infrastructure systems. *Canadian Journal of Civil Engineering,32,* 72-85. doi: 10.1139/l04-072

Troschinetz, A.M., Mihelcic, J.R., & Bradof, K.L. (2007). Developing Sustainability Indicators for a University Campus. *International Journal of Engineering Education, 23,* 231-241.

---

[37]http://dx.doi.org/10.1016/j.eiar.2007.09.002
[38]http://pdf.wri.org/environmentalindicators_bw.pdf
[39]http://dx.doi.org/10.1016/j.jclepro.2006.04.004
[40]http://www.oecd.org/dataoecd/37/42/42495745.pdf
[41]http://www.globalreporting.org/ReportingFramework/ReportingFrameworkOverview/

9.3.2 Footprinting: Carbon, Ecological and Water[42]

9.3.2.1 Footprinting: Carbon, Ecological and Water

9.3.2.1.1 Learning Objectives

After reading this section, students should be able to

- understand what an environmental footprint is and its limitations
- conduct some basic footprinting calculations
- calculate and explain their own footprint

9.3.2.1.2 Basic Concepts of Footprinting

What is a common measure of the impact of an individual, institution, region or nation? This can be done by measuring the "footprint" of that entity. When discussing climate change and sustainability the concepts of carbon footprint and ecological footprint are often used. Understanding how these footprints are derived is important to the discourse as not all calculations are equal. These footprints can be calculated at the individual or household level, the institutional level (corporation, university, and agency), municipal level, sub-national, national or global. They are derived from the consumption of natural resources such as raw materials, fuel, water, and power expressed in quantities or economic value. The quantity consumed is translated into the footprint by using conversion factors generally based in scientific or economic values.

NOTE: There are many personal calculators available on the internet. Here are a few to try:

- EPA Household Emissions Calculator[43]
- Ecological Footprint[44]
- Earth Day Network Footprint[45]
- Cool Climate Network (UC Berkeley)[46]
- Carbon Footprint[47]

This chapter will discuss three types of footprints – ecological, carbon and water – and the methodologies behind them. Although efforts have been made to standardize the calculations comparisons must be approached with caution. Comparing individual, institutional or national footprints that are calculated by the same method can be helpful in measuring change over time and understanding the factors that contribute to the differences in footprints.

9.3.2.1.3 Ecological Footprint

9.3.2.1.3.1 Concept

The Merriam-Webster Dictionary defines footprint[48] as:

1. an impression of the foot on a surface;
2. the area on a surface covered by something

---

[42]This content is available online at <http://legacy.cnx.org/content/m41615/1.5/>.
[43]http://www.epa.gov/climatechange/emissions/ind_calculator.html
[44]http://www.myfootprint.org/
[45]http://files.earthday.net/footprint/index.html
[46]http://coolclimate.berkeley.edu/
[47]http://www.carbonfootprint.com/
[48]http://www.merriam-webster.com/dictionary/footprint

Similarly, the **ecological footprint** (EF) represents the area of land on earth that provides for resources consumed and that assimilates the waste produced by a given entity or region. It is a composite index (see Module Sustainability Metrics and Rating Systems (Section 9.3.1)) that represents the amount of biologically productive land and water area required to support the demands of the population in that entity or region The EF is beneficial because it provides a single value (equal to land area required) that reflects resource use patterns (Costanza, 2000 (p. 450)). The use of EF in combination with a social and economic impact assessment can provide a measure of sustainability's **triple bottom line** (Dawe, et al., 2004 (p. 450)). It can help find some of the "hidden" environmental costs of consumption that are not captured by techniques such as cost-benefit analysis and environmental impact (Venetoulis, 2001 (p. 450)). Using the ecological footprint, an assessment can be made of from where the largest impact comes (Flint, 2001 (p. 450)).

Next, we will discuss the how an EF is calculated.

9.3.2.1.3.2 Methodology

The ecological footprint methodology was developed by William Rees and Mathis Wackernagel (p. 450) (1996) (p. 450), and consists of two methodologies:

1. Compound calculation[49] is typically used for calculations involving large regions and nations and is shown in Figure Compound Calculation Steps for Ecological Footprint Analysis (p. 437). First, it involves a consumption analysis of over 60 biotic resources including meat, dairy produce, fruit, vegetables, pulses, grains, tobacco, coffee, and wood products. That consumption is then divided by biotic productivity (global average) for the type of land (arable, pasture, forest, or sea areas) and the result represents the area needed to sustain that activity. The second part of the calculation includes energy generated and energy embodied in traded goods. This is expressed in the area of forested land needed to sequester CO_2 emissions from both types of energy. Finally, equivalence factors are used to weight the six ecological categories based on their productivity (arable, pasture, forest, sea, energy, built-up land). The results are reported as global hectares (gha) where each unit is equal to one hectare of biologically productive land based on the world's average productivity. We derive sub-national footprints based on apportioning the total national footprint between sub-national populations. The advantage of this method is that it captures many indirect of effects of consumption so the overall footprint is more accurate.
2. Component-based calculation[50] resembles life-cycle analysis in that it examines individual products and services for their **cradle-to-grave** resource use and waste, and results in a factor for a certain unit or activity. The footprint is typically broken down into categories that include energy, transportation, water, materials and waste, built-up land, and food. This method is better for individuals or institutions since it accounts for specific consumption within that entity. However, it probably under-counts as not all activities and products could practically be measured or included. It also may double-count since there may be overlap between products and services.

---

[49] http://www.unesco.org/education/tlsf/mods/theme_b/popups/mod09t05s01.html
[50] http://www.footprintnetwork.org/en/index.php/GFN/page/glossary/#consumptioncomponents

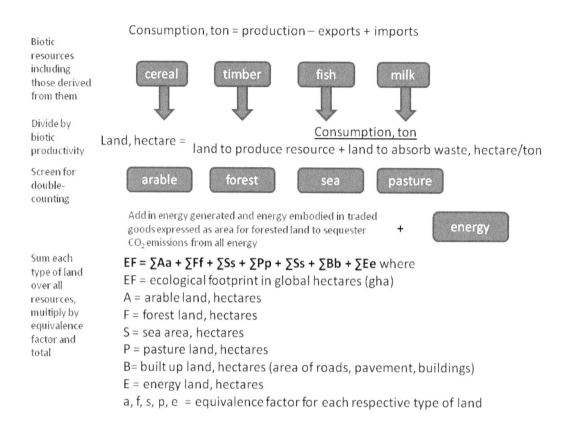

Figure 9.10: Compound Calculation Steps for Ecological Footprint Analysis Figure shows the compound calculation steps for ecological footprint analysis. *Source: C. Klein-Banai*[51].

9.3.2.1.3.3 What the Results Show

When looking at the sub-national level, it is useful to be able to examine different activities that contribute to the footprint such as energy, transportation, water, waste, and food. In both types of calculations, there is a representation of the energy ecological footprint. We utilize conversion factors that account for direct land use for mining the energy source and the land required to sequester any carbon emitted during combustion, construction, or maintenance of the power source. It should be noted that no actual component-based calculations have been done for nuclear power. The practice has been to consider it the same as coal so as to account for it in some way. A discussion of the merits of this method can be found in Wackernagel et al. (2005) (p. 450).

Transportation is another activity that can be examined at the sub-national level. The transportation footprint maybe considered part of the energy footprint, or separately, but is basically based on the energy consumption for transportation. It may also include some portion of the built-up land.

The hydroprint, or water-based footprint, measures the amount of water consumed in comparison to the amount of water in the land catchment system for the geographical area being footprinted. It can represent whether the entity is withdrawing more or less water than is naturally supplied to the area from rainfall.

---

[51]http://cnx.org/member_profile/cindykb

The wasteprint, or waste-based footprint, is calculated using commonly used component-based factors that have been calculated and compiled in a number of publications and books. Food production requires energy to grow, process and transport, as well as land for growing and grazing. The factors are derived using the compound calculation for a certain geographical area. See Case Study: Comparing Greenhouse Gas Emissions, Ecological Footprint and Sustainability Rating of a University (Section 9.3.3) for an example of this kind of ecological footprint analysis. This kind of analysis can show us how a nation, region, organization, or individual uses the planets resources to support its operation or life style, as well as what activities are the primary contributors to the footprint. In the next section, we will look at some national footprints.

9.3.2.1.3.4 Ecological Footprint Comparisons

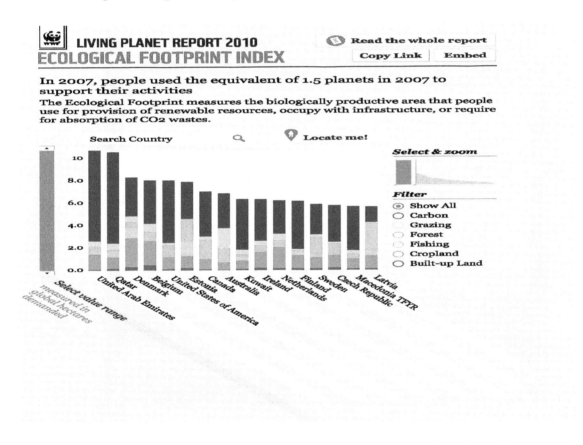

Figure 9.11: Ecological Footprints of Select Nations Graph shows the ecological footprints of select nations. The bars show average EF in global hectares per person for each nation. Each color on the bar represents the different types of land. *Source: ©2010 WWF (panda.org). Some rights reserved.*[52] *Living Planet Report, 2010*[53] *, figure under CC BY-SA 3.0 License*[54]

The Living Planet Report[55] prepared by the World Wildlife Fund[56] , the Institute of Zoology[57] in London, and Wackernagel's Global Footprint Network[58] reports on the footprints of various nations. Figure Ecological Footprints of Select Nations (Figure 9.11) displays the footprint of several nations as shown in the report. The bars show average EF in global hectares per person for each nation. Each color on the bar represents the different types of land. Here we see that the United Arab Emirates has the largest footprint of 10.2 gha per person, with the majority of its footprint due to carbon (same as energy land described above). Whereas Latvia has the lowest footprint displayed at 6.0 gha per person, with the majority of its footprint due to forestland.

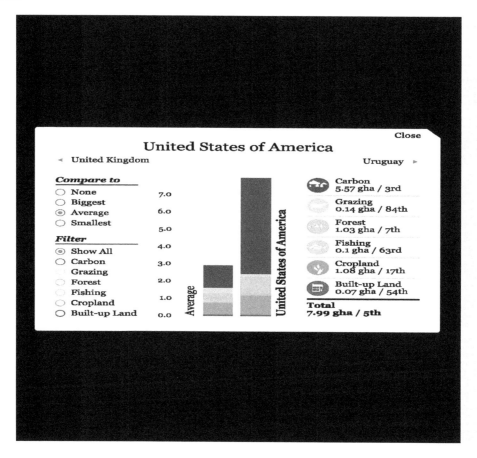

Figure 9.12: United States' Ecological Footprint Figure shows the United States' Ecological Footprint compared to the global average. *Source: ©2010 WWF (panda.org). Some rights reserved.*[59] *Living Planet Report, 2010*[60]*, figure under CC BY-SA 3.0 License*[61]

---

[52]http://wwf.panda.org/about_our_earth/all_publications/living_planet_report/2010_lpr/
[53]http://wwf.panda.org/about_our_earth/all_publications/living_planet_report/2010_lpr/
[54]http://creativecommons.org/licenses/by-sa/3.0/
[55]http://wwf.panda.org/about_our_earth/all_publications/living_planet_report/2010_lpr/
[56]http://www.worldwildlife.org/home-full.html
[57]http://www.zsl.org/science/
[58]http://www.footprintnetwork.org/en/index.php/GFN/page/glossary/
[59]http://wwf.panda.org/about_our_earth/all_publications/living_planet_report/2010_lpr/
[60]http://wwf.panda.org/about_our_earth/all_publications/living_planet_report/2010_lpr/
[61]http://creativecommons.org/licenses/by-sa/3.0/

Figure United States' Ecological Footprint (p. 440) shows the national footprint in 2007 of the United States as 7.99 gha per person both with a bar display and with specific metrics on the right that show the exact footprint and the United States' ranking among all nations in the report (e.g. carbon is 5.57 gha and ranks 3rd largest overall). The bar to the left expresses the world average. The United States' footprint of 7.99 gha stands in contrast to the earth's global biocapacity of 1.8 gha per person. Globally, the total population's footprint was 18 billion gha, or 2.7 gha per person. However, the earth's biocapacity was only 11.9 billion gha, or 1.8 gha per person. This represents an ecological demand of 50 percent more than the earth can manage. In other words, it would take 1.5 years for the Earth to regenerate the renewable resources that people used in 2007 and absorb CO_2 waste. Thus, earth's population used the equivalent of 1.5 planets in 2007 to support their lives.

9.3.2.1.4 Carbon Footprint

Since climate change (see Chapter Climate and Global Change) is one of the major focuses of the sustainability movement, measurement of greenhouse gases or carbon footprint is a key metric when addressing this problem. A greenhouse gas emissions (GHG) inventory is a type of carbon footprint. Such an inventory evaluates the emissions generated from the direct and indirect activities of the entity as expressed in carbon dioxide equivalents (see below). Since you cannot manage what you cannot measure, GHG reductions cannot occur without establishing baseline metrics. There is increasing demand for regulatory and voluntary reporting of GHG emissions such as Executive Order 13514[62] , requiring federal agencies to reduce GHG emissions, the EPA's Mandatory GHG Reporting Rule[63] for industry, the Securities and Exchange Commission's climate change disclosure guidance[64] , American College and University Presidents' Climate Commitment[65] (ACUPCC) for universities, ICLEI[66] for local governments, the California Climate Action Registry, and numerous corporate sustainability reporting initiatives.

9.3.2.1.4.1 Scoping the Inventory

The first step in measuring carbon footprints is conducting an inventory is to determine the scope of the inventory. The World Business Council for Sustainable Development[67] (WBCSD) and the World Resource Institute[68] (WRI) defined a set of accounting standards that form the Greenhouse Gas Protocol (GHG Protocol). This protocol is the most widely used international accounting tool to understand, quantify, and manage greenhouse gas emissions. Almost every GHG standard and program in the world uses this framework as well as hundreds of GHG inventories prepared by individual companies and institutions. In North America, the most widely used protocol was developed by The Climate Registry[69] .

The GHG Protocol also offers developing countries an internationally accepted management tool to help their businesses to compete in the global marketplace and their governments to make informed decisions about climate change. In general, tools are either sector-specific (e.g. aluminum, cement, etc.) or cross-sector tools for application to many different sectors (e.g. stationary combustion or mobile combustion).

---

[62]http://www.fedcenter.gov/Bookmarks/index.cfm?id=13641

[63]http://www.epa.gov/climatechange/emissions/ghgrulemaking.html

[64]http://www.sec.gov/rules/interp/2010/33-9106.pdf

[65]http://www.presidentsclimatecommitment.org/about/commitment

[66]http://www.iclei.org/

[67]http://www.wbcsd.org/templates/TemplateWBCSD5/layout.asp?type=p&MenuId=NjY&doOpen=1&ClickMenu=LeftMenu

[68]http://www.wri.org/

[69]http://www.theclimateregistry.org/

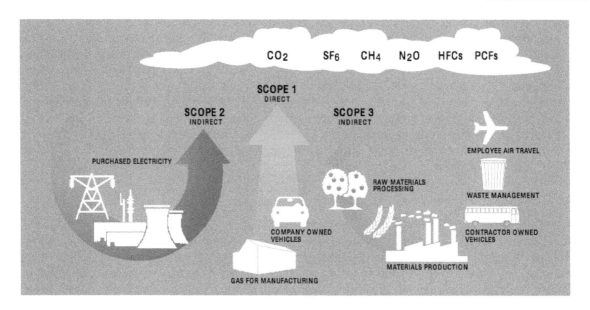

Figure 9.13: Scopes of a Greenhouse Gas Emissions Inventory Figure shows the three scopes of a greenhouse gas emissions inventory. *Source: New Zealand Business Council for Sustainable Development, The challenges of greenhouse gas emissions: The "why" and "how" of accounting and reporting for GHG emissions (2002, August), figure 3, p. 10[70].*

The WRI protocol addresses the scope by which reporting entities can set boundaries (see Figure Scopes of a Greenhouse Gas Emissions Inventory (Figure 9.13)). These standards are based on the source of emissions in order to prevent counting emissions or credits twice. The three scopes are described below:

- *Scope 1:* Includes GHG emissions from direct sources owned or controlled by the institution – production of electricity, heat or steam, transportation or materials, products, waste, and fugitive emissions. Fugitive emissions are due to intentional or unintentional release of GHGs including leakage of refrigerants from air conditioning equipment and methane releases from farm animals.
- *Scope 2:* Includes GHG emissions from imports (purchases) of electricity, heat or steam – generally those associated with the generation that energy.
- *Scope 3:* Includes all other indirect sources of GHG emissions that may result from the activities of the institution but occur from sources owned or controlled by another company, such as business travel; outsourced activities and contracts; emissions from waste generated by the institution when the GHG emissions occur at a facility controlled by another company, e.g. methane emissions from landfilled waste; and the commuting habits of community members.

Depending on the purpose of the inventory the scope may vary. For instance, the EPA mandatory reporting requirements for large carbon dioxide sources require reporting of only Scope 1 emissions from stationary sources. However, many voluntary reporting systems require accounting for all three scopes, such as the ACUPCC reporting. Numerous calculator tools have been developed, some publicly available and some proprietary. For instance many universities use a tool called the Campus Carbon Calculator[71] developed by Clean Air-Cool Planet[72], which is endorsed by the ACUPCC. Numerous northeastern universities collaborated to develop the Campus Carbon Calculator and the calculator has been used at more than 200

---

[70]http://www.nzbcsd.org.nz/climatechange/Climate_Change_Guide.pdf
[71]http://www.cleanair-coolplanet.org/toolkit/inv-calculator.php
[72]http://www.cleanair-coolplanet.org/toolkit/inv-calculator.php

campuses in North America. It utilizes an electronic Microsoft Excel workbook that calculates estimated GHG emissions from the data collected.

9.3.2.1.4.2 Methodology

GHG emissions calculations are generally calculated for the time period of one year. Figure Steps for Preparing a GHG Emissions Report (Figure 9.14) shows the steps for reporting GHG emissions. It is necessary to determine what the baseline year is for calculation. This is the year that is generally used to compare future increases or decreases in emissions, when setting a GHG reduction goal. The Kyoto Protocol[73] proposes accounting for greenhouse gas emissions from a baseline year of 1990. Sometimes calculations may be made for the current year or back to the earliest year that data is available.

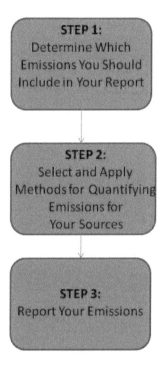

Figure 9.14: Steps for Preparing a GHG Emissions Report Figure shows the required steps to take when preparing a GHG emissions report. *Source: C. Klein-Banai*[74]

Next, the institutional or geographic boundaries need to be defined. Also, the gases that are being reported should be defined. There are six greenhouse gases defined by the Kyoto Protocol. Some greenhouse gases, such as carbon dioxide, occur naturally and are emitted to the atmosphere through natural and **anthropogenic** processes. Other greenhouse gases (e.g. fluorinated gases) are created and emitted solely

---

[73]http://ec.europa.eu/clima/policies/brief/eu/index_en.htm
[74]http://cnx.org/member_profile/cindykb

through human activities. The principal greenhouse gases that enter the atmosphere because of human activities are:

- Carbon Dioxide (CO2)[75] : Carbon dioxide is released to the atmosphere through the combustion of fossil fuels (oil, natural gas, and coal), solid waste, trees and wood products, and also as a result of non-combustion reactions (e.g. manufacture of cement). Carbon dioxide is **sequestered** when plants absorb it as part of the biological carbon cycle.
- Methane (CH4)[76] : Methane is emitted during the production and transport of coal, natural gas, and oil. Methane emissions also come from farm animals and other agricultural practices and the degradation of organic waste in municipal solid waste landfills.
- Nitrous Oxide (N2O)[77] : Nitrous oxide is emitted during agricultural and industrial activities, and combustion of fossil fuels and solid waste.
- Fluorinated Gases[78] : Hydrofluorocarbons, perfluorocarbons, and sulfur hexafluoride are synthetic, powerful greenhouse gases that are emitted from a variety of industrial processes. Fluorinated gases are sometimes used as substitutes for ozone-depleting substances[79] (i.e. Chlorofluorocarbons (CFCs), hydrochlorofluorocarbon (HCFCs), and halons). CFCs and HCFCs are gases comprised of chloride, fluoride, hydrogen, and carbon. Halons are elemental gases that include chlorine, bromine, and fluorine. These gases are typically emitted in smaller quantities, but because they are potent greenhouse gases, they are sometimes referred to as High **Global Warming Potential** gases ("High GWP gases").

Each gas, based on its atmospheric chemistry, captures different amounts of reflected heat thus contributing differently to the greenhouse effect, which is known as its global warming potential. Carbon dioxide, the least capture efficient of these gases, acts as the reference gas with a global warming potential of 1. Table Global Warming Potentials (Table 9.5: Global Warming Potentials) shows the global warming potential for the various GHGs.

---

[75]http://www.epa.gov/climatechange/emissions/co2.html
[76]http://www.epa.gov/methane/sources.html
[77]http://www.epa.gov/nitrousoxide/sources.html
[78]http://www.epa.gov/highgwp/sources.html
[79]http://www.epa.gov/ozone/

Global Warming Potentials

Gas	GWP
CO2	1
CH4	21
N2O	310
HFC-23	11,700
HFC-32	650
HFC-125	2,800
HFC-134a	1,300
HFC-143a	3,800
HFC-152a	140
HFC-227ea	2,900
HFC-236fa	6,300
HFC-4310mee	1,300
CF4	6,500
C2F6	9,200
C4F10	7,000
C6F14	7,400
SF6	23,900

Table 9.5: *Source: C. Klein-Banai [80] created table using data from Climate Change 2007: The Physical Science Basis: Contribution of Working Group I to the Fourth Assessment Report of the Intergovernmental Panel on Climate Change, Cambridge University Press, section 2.10.2* [81]

GHG emissions cannot be easily measured since they come from both mobile and stationary sources. Therefore, emissions must be calculated. Emissions are usually calculated using the formula:

$$A \times F_g = E \tag{9.1}$$

where A is the quantification of an activity in units that can be combined with emission factor of greenhouse gas g (Fg) to obtain the resulting emissions for that gas (Eg).

Examples of activity units include mmbtu (million British Thermal Units) of natural gas, gallons of heating oil, kilowatt hours of electricity, and miles traveled. Total GHG emissions can be expressed as the sum of the emissions for each gas multiplied by its global warming potential (GWP). GHG emissions are usually reported in metric tons of carbon dioxide equivalents (metric tons CO_2-e):

$$GHG = \sum_g E_g GWP_g \tag{9.2}$$

Eg is usually estimated from the quantity of fuel burned using national and regional average emissions factors, such as those provided by the US Department of Energy's Energy Information Administration[82].

---

[80]http://cnx.org/member_profile/cindykb
[81]http://www.ipcc.ch/publications_and_data/ar4/wg1/en/ch2s2-10-2.html
[82]http://www.eia.doe.gov/environment/

Emission factors can be based on government documents and software from the U.S. Department of Transportation[83] , the U.S. Environmental Protection Agency (EPA)[84] , and the U.S. Department of Energy[85] , or from specific characteristics of the fuel used – such as higher heating value and carbon content. Scope 3 emissions that are based on waste, materials, and commuting are more complex to calculate. Various calculators use different inputs to do this and the procedures are less standardized. See Case Study: Comparing Greenhouse Gas Emissions, Ecological Footprint and Sustainability Rating of a University (Section 9.3.3) for an example of these kinds of calculations.

Greenhouse gas emissions inventories are based on standardized practice and include the steps of scoping, calculating, and reporting. They are not based on actual measurements of emissions, rather on calculations based on consumption of greenhouse gas generating materials such as fossil fuels for provision of energy and transportation or emissions from waste disposal. They can be conducted for buildings, institutions, cities, regions, and nations.

9.3.2.1.4.3 Carbon Footprint Comparisons

Comparison of carbon footprints reveal interesting differences between countries, particularly when compared to their economic activity. The World Bank[86] tracks data on countries and regions throughout the world as part of their mission to "fight poverty. . .and to help people help themselves and their environment" (World Bank, 2011 (p. 450)). Table Gross Domestic Product (GDP) and Emissions for Select Regions, 2007 (Table 9.6: Gross Domestic Product (GDP) and Emissions for Select Regions, 2007) shows the results for GHG emissions and **gross domestic product** for various regions of the world. It is interesting to note that the United States' emissions per capita (19.34 mt e-CO_2) are more than four times the world average. The United States' economy makes up one fourth of the world GDP.

Gross Domestic Product (GDP) and Emissions for Select Regions, 2007

Country Name	CO2 emissions (metric ton)	CO2 emissions (metric tons per capita)	GDP (current US$ millions)	GDP per capita (current US$)
East Asia & Pacific (all income levels)	10,241,229	4.76	$11,872,148	$5,514
Europe & Central Asia (all income levels)	6,801,838	7.72	$20,309,468	$23,057
Latin America & Caribbean (all income levels)	1,622,809	2.87	$3,872,324	$6,840
Latin America & Caribbean (developing only)	1,538,059	2.75	$3,700,320	$6,610
				continued on next page

Least developed countries: UN classification	185,889	0.23	$442,336	$553
Middle East & North Africa (all income levels)	1,992,795	5.49	$1,924,470	$5,304
South Asia	1,828,941	1.20	$1,508,635	$991
Sub-Saharan Africa (all income levels)	684,359	0.86	$881,547	$1,102
United States	5,832,194	19.34	$14,061,800	$46,627
World	30,649,360	4.63	$55,853,288	$8,436

Table 9.6: Table shows the GDP and emissions for select regions in 2007. *Source: C. Klein-Banai*[87] *created table using data from The World Bank, "World Development Indicators"*[88]

9.3.2.1.5 Water Footprint

The water footprint of production is the volume of freshwater used by people to produce goods, measured over the full supply chain, as well as the water used in households and industry, specified geographically and temporally. This is slightly different from the hydroprint described above which simply compares the consumption of water by a geographic entity to the water that falls within its watershed. If you look at the hydrologic cycle (see module Water Cycle and Fresh Water Supply (Section 5.2)), water moves through the environment in various ways. The water footprint considers the source of the water as three components:

- Green water footprint: The volume of rainwater that evaporates during the production of goods; for agricultural products, this is the rainwater stored in soil that evaporates from crop fields.
- Blue water footprint: The volume of freshwater withdrawn from surface or groundwater sources that is used by people and not returned; in agricultural products this is mainly accounted for by evaporation of irrigation water from fields, if freshwater is being drawn.
- Grey water footprint: the volume of water required to dilute pollutants released in production processes to such an extent that the quality of the ambient water remains above agreed water quality standards.

The water footprint of an individual is based on the direct and indirect water use of a consumer. Direct water use is from consumption at home for drinking, washing, and watering. Indirect water use results from the freshwater that is used to produce goods and services purchased by the consumer. Similarly, the water footprint of a business or institution is calculated from the direct and indirect water consumption.

---

[87]http://cnx.org/member_profile/cindykb
[88]http://data.worldbank.org/indicator?display=default

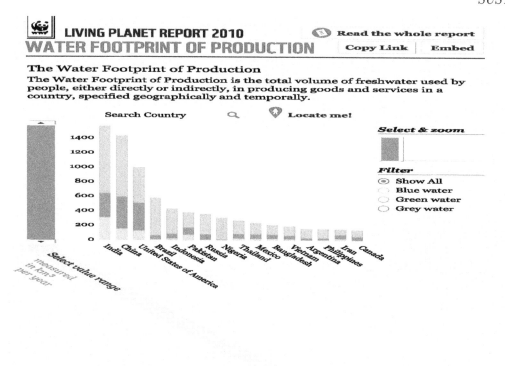

Figure 9.15: Water Footprint of Production of Select Countries Graph shows the water footprint of production of select countries. *Source: ©2010 WWF (panda.org). Some rights reserved.*[89] *Living Planet Report, 2010*[90], *figure under CC BY-SA 3.0 License*[91]

Figure Water Footprint of Production of Select Countries (Figure 9.15) shows the water footprint of production for several countries as a whole. In this report, due to lack of data, one unit of return flow is assumed to pollute one unit of freshwater. Given the negligible volume of water that evaporates during domestic and industrial processes, as opposed to agriculture, only the grey water footprint for households and industry was included. This figure does not account for imports and exports it is only based on the country in which the activities occurred not where they were consumed.

In contrast, the water footprint of a nation accounts for all the freshwater used to produce the goods and services consumed by the inhabitants of the country. Traditionally, water demand (i.e. total water withdrawal for the various sectors of economy) is used to demonstrate water demand for production within a nation. The internal water footprint is the volume of water used from domestic water resources; the external water footprint is the volume of water used in other countries to produce goods and services imported and consumed by the inhabitants of the country. The average water footprint for the United States was calculated to be $2480m^3/cap/yr$, while China has an average footprint of $700m^3/cap/yr$. The global average water footprint is $1240m^3/cap/yr$. As for ecological footprints there are several major factors that determine the water footprint of a country including the volume of consumption (related to the gross national income); consumption pattern (e.g. high versus low meat consumption); climate (growth conditions); and agricultural practice (water use efficiency) (Hoekstra & Chapagain, 2007 (p. 450)).

---

[89]http://www.panda.org/lpr/gwater
[90]http://www.panda.org/lpr/gwater
[91]http://creativecommons.org/licenses/by-sa/3.0/

Using average water consumption for each stage of growth and processing of tea or coffee, the "virtual" water content of a cup can be calculated (Table Virtual Water Content of a Cup of Tea or Coffee (Table 9.7: Virtual Water Content of a Cup of Tea or Coffee)). Much of the water used is from rainfall that might otherwise not be "utilized" to grow a crop and the revenue from the product contributes to the economy of that country. At the same time, the result is that many countries are "importing" water to support the products they consume.

Virtual Water Content of a Cup of Tea or Coffee

Drink	Preparation	Virtual water content (l/cup)
Coffee	Standard cup of coffee	140
	Strong coffee	200
	Instant coffee	80
Tea	Standard cup of tea	34
	Weak tea	17

Table 9.7: Table shows the virtual water content for a cup of tea or coffee. *Source: C. Klein-Banai*[92] *created table using data from Chapagain and Hoekstra (2007)* (p. 450). alt="Virtual Water Content of a Cup of Tea or Coffee" longdesc="Table shows the virtual water content for a cup of tea or coffee."

To learn more about other countries' water footprints, visit this interactive graph[93] . To calculate your own water footprint, visit the Water Footprint Calculator[94] .

The water footprint reveals that much more water is consumed to make a product than appears in using a simple calculation. It is not just the water content of the product but includes all water used in the process to make it and to manage the waste generated from that process.

9.3.2.1.6 Summary

Footprinting tools can be useful ways to present and compare environmental impact. They are useful because they can combine impacts from various activities into one measure. However, they have limitations. For instance, in a carbon footprint or greenhouse gas emissions inventory, many of the "conventional" environmental impacts such as hazardous waste, wastewater, water consumption, stormwater, and toxic emissions are not accounted for, nor are the impacts of resource consumption such as paper, food, and water generally measured. Perhaps most importantly, certain low-carbon fuel sources (e.g. nuclear power) that have other environmental impacts (e.g. nuclear waste) are neglected. Finally, the scope of the emissions inventory does not include upstream emissions from the manufacture or transport of energy or materials. This suggests that there is a need to go beyond just GHG emissions analyses when evaluating sustainability and include all forms of energy and their consequences.

The ecological footprint can be misleading when it is looked at in isolation, for instance with an urban area, the resources needed to support it will not be provided by the actual geographic area since food must be "imported" and carbon offset by natural growth that does not "fit" in a city. However, cities have many other efficiencies and advantages that are not recognized in an ecological footprint. When looked at on a national level it can represent the inequities that exist between countries.

It is interesting to contrast the water and ecological footprints, as well. The water footprint explicitly considers the actual location of the water use, whereas the ecological footprint does not consider the place of land use. Therefore it measures the volumes of water use at the various locations where the water

---

[92]http://cnx.org/member_profile/cindykb
[93]http://www.panda.org/lpr/gwater
[94]http://www.waterfootprint.org/

is appropriated, while the ecological footprint is calculated based on a global average land requirement per consumption category. When the connection is made between place of consumption and locations of resource use, the consumer's responsibility for the impacts of production at distant locations is made evident.

9.3.2.1.7 Review Questions

Question 9.3.2.1
Choose a calculator from the box and calculate your own footprint. How does it compare to the national or global average? What can you do to reduce your footprint?

Question 9.3.2.2
Discuss what kind of inequities the various footprints represent between nations and the types of inequities.

Question 9.3.2.3
How might the "food print" of a vegetarian differ from a carnivore?

9.3.2.1.8 References

Chambers, N., Simmons, C. & Wackernagel, M. (2000). *Sharing Nature's Interest: Ecological Footprints as an Indicator of Sustainability*. London: Earthscan Publications Ltd.

Chapagain, A.K. & Hoekstra, A.Y. (2007). The water footprint of coffee and tea consumption in the Netherlands. *Ecological Economics, 64*, 109-118.

Constanza, R. (2000). The dynamics of the ecological footprint concept. *Ecological Economics,32*, 341-345.

Dawe, G.F.M., Vetter, A. & Martin. S. (2004). An overview of ecological footprinting and other tools and their application to the development of sustainability process. *International Journal of Sustainability in Higher Education, 4*, 340-371.

Flint, K. (2001). Institutional ecological footprint analysis: A case study of the University of Newcastle, Australia. *International Journal of Sustainability in Higher Education, 2*, 48-62.

Hoekstra,Y. & Chapagain, A. K. (2007). Water footprints of nations: Water use by people as a function of their consumption pattern. *Water Resour Manage, 21*, 35-48.

Klein-Banai, C. (2007). Greenhouse gas inventory for the University of Illinois at Chicago. *UIC GHG Inventory,*Retrieved November 21, 2009 from http://www.uic.edu/sustainability/reports/Appendix%206%20GHGEmissionsFY2005-2006.pdf[95]

Rees, W.E. and Wackernagal, M. (1996). Urban ecological footprints and why cities cannot be sustainable – and why they are a key to sustainability. *Environmental Impact Assessment Review, 16*, 223-248.

Venetoulis, J. (2001). Assessing the ecological impact of a university: The ecological footprint for the University of Redlands. *International Journal of Sustainability in Higher Education, 2*, 180-196.

Wackernagel, M., Monfreda, C., Moran, D., Wermer, P., Goldfinger, S., Deumling, D., & Murray, M. (2005, May 25). National footprint and biocapacity accounts 2005: The underlying calculation method. *Global Footprint Network.* Retrieved March 2, 2010 from http://www.footprintnetwork.org/download.php?id=5[96] .

World Bank (2011). About Us. Retrieved September 20, 2011 from http://go.worldbank.org/3QT2P1GNH0[97] .

---

[95]http://www.uic.edu/sustainability/reports/Appendix%206%20GHGEmissionsFY2005-2006.pdf
[96]http://www.footprintnetwork.org/download.php?id=5
[97]http://go.worldbank.org/3QT2P1GNH0

9.3.3 Case Study: Comparing Greenhouse Gas Emissions, Ecological Footprint and Sustainability Rating of a University[98]

9.3.3.1 Case Study: Comparing Greenhouse Gas Emissions, Ecological Footprint and Sustainability Rating of a University

How do different measures of sustainability compare when looking at one institution? This case study compares these different measures for the University of Illinois at Chicago (UIC). Located just southwest of downtown Chicago, UIC has 13 colleges serving 27,000 students and 12,000 employees, with over 100 buildings on 240 acres (97 hectares) of land. The activities of the faculty, staff and students and the buildings and grounds have an impact on the sustainability of the institution. This case study will look at the results of the greenhouse gas emission inventory, ecology footprint, and sustainability rating.

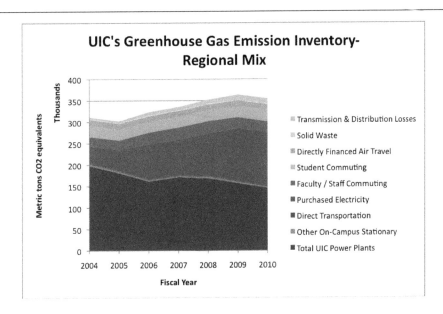

Figure 9.16: Greenhouse Gas Emissions Inventory UIC's Greenhouse gas emissions profile for FY2004-2010, using the regional mix for purchased electricity. *Source: C. Klein-Banai*[99]

Figure Greenhouse Gas Emissions Inventory (Figure 9.16) displays UIC's GHG emissions profile for seven years. The emissions were calculated using the Campus Carbon Calculator[100] developed by the not-for-profit organization, Clean Air-Cool Planet. While this tool has a number of limitations it has been used by many of the over 670 colleges and universities who are signatory to the American College and University Presidents Climate Commitment[101] (ACUPCC) to simplify the emissions inventory profile. The tool is also recommended by the ACUPCC as a standard method of emissions calculation for United States universities. It is based on the World Resources Institute (WRI) and World Business Council for Sustainable Development (WBSCD) Greenhouse Gas (GHG) Protocol Initiative[102] that developed GHG emissions inventory standards. UIC's emissions were calculated using the regional average electricity sources for the electric grid servicing

---

[98]This content is available online at <http://legacy.cnx.org/content/m41605/1.4/>.

[99]http://cnx.org/member_profile/cindykb

[100]http://www.cleanair-coolplanet.org/toolkit/inv-calculator.php

[101]http://www.presidentsclimatecommitment.org/about/commitment

[102]http://www.ghgprotocol.org/

the Chicago area. However, until August of 2009, UIC purchased electricity from Commonwealth Edison which has a much lower greenhouse gas emissions factor due to the high percentage of nuclear power in the Chicago region.

UIC operates two combined heat and power plants. However, the university has increasingly lowered its production of electricity from natural gas by purchasing more electricity through block purchases (for defined amounts of electricity for a certain period of time) due to the relatively low cost of purchasing electricity as compared to self-generating. This strategy has increased UIC's emissions as the regional mix has a fair amount of coal-powered plants providing electricity. Nevertheless, a downward trend in emissions is beginning in spite of the increased electricity purchases between 2009 and 2010. This may be due to overall reduction in energy consumption on campus, which is reducing the GHG emissions.

Figure Breakdown of UIC's Greenhouse Gas Emissions (Figure 9.17) illustrates the relative contribution to UIC's 2010 emissions profile, with 77 percent of emissions coming from buildings (power plants, purchased electricity, and other on-campus stationary, i.e. natural gas supply to the buildings), 20 percent due to transportation (campus fleet , commuting to campus, and air travel), and less than one percent for emissions due to waste sent to the landfill (which generates methane).

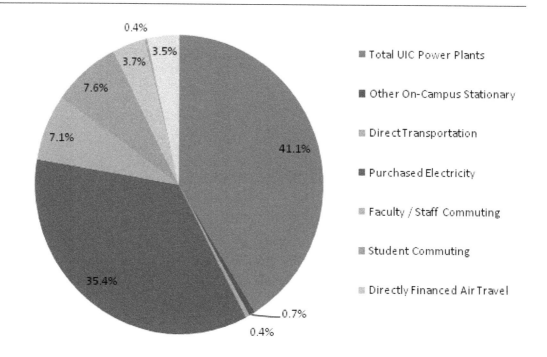

Figure 9.17: Breakdown of UIC's Greenhouse Gas Emissions Figure shows the breakdown of UIC's greenhouse gas emissions inventory for the fiscal year 2010, in metric tons of carbon dioxide equivalents (mt CO_2-e). Total emissions: 354,758 mt CO_2-e. *Source: C. Klein-Banai*[103]

UIC's total emissions for fiscal year 2010 were 354,758 mt CO_2-e, which amounts to 13.14 mt CO_2-e per full-time equivalent student enrolled. Table Comparison of GHG Emissions (Table 9.8: Comparison of GHG Emissions) compares UIC's emissions to those of the city of Chicago, state of Illinois, and the United States.

---

[103]http://legacy.cnx.org/content/m41605/latest/ http://cnx.org/member_profile/cindykb

Comparison of GHG Emissions

Entity	GHG emissions, million MT CO 2 -e	Most Recent Year Reported
US	6,633.20	2009
Illinois	274.9	2003
Chicago	36.2	2005
UIC	0.4	2010

Table 9.8: *Sources: C. Klein-Banai*[104] *created table using data from UIC Climate Action Plan, Chicago Climate Action Plan, U.S. EPA.*

An Ecological Footprint Analysis (EFA) was conducted using data from fiscal year 2008, including much of the same data used for the GHG emissions inventory. In addition, water, food, recycling, and built-up land data were used to calculate the number of global hectares required to provide the resources and absorb the waste and GHG emissions produced to support UIC's activities. The results are displayed in Table UIC's Ecological Footprint Using FY2008 Data (Table 9.9: UIC's Ecological Footprint Using FY2008 Data). The total footprint was 97,601 global hectares, on a per capita basis this is equivalent to 2.66 gha/person. This is in contrast to about 8.00 gha/person nationally in the United States, although one must use caution in making comparisons because the scope and methodology of the analysis differ.

UIC's Ecological Footprint Using FY2008 Data

Category	Global Hectares	Percent
Energy	70,916	72.7%
Transportation	12,293	12.6%
Water	139	0.1%
Materials and waste	11,547	11.8%
Built-up land	172	0.2%
Food	2,533	2.6%
TOTAL, Global Hectares	**97,601**	**100.0%**

Table 9.9: Composite Indicator: Sustainability Tracking, Assessment and Rating System. *Source: C. Klein-Banai*[105] .

The STARS system (see module Sustainability Metrics and Rating Systems (Section 9.3.1)) was used to rate UIC. The university received 39.1 points, for a Bronze rating. The points break down into the categories shown in Table STARS Points Received by UIC by Category (Table 9.10: STARS Points Received by UIC by Category). There are three main categories of points – Education & Research; Operations; and Planning, Administration & Engagement. Within each of the categories there are sub-categories such as Curriculum, Climate, and Coordination & Planning. Within those sub-categories there are specific strategies that address them, with varying amounts of points that depend on the assessed weight of each strategy. Each category's individual percentage score is weighted equally to the others. In addition, four innovation strategies are available for which an institution can receive one point. These points are not attributed to a particular category.

---

[104]http://cnx.org/member_profile/cindykb
[105]http://cnx.org/member_profile/cindykb

STARS Points Received by UIC by Category

Points	Received	Possible	% Per Category	Weight
Education & Research			38.61%	33.33/100
Co-Curricular Education	11.75	18.00		
Curriculum	18.89	55.00		
Research	7.97	27.00		
Operations			23.78%	33.33/100
Buildings	0.23	13.00		
Climate	1.75	16.50		
Dining Services	1.25	8.50		
Energy	3.44	16.50		
Grounds	1.00	3.25		
Purchasing	1.76	7.50		
Transportation	5.71	12.00		
Waste	6.89	12.50		
Water	1.75	10.25		
Planning, Administration & Engagement			54.91%	33.33/100
Coordination and Planning	15.00	18.00		
Diversity and Affordability	13.50	13.75		
Human Resources	19.75	19.75		
Investment	0.00	16.75		
Public Engagement	6.66	31.75		
Innovation	0.00	4.00		

Table 9.10: *Source: C. Klein-Banai[106] with data from STARS[107]*

This reporting system shows that UIC's strengths lie in the areas outside of operations, which are what is measured with an EFA or GHG emissions inventory. Most points were gained for Planning, Administration & Engagement. This rating system can be used to identify specific areas that can be targeted for advancing sustainability initiatives in a much broader realm than the other two metric allow. This case study demonstrates the different types of information and sustainability tracking that can be done using different types of measures of sustainability. Whether you use one measure or several depends on the purpose and scope of the sustainability reporting.

9.3.3.1.1 References

Klein-Banai, C, Theis, T.L., Brecheisen, T.A. & Banai, A. (2010). A Greenhouse Gas Inventory as a Measure of Sustainability for an Urban Public Research University, *Environmental Practice*, *12*, 25-47.

Klein-Banai, C & Theis, T.L. (2011). An urban university's ecological footprint and the effect of climate change, *Ecological Indicators*, *11*, 857–860.

---

[106]http://cnx.org/member_profile/cindykb
[107]https://stars.aashe.org/institutions/university-of-illinois-chicago-il/report/2011-01-31/

UIC Office of Sustainability. (2011). *State of Sustainability Univer-sity of Illinois at Chicago Biennial Report.* Retrieved May 30, 2011 from http://www.uic.edu/sustainability/reports/UIC.STARS_report.2010.pdf[108] .

9.3.4 Food Miles[109]

9.3.4.1 Learning Objectives

After reading this module, students should be able to

- understand what food miles are and why they are used.
- compare the strengths and limitations of the use of food miles.
- explore the implications of food miles in decision-making strategies.

9.3.4.2 Introduction

Efforts to explore the impacts of the items on our dinner tables led to the broad concept of **food miles** (the distance food travels from production to consumption) as being a quick and convenient way to com-pare products. With increasing globalization, our plates have progressively included food items from other continents. Previously it would have been too expensive to transport these products. However, changes to agricultural practices, transportation infrastructure, and distribution methods now mean that people in the United States can start the day with coffee from Brazil, have a pasta lunch topped with Italian cheeses, snack on chocolate from Côte d'Ivoire, and end with a dinner of Mediterranean bluefin tuna and Thai rice. How-ever, the globalization that has led to increased availability of these products comes with associated costs, such as the emission of greenhouse gases and other pollutants, increased traffic congestion, lack of support for local economies, less fresh food, and decreased **food security**. Therefore, the concept of measuring food miles was meant to provide an easy comparison of the relative impacts of our food choices.

Many individuals, groups, and businesses today measure or calculate food miles. But, when Andrea Paxton, a U.K.-based environmental activist, coined the term in the 1990s the concept of food miles was intended to encompass more than simply a distance. The point was to broaden awareness that our food choices have consequences that are often not apparent. Consumers frequently do not know the histories be-hind their food purchases, and markets often cannot supply the information because of the many production processes and distribution methods used.

While the distance food travels does determine some of the environmental, social, and economic impacts, there can be other hidden consequences not so easily measured. Exploration of the utility of food miles in the general sense of knowing the impacts of our purchasing decisions has resulted in a broadening awareness of the complexity of globalization. Although consumers can use the easy-to-compare numbers representing food miles, that metric cannot reflect all of the impacts of food purchasing decisions.

9.3.4.3 Calculating Food Miles

In some cases it is easy to use food miles, such as comparing two watermelons grown using the same methods and both transported by truck to your store. However, many of our food products contain components with different origins. In that case, food miles are calculated as a weighted average to create a single number that takes into consideration the weight and distance of each item. For example, to calculate the food miles for a simple fruit salad that contains only apples, bananas, and honey, you need to know the distance that each ingredient traveled to reach your market and the relative amount of each product. Figure **Food Miles for Fruit Salad** (Figure 9.18) illustrates the food miles for this simple fruit salad.

---

[108]http://www.uic.edu/sustainability/reports/UIC.STARS_report.2010.pdf
[109]This content is available online at <http://legacy.cnx.org/content/m38680/1.4/>.

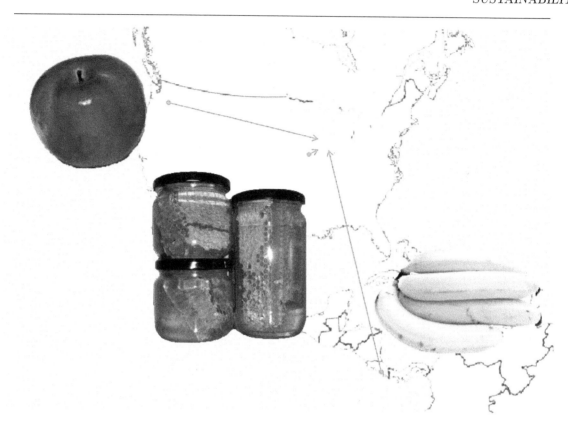

Figure 9.18: Food Miles for Fruit Salad The various ingredients in this simple fruit salad travel different distances to Illinois' supermarkets. *Source. D. Ruez adapted from TUBS*[110], *akarlovic*[111], *Fir0002*[112], *and Abrahami*[113]

Most of our food from supermarkets is marked with a country or state of origin. That alone is usually enough to get an estimate of the distance, especially if the location can be narrowed down by finding out the part of the country or state that most commonly produces the product. If the fruit salad in Figure **Food Miles for Fruit Salad** (Figure 9.18) is being made in Chicago, Illinois, and the apples are from the state of Washington, the likely origin is in the center part of the state. The travel distance is approximately 2,000 miles (3,219 km). Bananas from Costa Rica traveled about 2,400 miles (3,862 km) to Chicago, and there are honey producers only 160 miles (257 km) from Chicago. A simple average of the miles the ingredients traveled would not take into account that the fruit salad probably would not contain equal amounts of the three items. If the recipe called for 2 pounds (.9 kg) of apples, 2 pounds (.9 kg) of bananas, and a $\frac{1}{4}$ pound (.1 kg) of honey, the miles would be weighted toward the distances traveled by the fruit: 2080 food miles per pound of fruit salad (or 3,347 km/kg of fruit salad).

---

[110]http://commons.wikimedia.org/wiki/File:BLANK_in_North_America_%28-mini_map_-rivers%29.svg
[111]http://commons.wikimedia.org/wiki/File:Med_u_sacu_karlovic1.jpg
[112]http://commons.wikimedia.org/wiki/File:Bananas_white_background.jpg
[113]http://commons.wikimedia.org/wiki/File:Cortland_apples.jpg

9.3.4.4 Benefits

The benefits of using food miles in evaluating food choices match the three main categories that represent sustainability: environmental, social, and economic. All methods of transporting food over long distances, and most methods used to transport over short distances, involve fossil fuels. Burning of fossil fuels creates greenhouse gases, which contribute to climate change. Using fossil fuels also results in the emission of other gases and particulates that degrade air quality. Longer transportation distances intensify traffic congestion, resulting in lost productivity, and increase the need for more extensive infrastructure (such as more highways) that negatively impact the environment by increasing the amount of impervious cover and by requiring more natural resources. Increased roadways also encourage sprawl, leading to more inefficient development patterns. Finally, traffic congestion and air pollution from driving contribute to an estimated 900,000 fatalities per year worldwide.

Use of food miles is often tied to **locavore** movements, which emphasizes consumption of locally-grown food products. Local food is usually fresher, with harvesting waiting until produce is ripe, and has less processing and fewer preservatives. Many people think locally-grown food tastes better, but others chose to be a locavore because it strengthens local cultural identity or because the safety of the food is being controlled by people who also consume the products themselves. Eating local foods also promotes food security because availability and price of imported foods is more dependent on fluctuating fuel costs and sociopolitical conflicts elsewhere.

The production of food in developing countries, and the subsequent exporting of those products, has several types of impacts. The environmental burden of soil degradation, water depletion, and others, are imposed on developing countries, while more prosperous countries enjoy the benefits. This can be especially problematic because some developing countries do not have the policies to require, or the resources to implement, more environmentally-friendly food production practices. In particular, the low prices paid to food producers in developing countries do not include sufficient funds, or requirements, for practices to preserve or restore ecosystem quality. Moreover, developing countries disproportionately suffer malnutrition, yet the success of large-scale transport of food encourages cultivation of products to be exported instead of planting nutritious foods to be self-sustaining.

Some businesses are embracing the basic concepts of food miles because transporting food over shorter distances uses less fuel, and is therefore cheaper. Additionally, food that covers longer distances usually requires more packaging, which adds to the cost. By focusing on local foods, local economies are supported. This has led to clearer labeling of food products, giving consumers the ability to make more informed decisions about their purchases.

9.3.4.5 Criticism

Although the concept of food miles is useful, it has been heavily criticized for being too simplistic. For example, all miles are not created equally. The consumption of fuel varies by the mode of transportation and the amount being moved. If you compare the consumption required to move one pound of a product, ocean freighters are the most efficient of the common methods, followed by trains, trucks, and finally planes. When a combination of transportation methods is used, making a comparison with food miles becomes even more complex. This is especially a problem because most of us drive a personal vehicle to get our groceries. That means that it may be more efficient (from a total fuel consumption perspective) to drive 1 mile (1.6 km) to a local supermarket who imports beef from Australia, than to drive 40 miles (64 km) to visit a market selling locally-produced beef.

Food miles also do not take into consideration the variables of production before the products are transported. Growing outdoors requires different amounts of energy input than greenhouses. A commonly cited example is that of tomatoes; heating greenhouses to grow tomatoes in the United Kingdom consumes much more energy than growing tomatoes in warm Spain and importing them. Use of chemical fertilizers and pesticides affect environmental quality and production levels differently than organic farming. Because soil quality varies, locally-grown foods, in some cases, require more of the chemical additives. Some areas may have newer equipment, better climate, increased access to water, or other factors that determine the overall efficiency of food production. Growing rice in deserts or oranges in the Arctic would have more environmental impacts than the transportation of those products from locales where they can be grown more efficiently (from both an environmental and economic perspective). Understanding these production variables is critical because several recent studies have suggested that as much as 80% of greenhouse-gas generation from food consumption comes from the production phase. See References (Section 9.3.4.9: References) for further reading.

There are also benefits to globalization and increased transport of food. There is now more widespread access to a broader range of food products. This can lead to increased appreciation for other cultures and greater international cooperation. Long-distance transport of food products can also provide jobs to developing nations by giving them access to larger, more prosperous markets internationally. Jobs and economic incentives from food production are some of the few widespread opportunities for developing countries, and these may lead to growth in other economic areas.

Criticism of the use of food miles can be unfairly disapproving of products that travel long distances. However, simple calculations of food miles have also been said to underrepresent the importance of travel distances. Most food is transported with some packaging, and that packaging also requires energy input for its production and transport. Because products that move shorter distances usually have less packaging, the difference in calculated food miles may underestimate the actual environmental impact. Local foods also require less energy and resource consumption because of reduced need for transportation infrastructure, chemical additives and preservatives, and refrigeration.

The impacts during the production phase also vary between types of foods, which can also result in underestimates of the impacts. Production of meats, especially red meats, requires large amounts of land to generate the crops needed for animal feed. Because not all energy is passed from feed to the animal, using meats for our food is inefficient from an energy perspective. It takes over 8 pounds of grain to feed a cow enough to generate 1 pound of weight gain. That grain must be grown on land that can long longer produce food directly for human consumption. The amount of land required to produce animal feed is known as **ghost acres**. Ghost acres also extend to the areas required to provide the fuel, water, and other resources needed for animal feed, and for the overall support of animals[114]. While some other meats such as pork, poultry, and especially fish, use proportionally less feed, there are other concerns about the environmental impacts of diets with large amounts of meat.

Confined animal feeding operations (CAFOs), high-density animal farms, have become the primary source of livestock for meat in the U.S., Europe, and many other countries. The technological innovations employed in these operations have increased the speed and volume of meat production, but have raised health concerns. Antibiotics and hormones used increasingly on animals in CAFOs may be passed on to humans during consumption, even though there is currently no way of knowing a safe level of those substances in our diets. The overuse of antibiotics in CAFOs also results in antibiotic-resistant pathogens. In addition to the impacts from the ghost acres, there are other ecological impacts such as pollution from massive amounts of concentrated manure. Although the distance meat is transported has an environmental impact, the other concerns are more significant.

---

[114]In other environmental contexts, ghost acres refer more broadly to all land areas being used indirectly to support human activity and areas not usable due to other human influences

Figure 9.19: Confined Animal Feeding Operations (CAFOs) This image shows a CAFO for cattle. CAFOs have raised health concerns for human consumption of the meat produced in them. *Source: eutrophication&hypoxia*[115]

9.3.4.6 Implementation

The ongoing investigations of food miles have affected businesses, groups, and individuals in various ways. As mentioned above, paying closer attention to the distance food travels can be a good business strategy because fuel costs money. Centralization of processing and distribution centers in the United States has resulted in a relative frequent occurrence of shipping produce thousands of miles only to end up in supermarkets back near its origin. In many cases the initial savings from building fewer centralized facilities is exceeded in the long-term by the continual shipping costs. As a result, some retailers are encouraging outside scrutiny of their habits, because it can result in increased profits. At the other extreme, the rise in food miles in some cases is driven entirely by money. Fish caught offshore Norway and the United Kingdom, for example, is sent to China for cheaper processing before being returned to European markets.

An awareness of the impact of food miles has led to many groups advocating local foods. Local farmers' markets have appeared and expanded around the United States and elsewhere, providing increased access to fresh foods. **Community-supported agriculture** programs create share-holders out of consumers,

---

[115]http://www.flickr.com/photos/48722974@N07/5249420021/in/photostream/

making them more personally invested in the success of local economies, while farmers gain some financial security. Campaigns by community groups are influencing retailers and restaurants by scrutinizing the food-purchasing decisions. The reciprocal is also true as retailers and restaurants advertise their sustainability efforts. See Resources (Section 9.3.4.10: Resources for locating farmers' markets in Illinois:) for examples of local farmers' markets in Illinois.

Figure 9.20: **Illinois Farmer's Market** Colorful produce at an Illinois farmer's market. *Source: Maycomb Paynes*[116]

Yet, there are challenges to the implementation of food miles as a concept. Suppliers, such as individual farmers, might opt for the reliable annual purchase from a mass-distributor. Consumers might make decisions solely on the sticker price, not knowing the other impacts, or consumers might know the impacts but choose the immediate economic incentive. Some of these challenges can be addressed by education. This can include efforts such as eco-labeling – labels, often by third parties, that independently attest to the environmental claims of products. This can influence some consumers, but larger buyers like school systems and restaurant chains may require other incentives to change purchasing practices. The source of these incentives, or alternatively, regulations, might come from government agencies, especially those with desires to support local economies. However, there is no consensus regarding who should be evaluating and monitoring food miles.

---

[116]http://www.flickr.com/photos/24730945@N03/5025234118/

9.3.4.7 Summary

The criticisms of food miles are valid, and work is continually being done incorporate the many factors that more completely show the environmental impacts of transporting food. This can be a time consuming process, and the many variables are usually not readily available to consumers. A frozen pizza might contain many types of ingredients from various areas that are transported to individual processing plants before being assembled in another location and forwarded to distribution centers before being shipped to stores. Even if this process is eventually simplified, eating decisions should not be made solely on the basis of food miles, which cannot account for the variations in transportation and production methods or the social and economic impacts.

This does not mean that food miles are never a useful tool. When comparing similar products (e.g., onions to onions) with other similar externalities (e.g., production and transportation methods), food miles provide a convenient way for consumers to begin to make informed decisions about their purchases. Even though food transportation is a relatively small portion of the overall impact of our food consumption, changes to any phase of the process can have a positive additive effect and make a real contribution to environmental health. Moreover, most of the benefits for using food miles can likewise apply to many of our non-food purchases, with allowances for some of the same drawbacks. Additionally, the discussion could be expanded to include other kinds of decisions, such as where to live in relation to location of job, and where to take a vacation. In general, the concept of food miles reflects the need to understand how hidden influences generate environmental, social, and economic impacts.

9.3.4.8 Review Questions

Question 9.3.4.1
What are some of the problems with comparing food miles for a cheeseburger to those for a vegetarian salad?

Question 9.3.4.2
Why might food producers in isolated but prosperous areas (like Hawaii or New Zealand) argue against the use of food miles?

Question 9.3.4.3
Do you think increased reliance on food miles is good or bad for rural areas in developing countries? Explain your decision.

9.3.4.9 References

Cleveland, D. A., Radka, C. N., Müller, N. M., Watson, T. D., Rekstein, N. J., Wright, H. V. M., et al. (2011). Effect of localizing fruit and vegetable consumption on greenhouse gas emissions and nutrition, Santa Barbara County. *Environmental Science & Technology*, 45,4555-4562. doi: 10.1021/es1040317

Saunders, C., Barber, A., & Taylor, G. (2006). Food miles – comparative energy/emissions performance of New Zealand's Agriculture Industry. *Lincoln University Agribusiness & Economics Research Unit Research Report*, 285, 1-105.

Weber, C. L., & Matthews, H. S. (2008). Food-miles and the relative climate impacts of food choices in the United States. *Environmental Science & Technology*, 42, 3508-3513. doi: 10.1021/es702969f

9.3.4.10 Resources for locating farmers' markets in Illinois:

- Local Harvest http://www.localharvest.org[117]
- Illinois Stewardship Alliance http://www.ilstewards.org[118]

---

[117]http://www.localharvest.org/
[118]http://www.ilstewards.org/

- Slow Food Chicago http://www.slowfoodchicago.org[119]
- Illinois Farmers Markets, Illinois Department of Agriculture http://www.agr.state.il.us/markets/farmers/[120]

9.3.5 Environmental Performance Indicators[121]

9.3.5.1 Learning Objectives

After reading this module, students should be able to

- understand the data included in creating an environmental performance indicator
- be able to state some general strengths and weaknesses of the environmental sustainability index and emergy performance index
- know the differences between some of the major environmental performance indicators

9.3.5.2 Introduction

Because there are so many types of environmental problems, there are many projects designed to address these concerns and likewise many methods to assess them. Collectively, the methods for assessing environmental impactsand the uses of natural resources (both living and non-living) are called **environmental performance indicators**. Generally, performance indicators are used in fields ranging from marketing and economics to education and legal studies to measure a project's progress and/or success. Some indicators can evaluate the actions of a single individual, while others are broad enough to reflect the efforts of entire nations or even the globe. Specifically, **environmental performance indicators (EPIs)** examine environmental issues such as pollution, biodiversity, climate, energy, erosion, ecosystem services, environmental education, and many others. Without these EPIs, the success or failure of even the most well-intentioned actions can remain hidden.

Because of the diversity of observational scales and topics, not all EPIs are useful in all scenarios. However, all EPIs should indicate whether the state of the environment is changed positively or negatively, and they should provide a measure of that change. An EPI is also more meaningful if it can quantify the results to facilitate comparison between different types of activities. But before an EPI is selected, targets and baselines must be clearly articulated. Vague targets are difficult to evaluate, and the results may be uninformative. The EPI selected must use indicators that are definitively linked to the targets, are reliable and repeatable, and can be generated in a cost and time efficient manner.

To evaluate an activity, an EPI needs to include information from up to four types of indicators: **inputs**, **outputs**, **outcomes**, and **impacts**. Inputs are the natural resources or ecosystem services being used. Outputs are the goods or services that result from that activity. While outputs can often be quantified, outcomes typically cannot be and instead represent environmental, social, and economic dimensions of well-being. In some cases it is useful to think of outcomes as why an output was sought; however, outcomes can also be unanticipated or unwanted effects of an output. Impacts refer to the longer-term and more extensive results of the outcomes and outputs, and can include the interaction of the latter two indicators.

For example, coal can be an input for an electricity-generating plant because we need the output (electricity) to turn on lights in our homes. Two outcomes would include the ability to read at night because of the electricity and the visible air pollution from the power plant smoke stacks. An impact of being able to read more can be a better-educated person, while an impact of the greenhouse gas emissions from burning coal is increased potential for global climate change. This is a simplistic example which does not include the majority of relevant indicators (inputs, outputs, outcomes, and impacts) for a complete and more meaningful analysis.

---

[119]http://www.slowfoodchicago.org/
[120]http://www.agr.state.il.us/markets/farmers/
[121]This content is available online at <http://legacy.cnx.org/content/m38877/1.5/>.

We can then evaluate each of the indicators. Is the input (coal) an appropriate choice? Is there enough for the practice of burning it to continue? Are there problems, such as political instability that could interrupt continued access? Does the output (electricity) sufficiently address the problem (in this case, energy for turning on lights)? Is the output produced and delivered in a timely manner? Is it provided to the appropriate consumers and in a quantity that is large enough? Does the output create the desired outcome (being able to read at night)? Does it also result in unwanted outcomes (air pollution)? Do the outcomes result in long-term impacts (such as life-long learning or decade-long climate change) that are widespread?

Note that outcomes and impacts can be either positive or negative. The strength of an EPI lies in its ability to look at the bigger picture and include multiple variables – particularly with regard to the impacts. However, whether an impact is considered meaningful depends on the values and perspectives of the individuals and groups involved. Judgment plays a role because of the difficulty in comparing completely different impacts. How do you compare life-long learning and climate change in the above example about the use of coal?

9.3.5.3 Uses

Monitoring the impacts of both short-term and long-term activities with EPIs allows decision makers to make changes that result in performance with lesser environmental impacts. In some cases, changes can be made to ongoing projects, or the results of an EPI can be used for publicity if the performance data indicate the activity is environmentally-sound. In other cases, the EPI establishes a performance benchmark against which other projects are measured, or the results are used in the strategic planning phase while projects are in development. In this way, past successes and failures can both be incorporated into future plans.

Use of EPIs requires production of multiple data points. A single application of an EPI does not mean much until placed into a larger context. For example, an EPI might evaluate the impact of your city's recycling efforts (see Figure **Municipal Solid Waste Recycling Rates** (Figure 9.21)), but that result can be difficult to interpret without additional data that can be presented in multiple ways:

- Absolute values: Is the impact greater or less than that of other cities? How does the total cost of the recycling program compare?
- Normalized values: How does the per person impact compare to another city, country, business, etc.? What is the amount of aluminum recycled per dollar spent on recycling?
- Trends: Is your city improving, or is the progress your city sees in recycling better than that that of other cities? This could be asked of either absolute or normalized data: Is the total amount of aluminum recycled in your city increasing? Is the per-person amount of aluminum recycled in your city increasing?

Figure 9.21: Municipal Solid Waste Recycling Rates Municipal solid waste recycling rates in the United States from 1960-2007. *Source: EPA*[122]

9.3.5.4 Major EPI Areas

Most EPIs focus on one or a few categories of environmental problems and do not attempt to be all-inclusive methods of evaluating sustainability. A few of the more common categories are briefly described below.

Biodiversity is the number and variety of forms of life, and can be calculated for a particular tree, an ecosystem, a nation, or even the planet. Food, fuel, recreation, and other ecosystem services are dependent on maintaining biodiversity. However, biodiversity is threatened by overuse and habitat destruction (see Figure **Endangered Animals** (Figure 9.22)). Because the actual number of species alive is not known, biodiversity indicators often use proxy data. These include patterns of habitat preservation and resource use, because they are the primary factors influencing biodiversity. The better-known groups of organisms, such as birds and mammals, are also monitored for a direct count of biodiversity, but vertebrates are a tiny proportion of life and cannot accurately reflect changes in all species.

[122]http://commons.wikimedia.org/wiki/File:EPA_2007_MSW_recycling_rates.gif

Number of globally threatened mammal species in each country in 2000

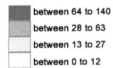

between 64 to 140

between 28 to 63

between 13 to 27

between 0 to 12

Figure 9.22: Endangered Animals Illustration shows the number of endangered animals in each country of the world. *Source: World Atlas of Biodiversity*[123]

Wood is harvested for timber and fuel, but forests are also cleared for agricultural fields and housing developments. Such deforestation frequently leads to rapid soil erosion and extinctions. Cutting of forests also results in changes to the water cycle, altering precipitation patterns and rates, and nutrient cycles, such as the release of carbon dioxide into the atmosphere. At the same time as deforestation takes its toll in places, trees are being planted elsewhere. Developed countries are increasing their forested areas, but this is commonly being done at the expense of developing countries, which are exporting their wood (see Figure **Deforestation at the Haiti/Dominican Republic Border** (Figure 9.23)). Forestry indicators in EPIs include the annual change in forested areas, but can be broken down into the types of forests because each has different environmental impacts. Another indicator is the use of non-sustainable wood resources. Tree farms and some harvesting methods provide renewable supplies of wood, while clear-cutting tropical forests does not. Irresponsible wood harvesting produces negative results for ecosystem health.

[123]http://commons.wikimedia.org/wiki/File:EspecesMammiferesMenacees_fr.svg

Figure 9.23: Deforestation at the Haiti/Dominican Republic Border Satellite photograph
show deforestation of Haiti (on the left) at the border with the Dominican Republic (on the right).
Deforestation on the Haitian side of the border is much more severe. *Source: NASA*[124]

Air, water, and land pollution directly, and adversely, impacts human and ecosystem health. It also has
economic consequences from the damage of natural resources and human structures. In many cases the level
of pollutants can be measured either in the environment or at the point of emissions. Additional indicators
include whether pollution monitoring even occurs, to what extent legal maximum levels are enforced, and
whether regulations are in place to clean up the damage. Visit the EPA's MyEnvironment[125] application to
learn more about environmental issues in your area.

Greenhouse gas emissions and ozone depletion are results of air pollution, but are frequently placed
in a separate category because they have global impacts regardless of the source of the problem. Levels
of greenhouse gases and ozone-depleting substances in the atmosphere can be measured directly, or their
impacts can be measured by looking at temperature change and the size of the ozone hole. However, those
methods are rarely part of EPIs because they do not assign a particular source. Instead, EPIs include the
actual emissions by a particular process or area.

---

[124]http://commons.wikimedia.org/wiki/File:Haiti_deforestation.jpg
[125]http://www.epa.gov/myenvironment/

9.3.5.5 Examples of EPIs

There are dozens of EPIs that can be used to evaluate sustainability. Below are two examples of multi-component methods that allow comparisons at a national level, which is necessary for promoting many types of systemic change.

9.3.5.5.1 Environmental Sustainability Index

The **environmental sustainability index (ESI)** was created as a joint effort of Yale and Columbia universities in order to have a way to compare the sustainability efforts and abilities of countries. Visit the ESI website[126] for more information such as maps and data. First presented in 2000 at the World Economic Forum, the ESI has quickly gained popularity because it aids decision-making by providing clear comparisons of environmental statistics. The basic assumption of the ESI is that sustainable development, the use of resources in a way to meet societal, economic, and environmental demands for the long-term, requires a multi-faceted approach. Specifically, the ESI uses 76 variables to create 21 indicators of sustainability.

The indicators cover five categories, with each description below indicating the condition that is more sustainable:

- environmental systems – maintaining and improving ecosystem health
- reducing environmental stress – reducing anthropogenic stress on the environment
- reducing human vulnerability – having fewer negative impacts on people from the environment
- capacity to respond to environmental challenges – fostering social infrastructures that establish ability and desire to respond effectively to environmental challenges
- global stewardship efforts – cooperating with other countries to address environmental problems.

The ESI scores range from 0, least sustainable, to 100, most sustainable, and is an equally-weighted average of the 21 individual indicators. The highest-ranked countries in 2005 (Finland, Norway, Uruguay, Sweden, and Iceland) all had in common abundant natural resources and low human-population densities. At the other extreme, the lowest-ranked countries (North Korea, Iraq, Taiwan, Turkmenistan, and Uzbekistan) had fewer natural resources, particularly when compared per capita, and have made policy decisions often against their own long-term best interests. However, it is important to note that most countries do not excel, or fail, with regard to all 21 indicators; every nation has room for improvement. Each country will also have its own environmental priorities, attitudes, opportunities, and challenges. For example, the United States scores high in the capacity to respond to environmental challenges, but low in actually reducing environmental stress.

ESI scores have sparked some healthy competition between nations; no one wants to be seen as under-performing compared to their peers. After the pilot ESI rankings in 2000 and the first full ESI rankings in 2002, Belgium, Mexico, the Philippines, South Korea, and the United Arab Emirates, all initiated major internal reviews that resulted in the initiation of efforts to improve environmental sustainability. Because ESI data are presented not only as an overall average but also as 21 independent indicators, countries can focus their efforts where most improvement could be made. Countries dissatisfied with their rankings have also begun to make more of their environmental data accessible. Initial rankings by ESI score had missing or estimated data in many cases, but by making more data available, more accurate overall assessments are possible. For example, the Global Environmental Monitoring System Water Program, an important source of water quality information, had data contributions increase from less than 40 countries to over 100 as a result of the ESI.

Several similar ranking methodologies have emerged from the ESI. They vary in the number and type of variables included and indicators produced. Some also calculate an overall average by weighting some indicators more than others. However, they all share the same 0-100 scale and have individual indicators that allow targeted improvement of the overall scores.

---

[126]http://sedac.ciesin.columbia.edu/es/esi/

9.3.5.5.2 Emergy Performance Index

One drawback of the ESI is that the indicators measure items as different as percentage of endangered animals, recycling rates, government corruption, and child mortality rates. The scope of the variables has been criticized because they may not be comparable in importance, and many others could be added. The term, **emergy**, is a contraction of EMbodied enERGY. The **emergy performance index (EMPI)** differs in omitting the social variables, and instead creates a single unit that can be used to describe the production and use of any natural or anthropogenic resource.

The first step of calculating EMPI is to inventory all material and energy inputs and outputs for all processes and services. Every process and service is then converted to its equivalent in emergy. The amounts of emergy of each type are summed. There are several possible ways to group emergy by type and to combine the data, but generally the goal is to create either a measure of emergy renewability (as an indicator of stress on the environment) or emergy sustainability (which combines renewability with the total productivity and consumption or emergy).

Calculating the emergy equivalents of materials and energy can be done easily with a conversion table, but creating the table can be a challenge. Burning coal releases an amount of energy that is easy to measure and easy to convert to emergy. However, determining the amount of energy required to create coal is nearly impossible. Similarly, how can you quantify the emergy conversion factor for objects like aluminum or for ecosystem services like rainfall? It is difficult, but possible, to place a dollar value on those objects and services, but assigning an energy equivalent is even more tenuous. While converting everything to a common unit, emergy, simplifies comparisons of diverse activities and processes like soil erosion and tourism, there are concerns about the accuracy of those conversions.

9.3.5.6 Comparisons

There are no perfect measures of sustainability, and different indicators can sometimes give conflicting results. In particular this happens when perspectives on the most important components of sustainability, and the methods to address them, differ. Therefore, it is often useful to examine the main characteristics of several Environmental Performance Indicators to find the one most appropriate for a particular study. As an example, ESIs, EMPIs, and ecological footprinting (discussed in a previous section) are compared below.

Ecological footprinting (EF) has units that are the easiest to understand – area of land. Both EF and EMPI employ only a single type of unit, allowing for use of absolute variables and permitting quantitative comparisons. However, EF does not use multiple indicators to allow for focused attention on impacts. EMPI can also be used as scaled values (such as the proportion of emergy from renewable sources), in the same manner as ESI. However, ESI combines multiple units of measurements, which can provide a more holistic perspective, but at the same time leads to concerns about combining those data.

Of the three, ESI and EMPI take into account wastefulness and recycling, and only ESI includes the effects of all emissions. But while ESI includes the most variables, it is the most complex to calculate; the simplest to calculate is EF.

Because ESI includes social and economic indicators, it can only compare nations (or in some cases, states or other levels of governments). EF and EMPI are effective at comparing countries, but can also be used at scales from global down to individual products.

All three of the EPIs compared here can be useful, but each has their limitations. Additionally, there are scenarios where none of these are useful. Specific environmental education projects, for example, would require different types of performance indicators.

9.3.5.7 Review Questions

Question 9.3.5.1
What is the difference between energy and emergy?

Question 9.3.5.2
In what way(s) is ESI a better method of assessing sustainability than EF and EMPI?

Question 9.3.5.3

The ESI creates indicators in five areas. In which of the areas do you think the indicators are the least reliable?

Question 9.3.5.4

Why do EPIs require multiple data points to be useful?

9.3.5.8 Additional Resources

Environmental Sustainability Index (http://sedac.ciesin.columbia.edu/es/esi/[127])
    EPA MyEnvironment (http://www.epa.gov/myenvironment/[128])

9.3.6 Case Study: UN Millennium Development Goals Indicator[129]

In 2000 the United Nations created the Millennium Development Goals (MDGs)[130] to monitor and improve human conditions by the year 2015. This framework was endorsed by all UN member nations and includes goals in eight areas: hunger/poverty, universal primary education, gender equity, infant mortality, maternal health, disease, global partnerships, and environmental sustainability.

Each of the MDGs on basic human rights has one or more targets, with each target having specific indicators for assessment. Most of the targets have a baseline year of 1990 and specify an achievement rate. For example, one target is to halve the proportion of people suffering from hunger. By specifying a proportion, targets can be monitored separately at national, regional, and global levels. Visit the interactive map at MDGMonitor[131] to track and monitor progress of the Millennium Development Goals.

The underlying principle of the MDGs is that the world has sufficient knowledge and resources to implement sustainable practices to improve the life of everyone. Annual progress reports suggest that this principle may be realistic only for some targets. The targets within environmental sustainability are the implementation of national policies of sustainable development, increased access to safe drinking water, and improvements to urban housing. There are success stories: efforts to increase availability of clean water have resulted in improvements faster than expected. However, not all indicators are showing improvement. Impacts of climate change are accelerating, and risks of physical and economic harm from natural disasters are increasing. Moreover, these impacts and risks are concentrated in poorer countries – those least able to handle the threats. Overall, results are mixed.

The worldwide rate of deforestation is still high but has slowed. Large-scale efforts to plant trees in China, India, and Viet Nam have resulted in combined annual increases of about 4 million hectares of forests since 2000. Unfortunately, that is about the same rate of forest loss in South America and Africa each. Globally, the net loss of forest from 2000 to 2010 was 5.2 million hectares per year, down by a third from the 1990s.

The world will likely meet the target of halving the proportion of people without access to clean water, with the majority of progress made in rural areas. By 2008 most regions exceeded or nearly met the target levels. The exceptions were Oceania and sub-Saharan Africa, which had only 50% and 60% respectively of their populations with access to improved water sources. Those regions will almost certainly miss the target. They, and most other developing regions, will also miss the target of halving the proportion of the population lacking improved sanitation facilities. In fact, the total number of people without such access is expected to grow until at least 2015.

From 1990 to 2007, emissions of carbon dioxide rose in developed regions by 11%; in developing regions, which have much higher rates of population growth, emissions increased by 110%. While most indicators

[127]http://sedac.ciesin.columbia.edu/es/esi/
[128]http://www.epa.gov/myenvironment/
[129]This content is available online at <http://legacy.cnx.org/content/m41602/1.3/>.
[130]http://www.un.org/millenniumgoals/
[131]http://www.mdgmonitor.org/map.cfm?goal=&indicator=&cd

have shown either progress or minimal additional harm, carbon dioxide emissions stand out as one of the
significant failures in achieving global sustainability.

Efforts to preserve biodiversity have made only minimal progress. One target was to have 10% of each of
the world's terrestrial ecosystem types protected by 2010; only half were. The proportion of key biodiversity
areas protected stagnated in the 2000s, after showing faster improvements in the 1970s-1990s. As a result,
the number of birds and mammals expected to go extinct in the near future has increased.

The environmental sustainability target for urban housing was meant to significantly improve the lives
of 100 million slum-dwellers by 2020. This target differed from most others not only by using a later date
of 2020, but by lacking a specified proportion of the population. Setting a target as an absolute value for
the entire globe obscures the progress in individual countries, so this criterion may be revisited. From 1990
to 2010, the proportion of slum-dwellers decreased from 46% to 33%. However, during the same time, the
number of people living in slums increased from 657 million to 828 million. Over 200 million slum-dwellers
achieved access to clean water and improved sanitation facilities, so the target was met. However, it is widely
acknowledged that the target was set too low.

Even as we continue to strive toward the MDGs 2015 target date, it is also necessary to think beyond
them. Changing demographics will drive shifts in the global economy and the use of resources. Increased
effects of climate change will result in greater volatility, while technological developments can open new
opportunities. In light of these changes, evaluation of the MDGs must assess their utility after 2015. Should
the general framework stay in place, should it be modified with new approaches, or should it be replaced
with something fundamentally different?

9.4 Sustainability and Business[132]

9.4.1 Learning Objectives

After reading this module, students should be able to

- understand how businesses incorporate sustainability into their plans, the basis of sustainable product
  chains, and factors that need to be considered in measuring and assessing sustainable performance

9.4.2 Introduction

Throughout this text the integrative nature of environmental, social, and economic sustainability has been
stressed. In this chapter, various ways of framing the sustainability paradigm and measuring progress toward
its achievement have been presented. This section focuses more directly on businesses, and how they attempt
to incorporate sustainability into their decisions and plans. The business sector, continually seeking ways to
create competitive advantages, has become acutely aware of the general value of adjusting various business
models to accommodate consumers' desires for sustainable products and services. Still, the broad definition of
sustainable development provided by the Brundtland report is a difficult one to make operational. The World
Business Council for Sustainable Development[133] has adapted Brundtland to a view more understandable
to business interests, focusing on living within the "interest" of natural systems and being cautious about
drawing down the "principal" (i.e. degrading natural ecosystems), but there remain substantial differences
on precisely how to measure progress toward the goals of the sustainability paradigm.

It is a common practice for businesses to refer to the **triple bottom line**, a reference to the value of
a business going beyond dollar profitability to include social and environmental costs and benefits as well.
Indeed, many of the tools and indices outlined in Module **Life Cycle Assessment** (Section 9.2) and Module
Sustainability Metrics and Rating Systems (Section 9.3.1) are widely used by businesses to measure
progress toward corporate goals. However, there is no agreed upon way of using these tools, and many
businesses have developed their own methods for assessing progress. This has, inevitably perhaps, led to

---

[132]This content is available online at <http://legacy.cnx.org/content/m42273/1.3/>.
[133]http://www.wbcsd.org/

claims and counter-claims by various parties about the "sustainability" of their products or services. Such claims usually find their way into corporate brochures and advertising so that, often without substantive backing or very subjective analysis, the impression of significant corporate sustainability is created, practices known generally as **greenwashing**. Greenwashing is a concern because these kinds of advertising messages can mislead consumers about the "the environmental practices of a company or the environmental benefits of a product or service" (Greenpeace, 2011 (p. 474)). Nevertheless, businesses must ultimately generate profits to remain viable, and increasingly they are being held to account for their impacts on all aspects of business operations, however difficult it may be to assign value to decisions made under conditions of considerable uncertainty. The intergenerational mandate of Brundtland and the nature of modern environmental problems facing society ask that business plans extend far beyond the usual five to ten year range.

9.4.3 Tools for Assessing Sustainability in Business

One useful organizational framework for envisioning different kinds of costs and benefits that businesses encounter is referred to as Total Cost Assessment (TCA). TCA assigns levels of uncertainty to the types of costs associated with various aspects of business activities. Typically five such types are recognized:

- Type I (Direct Costs) – Costs associated with direct operation of the manufacturing or service enterprise that can be readily attributed to a specific activity. Labor, medical, materials, land, and energy are examples of this type of cost.
- Type II (Indirect Costs) – Costs similar to Type I that are not easily assigned to a specific activity and thus are born more generally by the company. These include various kinds of overhead costs, outsourced services and subcontracts (e.g. component subassemblies, janitorial needs), and general support activities such as central offices for purchasing, human resources, etc.
- Type III (Contingent Liability Costs) – These are costs associated with environmental cleanup, non-compliance fines, product or service liability, civil suits, and accidents.
- Type IV (Internal Intangible Costs/Benefits) – These are costs and benefits that accrue to a business that are connected to a variety of intangibles such as worker morale, consumer loyalty, corporate image, and branding of products and services.
- Type V (External Costs) – Put simply, Type V costs are those associated with environmental degradation. They are "external" in the sense that normal financial accounting does not include them; the damage is born in a general sense by society at large. Environmental protection requirements that are enforceable by various laws (see section Government and Laws on the Environment), and mandated market or taxation mechanisms, are policy decisions meant to internalize these costs, forcing the generator of the pollution to either pay for the damage or prevent damage in the first place.

Taken as a whole, these cost/benefit types include all three of the basic elements of the sustainability paradigm. However Type IV and V costs are often difficult to assign a dollar value to; indeed even if this can be done, projecting their value into the future is an uncertain science.

Life cycle assessment (LCA) can also be used to visualize and organize a sustainability model for businesses (See Module **Life Cycle Assessment** (Section 9.2) for more information). Recall that LCA grew out of industry's needs to understand how product manufacturing systems behave, and to develop workable models that could be used to control and optimize material and energy flows, ensure product quality, manage environmental impacts, and minimize costs (these functions are collectively referred to as the supply chain). An expanded use of LCA incorporates the complete **product chain**, examining consumer uses, benefits and costs, and the post-consumer disposition of the product. This has led to product conceptualization and development, and in some cases regulatory reform, that incorporate business practices and plans built upon the concept of **eco-efficiency**, and **extended product/producer responsibility** (EPR). Eco-efficiency is an evolutionary business model in which more goods and services are created with less use of resources, and fewer emissions of waste and pollution. Extended product/producer responsibility involves the creation of financial incentives, and legal disincentives, to encourage manufacturers to make more environmentally friendly products that incorporate **end-of-life costs** into product design and business plans. For example one business model that is conducive to EPR is a "lease-and-take-back" model in which products must eventually come back to the manufacturer or retailer, who then must reckon with the best way to minimize end-of-life costs. Remanufacturing, recycling, and reuse of materials are the intended results of EPR, but ordinary disposal, including landfilling or incineration, can also be an option.

Figure **LCA Framework Applied to Product Development** (Figure 9.24), illustrates in a general way how the LCA framework can be structured for understanding how product development can benefit from the various material and information transfers and feedback loops along the product chain. Such a figure illustrates the complexities involved in creating, marketing, and discerning the impacts of a product or service, and raises the general concept of what is often referred to as **product stewardship**, an approach in which products are conceived, designed, manufactured, and marketed within a **systems thinking** context. It is a way of framing environmental problems that recognizes the three parts of the sustainability paradigm, and incorporates the concepts of sustainable manufacturing, marketing, utility-to-society, impacts of the use of the product, and end-of-life disposition of the product.

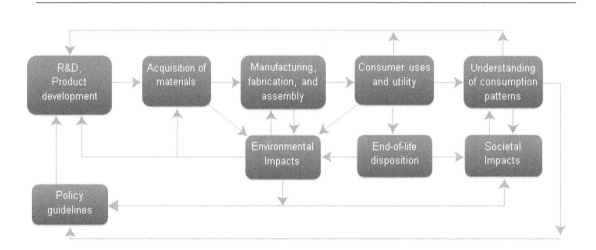

Figure 9.24: LCA Framework Applied to Product Development. Generalized view of the life cycle product chain, showing major material and information transfers and feedback loops. *Source: Tom Theis*[134]

9.4.4 Creating Uniformity

The problem of lack of uniformity in measuring, assessing, and valuing business actions taken at least in part for the sake of sustainability might be dealt with more effectively through the development of uniform standards and metrics that are applied by an agreed upon authority who uses transparent methodologies and reporting techniques so that other companies, and consumers, can make more objective judgments about comparative performances. From what has been presented in this section this may appear to be a near-impossible task. Yet attempts in this direction are being made, for example by the aforementioned World Business Council for Sustainable Development, the Organization for Economic Cooperation and Development[135], and the United Nations Millennium Development Goals[136]. One of the more popular approaches

---

[134]http://cnx.org/member_profile/theist
[135]http://www.oecd.org/
[136]http://www.un.org/millenniumgoals/environ.shtml

for measuring and ranking corporate sustainability has been developed by the Dow Jones Corporation (DJC), through its Sustainability Index[137] (DJSI). It may seem ironic that such a bastion of the free market economy has put together a system for measuring and assessing corporate sustainability, yet the size and general acceptability of DJC by corporations and investors work in favor of the establishment of an objective and transparent index. The DJSI itself was created in 1999 in response to the need, articulated from many sectors including consumers, for a way to assess progress toward sustainable corporate responsibility. The index contains three general evaluative sectors – economic, social, and environmental – that reflect the Brundtland definition. Each sector is composed, in turn, of specific categories as follows:

Economic

- Codes of Conduct/Compliance/Corruption and Bribery
- Corporate Governance
- Risk and Crisis Management
- Industry-specific Criteria

Social

- Corporate Citizenship and Philanthropy
- Labor Practice Indicators
- Human Capital Development
- Social Reporting
- Talent Attraction and Retention
- Industry-specific Criteria

Environmental

- Environmental Performance (Eco-efficiency)
- Environmental Reporting
- Industry-specific Criteria

Each of these categories is composed of quantitative measures and assigned a specific, and constant, weighting. From the data gathered, a "best-in-class" (i.e. industry class) ranking is published annually. The index has engendered considerable corporate competition such that mere attainment of the previous year's statistics, for a given company, usually results in a drop in rank. Of course one can argue with the choice of categories, or the data that are gathered and the way categories are parameterized, or with the weighting scheme used, but the important aspects of DJSI (and other sustainability rankings) is its comprehensiveness, uniformity, and transparency.

9.4.5 Summary

In the final analysis, no economy can move in the direction of sustainability without the active participation of the business sector. In other words, significant progress cannot be achieved through government or individual actions alone. As noted above, this creates difficulties and conflicts for businesses. As they continue to work together in the future, businesses and sustainability experts face many questions such as: What are the best measures of sustainability and how should businesses develop and plan for delivering more sustainable products and services? Is reliance on eco-efficiency enough to reduce the impacts of increasing consumption? Should businesses play a more significant role in educating consumers on the factors that affect sustainable development? How can businesses adapt to uncertainties that lie beyond the near term? What is the role of government in overseeing or regulating business activities that contribute to sustainability?

---

[137]http://www.sustainability-index.com/

9.4.6 Review Questions

Question 9.4.1
Find a product chain for the manufacture of a major consumer item such as a flat screen television, a computer, or an automobile and cast the stages of the chain in life cycle form as shown in Figure **LCA Framework Applied to Product Development** (Figure 9.24). As part of your answer, define the various information transfers and feedback loops involved.

Question 9.4.2
Consider the various types of costs in the total cost accounting framework. In proceeding from Type I to Type V, give reasons why uncertainties usually increase at each level?

Question 9.4.3
What are the main attributes of a sound index for measuring progress toward sustainability of products and services?

9.4.7 Resources

The World Business Council for Sustainable Development[138]

9.4.8 References

Greenpeace   (2011).   Greenwashing.   *Greenpeace.*   Retrieved   December   17,   2011   from http://stopgreenwash.org/[139]

---

[138]http://www.wbcsd.org/home.aspx
[139]http://stopgreenwash.org/

Chapter 10

Sustainability: Ethics, Culture, and History

10.1 The Human Dimensions of Sustainability: History, Culture, Ethics[1]

Figure 10.1: *Source: Earth Day Network*[2]

Once we begin talking about sustainability, it's hard to stop. That's because sustainability is truly the science of everything, from technical strategies for repowering our homes and cars, to the ecological study of biodiversity in forests and oceans, to how we think and act as human beings. This latter category—the "human dimensions" of sustainability—is the focus of this chapter. Much sustainability discourse focuses on scientific, technical and regulatory issues, but there is increasing awareness that without changes in people's attitudes and patterns of behavior, and how these attitudes are reflected in public policymaking priorities, meaningful reform toward a more sustainable management of natural resources will be impossible. One key to this problem is that we are accustomed to thinking of the environment as a remote issue. Even the words "environment" and "nature" themselves suggest the habitual view we take of ourselves as somehow independent of or superior to the planet's material resources and processes. The truth is different. Humanity is but a thread of nature's web, albeit an original and brilliant thread. So brilliant indeed that we are now shaping the evolution of the web itself, to our short-term advantage, but in ways that cannot be sustained.

One example of the centrality of the human dimensions component of sustainability studies is the fact that sustainable technologies of food and energy production are increasingly available, but have yet to be adapted on the necessary scale to make a difference to humanity's overall environmental footprint on the planet. Many look to technology for answers to our myriad environmental problems, but the fact that even the limited technological innovations that exist lack support and have been inadequately deployed is a complex human issue, touching an essential resistance to change in our economic and political structures, our lifestyles and culture and, at the micro-level, basic human psychology and behavior. This chapter will explore these human dimensions of the sustainability challenge, with an emphasis on the historical and cultural factors that have placed us on our dangerously unsustainable path, and which make changing course so challenging.

Sustainability in human terms is, first and foremost, a commonsense goal: to ensure that conditions on earth continue to support the project of human civilization, that widely diverse populations of the global community not slip into protracted crisis on account of deteriorating environmental conditions and depleted resources. This preventive dimension of sustainability discourse inevitably involves doom projections. Despite the popularity of apocalyptic, end-of-the-world scenarios in Hollywood movies, science fiction, and some corners of the blogosphere, the biological end of the human race remains scarcely imaginable—we will continue on, in some form. But in the emerging perfect storm of food stock declines, water scarcity, climate disruption, and energy shortfalls, there now exist measurable global-scale threats to social order and basic living standards that are the material bedrock of civic society as we recognize it.

The dramatic environmental changes underway on earth are already impacting human social systems. Droughts, floods, and rising sea levels are taking lives, damaging infrastructure, reducing crop yields and creating a new global underclass of environmental refugees. The question is how much more serious will these impacts become and how soon? There are no reassuring answers if we continue on a business-as-usual path. One thing about sustainability in the twenty-first century is certain: individual nations and the international community together will need to both **mitigate** the projected declines of the planet's ecosystems, and at the same time **adapt** to those that are irreversible. As one popular sustainability policy mantra has it: "we must strive to avoid the unmanageable, while managing the unavoidable."

The environmental historian Sing Chew sees in the cluster of environmental crises of the early 21st century the hallmarks of a potential new Dark Age, that is, a period of conflict, resource scarcity and cultural impoverishment such as has afflicted the global human community only a few times over the past five millennia. The goal of sustainability, in these terms, is clear and non-controversial: to avoid a new and scaled-up Dark Age in which the aspirations of billions of people, both living and yet unborn, face brutal constraints. The implications of sustainability, in this sense, extend well beyond what might ordinarily considered "green" issues, such as preserving rainforests or saving whales. Sustainability is a human and social issue as much as it is "environmental." Sustainability is about people, the habitats we depend on for services vital to us, and our ability to maintain culturally rich civic societies free from perennial crises in food, water, and energy supplies.

[2]http://cdn.earthday.advomatic.com/sites/default/files/imagecache/frontpage_slide/marquee-edn_0.jpg

10.2 It's Not Easy Being Green: Anti-Environmental Discourse, Behavior, and Ideology[3]

10.2.1 Learning Objectives

After reading this module, students should be able to

- understand the complex connections that tie our modern lifestyles and the consumption of goods to human and environmental impacts across the world
- relate our habits of consumption to the long history of human social development on evolutionary time scales
- apply the working distinction between "society" and "culture" outlined in this section to explain the different and often conflictual attitudes toward the environment that exist today

10.2.2 Introduction

The consensus view among scientists and professional elites in the early twenty-first century, as it has been among environmental activists for a much longer time, is that our globalized industrial world system is on an unsustainable path. Inherent in this view is a stern judgment of the recent past: we have not adapted well, as a species, to the fruits of our own brilliant technological accomplishments, in particular, to the harnessing of fossil fuels to power transport and industry.

Taking the long view of human evolution, it is not surprising to find that we are imperfectly adapted to our modern industrialized world of cars, computers, and teeming cities, or that human societies organized for so many millennia around the problem of scarcity should treat a sudden abundance of resources with the glee of a kid in a candy store. In evolutionary terms, we have simply not had sufficient time to adapt to the windfall of change. Though rapid advances in the biophysical sciences in recent decades mean that we mostly understandour maladaptation to industrialization and the great dangers it poses, our political decision-making and consumption patterns have barely changed on the basis of this understanding. This sobering fact tells us that, at this moment in human history, social behavior and political decision-making are not being driven by knowledge, but rather by entrenched attitudes that perpetuate an unsustainable drawdown of earth's resources. In short, human decision making and consumption of material goods in our fossil-fuel age continues to largely take place outside of an awareness of the strained and finite nature of our planet's ecosystem services.

It is the character of modern consumer society to promote the idea that nothing is connected, that the jeans we wear, or the food we eat, are matters of personal choice without any greater context beyond a concern for immediate pleasure and peer approval. Sustainability, by contrast, teaches that everything is connected. That favorite pair of jeans, for instance, is dependent on cheap labor in developing countries, on heavily fertilized cotton plantations, and enormous volumes of water expended throughout the jeans' lifecycle, from the irrigation to grow the cotton to the washing machine that cleans them. Or let's take that "cheap" fast food lunch from yesterday: it most likely contained processed soybeans from a recently cleared stretch of the Amazon rainforest, and artificial sweeteners made from corn whose enormous production quotas are subsidized by government tax revenues. The corn-based sweetener, in turn, turns out to be a principal cause of the national obesity epidemic, a key contributor to spiraling health care costs. Thus the "value meal" turns out not to be so economical after all, once the systems-wide effects are factored in.

A twenty minute video, The Story of Stuff[4] , tells the complicated story of how our "stuff" moves from extraction to sale to disposal.

---

[3]This content is available online at <http://legacy.cnx.org/content/m41067/1.4/>.

[4]http://www.youtube.com/storyofstuffproject#p/u/22/9GorqroigqM

The Story of Stuff

This media object is a Flash object. Please view or download it at
<http://www.youtube.com/v/9GorqroigqM?version=3&hl=en_US>

Figure 10.2

Figure 10.3: Fast Food Industry's Environmental Impact? Here's food for thought. Though we are accustomed to measuring the impact of a fast food diet on our physical health, there is much less readily available information on the global network of agricultural providers that supports the fast food industry, and on its environmental impacts on land use, water resources, and human communities. *Source: Created by CrazyRob926[5]*

10.2.3 Connectivity

To think about sustainability in these terms may sound exhausting. But because we live in a world characterized by **connectivity**, that is, bycomplex chains linking our everyday lives to distant strangers and ecosystems in far flung regions of the earth, we have no choice. In the end, we must adapt our thinking to a complex, connected model of the world and our place in it. Persisting with only simple, consumerist frames of understanding—"I look great!" "This tastes delicious!"—for a complex world of remote impacts and finite resources renders us increasingly vulnerable to episodes of what ecologists call system collapse, that is, to the sudden breakdown of ecosystem services we rely upon for our life's staple provisions.

In the early twenty-first century, vulnerability to these system collapses varies greatly according to where one lives. A long-term drought in India might bring the reality of aquifer depletion or climate change home to tens of thousands of people driven from their land, while the life of a suburban American teenager is not obviously affected by any resource crisis. But this gap will narrow in the coming years. Overwhelming scientific evidence points to rapidly increasing strains this century on our systems of food, water, and energy provision as well as on the seasonable weather to which we have adapted our agricultural and urban regions. In time, no one will enjoy the luxury of remaining oblivious to the challenges of sustainability. Drought, for example, is one of the primary indices of global ecosystem stress, and arguably the most important to humans. According to the United Nations Food and Agriculture Organization, without wholesale reformation of water management practices on a global scale, two-thirds of the world's population will face water shortages by 2025, including densely populated regions of the United States.

So how did we arrive at this point? Without you or I ever consciously choosing to live unsustainably, how has it nevertheless come about that we face environmental crises of global scale, circumstances that will so decisively shape our lives and those of our children? Here's one explanatory narrative, framed by the long view of human evolution.

Since the emergence of the first proto-human communities in Africa millions of years ago, we have spent over 99% of evolutionary time as nomadic hunters and gatherers. A fraction of the balance of our time on earth spans the 10,000 years of human agriculture, since the end of the last Ice Age. In turn, only a third of that fractional period has witnessed the emergence of the institutions and technologies—writing, money, mathematics, etc.—that we associate with human "civilization." And lastly, at the very tip of the evolutionary timeline, no more than a blink of human species history, we find the development of the modern industrialized society we inhabit. Look around you. Observe for a moment all that is familiar in your immediate surroundings: the streetscape and buildings visible through the window, the plastic furnishings in the room, and the blinking gadgets within arm's length of where you sit. All of it is profoundly "new" to human beings; to all but a handful of the tens of thousands of generations of human beings that have preceded us, this everyday scene would appear baffling and frightening, as if from another planet.

10.2.4 Normalization

In this sense, the real miracle of human evolution is that cars, computers, and cities appear so normal to us, even sometimes "boring" and monotonous! Our perception of the extraordinary, rapid changes in human societies in the past two centuries—even the past half-century—is deadened by virtue of what is our greatest evolutionary acquirement, namely **normalization**, an adaptive survival strategy fundamental to human success over the millennia. The ability to accept, analyze, and adapt to often fluctuating circumstances is our great strength as a species. But at this point in human history it is also a grave weakness, what, in the language of Greek tragedy might be called a "fatal flaw."

To offer an analogy, for many centuries slavery appeared normal to most people across the world—until the late eighteenth century, when a handful of humanitarian activists in Britain began the long and difficult process of de-normalizing human bondage in the eyes of their compatriots. The task of sustainability ethics is analogous, and no less difficult, in that it lays out the argument for wholesale and disruptive attitude adjustment and behavior change in the general population. Given the long-term adaptation of the human species to the imperatives of hunter-gathering, our decision-making priorities and consumption drives still

---
[5]http://en.wikipedia.org/wiki/File:Generic_Fastfood.jpg

tend toward the simple necessities, based on the presumption of relative and seasonal scarcity, and with little emotional or social reward for restraint in the face of plenty, for viewing our choices in global terms, or for measuring their impacts on future generations.

A working distinction between the historical evolution of human *society* and human *culture* is useful to understanding the social and psychological obstacles to achieving sustainability. As both individuals and societies, we work hard to insulate ourselves from unpleasant surprises, shocks, and disorder. We crave "security," and our legal and economic institutions accordingly have evolved over the millennia to form a buffer against what Shakespeare's Hamlet called "the thousand natural shocks that flesh is heir to." For instance, the law protects us from violent physical harm (ideally), while insurance policies safeguard us from financial ruin in the event of an unexpected calamity. .

In one sense, this security priority has determined the basic evolution of human societies, particularly the decisive transition 10,000 years ago from the variable and risky life of nomadic hunter communities to sedentary farming based on an anticipated stability of seasonal yields. Of course, the shift to agriculture only partially satisfied the human desire for security as farming communities remained vulnerable to changing climatic conditions and territorial warfare. Global industrialization, however, while it has rendered vast populations marginal and vulnerable, has offered its beneficiaries the most secure insulation yet enjoyed by humans against "the slings and arrows of outrageous fortune." This success has been a double-edged sword, however, not least because the industrialized cocoon of our modern consumer lifestyles relentlessly promotes the notion that we have transcended our dependence on the earth's basic resources. As it stands, we look at our highly complex, industrialized world, and adapt our expectations and desires to its rewards. It is never our first instinct to ask whether the system of rewards itself might be unsustainable and collapse at some future time as a result of our eager participation.

10.2.5 Sustainability Obstacles and Support

In terms of the evolutionary argument I am outlining here, our ability to grasp the sustainability imperative faces two serious obstacles. The first is psychological, namely the inherited mental frameworks that reward us for the normalization and simplification of complex realities. The second is social, namely our economic and institutional arrangements designed to protect us from material wants, as well as from risk, shock, disorder and violent change. Both these psychological and social features of our lives militate against an ecological, systems-based worldview.

Luckily, our *cultural* institutions have evolved to offer a counterweight to the complacency and inertia encouraged by the other simple, security-focused principles governing our lives. If society is founded upon the principle of security, and promotes our complacent feeling of independence from the natural world, we might think of culture as the conscience of society. What culture does, particularly in the arts and sciences, is remind us of our frailty as human beings, our vulnerability to shocks and sudden changes, and our connectedness to the earth's natural systems. In this sense, the arts and sciences, though we conventionally view them as opposites, in fact perform the same social function: they remind us of what lies beyond the dominant security paradigm of our societies—which tends to a simplified and binary view of human being and nature—by bringing us closer to a complex, systemic understanding of how the natural world works and our embeddedness within it. Whether by means of an essay on plant biology, or a stage play about family breakdown (like *Hamlet*), the arts and sciences model complex worlds and the systemic interrelations that shape our lives. They expose complexities and connectivities in our world, and emphasize the material consequences of our actions to which we might otherwise remain oblivious. The close relation between the arts and sciences in the Western world is evidenced by the fact that their concerns have largely mirrored each other over time, from the ordered, hierarchical worldview in the classical and early modern periods, to the post-modern focus on connectivity, chaos, and emergence.

Life in the pre-modern world, in the memorable words of the English philosopher Thomas Hobbes, was mostly "nasty, brutish, and short." By contrast, social and economic evolution has bestowed the inhabitants of the twenty-first century industrialized world with a lifestyle uniquely (though of course not wholly) insulated from physical hardship, infectious disease, and chronic violence. This insulation has come at a cost, however, namely our disconnection from the basic support systems of life: food, water and energy. This is a very recent development. At the beginning of the 20th century, for example, almost half of Americans grew up on farms. Now, fewer than two percent do. We experience the staples of life only at their service endpoints: the supermarket, the faucet, the gas station. In this context, the real-world sources of food, water, and energy do not seem important, while supplies appear limitless. We are not prepared for the inevitable shortages of the future.

On the positive side, it is possible to imagine that the citizens of the developed world might rapidly reconnect to a systems view of natural resources. One product of our long species evolution as hunters and agricultural land managers is an adaptive trait the ecologist E. O. Wilson has called "biophilia," that is, a love for the natural world that provides for us. In the few centuries of our fossil fuel modernity, this biophilia has become increasingly aestheticized and commodified—as landscape art, or nature tourism—and consequently marginalized from core social and economic decision structures. In the emerging age of environmental decline and resource scarcity, however, our inherited biophilia will play a key role in energizing the reform of industrialized societies toward a sustainable, renewable resource and energy future.

10.2.6 Review Questions

Question 10.2.1
How has the human capacity for *normalization* both helped and hindered social development, and what are its implications for sustainable reform of our industries, infrastructure, and way of life?

Question 10.2.2
Take an everyday consumer item—running shoes, or a cup of coffee—and briefly chart its course through the global consumer economy from the production of its materials to its disposal. What are its environmental impacts, and how might they be reduced?

10.3 The Industrialization of Nature: A Modern History (1500 to the present)[6]

10.3.1 Learning Objectives

After reading this module, students should be able to

- reproduce a basic timeline of global economic development since 1500, and outline the historical webs of trade linking sources of major raw materials—e.g. spices, cotton, oil—to their consumer markets on a world map
- define the historical development of core and periphery nations in the world economy
- understand the concept of *externalization* of environmental costs, and its role as a principle driver of unsustainable industrial development

10.3.2 Introduction

It is a measure of our powers of normalization that we in the developed world take the existence of cheap energy, clean water, abundant food, and international travel so much for granted, when they are such recent endowments for humanity, and even now are at the disposal of considerably less than half the global population. It is a constant surprise to us that a situation so "normal" could be having such abnormal effects on the biosphere—degrading land, water, air, and the vital ecosystems hosting animals and fish. How did we get here? How can we square such apparent plenty with warnings of collapse?

---

[6]This content is available online at <http://legacy.cnx.org/content/m40821/1.5/>.

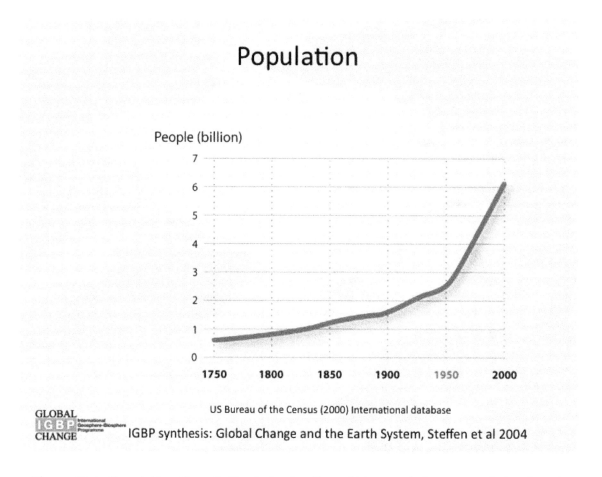

Figure 10.4: Population Growth Graph showing the rapid increase in human population since the beginning of the Industrial Age, with exponential rise since the mid-twentieth century. *Source: IGBP synthesis: Global Change and the Earth System, Steffen et al 2004*[7]

Raw figures at least sketch the proportions of global change over the last 500 years. In 1500, even after several centuries of rapid population growth, the global population was no more than 500 million, or less than half the population of India today. It is now fourteen times as large, almost 7 billion. Over the same period, global economic output has increased 120 times, most of that growth occurring since 1820, and with the greatest acceleration since 1950. This combination of rampant population and economic growth since 1500 has naturally had major impacts on the earth's natural resources and ecosystem health. According to the United Nations Millennium Ecosystem Assessment, by the beginning of the 21st century, 15 of the world's 24 ecosystems, from rainforests to aquifers to fisheries, were rated in serious decline.

10.3.3 Economic Development

Fundamental to significant changes in human history has been social reaction to resource scarcity. By 1500, Europeans, the first engineers of global growth, had significantly cleared their forests, settled their most productive agricultural lands, and negotiated their internal borders. And yet even with large-scale internal development, Europe struggled to feed itself, let alone to match the wealth of the then dominant global

---

[7]http://en.wikipedia.org/wiki/File:Populationgrowth.jpg

empires, namely China and the Mughal States that stretched from the Spice Islands of Southeast Asia to the busy ports of the Eastern Mediterranean. As a consequence of resource scarcity, European states began to sponsor explorations abroad, in quest initially for gold, silver, and other precious metals to fill up their treasuries. Only over time did Europeans begin to perceive in the New World the opportunities for remote agricultural production as a source of income. Full-scale colonial settlement was an even later idea.

The new "frontiers" of European economic development in the immediate pre-industrial period 1500-1800 included tropical regions for plantation crops, such as sugar, tobacco, cotton, rice, indigo, and opium, and temperate zones for the cultivation and export of grains. The seagoing merchants of Portugal, France, Spain, Britain and the Netherlands trawled the islands of the East Indies for pepper and timber; established ports in India for commerce in silk, cotton and indigo; exchanged silver for Chinese tea and porcelain; traded sugar, tobacco, furs and rice in the Americas; and sailed to West Africa for slaves and gold. The slave trade and plantation economies of the Americas helped shift the center of global commerce from Asia to the Atlantic, while the new oceangoing infrastructure also allowed for the development of fisheries, particularly the lucrative whale industry. All these commercial developments precipitated significant changes in their respective ecosystems across the globe—deforestation and soil erosion in particular—albeit on a far smaller scale compared with what was to come with the harnessing of fossil fuel energy after 1800.

The 19th century witnessed the most rapid global economic growth seen before or mostly since, built on the twin tracks of continued agricultural expansion and the new "vertical" frontiers of fossil fuel and mineral extraction that truly unleashed the transformative power of industrialization on the global community and its diverse habitats. For the first time since the human transition to agriculture more than 10,000 years before, a state's wealth did not depend on agricultural yields from contiguous lands, but flowed rather from a variety of global sources, and derived from the industrialization of primary products, such as cotton textiles, minerals and timber. During this period, a binary, inequitable structure of international relations began to take shape, with a *core* of industrializing nations in the northern hemisphere increasingly exploiting the natural resources of undeveloped *periphery* nations for the purposes of wealth creation.

Figure 10.5: Trade Map, Late 20th Century This map shows the "core" industrialized nations of the northern hemisphere, and the "periphery" nations of the tropics and south dependent on subsistence agriculture and natural resource extraction. This unequal relationship is the product of hundreds of years of trade and economic globalization *Source: Created by Naboc1, based on a list in Christopher Chase-Dunn, Yukio Kawano and Benjamin Brewer, Trade Globalization since 1795, American Sociological Review, 2000 February, Vol. 65* [8]

10.3.4 The Great Acceleration

Despite the impact of the world wars and economic depression on global growth in the early 20th century, the new technological infrastructure of the combustion engine and coal-powered electricity sponsored increased productivity and the sanitization of growing urban centers. Infectious diseases, the scourge of humanity for thousands of years, retreated, more than compensating for losses in war, and the world's population continued to increase dramatically, doubling from 1 to 2 billion in 50 years, and with it the ecological footprint of our single species.

Nothing, however, is to be compared with the multiplying environmental impacts of human activities since 1950, a period dubbed by historians as "The Great Acceleration." In the words of the United Nations Millennium Ecosystem Assessment, "over the past 50 years, humans have changed ecosystems more rapidly and extensively than in any comparable period of time in human history, largely to meet rapidly growing demands for food, fresh water, timber, fiber, and fuel. This has resulted in a substantial and largely irreversible loss in the diversity of life on Earth." The post-WWII global economic order promoted liberal and accelerated trade, capital investment, and technological innovation tethered to consumer markets, mostly free of environmental impact considerations. The resultant economic growth, and the corresponding drawdown of natural resources, are **nonlinear** in character, which is, exhibiting an unpredictable and exponential rate of increase.

All systems, human and natural, are characterized by nonlinear change. We are habituated to viewing our history as a legible story of "progress," governed by simple cause-and-effect and enacted by moral agents, with the natural world as a backdrop to scenes of human triumph and tragedy. But history, from a sustainability viewpoint, is ecological rather than dramatic or moral; that is, human events exhibit the same patterns

---

[8]http://en.wikipedia.org/wiki/File:World_trade_map.PNG

of systems connectivity, complexity, and non-linear transformation that we observe in the organic world, from the genetic makeup of viruses to continental weather systems. The history of the world since 1950 is one such example, when certain pre-existing conditions—petroleum-based energy systems, technological infrastructure, advanced knowledge-based institutions and practices, and population increase—synergized to create a period of incredible global growth and transformation that could not have been predicted at the outset based upon those conditions alone. This unforeseen Great Acceleration has brought billions of human beings into the world, and created wealth and prosperity for many. But nonlinear changes are for the bad as well as the good, and the negative impacts of the human "triumph" of postwar growth have been felt across the biosphere. I will briefly detail the human causes of the following, itself only a selective list: soil degradation, deforestation, wetlands drainage and damming, air pollution and climate change.

10.3.4.1 Soil Degradation

Since the transition to agriculture 10,000 years ago, human communities have struggled against the reality that soil suffers nutrient depletion through constant plowing and harvesting (mostly nitrogen loss). The specter of a significant die-off in human population owing to stagnant crop yields was averted in the 1970s by the so-called "Green Revolution," which, through the engineering of new crop varieties, large-scale irrigation projects, and the massive application of petroleum-based fertilizers to supplement nitrogen, increased staple crop production with such success that the numbers suffering malnutrition actually declined worldwide in the last two decades of the 20th century, from 1.9 to 1.4 billion, even as the world's population increased at 100 times background rates, to 6 billion. The prospects for expanding those gains in the new century are nevertheless threatened by the success of industrial agriculture itself. Soil depletion, declining water resources, and the diminishing returns of fertilizer technology—all the products of a half-century of industrial agriculture—have seen increases in crop yields level off. At the same time, growing populations in developing countries have seen increasing clearance of fragile and marginal agricultural lands to house the rural poor.

It has been estimated that industrial fertilizers have increased the planet's human carrying capacity by two billion people. Unfortunately, most of the chemical fertilizer applied to soils does not nourish the crop as intended, but rather enters the hydrological system, polluting aquifers, streams, and ultimately the oceans with an oversupply of nutrients, and ultimately draining the oxygen necessary to support aquatic life. As for the impact of fertilizers on soil productivity, this diminishes over time, requiring the application of ever greater quantities in order to maintain yields.

10.3.4.2 Deforestation

Arguably the biggest losers from 20th century economic growth were the forests of the world's tropical regions and their non-human inhabitants. Across Africa, Asia, and the Americas, approximately one-third of forest cover has been lost. Because about half of the world's species inhabits tropical rainforests, these clearances have had a devastating impact on **biodiversity**, with **extinction** rates now greater than they have been since the end of the dinosaur era, 65 million years ago. Much of the cleared land was converted to agriculture, so that the amount of irrigated soils increased fivefold over the century, from 50 to 250m hectares. Fully 40% of the terrestrial earth's total organic output is currently committed to human use. But we are now reaching the ceiling of productive land expansion, in terms of sheer area, while the continued productivity of arable land is threatened by salinity, acidity and toxic metal levels that have now degraded soils across one third of the earth's surface, some of them irreversibly.

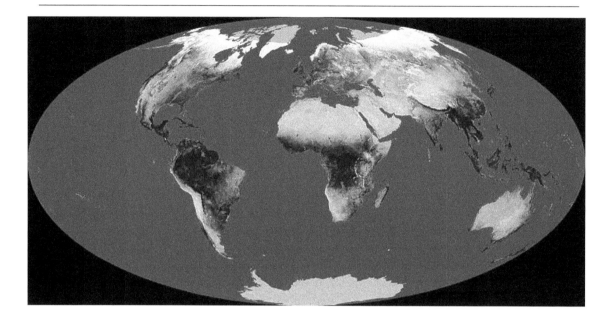

Figure 10.6: Global Forest Map Since the middle of the twentieth century, the global logging industry, and hence large-scale deforestation, has shifted from the North Atlantic countries to the forests of tropical regions such as Indonesia and the Amazon Basin in Latin America. This tropical "green belt" is now rapidly diminishing, with devastating consequences for local ecosystems, water resources, and global climate. *Source: NASA*[9]

10.3.4.3 Wetlands Drainage and Damming

Meanwhile, the worlds' vital wetlands, until recently viewed as useless swamps, have been ruthlessly drained—15% worldwide, but over half in Europe and North America. The draining of wetlands has gone hand in hand with large-scale hydro-engineering projects that proliferated through the last century, such that now some two-thirds of the world's fresh water passes through dam systems, while rivers have been blocked, channeled, and re-routed to provide energy, irrigation for farming, and water for urban development. The long-term impacts of these projects were rarely considered in the planning stages, and collectively they constitute a wholesale re-engineering of the planet's hydrological system in ways that will be difficult to adapt to the population growth demands and changing climatic conditions of the 21st century. As for the world's oceans, these increasingly show signs of acidification due to carbon emissions, threatening the aquatic food chain and fish stocks for human consumption, while on the surface, the oceans now serve as a global conveyor belt for colossal amounts of non-degradable plastic debris.

---

[9]http://earthobservatory.nasa.gov/IOTD/view.php?id=8622

Figure 10.7: Mississippi Watershed Map The catchment area of the Mississippi River covers almost 40% of the U.S. continental landmass, collecting freshwater from 32 states. Included in the runoff that feeds the river system are large quantities of agricultural fertilizer and other chemicals that eventually drain into the Gulf of Mexico, creating an ever-growing "dead zone." *Source: Environmental Protection Agency*[10]

10.3.4.4 Air Pollution

In many parts of the world, pollution of the air by industrial particles is now less a problem than it was a century ago, when newspapers lamented the "black snow" over Chicago. This is due to concerted efforts by a clean air caucus of international scope that arose in the 1940s and gained significant political influence with the emergence of the environmental movement in the 1970s. The impact of the post-70s environmental movement on the quality of air and water, mostly in the West, but also developing countries such as India, is the most hopeful precedent we have that the sustainability issues facing the world in the new century might yet be overcome, given political will and organization equal to the task.

10.3.4.5 Climate Change

Air pollution is still a major problem in the megacities of the developing world, however, while a global change in air chemistry—an increase of 40% in the carbon load of the atmosphere since industrialization—is ushering in an era of accelerated climate change. This era will be characterized by increased droughts and floods, higher sea levels, and extreme weather events, unevenly and unpredictably distributed across the globe, with the highest initial impact in regions that, in economic and infrastructural terms, can least support climate disruption (for example, sub-Saharan Africa). The environmental historian J. R. McNeil estimates that between 25 and 40 million people died from air pollution in the 20th century. The death toll arising from climate change in the 21st century is difficult to predict, but given the scale of the disruption to weather systems on which especially marginal states depend, it is likely to be on a much larger scale.

---

[10]http://en.wikipedia.org/wiki/File:Mississippi_River_basin.jpg

10.3.5 Summary

From the Portuguese sea merchants of the 16th century in quest of silver and spices from Asia, to the multinational oil companies of today seeking to drill in ever more remote and fragile undersea regions, the dominant view driving global economic growth over the last half millennium has been **instrumentalist**, that is, of the world's ecosystems as alternately a source of raw materials (foods, energy, minerals) and a dump for the wastes produced by the industrialization and consumption of those materials. The instrumentalist economic belief system of the modern era, and particularly the Industrial Age, is based on models of perennial growth, and measures the value of ecosystems according to their production of resources maximized for efficiency and hence profit. In this prevailing system, the cost of resource extraction to the ecosystem itself is traditionally not factored into the product and shareholder values of the industry. These costs are, in economic terms, **externalized**.

A future economics of sustainability, by contrast, would prioritize the management of ecosystems for resilience rather than pure capital efficiency, and would incorporate the cost of ecosystem management into the pricing of goods. In the view of many sustainability theorists, dismantling the system of "unnatural" subsidization of consumer goods that has developed over the last century in particular is the key to a sustainable future. Only a reformed economic system of natural pricing, whereby environmental costs are reflected in the price of products in the global supermarket, will alter consumer behavior at the scale necessary to ensure economic and environmental objectives are in stable alignment, rather than in constant conflict. As always in the sustainability paradigm, there are tradeoffs. A future economy built on the principle of resilience would be very different from that prevalent in the economic world system of the last 500 years in that its managers would accept reduced productivity and efficiency in exchange for the long-term vitality of the resource systems on which it depends.

10.3.6 Review Questions

Question 10.3.1
What are the major technological and economic developments since 1500 that have placed an increased strain on the planet's ecosystem services? What is the role of carbon-based energy systems in that history?

Question 10.3.2
What is the so-called Great Acceleration of the 20th century? What were its principal social features and environmental impacts?

Question 10.3.3
What is the Green Revolution? What were its successes, and what problems has it created?

10.4 Sustainability Studies: A Systems Literacy Approach[11]

10.4.1 Learning Objectives

After reading this module, students should be able to

- define systems literacy, how it is tailored specifically to the understanding and remedy of environmental problems, and the ways in which it differs from traditional disciplinary approaches to academic learning
- define bio-complexity as a scientific principle, and its importance as a concept and method for students in the environmental humanities and social sciences
- identify a potential research project that would embrace applications of one or more of the following sustainability key terms: resilience and vulnerability, product loops and lifecycles, and carbon neutrality

---

[11]This content is available online at <http://legacy.cnx.org/content/m41039/1.5/>.

10.4.2 Introduction

Transition to a sustainable resource economy is a dauntingly large and complex project, and will increasingly drive research and policy agendas across academia, government, and industry through the twenty-first century. To theorize sustainability, in an academic setting, is not to diminish or marginalize it. On the contrary, the stakes for sustainability education could not be higher. The relative success or failure of sustainability education in the coming decades, and its influence on government and industry practices worldwide, will be felt in the daily lives of billions of people both living and not yet born.

The core of sustainability studies, in the academic sense, is **systems literacy**—a simple definition, but with complex implications. Multiple indicators tell us that the global resource boom is now reaching a breaking point. The simple ethos of economic growth—"more is better"—is not sustainable in a world of complex food, water and energy systems suffering decline. The grand challenge of sustainability is to integrate our decision-making and consumption patterns—along with the need for economic viability—within a sustainable worldview. This will not happen by dumb luck. It will require, first and foremost, proper education. In the nineteenth and twentieth centuries, universal literacy—reading and writing—was the catch-cry of education reformers. In the twenty-first century, a new global literacy campaign is needed, this time systems literacy, to promote a basic understanding of the complex interdependency of human and natural systems.

Here I will lay out the historical basis for this definition of sustainability in terms of systems literacy, and offer specific examples of how to approach issues of sustainability from a systems-based viewpoint. Systems literacy, as a fundamental goal of higher education, represents the natural evolution of **interdisciplinarity**, which encourages students to explore connections between traditionally isolated disciplines and has been a reformist educational priority for several decades in the United States. Systems literacy is an evolved form of cross-disciplinary practice, calling for intellectual competence (not necessarily command) in a variety of fields in order to better address specific real-world environmental problems.

For instance, a student's research into deforestation of the Amazon under a sustainability studies paradigm would require investigation in a variety of fields not normally brought together under the traditional disciplinary regime. These fields might include plant biology, hydrology, and climatology, alongside economics, sociology, and the history and literature of post-colonial Brazil. Systems literacy, in a nutshell, combines the study of social history and cultural discourses with a technical understanding of ecosystem processes. Only this combination offers a comprehensive view of real-world environmental challenges as they are unfolding in the twenty-first century.

From the viewpoint of systems literacy sustainability studies works on two planes at once. Students of sustainability both acknowledge the absolute interdependence of human and natural systems—indeed that human beings and all their works are nothing if not natural—while at the same time recognizing that to solve our environmental problems we must often speak of the natural world and human societies as if they were separate entities governed by different rules. For instance, it is very useful to examine aspects of our human system as **diachronic**—as progressively evolving over historical time—while viewing natural systems more according to **synchronic** patterns of repetition and equilibrium. The diachronic features of human social evolution since 1500 would include the history of trade and finance, colonization and frontier development, and technology and urbanization, while examples of nature's synchronicity would be exemplified in the migratory patterns of birds, plant and animal reproduction, or the microbial ecology of a lake or river. A diachronic view looks at the changes in a system over time, while the synchronic view examines the interrelated parts of the system at any given moment, assuming a stable state.

While the distinction between diachronic and synchronic systems is in some sense artificial, it does highlight the structural inevitability of dysfunction when the two interlocked systems operate on different timelines and principles. The early twentieth century appetite for rubber to service the emerging automobile industry, for instance, marks an important chapter in the "heroic" history of human technology, while signifying a very different transition in the history of forest ecosystems in Asia and Latin America. Human history since the agricultural transition 10,000 years ago, and on a much more dramatic scale in the last two hundred years, is full of such examples of new human technologies creating sudden, overwhelming demand for a natural resource previously ignored, and reshaping entire ecosystems over large areas in order to extract, transport and industrialize the newly commodified material.

10.4.3 Biocomplexity

For students in the humanities and social sciences, sustainability studies requires adoption of a new conceptual vocabulary drawn from the ecological sciences. Among the most important of these concepts is *complexity*. **Biocomplexity**—the chaotically variable interaction of organic elements on multiple scales—is the defining characteristic of all ecosystems, inclusive of humans. Biocomplexity science seeks to understand this nonlinear functioning of elements across multiple scales of time and space, from the molecular to the intercontinental, from the microsecond to millennia and deep time. Such an approach hasn't been possible until very recently. For example, only since the development of (affordable) genomic sequencing in the last decade have biologists begun to investigate how environments regulate gene functions, and how changes in biophysical conditions place pressure on species selection and drive evolution.

Figure 10.8: The Biocomplexity Spiral The biocomplexity spiral illustrates the concept of biocomplexity, the chaotically variable interaction of organic elements on multiple scales. *Source: U.S. National Science Foundation*[12]

How is the concept of complexity important to sustainability studies? To offer one example, a biocomplexity paradigm offers the opportunity to better understand and defend *biodiversity*, a core environmental

---

[12]http://en.wikipedia.org/wiki/File:Biocomplexity_spiral.jpg

concern. Even with the rapid increase in knowledge in the biophysical sciences in recent decades, vast gaps exist in our understanding of natural processes and human impacts upon them. Surprisingly little is known, for example, about the susceptibilities of species populations to environmental change or, conversely, how preserving biodiversity might enhance the resilience of an ecosystem. In contrast to the largely reductionist practices of twentieth-century science, which have obscured these interrelationships, the new biocomplexity science begins with presumptions of ignorance, and from there goes on to map complexity, measure environmental impacts, quantify risk and resilience, and offer quantitative arguments for the importance of biodiversity. Such arguments, as a scientific supplement to more conventional, emotive appeals for the protection of wildlife, might then form the basis for progressive sustainability policy.

But such data-gathering projects are also breathtaking in the demands they place on analysis. The information accumulated is constant and overwhelming in volume, and the methods by which to process and operationalize the data toward sustainable practices have either not yet been devised or are imperfectly integrated within academic research structures and the policy-making engines of government and industry. To elaborate those methods requires a humanistic as well as scientific vision, a need to understand complex interactions from the molecular to the institutional and societal level.

A practical example of biocomplexity as the frame for studies in environmental sustainability are the subtle linkages between the hypoxic "dead zone" in the Gulf of Mexico and farming practices in the Mississippi River watershed. To understand the impact of hydro-engineered irrigation, nitrogen fertilizer, drainage, and deforestation in the Midwest on the fisheries of the Gulf is a classic biocomplexity problem, requiring data merging between a host of scientific specialists, from hydrologists to chemists, botanists, geologists, zoologists and engineers. Even at the conclusion of such a study, however, the human dimension remains to be explored, specifically, how industry, policy, culture and the law have interacted, on decadal time-scales, to degrade the tightly coupled riverine-ocean system of the Mississippi Gulf. A quantitative approach only goes so far. At a key moment in the process, fact accumulation must give way to the work of narrative, to the humanistic description of desires, histories, and discourses as they have governed, in this instance, land and water use in the Mississippi Gulf region.

To complexity should be added the terms **resilience** and **vulnerability**, as core concepts of sustainability studies. The resilience of a system—let's take for example, the wildlife of the Arctic Circle—refers to the self-renewing stability of that system, its ability to rebound from shocks and threats within the range of natural variability. The vulnerability of Artic wildlife, conversely, refers to the point at which resilience is eroded to breaking point. Warming temperatures in the Arctic, many times the global average, now threaten the habitats of polar bear and walruses, and are altering the breeding and migratory habits of almost all northern wildlife populations. The human communities of the Arctic are likewise experiencing the threshold of their resilience through rising sea levels and coastal erosion. Entire villages face evacuation and the traumatic prospect of life as environmental refugees.

As mentioned earlier, we have grown accustomed to speaking of "nature" or "the environment" as if they were somehow separate from us, something that might dictate our choice of holiday destination or wall calendar, but nothing else. A useful counter-metaphor for sustainability studies, to offset this habitual view, is to think of human and natural systems in *metabolic* terms. Like the human body, a modern city, for example, is an energy-dependent system involving inputs and outputs. Every day, millions of tons of natural resources (raw materials, consumer goods, food, water, energy) are pumped into the world's cities, which turn them out in the form of waste (landfill, effluent, carbon emissions, etc.).

Unlike the human body, however, the **metabolism** of modern cities is not a closed and self-sustaining system. Cities are consuming resources at a rate that would require a planet one and a half times the size of Earth to sustain, and are ejecting wastes into the land, water, and air that are further degrading the planet's ability to renew its vital reserves. Here, another body metaphor—the environmental "**footprint**"—has become a popular means for imagining sufficiency and excess in our consumption of resources. The footprint metaphor is useful because it provides us an image measurement of both our own consumption volume and the environmental impact of the goods and services we use. By making sure to consume less, and to utilize only those goods and services with a responsibly low footprint, we in turn reduce our own footprint on the planet. In important ways, the problem of unsustainability is a problem of waste. From a purely instrumentalist or consumerist viewpoint, waste is incidental or irrelevant to the value of a product. A metabolic view of systems, by contrast, promotes sustainability concepts such as **closed loops** and **carbon neutrality** for the things we manufacture and consume, whereby there are no toxic remainders through the entire **lifecycle** of a product. In this sense, systems literacy is as much a habit or style of observing the everyday world as it is an academic principle for the classroom. Because in the end, the fate of the world's ecosystems will depend not on what we learn in the classroom but on the extent to which we integrate that learning in our lives beyond it: in our professional practice and careers, and the lifestyle and consumer choices we make over the coming years and decades. If systems literacy translates into a worldview and way of life, then sustainability is possible.

10.4.4 Review Questions

Question 10.4.1
What are *synchronic* and *diachronic* views of time, and how does the distinction help us to understand the relation between human and natural systems, and to potentially rewrite history from an environmental point of view?

Question 10.4.2
How is a *bio-complex* view of the relations between human and natural systems central to sustainability, in both theory and practice?

10.5 The Vulnerability of Industrialized Resource Systems: Two Case Studies[13]

10.5.1 Introduction

Sustainability is best viewed through specific examples, or case studies. One way of conceiving sustainability is to think of it as a map that shows us connections between apparently unrelated domains or sequences of events. To cite an earlier example, what do the cornfields of Illinois have to do with the decline of fisheries in the Gulf of Mexico? To the uneducated eye, there is no relationship between two areas so remote from each other, but a sustainable systems analysis will show the ecological chain linking the use of chemical fertilizers in the Midwest, with toxic runoff into the Mississippi Basin, with changes in the chemical composition in the Gulf of Mexico (specifically oxygen depletion), to reduced fish populations, and finally to economic and social stress on Gulf fishing communities. Here, I will look at two case studies in greater detail, as a model for the systems analysis approach to sustainability studies in the humanities. The first concerns the alarming worldwide decline of bee populations (Section 10.6) since 2006, owing to a new affliction named Colony Collapse Disorder (CCD). The second case study examines the BP oil disaster in the Gulf of Mexico (Section 10.7) in 2010, considered in the larger historical context of global oil dependency.

10.5.2 Our Faustian Bargain

Before the emergence of coal and later oil as highly efficient and adaptable energy sources, human beings relied on mostly renewable sources of energy, principally their own muscle power, supplemented to varying degrees by the labor of domesticated farm animals, wood and peat for fuel, and the harnessing of wind and water for milling and sailing. An extraordinary and rapid transformation occurred with the extraction of latent solar power from ancient organic deposits in the earth. On the eve of industrialization, around 1800, the raw muscle power of human beings was responsible for probably 70% of human energy expenditure, while slavery—a brutal system for the concentration of that energy—functioned as a cornerstone of global economic growth. In the 1500-1800 period, in addition to the ten million or more Africans transported to

---

[13]This content is available online at <http://legacy.cnx.org/content/m41068/1.4/>.

slave colonies in the Americas, several times as many Indian and Chinese laborers, under various regimes of servitude, migrated across the globe to answer labor "shortages" within the globalizing Atlantic economy.

But technical improvements in the steam engine revolutionized this longstanding energy equation. Already by 1800, a single engine could produce power the equivalent of two hundred men. Today, a single worker, embedded within a technologized, carbon-driven industry, takes a week to produce what an 18th century laborer would take four years to do, while the average middle-class household in the industrialized world consumes goods and energy at a rate equivalent to having 100 slaves at their disposal round-the-clock.

In the famous medieval story of Faust, a scholar who dabbles in black magic sells his soul in exchange for extraordinary powers to satisfy his every desire. The Faust story provides an excellent analogy for our 200-year love affair with cheap fossil fuel energy. Our planetary carbon endowment has provided us with extraordinary powers to bend space and time to the shape of our desires and convenience, and fill it with cool stuff. But petroleum and coal are finite resources, and such is the environmental impact of our carbon-based Faustian lifestyle that scientists have now awarded our industrial period, a mere blink in geological time, its own title in the 4 billion year history of the planet: the **Anthropocene**. We are no longer simply biological creatures, one species among thousands, but biophysical agents, reshaping the ecology of the entire planet, and shaping the fates of all species.

Figure 10.9: Faust and Mephistopheles Mephistopheles, the devil figure in Goethe's play Faust, tempts Faust with the exhilaration of flight. From the air, it is easy for Faust to imagine himself lord of the earth, with no limits to his powers. *Source: Public Domain. Illustration by Alphonse de Neuville*[14]

In short, we are all Fausts now, not the insignificant, powerless creatures we sometime feel ourselves to be, but rather, the lords of the planet. How this came to pass is an object lesson in complex diachronic evolution. Without any single person deciding, or any law passed, or amendment made to the constitution, we have transformed ourselves over but a few centuries from one struggling species among all the rest, to being planetary managers, now apparently exempted from the evolutionary struggle for survival with other species, with the fate of animals, birds, fish, plants, the atmosphere, and entire ecosystems in our hands. This Faustian power signals both our strength and vulnerability. We are dependent on the very ecosystems we dominate. That is, we have become carbon-dependent by choice, but we are ecosystem-dependent by necessity. We may all be supermen and wonderwomen relative to the poor powers of our forebears, but we still require food, clean water, and clean air. The billion or more people on earth currently not plugged into the carbon energy grid, and hence living in dire poverty, need no reminding of this fact. Many of us in the developed world do, however. Our civilization and lifestyles as human beings have changed beyond recognition, but our biological needs are no different from our species ancestors on the East African savannah a million years ago. In sum, the lesson of the Faust story is hubris. We are not exempt from natural laws,

---

[14]http://en.wikipedia.org/wiki/File:Faust_et_mephistopheles.jpg

as Faust recklessly hoped.

To understand the impact of our fossil fuel based, industrialized society on the planet we inhabit requires we think on dual time scales. The first is easy enough, namely, the human scale of days and years. For example, consider the time it takes for liquid petroleum to be extracted from the earth, refined, transported to a gas station, and purchased by you in order to drive to school or the shopping Mall. Or the time it takes for that sweater you buy at the mall to be manufactured in China or Indonesia and transported thousands of miles to the shelf you grab it from. This is an oil-dependent process from beginning to end: from the petroleum-based fertilizers that maximized the productive efficiency of the cotton plantation, to powering the machinery in the factory, to the massive goods ship transporting your sweater across the oceans, to the lights in the store that illuminate your sweater at the precise angle for it to catch your eye.

Now consider the second time scale, to which we are usually oblivious—the thousands or millions of years it has taken for terrestrial carbon to form those reserves of liquid petroleum that brought you your sweater. This is a process describable only on a geological time scale, the costs of the disruption to which have been wholly omitted from the sticker price of the sweater. What are the environmental, and ultimately human costs that have been externalized? In powering our modern societies through the transference of the earth's carbon reserves from long-term storage and depositing it in the atmosphere and oceans, we have significantly altered and destabilized the earth's carbon cycle. There is now 40% more carbon in the atmosphere and oceans than in 1800, at the outset of the industrial age. The earth's climate system is reacting accordingly, to accommodate the increased nonterrestrial carbon load. The result is altered weather patterns, increasing temperatures, glacial melt, and sharp increases in droughts, floods, and wildfires. The cost to the global economy of these climate disruptions this century has been projected in the trillions of dollars, even before we consider the human costs of climate change in mortality, homelessness, impoverishment, and social instability.

Extracting carbon from the earth, and transforming it into energy, fertilizers, and products has enabled an almost magical transformation of human lives on earth, as compared to those of our premodern ancestors. The house you live in, the clothes you wear, the food you eat, the gadgets you use, and all the dreams you dream for your future, are carbon-based dreams. These amazing fossil-fuel energy sources—oil, coal, gas—have created modernity itself: a crest of population growth, economic development, prosperity, health and longevity, pulling millions out of poverty, and promoting, life, liberty, and happiness. This modernity is truly a thing of wonder, involving the high-speed mass transport of people, goods, and information across the globe, day after day. Regardless of the season, it brings us apples from New Zealand, avocadoes from Mexico, and tomatoes that have traveled an average of 2000 miles to reach the "fresh produce" section of our supermarkets. Having bought our groceries for the week, we jump in our car and drive home. Because our species ancestors were both nomads and settlers, we love our cars and homes with equal passion. We value both mobility and rootedness. Done with roaming for the day, we cherish our indoor lives in atmospherically controlled environments: cool when hot outside, toasty when cold, light when dark, with digital devices plugged in and available 24/7. A miraculous lifestyle when one sits back to reflect, and all the result of ongoing carbon-intensive investments in human comfort and convenience.

But it is also a 200-year chemistry experiment, with our planet as the laboratory. We are carbon beings in our own molecular biology; we touch and smell it; we trade, transport, and spill it; we consume and dispose of it in the earth and air. Intensifying heat and storms and acidifying oceans are carbon's elemental answer to the questions we have posed to the earth system's resilience. Mother Nature is having her say, acting according to her nature, and prompting us now to act according to our own mostly forgotten natures—as beings dependent on our ecosystem habitat of sun, rain, soil, plants, and animals, with no special allowance beyond the sudden responsibility of reformed stewardship and management.

The 2010 BP oil spill in the Gulf of Mexico (Section 10.7) was a spectacular warning that the 200-year era of cheap fossil fuel energy is drawing to a close. With viable oil reserves likely to be exhausted in the next decade or so, and the dangers to global climate associated with continued reliance on coal and natural gas, the transition to a sustainable, low-carbon global economy—by means that do not impoverish billions of people in the process—looms as nothing less than the Great Cause of the 21st century, and without doubt the greatest challenge humanity has faced in its long residence on earth. The stakes could not be higher for this task, which is of unprecedented scope and complexity. If enormous human and financial resources were expended in meeting the greatest challenges faced by the international community in the 20th century—the defeat of fascism, and the hard-earned progress made against poverty and infectious diseases—then the low-carbon sustainability revolution of our century will require the same scale of resources and more. At present, however, only a tiny fraction of those resources have been committed.

10.6 Case Study: Agriculture and the Global Bee Colony Collapse[15]

Two thousand years ago, at the height of the Roman Empire, the poet Virgil wrote lovingly about the practice of beekeeping, of cultivating the "aerial honey and ambrosial dews" he called "gifts of heaven" (*Georgics* IV: 1-2[16]). Bees represent a gift to humanity even greater that Virgil knew. In addition to satisfying the human appetite for honey, the Italian honeybee, *Apis melliflora*, is the world's most active pollinator, responsible for over 80 of the world's most common nongrain crops, including apples, berries, almonds, macadamias, pumpkins, melons, canola, avocadoes, and also coffee beans, broccoli and lettuce. Even the production chain of the enormous meat and cotton industries relies at crucial points on the ministrations of the humble honeybee. We depend on pollinated fruits, nuts and seeds for a third of our caloric intake, and for vital vitamins, minerals and antioxidants in our diet. In total, around 80% of the foods we eat are to some degree the products of bee pollination, representing one third of total agricultural output.

Given the $1 trillion value of pollinated produce, any threat to the health of honey bees represents a serious threat to the human food chain—a classic sustainability issue. With the industrialization of the global agricultural system over the last 50 years—including crop monoculture and mass fertilization—bees have indeed faced a series of threats to their ancient role, the most recent of which, so-called Colony Collapse Disorder, is the most serious yet.

---

[15]This content is available online at <http://legacy.cnx.org/content/m41055/1.5/>.

[16]http://www.theoi.com/Text/VirgilGeorgics2.html#4

Figure 10.10: Busy Bee Hive A forager honeybee comes in for landing at a healthy hive, her legs dusted with pollen. Colony Collapse Disorder has devastated tens of thousands of such hives. *Source: Ken Thomas*[17]

In his poetic primer on beekeeping, Virgil includes a moving description of a bee colony suffering mysterious decline:

Observe the symptoms when they fall away

And languish with insensible decay.

They change their hue; with haggard eyes they stare . . .

The sick, for air, before the portal gasp,

Their feeble legs within each other clasp,

Or idle in their empty hives remain,

---

[17]http://en.wikipedia.org/wiki/File:Honeybees-27527-2.jpg

Benumbed with cold, and listless of their gain. (368-78)

Beekeepers worldwide faced an even worse predicament in late 2006: the mysterious disappearance of entire hives of bees. Over the winter, honeybees enter a form of survival hibernation. Their populations suffer inevitable losses, but these are replenished by the Queen's renewed laying of eggs once winter thaws. In the spring of 2007, however, hundreds of thousands of colonies in the United States did not survive the winter. A full 30% of all honeybee colonies died. Each spring since has witnessed even worse declines. Similar losses afflicted Europe and Asia. Worldwide, millions of colonies and billions of bees have perished since 2006 on account of the new bee plague.

Because the global commercial value of bee pollination is so enormous, well-funded research into colony collapse began immediately. A number of theories, some credible, some not, were quickly advanced. Several studies pointed to new or enhanced viral strains, while others suggested the toxic effect of industrial fertilization. Still others claimed that mobile phone towers were interfering with the bees' navigations systems. Because the honeybee is a charismatic creature and features so prominently in our cultural lore—we admire their industriousness, fear their stings, call our loved ones "honey," and talk much of Queen Bees—the story of colony collapse was quickly taken up by the media. A flurry of news stories announced CCD as an epic "disaster" and profound "mystery," which was true in simple terms, but which cast bee decline as a new and sudden calamity for which some single culprit must be responsible.

The truth, as it is now unfolding, is more complex, and shows the importance of viewing the interactions between human and natural ecologies in systemic terms. In strictly pathogenic terms, CCD is caused by the combination of a virus (called *Iridoviridae* or IIV) and a microsporidian fungus called *Nosema*. The specific interaction between the pathogens, and why they cause bees in their millions to vacate their hives, is not understood. What is becoming clear, however, is the increasing burden being placed on bees by the human agricultural system, a burden that has rendered bees increasingly vulnerable to epidemic infection. Humans have been keeping bees for eight thousand years, and European bees were at the vanguard of the successful crop colonization of the Americas. But the numbers of bees in the United States had already declined by a third since 1950 before the arrival of CCD, owing to various viral and mite infestations, and the large scale changes in bee habitat and lifestyle.

Before the industrialization of farming, bees came from neighboring wildlands to pollinate the diverse range of crops available to them on small plots. But the conversion, for economic reasons, of arable land into enormous monocrop properties in the last sixty years, and hence the diminishment of proximate wildflower habitats, has necessitated a different system, whereby bees are trucked around the country to service one crop at a time, be it peppers in Florida, blueberries in Maine, or almonds in California. At the height of the recent almond boom, the California crop required almost the entire bee population of the United States to be fully pollinated. Wholesale suburbanization is also to blame for the destruction of the bees' natural wildflower habitats. Be it a thousand acre cornfield or a suburban street of well-tended green lawns, to a bees' eyes, our modern landscape, engineered to human needs, is mostly a desert.

Studies that have not identified specific culprits for CCD have nevertheless shown the extent of the long-term decline in bee health wrought by their conscription to industrial agriculture. For instance, researchers found no fewer than 170 different pesticides in samples of American honeybees, while other studies found that even bees not suffering CCD habitually carry multiple viral strains in their systems. The combined toxic and viral load for the average honeybee is enormous. In the words of Florida's state apiarist, "I'm surprised honey bees are alive at all." (Jacobsen, 2008, p. 137 (p. 501)) A further study showed a decline in the immune systems of bees owing to lack of diverse nutrition. Pollinating only almonds for weeks on end, then travelling on a flatbed truck for hundreds of miles in order to service another single crop, is not the lifestyle bees have adapted to over the near 80 million years of their existence. As Virgil warned, "First, for thy bees a quiet station find." The lives of modern bees have been anything but quiet, and the enormous changes in their habitat and lifestyle have reduced their species' resilience.

The most important lesson of recent research into CCD is not the identification of IIV and *Nosema* as the specific contributors, but the larger picture it has provided of a system under multiple long-term stresses. Complex systems, such as bee pollination and colony maintenance, are not characterized by linear development, but rather by sudden, nonlinear changes of state called **tipping points**. CCD is an example of a potential tipping point in a natural system on which humans depend, in which sudden deterioration overtakes a population beyond its ability to rebound. Everything seems fine, until it isn't. One day we have almonds, berries, melon, and coffee on our breakfast menu. The next day there's a critical shortage, and we can't afford them.

In sustainability terms, bee colony collapse is a classic "human dimensions" issue. CCD will not be "solved" simply by the development of a new anti-viral drug or pesticide targeting the specific pathogens responsible. Part of what has caused CCD is the immunosuppressive effects of generations of pesticides developed to counter previous threats to bee populations, be they microbes or mites. Our chemical intervention in the lifecycle of bees has, in evolutionary terms, "selected" for a more vulnerable bee. That is, bees' current lack of resilience is a systemic problem in our historical relationship to bees, which dates back thousands of years, but which has altered dramatically in the last fifty years in ways that now threaten collapse. And this is to say nothing of the impact of bee colony collapse on other pollination-dependent animals and birds, which would indeed be catastrophic in biodiversity terms.

That we have adapted to bees, and they to us, is a deep cultural and historical truth, not simply a sudden "disaster" requiring the scientific solution of a "mystery." In the light of sustainability systems analysis, the bee crisis appears entirely predictable and the problem clear cut. The difficulty arises in crafting strategies for how another complex system on a massive scale, namely global agriculture, can be reformed in order to prevent *its* collapse as one flow-on effect of the global crisis of the vital honey bee. The incentive for such reform could not be more powerful. The prospect of a future human diet without fruits, nuts and coffee is bleak enough for citizens of the developed world and potentially fatal for millions of others in the long term.

10.6.1 Review Questions

Question 10.6.1
What is the long history of the human relationship to bees, and what radical changes in that relationship have occurred over the last fifty years to bring it to the point of collapse? What are the implications of bee colony collapse for the global food system?

10.6.2 References

Jacobsen, R. (2008). Fruitless Fall: The Collapse of the Honey Bee and the Coming Agricultural Crisis. New York: Bloomsbury

10.7 Case Study: Energy and the BP Oil Disaster[18]

On the night of April 20, 2010, the Deepwater Horizon oil rig, one of hundreds operating in the Gulf of Mexico, exploded, killing eleven men, and placing one of the most rich and diverse coastal regions on earth in imminent danger of petroleum poisoning. BP had been drilling in waters a mile deep, and in the next two days, as the rig slowly sank, it tore a gash in the pipe leading to the oil well on the ocean floor. Over the next three months, two hundred million gallons of crude oil poured into the Gulf, before the technological means could be found to seal the undersea well. It was the worst environmental disaster in American history, and the largest peacetime oil spill ever.

---

[18]This content is available online at <http://legacy.cnx.org/content/m41066/1.5/>.

Figure 10.11: The Deepwater Horizon Oil Rig on Fire The Deepwater Horizon oil rig on fire, April, 2010. It would later sink, precipitating the worst environmental disaster in United States history. *Source: Public Domain U.S. Coast Guard*[19]

The BP oil disaster caused untold short- and long-term damage to the region. The initial impact on the Gulf—the oil washing up on beaches from Texas to Florida, and economic hardship caused by the closing down of Gulf fishing—was covered closely by the news media. The longer term impacts of the oil spill on wetlands erosion, and fish and wildlife populations, however, will not likely receive as much attention.

Much public debate over the spill has focused on the specific causes of the spill itself, and in apportioning responsibility. As with the example of bee colony collapse, however, the search for simple, definitive causes can be frustrating, because the breakdown is essentially systemic. Advanced industries such as crop pollination and oil extraction involve highly complex interactions among technological, governmental, economic, and natural resource systems. With that complexity comes vulnerability. The more complex a system, the more points at which its resiliency may be suddenly exposed. In the case of the Deepwater Horizon rig, multiple technological "safeguards" simply did not work, while poor and sometimes corrupt government oversight of the rig's operation also amplified the vulnerability of the overall system—a case of governmental system failure making technological failure in industry more likely, with an environmental disaster as the result.

In hindsight, looking at all the weaknesses in the Gulf oil drilling system, the BP spill appears inevitable.

---

[19]http://en.wikipedia.org/wiki/File:Deepwater_Horizon_offshore_drilling_unit_on_fire_2010.jpg

But predicting the specific vulnerabilities within large, complex systems ahead of time can be next to impossible because of the quantity of variables at work. Oil extraction takes place within a culture of profit maximization and the normalization of risk, but in the end, the lesson of BP oil disaster is more than a cautionary tale of corporate recklessness and lax government oversight. The very fact that BP was drilling under such risky conditions—a mile underwater, in quest of oil another three miles under the ocean floor—is an expression of the global demand for oil, the world's most valuable energy resource. To understand that demand, and the lengths to which the global energy industry will go to meet it, regardless of environmental risk, requires the longer view of our modern history as a fossil-fueled species.

10.7.1 Review Questions

Question 10.7.1
In what ways is the BP Oil Disaster of 2010 an example of complex human systems failure, and what are its longer chains of causation in the history of human industrialization?

10.8 Sustainability Ethics[20]

10.8.1 Learning Objectives

After reading this module, students should be able to

- understand the principle of the *intergenerational social contract* at the core of sustainability ethics
- define the global terms of responsibility for action on sustainability, both the *remote responsibilities* applicable to you as an individual consumer, and the historically-based concept of *shared but differentiated responsibilities* driving negotiations between nations in different hemispheres

10.8.2 Developing an Ethics of Sustainability

The 1987 United Nations Brundtland definition of sustainability[21] embodies an *intergenerational contract*: to provide for our present needs, while not compromising the ability of future generations to meet their needs. It's a modest enough proposal on the face of it, but it challenges our current expectations of the intergenerational contract: we expect each new generation to be better off than their parents. Decades of technological advancement and economic growth have created a mindset not satisfied with "mere" sustainability. We might call it turbo-materialism or a **cornucopian** worldview: namely that the earth's bounty, adapted to our use by human ingenuity, guarantees a perpetual growth in goods and services. At the root of the cornucopian worldview lies a brand of technological triumphalism, an unshakeable confidence in technological innovation to solve all social and environmental problems, be it world hunger, climate change, or declining oil reserves. In sustainability discourse, there is a wide spectrum of opinion from the extremes of cornucopian optimism on one side and to the doom-and-gloom scenarios that suggest it is already too late to avert a new Dark Age of resource scarcity and chronic conflict on the other.

---

[20]This content is available online at <http://legacy.cnx.org/content/m41069/1.6/>.
[21]http://en.wikipedia.org/wiki/Our_Common_Future

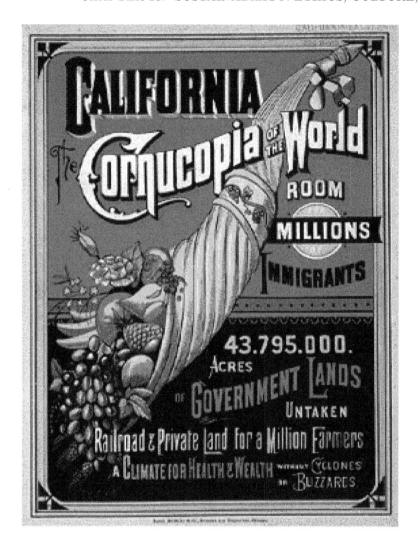

Figure 10.12: **California, the Cornucopia of the World** Cover of an 1885 promotional book prepared by the California Immigration Commission. *Source: The California State Library*[22]

For every generation entering a Dark Age, there were parents who enjoyed a better life, but who somehow failed to pass along their prosperity. No one wants to fail their children in this way. To this extent, biology dictates multigenerational thinking and ethics. Though it might not always be obvious, we are all already the beneficiaries of multi-generational planning. The world-leading American higher education system, for example, depends upon an intergenerational structure and logic—a financial and human investment in the future committed to by multiple generations of Americans going back to the 19th century. But conversely, in terms of vulnerability, just as higher education in the United States is neither necessarily permanent nor universal, but a social institution built on an unwritten contract between generations, so the lifestyle benefits of advanced society as we know it will not simply perpetuate themselves without strenuous efforts to place them on a sustainable footing.

Our current problem lies in the fact that multigenerational thinking is so little rewarded. Our economic and political systems as they have evolved in the Industrial Age reward a mono-generational mindset driven

---

[22]http://www.library.ca.gov/calhist/

by short-term profits and election cycles. In the West, for example, there is no significant political philosophy, regulatory system, or body of law that enshrines the idea that we act under obligation to future generations, despite widely held views that we naturally must. One challenge of sustainability is to channel our natural biological interest in the future into a new ethics and politics based on multigenerational principles. Many indigenous communities in the world, marginalized or destroyed by colonialism and industrialization, have long recognized the importance of sustainability in principles of governance, and provide inspiring models. The Great Law of the Iroquois Confederacy, for example, states that all decisions made by its elders should be considered in light of their impact seven generations into the future.

To embrace an ethics of sustainability is to accept that our rapid industrialization has placed us in the role of planetary managers, responsible for the health, or ruinous decline, of many of the globe's vital ecosystems. This ethics requires we activate, in the popular sense, both sides of our brain. That is, we must toggle between a rational consideration of our environmental footprint and practical issues surrounding the reinvention of our systems of resource management, and a more humble, intuitive sense of our dependence and embeddness within the web of life. Both reason and emotion come into play. Without emotion, there can be no motivation for change. Likewise, without an intellectual foundation for sustainability, our desire for change will be unfocused and ineffective. We are capable of adapting to a complex world and reversing broad-based ecosystem decline. But to do so will require technical knowledge wedded to an ethical imagination. We need to extend to the natural world the same moral sense we intuitively apply to the social world and our relations with other people.

Sustainability ethics thus does not need to be invented from whole cloth. It represents, in some sense, a natural extension of the ethical principles dominant in the progressive political movements of the 20th century, which emphasized the rights of historically disenfranchised communities, such as women, African-Americans, and the global poor. Just as we have been pressed to speak for dispossessed peoples who lack a political voice, so we must learn the language of the nonhuman animal and organic world, of "nature," and to speak for it. Not simply for charity's sake, or out of selfless concern, but for our own sake as resource-dependent beings.

10.8.3 Remote Responsibilities

What distinguishes an ethics of sustainability from general ethical principles is its emphasis on **remote responsibilities**, that is, our moral obligation to consider the impact of our actions on people and places far removed from us. This distance may be measured in both space and time. First, in spatial terms, we, as consumers in the developed world, are embedded in a global web of commerce, with an ethical responsibility toward those who extract and manufacture the goods we buy, whether it be a polo shirt from Indonesia, or rare metals in our computer extracted from mines in Africa. The economic and media dimensions of our consumer society do not emphasize these connections; in fact, it is in the interests of "consumer confidence" (a major economic index) to downplay the disparities in living standards between the markets of the developed world and the manufacturing countries of the global south (Africa, Asia, Latin America), which serve as the factories of the world.

Second, as for sustainability ethics considered in temporal terms, the moral imagination required to understand our remote responsibilities poses an even greater challenge. As we have seen, the landmark United Nations Brundtland Report[23] establishes an ethical contract between the living and those yet to be born. For an industrial civilization founded on the no-limits extraction of natural resources and on maximizing economic growth in the short term, this is actually a profoundly difficult challenge to meet. More than that, the practical ethical dilemmas it poses to us in the present are complex. How, for instance, are we to balance the objectives of economic development in poorer nations—the need to lift the world's "bottom billion" out of poverty—with the responsibility to conserve resources for future generations, while at the same time making the difficult transition from industrialized fossil fuels to a low-carbon global economy?

The issue of fairness with regard to individual nations' carbon emissions reduction mandates is a specific example of how ethical issues can complicate, or even derail, negotiated treaties on environmental sustain-

---

[23]http://en.wikipedia.org/wiki/Our_Common_Future

ability, even when the parties agree on the end goal. In the view of the developing countries of the global south, many of them once subject to colonial regimes of the north, the advanced industrialized countries, such as the United States and Europe, should bear a heavier burden in tackling climate change through self-imposed restraints on carbon consumption. They after all have been, over the last 200 years, the principal beneficiaries of carbon-driven modernization, and thus the source of the bulk of damaging emissions. For them now to require developing nations to curb their own carbon-based modernization for the benefit of the global community reeks of neo-colonial hypocrisy. Developing nations such as India thus speak of **common but differentiated responsibilities** as the ethical framework from which to justly share the burden of transition to a low-carbon global economy.

From the point of view of the rich, industrialized nations, by contrast, whatever the appearance of historical injustice in a carbon treaty, all nations will suffer significant, even ruinous contractions of growth if an aggressive mitigation agreement among all parties is not reached. Some commentators in the West have further argued that the sheer scale and complexity of the climate change problem means it cannot effectively be addressed through a conventional rights-based and environmental justice approach. To this degree at least, the sustainability issue distinguishes itself as different in degree and kind from the landmark social progressive movements of the 20th century, such as women's emancipation, civil rights, and multiculturalism, to which it has often been compared.

Disputes over the complex set of tradeoffs between environmental conservation and economic development have dominated environmental policy and treaty discussions at the international level for the last half century, and continue to stymie progress on issues such as climate change, deforestation, and biofuels. These problems demonstrate that at the core of sustainability ethics lies a classic *tragedy of the commons*, namely, the intractable problem of persuading individuals, or individual nations, to take specific responsibility for resources that have few or no national boundaries (the atmosphere, the oceans), or which the global economy allows to be extracted from faraway countries, the environmental costs of which are thus "externalized" (food, fossil fuels, etc). How the international community settles the problem of shared accountability for a rapidly depleting global commons, and balances the competing objectives of economic development and environmental sustainability, will to a large extent determine the degree of decline of the planet's natural capital this century. One tragic prospect looms: If there is no international commitment, however patchwork, to protect the global resource commons, then the gains in economic prosperity, poverty alleviation and public health in the developing world so hard won by international agencies over the second half of the 20th century, will quickly be lost.

Figure 10.13: Tragedy of Commons The tragedy of the commons is evident in many areas of our lives, particularly in the environment. The over-fishing of our oceans that causes some marine life to be in danger of extinction is a good example. *Source: Food and Agriculture Organization of the United Nations*[24]

10.8.4 Precautionary Principle

The **precautionary principle** is likewise central to sustainability ethics. The margins of uncertainty are large across many fields of the biophysical sciences. Simply put, there is a great deal we do not know about the specific impacts of human activities on the natural resources of land, air, and water. In general, however, though we might not have known where the specific thresholds of resilience lie in a given system—say in the sardine population of California's coastal waters—the vulnerability of ecosystems to human resource extraction is a constant lesson of environmental history. A prosperous and vital economic engine, the Californian sardine fishery collapsed suddenly in the 1940s due to overfishing. The precautionary principle underlying sustainability dictates that in the face of high risk or insufficient data, the priority should lie with ecosystem preservation rather than on industrial development and market growth.

---

[24]http://www.fao.org/docrep/003/X7579E/x7579e05.gif

Figure 10.14: Great Fish Market by Jan Brueghel Though we might not have known where
the specific thresholds of resilience lie in a given system—say in the sardine population of California's
coastal waters—the vulnerability of ecosystems to human resource extraction is a constant lesson of
environmental history. *Source: Public Domain*[25]

Sustainability, in instances such as these, is not a sexy concept. It's a hard sell. It is a philosophy of
limits in a world governed by dreams of infinite growth and possibility. Sustainability dictates that we are
constrained by earth's resources as to the society and lifestyle we can have. On the other hand, sustainability
is a wonderful, inspiring concept, a quintessentially human idea. The experience of our own limits need not
be negative. In fact, what more primitive and real encounter between ourselves and the world than to feel
our essential dependence on the biospheric elements that surround us, that embeddedness with the air, the
light, the warmth or chill on our skins, and the stuff of earth we eat or buy to propel ourselves over immense
distances at speed unimaginable to the vast armies of humanity who came before us.

Sustainability studies is driven by an ethics of the future. The word itself, sustainability, points to proofs
that can only be projected forward in time. To be sustainable is, by definition, to be attentive to what is to
come. So sustainability requires imagination, but sustainability studies is also a profoundly historical mode,
committed toreconstruction of the long, nonlinear evolutions of our dominant extractivist and instrumentalist
views of the natural world, and of the "mind-forg'd manacles" of usage and ideology that continue to limit
our ecological understanding and inhibit mainstream acceptance of the sustainability imperative.

Sustainability studies thus assumes the complex character of its subject, multiscalar in time and space,
and dynamically agile and adaptive in its modes. Sustainability teaches that the environment is not a
sideshow, or a scenic backdrop to our lives. A few more or less species. A beautiful mountain range here or
there. Our relation to our natural resources is the key to our survival. That's why it's called "sustainability."

---

[25]http://en.wikipedia.org/wiki/File:An_Brueghel_the_Elder-Great_Fish_market.jpg

It's the grounds of possibility for everything else. Unsustainability, conversely, means human possibilities and quality of life increasingly taken away from us and the generations to come.

10.8.5 Review Questions

Question 10.8.1

What does it mean to say that global environmental problems such as climate change and ocean acidification represent a "tragedy of the commons?" How are global solutions to be tied to local transitions toward a sustainable society?

Question 10.8.2

How does sustainability imply an "ethics of the future?" And in what ways does sustainability ethics both borrow and diverge from the principles that drove the major progressive social movements of the 20th century?

Chapter 11

Sustainable Infrastructure

11.1 Sustainable Infrastructure - Chapter Introduction[1]

11.1.1 Introduction

At present 80% of the US population lives in urban regions, a percentage that has grown steadily over the past two hundred years. Urban infrastructures have historically supported several needs of the population served: the supply of goods, materials and services upon which we rely; collection, treatment and disposal of waste products; adequate transportation alternatives; access to power and communication grids; a quality public education system; maintenance of a system of governance that is responsive, efficient and fair; generation of sufficient financial and social capital to maintain and renew the region; and insurance of the basic elements of safety and public health. Collectively, these needs have been perceived as the basic attributes needed to make an urban region livable.

Urban infrastructures are designed and built in response to social needs and economies of scale that urbanization has brought about. Although our urban infrastructures are in many ways remarkable achievements of engineering design that were conceived and built during times of rapid urbanization, as they have aged and, inevitably, deteriorated; significant strains on their function and ability to provide services have become evident. In its program to identify the "grand challenges" facing society in the near future, the National Academy of Engineering has proposed several focus areas, among them the restoration and improvement of urban infrastructures. Such a challenge involves the need for renewal, but also presents opportunities for re-envisioning the basis of infrastructure design and function as we move forward. Urban infrastructures of the past were not generally conceived in concert with evolutionary social and ecological processes. This has resulted in several characteristic attributes: conceptual models of infrastructure that perceive local ecological systems either indifferently or as obstacles to be overcome rather than assets for harmonious designs; a general reliance on centralized facilities; structures that often lack operational flexibility such that alternative uses may be precluded during times of crisis; heavy use of impervious and heat absorbing materials; systems that have become increasingly costly to maintain and that are often excessively consumptive of natural resources on a life cycle basis; and a built environment the materials and components of which are often difficult to reuse or recycle.

The urban environment is an example of a complex human-natural system. The resiliency of such systems lies in their capacity to maintain essential organization and function in response to disturbances (of both long and short duration). A complimentary view, inspired by traditional ecological and economic thought focuses on the degree of damage a system can withstand without exhibiting a "regime" shift, defined as a transition that changes the structure and functioning of the system from one state to another as a result of one or more independent factors. Upon exceeding a given threshold, the system shifts to a new alternative state which may not be readily reversed through manipulation of causative factors. In the context of human-

---

[1]This content is available online at <http://legacy.cnx.org/content/m44985/1.1/>.

natural systems, regime shifts can have significant consequences, and not all shifts are preferred by the human component of the system. To the extent that change of some order is a given property of essentially all dynamic systems, "preferred" resiliency might be viewed as the extent to which human societies can adapt to such shifts with acceptable levels of impacts. Resilient infrastructures, then, are those which most readily facilitate such adaptation. Much of the foregoing discussion also applies to sustainability, with the added constraints of the sustainability paradigm: the equitable and responsible distribution of resources among humans, present and future, in ways that do not harm, and ideally reinforce, the social and biological systems upon which human society is based. Although there are important differences between those two concepts, there remains a close interrelationship that stems from the same need: to understand and design urban infrastructural systems that enhance human interactions with the environment.

It is beyond the scope of this book to present an exhaustive treatment of the urban environment, indeed there are many books and treatises on this topic. But in this chapter several important aspects of urban resiliency and sustainability are presented, beginning with the concept of a sustainable city, and proceeding through various elements of urban systems: buildings, energy and climate action planning, transportation, and stormwater management. The chapter concludes with a case study of a net zero energy home, one in which perhaps you can envision yourself inhabiting one day.

11.1.2 Further Reading

Nancy B. Grimm, Stanley H. Faeth, Nancy E. Golubiewski, Charles L. Redman, Jianguo Wu, Xuemei Bai, and John M. Briggs (2008). "Global Change and the Ecology of Cities", Science 8 February 2008: Vol. 319 no. 5864 pp. 756-760 DOI: 10.1126/science.1150195.

11.2 The Sustainable City[2]

11.2.1 Learning Objectives

After reading this module, students should be able to

- imagine what a sustainable city will look like and what it will mean to live in one
- understand how technology will influence the form and pattern of the sustainable city
- explore the connections between the design of our cities and resource use
- recognize that sustainability means we will have to share the earth's bounty with all of the earth's inhabitants
- think about how one's lifestyle will have to be altered in order to live more sustainably

---

[2]This content is available online at <http://legacy.cnx.org/content/m44935/1.2/>.

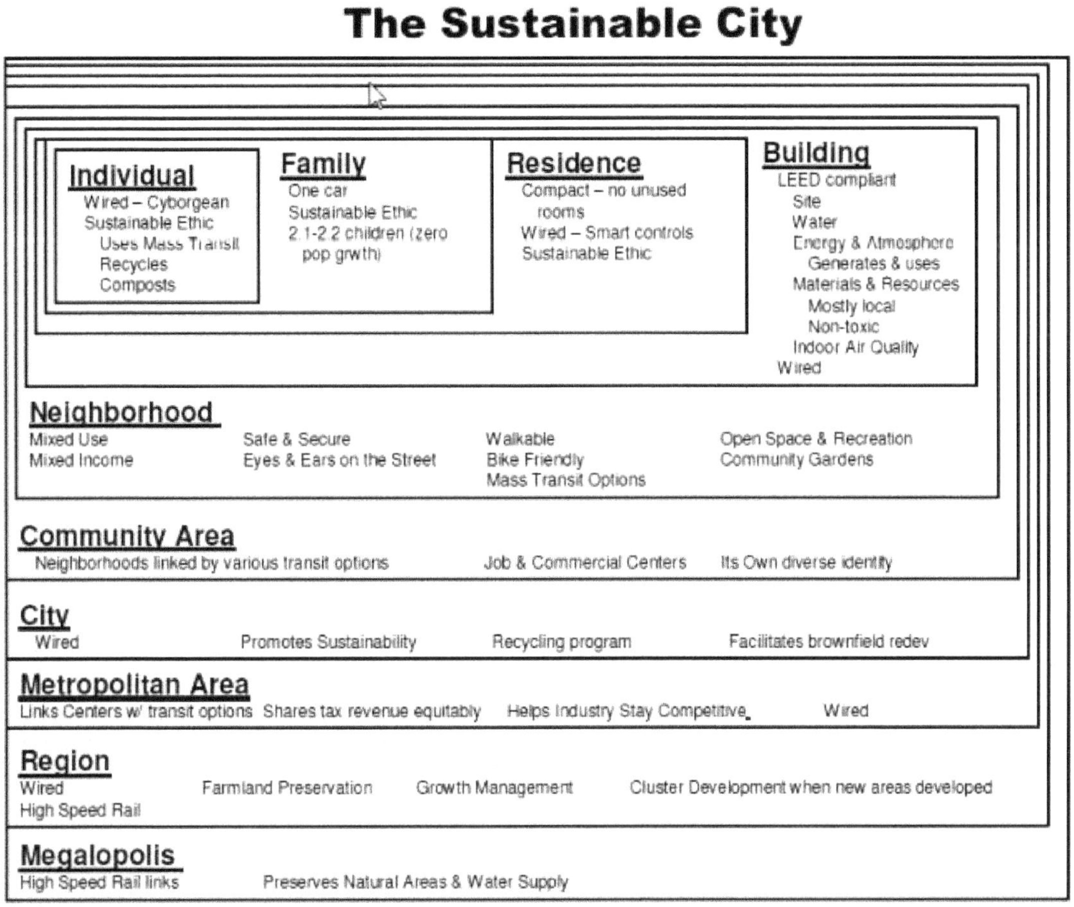

The Sustainable City

Individual
Wired – Cyborgean
Sustainable Ethic
Uses Mass Transit
Recycles
Composts

Family
One car
Sustainable Ethic
2.1-2.2 children (zero pop grwth)

Residence
Compact – no unused rooms
Wired – Smart controls
Sustainable Ethic

Building
LEED compliant
Site
Water
Energy & Atmosphere
Generates & uses
Materials & Resources
Mostly local
Non-toxic
Indoor Air Quality
Wired

Neighborhood
Mixed Use   Safe & Secure   Walkable   Open Space & Recreation
Mixed Income   Eyes & Ears on the Street   Bike Friendly   Community Gardens
                                           Mass Transit Options

Community Area
Neighborhoods linked by various transit options   Job & Commercial Centers   Its Own diverse identity

City
Wired   Promotes Sustainability   Recycling program   Facilitates brownfield redev

Metropolitan Area
Links Centers w/ transit options   Shares tax revenue equitably   Helps Industry Stay Competitive   Wired

Region
Wired   Farmland Preservation   Growth Management   Cluster Development when new areas developed
High Speed Rail

Megalopolis
High Speed Rail links   Preserves Natural Areas & Water Supply

Figure 11.1

11.2.2 Introduction

Sustainability, from science to philosophy to lifestyle, finds expression in the way we shape our cities. Cities are not just a collection of structures, but rather groups of people living different lifestyles together. When we ask if a lifestyle is sustainable, we're asking if it can endure. Some archaeologists posit that environmental imbalance doomed many failed ancient civilizations.

What could the sustainable city look like, how would it function, and how can we avoid an imbalance that will lead to the collapse of our material civilization? This module will make some educated guesses based upon the ideas and practices of some of today's bold innovators.

Throughout history settlement patterns have been set by technology and commerce. Civilizations have produced food, clothing and shelter, and accessed foreign markets to purchase and sell goods. Workers traditionally had to live near their place of occupation, although in modern industrial times advanced transportation systems have enabled us to live quite a distance from where we work.

In hindsight we can see how reliance on water and horse-drawn transportation shaped historical civilizations and how this equation was radically altered with the rise of the automobile following World War II. While attempting to envision the "Sustainable City" we must discern what factors will influence its shape and form in the future.

11.2.3 Energy

For the last century energy has been affordable and plentiful, limited mainly by our technological ability to use it. Contemporary civilization consumes 474 exajoules (474×10^{18} J=132,000 TWh). This is equivalent to an average annual power consumption rate of 15 terawatts (1.504×10^{13} W).

The potential for renewable energy is: solar energy 1,600 EJ (444,000 TWh), wind power 600 EJ (167,000 Wh), geothermal energy 500 EJ (139,000 TWh), biomass 250 EJ (70,000 TWh), hydropower 50 EJ (14,000 TWh) and ocean energy 1 EJ (280 TWh).[3] Even though it is possible to meet all of our present energy needs with renewables, we do not do so because the way in which the market prices our fossil reserves. In the current framework, when a company exploits resources it normally does not account for the loss of resource base or for environmental damage. Gasoline has been cheap in the United States because its price does not reflect the cost of smog, acid rain, and their subsequent effects on health and the environment

let alone recognize that the oil reserves are being depleted. Scientists are working on fusion nuclear energy; if that puzzle is solved energy will be affordable, plentiful and carbon neutral. See Environmental and Resource Economics (Section 6.1) and Sustainable Energy Systems (Section 8.1) for more detail.

11.2.4 Materials & Waste

Scientists are producing materials not previously known to nature with unpredictable effects on bio-systems. Some, such as dioxin, are highly toxic; others (e.g. xenoestrogens[4] - which act as endocrine disruptors) have more subtle effects. In the future the government will likely continue to expand its regulation of the production, use and disposal of chemicals. Even heretofore benign processes, such as the production of garbage and greenhouse gases, will probably need to be controlled as civilization exceeds the capacity of natural systems to absorb and recycle our waste products.

Recycling and composting will reduce waste streams and "material exchanges" will take waste from one group and transfer it efficiently to others, thus reducing trash volume. Chicago's Rebuilding Exchange[5] , for instance, allows donors to take a tax deduction while it chargers buyers a greatly reduced fee to reuse materials that would otherwise be sent to the landfill. Although the Rebuilding Exchange is a physical location, similar material exchanges could be virtual as they connect seller/donors to buyers/users online. Old landfills might be mined as raw material use by a larger developed world (the addition of Asia's billions) creates demand while technology drives down the cost of extraction. These modern economic realities, along with the arrival of useful technology, represent the rise of collaborative consumption[6] .

Long before modern lighting and HVAC systems were developed, buildings relied upon natural light and ventilation. With support from a growing body of science supporting the public health benefits, contemporary designers are rediscovering the role biophilia – the human affinity for nature – plays in the spaces we occupy. When adjacent to residential areas, green spaces have been shown to create neighborhoods with fewer violent and property crimes and where neighbors tend to support and protect one another.

Studies have shown that natural daylight increases commercial sales
and green schools improve test scores
. Biomimicry is also part of the green revolution. The idea behind biomimicry is that nature has already solved many of the challenges that face us. One example is the development of new friction-free surfaces, modeled on the slippery skin of the Arabian Peninsula's sandfish lizard, an advance that could eliminate the use of ball bearings in many products as well as industrial diamond dust in automobile air bags. The pearl oyster uses carbon dioxide to construct its calcium carbonate shell, so a Canadian company developed

---

[4]http://en.wikipedia.org/wiki/Xenoestrogen
[5]http://www.rebuildingexchange.org/
[6]http://en.wikipedia.org/wiki/Collaborative_consumption

a technology that reduces large amounts of CO^2 in cement production. 300,000 buildings in Europe use self-cleaning glass that mimics the way water balls up on lotus leaves and simply rolls off.

In the future, we should see more of a return to natural systems as well as the use of new materials that mimic nature in our sustainable city.

11.2.5 Social Equity

Perhaps the most significant development that separates sustainability from its conservation antecedents is the element of social equity. The environmental and conservation movements have been criticized in the past for being too "white collar" and promoting the interests of the "haves"; these movements have traditionally not dealt with the needs of the underclass in the U.S. and, especially, developing countries. In Agenda 21[7] , the manifesto of the Earth Summit[8] conference on the environment held in Rio de Janeiro in 1992, sustainable development was viewed as the strategy that would be needed to increase the basic standard of living of the world's expanding population without unnecessarily depleting our finite natural resources and further degrading the environment upon which we all depend.

The challenge, as viewed at the Earth Summit, was posed in terms of asking humanity to collectively step back from the brink of environmental collapse and, at the same time, lift its poorest members up to the level of basic human health and dignity.

The concept of **ecological footprint** asks each of us to limit resource use to our equitable share. Sitting on the apex of civilization the Western world is being asked to share the earth's bounty with the masses of Asia, South America and Africa. If technology continues to advance we can do this without significant long-term degradation of our standard of living. Short-term economic dislocations are inevitable, however, as increasing demand from China and India bring us to peak oil and rising transportation costs will highlight the nexus between location efficiency and affordable housing. The Center for Neighborhood Technology[9] , for instance, has mapped 337 metropolitan areas[10] covering 80% of the United States population showing how efficient (near mass transit) locations reduce the cost of living (housing + utilities transportation) and vice versa. The reality of rising transportation costs could have a significant impact on the shape of the city. Lookin target-id="targetid"g backward we also realize that racial politics were one of the dynamics that fueled suburban expansion in the 50's and 60's decimating many of our urban centers. The Sustainable City of the future, if it works, will have stably integrated mixed income neighborhoods.

11.2.6 Technology

Computers brought intelligence to the Machine Age and transformed it into the Information Age. Markets run on information and better information will help the markets perform more efficiently. Whereas in the past surrogate measures were developed to guess at impacts, information technology can track actual use. For example, do we charge everyone the same fee for water and sewers or do we measure their use, charge proportionally, and thus encourage landowners to reduce their use? In Miami the (congestion pricing) charge for driving in the special lanes goes up instantaneously with actual traffic conditions. As the old adage goes, "What gets measured gets managed," and as technology increases the precision to which environmental measures, consumption, and behavior increases, our ability to manage, and therefore reduce negative impacts, will increase.

In the past humans have been one of the beasts of burden and workers have been needed to produce and move goods. Modern factories reduce human labour needs and artificial intelligence will soon carry most of the load in our partnership with machines. In the Information Age humans should no longer have to live and work near the factories and centers of commerce and jobs will move from the production of goods to the provision of services. People may choose to live in exciting urban centers, but if one wants a bucolic life style telework will offer an alternative.

---

[7]http://www.un.org/esa/dsd/agenda21/

[8]http://en.wikipedia.org/wiki/Earth_Summit

[9]http://www.cnt.org/

[10]http://htaindex.cnt.org/

11.2.7 Shrinking Cities

Many American cities have declined in population from highs immediately following World War II, even as the host metropolitan area has continued to grow. While populations have declined poverty and other social problems have been concentrated.[11] In the United States, nearly 5,000,000 acres of vacant property (including brownfields) exist. This is equivalent to the combined land area of the nation's 60 largest cities.

Some Shrinking Cities

City	Year	Population	Population Loss
Detroit	1950	1,850,000	
	2008	912,000	50.7%
Cleveland	1950	914,000	
	2008	433,000	52.6%
St. Louis	1960	750,000	
	2008	354,000	52.8%
Akron	1960	290,000	
	2008	207,000	28.6%
Cincinnati	1950	503,000	
	2008	333,000	33.8%
Dayton	1960	262,000	
	2008	155,000	40.8%
Flint	1960	196,000	
	2008	112,000	42.9%
Gary	1960	178,000	
	2008	96,000	46.1%
Canton	1950	116,000	
	2008	78,000	32.8%
Youngstown	1960	168,000	
	2008	72,000	57.1%

Data from U.S. Census Bureau

Figure 11.2

The traditional planning approach has been to focus on managing growth and new development through time-honored tools such as comprehensive planning, zoning, subdivision regulations, and urban growth boundaries.

Central City Revitalization." Journal of the American Planning Association, 69(4), 381-396.

This growth-oriented approach to addressing the shrinking city is now criticized.

Cantz Verlag

Some commentators postulate that green infrastructure offers a better model for improving these cities health.

How could these factors manifest themselves in our sustainable city? They will influence its design and our settlement patterns will influence our lifestyles. You are not only what you eat but also where you live. For instance:

11.2.8 Transportation

Most agree that **walkability** is a key component of any sustainable neighborhood. Walkability not only reduces energy use, but also increases public health. How can we measure walkability? Walkscore.com[12] identifies and measures nearby amenities and provides a rating for specific locations and neighborhoods. Try it for where you live.

Sustainable cities could consist of walkable neighborhoods that separate pedestrian, bike and vehicular traffic and are connected to each other through multiple transportation modes, with biking and mass transit choices in addition to the automobile. Instead of averaging 10 (auto) trips per unit per day

most residents would not use an automobile daily and instead walk or bike or order online. Trip generation would be reduced through telework and ecommerce. Goods would be brought to residents in bulk delivery trucks using services like UPS, Fedex and Peapod. Under telework many would only visit an office to attend meetings once or twice a week (or less). Streets and intersections would be made less daunting to pedestrians through traffic calming techniques.

---

[12]http://www.walkscore.com/

Figure 11.3: Walkable Neighborhood Picture shows a bike path in Chapinero, Bogotá. *Source: Tequendamia (Own work) [CC-BY-SA-3.0[13]] via Wikimedia Commons[14]*

Most trips to other parts of the city would be made via mass transit. When an individual car is need it would be provided through car sharing, or taxis. Much to the dismay of science fiction fans, flying cars sound nice but it is difficult to see how they can be sustainable until a non-polluting, renewable energy source for air travel is obtained. Traffic congestion would be relieved not through artificial subsidies (overbuilding roads and providing free parking) but through congestion pricing, removal of free street parking, and providing viable bicycle and mass transit alternatives.

Even rural centers could be planned as concentrated walkable neighborhoods with viable transportation options. **Telework, e-commerce** and **low impact cluster development** would enable residents to enjoy country living without a guilty conscience. Think in terms of a kibbutz (collective farm) where most members do not own their own cars and rarely have to use this type of transportation.

Cities will continue to draw entrepreneurs and foster productivity.

Most of the population will reside in mega-regions and linking them through high-speed rail that connects to mass transit will be the key to long-term economic growth.

[13]http://creativecommons.org/licenses/by-sa/3.0/
[14]http://commons.wikimedia.org/wiki/File%3AChapinero_bike_path.JPG

11.2.9 Water

Traditional approaches have sought to rapidly move stormwater away from what we've built via gutters, sewers and artificial channels. While this approach on the micro scale is intended to prevent local flooding and undesired ponding, on the macro scale it may actually cause area wide flooding. It also short-circuits the opportunity for water to naturally soak into the ground – to water plants and recharge groundwater resources

, and, with traditional planting of lawns and other exotics, necessitates bringing more water in for irrigation.

Best water management practices for sustainable cities would include:

- Green Roofs
- Downspouts, Rain Barrels and Cisterns
- Permeable Paving
- Natural Landscaping
- Filter Strips
- Bioinfiltration using: Rain Gardens
- Drainage Swales
- Naturalized Detention Basins

Figure 11.4: Green Roof The green roof of City Hall in Chicago, Illinois *Source: TonyTheTiger [CC-BY-SA-3.0[15]] via Wikimedia Commons[16]*

These features are discussed in more detail in the Module Sustainable Stormwater Management (Section 11.6). The sustainable city would recharge its local aquifer and surface water would flow primarily from groundwater and not storm water discharge. Instead of charging a flat tax for storm and sanitary sewer services, technology allows districts to charge usage fees based upon volume, thus providing a financial incentive for sustainable design. Governmental bodies could use these tools to encourage the reorientation and designers could use the techniques outlined above as divert stormwater into the ground rather than directly into surface water.[17]

Working together, local government and project planners could also retrofit older urban streets with attractive walkable streetscapes, just as Lansing, Michigan has done as part of its combined sewer overflow project[18] (below).

Some visionaries see even more dramatic transformations in the way we deal with water. Sarah Dunn and Martin Felsen of Urbanlab[19] envision Chicago's evolution into a model city for "growing water[20]" by creating a series of Eco-Boulevards that function as a giant Living Machine – treating the city's waste and storm water naturally, using micro-organisms, small invertebrates such as snails, fish, and plants. Under their plan treated water would be returned to the Great Lakes Basin and create a closed water loop within Chicago, instead of being exported to the Mississippi and Gulf Coast.

11.2.10 Food

The ancients would wonder at modern supermarkets with their food from all over the world and fresh fruits and vegetables all year round. Yet most environmental activists advocate locally produced organic food. Peak oil will raise petrochemical costs and upset the dynamics of modern agriculture, but it will be difficult to change the acquired tastes of the consuming public.

USEPA is encouraging urban agriculture as one of the solutions to the shrinking city.

It sees urban agriculture as not only providing a use for vacant land, (thus addressing blight and the deleterious affect of neglect on property values) but also as a potential cleanup strategy for contamination. It addresses the problem of food deserts (lack of healthy, affordable, fresh produce) in blighted inner city neighborhoods while educating children and adults about farming and local enterprise. Practitioners have found that urban farming enhances social capital and community connections. Victory gardens produced about 40% of American vegetables consumed during World War II

and urban gardens could be a prime user of the compost that we could generate either through individual compost bins or through collective efforts performed on a large scale by our waste haulers.

Figure 11.5: Urban Agriculture Some new crops being started, protected by shade cloth barriers to the west. Note the new construction in the background. This area used to be all public housing. The high rise "warehouses of the poor" were torn down and are being replaced with mix of market-rate and low-income housing (also called mixed income housing.) The 1.5 acre parcel that City Farm sits on is owned by the City of Chicago and provided, rent-free, to this non-profit initiative. The property is valued at $8 million, however, so it's anyone's guess as to when the city decides to terminate the agreement and City Farm must move again. *Source: Linda from Chicago, USA (New crops) [CC-BY-2.0[21]] via Wikimedia Commons[22]*

Many of us might belong to food cooperatives where the members contract with organic farmers to purchase the food grown for them.

In Sustainable Cities farming will not just be an interim land use in blighted neighborhoods but, like Prairie Crossing in Grayslake, Illinois[23] , will be an integral part of the community plan. Some even forecast vertical farming[24] in the great cities of the world.

[21]http://creativecommons.org/licenses/by/2.0
[22]http://commons.wikimedia.org/wiki/File%3ANew_crops-Chicago_urban_farm.jpg
[23]http://www.prairiecrossing.com/farm/index.php
[24]http://www.spiegel.de/international/zeitgeist/vertical-farming-can-urban-agriculture-feed-a-hungry-world-a-775754.html

11.2.11 Buildings & Neighborhoods

Americans have come a long way from the pioneer one room log cabin and crowded immigrant tenement. The average American house size has more than doubled since the 1950s and now stands at 2,349 square feet.[25] Sustainability will probably mean more efficient use of smaller homes, and **McMansions** might become multi-family dwellings, putting pressure on local ordinances and home association rules.

Figure 11.6: McMansions Home with large garage and short driveway depth taking up a large amount of street frontage. Also evident: several cheaply installed neoclassical elements, a brick facade, no side windows, and poorly proportioned windows on the front. *Source: John Delano of Hammond, Indiana [CC0[26]] via Wikimedia Commons[27]*

Second (& third) homes? The Joint Center for Housing Studies at Harvard University showed a dramatic rise in vacation homes, from 3.1 million such units in the 1990 Census to over 6 million in the Housing Vacancy Survey ten years later.

If we want to equitably share the world's resources with emerging markets we'll have to figure out how to manage this desire to spend time in more than one place in a more conservative manner. Time-sharing addresses this need, as does the (still) growing hotel and vacation resort industry.

Homes use about 23% of all energy in the United States.

---

[26]http://creativecommons.org/publicdomain/zero/1.0/deed.en
[27]http://commons.wikimedia.org/wiki/File:McMansion,_Munster,_Indiana.JPG

In the future many of our homes will generate their own power (See **Case Study: A Net-Zero Energy Home in Urbana, Illinois** (Section 11.7)). Today ultra-efficient homes combine state-of-the-art, energy-efficient construction and appliances with commercially available renewable energy systems, such as solar water heating and solar electricity, so that the net energy use is zero or even less than zero (positive energy production).

There have been efforts since the 70's oil crisis to promote (mandatory) energy codes, but voluntary efforts such as Energy Star and LEED are the ones that have made substantial headway.

LEED

Leadership in Energy and Environmental Design, a voluntary effort by the U.S. Green Building Council , includes more than energy and also gives points for site, water, materials and resources, and indoor air quality. LEED in particular and sustainable construction in general have found widespread acceptance as even the National Association of Homebuilders has rolled out its own version of green construction . Since its inception in 1998, the U.S. Green Building Council has grown to encompass more than 10,000 projects in the United States and 117 countries covering 8 billion square feet of construction space and in April, 2011 LEED certified its 10,000th home in its LEED for Homes program . The U.S government's General Services Administration (GSA), the part of the federal government that builds and manages federal space, currently requires LEED Gold certification for all of its new buildings (up from Silver).

In addition to using fewer resources sustainable buildings reduce absenteeism, improve employee morale, and lead to improved educational performance.

In the Pacific Northwest the International Living Future Institute has set up a Living Building Challenge to go beyond LEED and design and build triple net zero (storm water, energy, wastewater) structures. As of Fall 2010 there were 70 registered projects .

What about the neighborhoods where we live and raise our families? Many now recognize that our grandparents' mixed-use, walkable neighborhoods were more sustainable than today's reality. The Congress for New Urbanism promotes mixed use in contrast to its predecessor, Congrès International d'Architecture Moderne (CIAM), which promoted separation of use. CIAM, active in the first part of the 20th century, proposed that the social problems faced by cities could be resolved by strict functional segregation, and the distribution of the population into tall apartment blocks at widely spaced intervals.

This view found its expression in Le Corbusier's The Radiant City (1935). Separation of Use heavily influenced subdivision and building codes that, in turn, shaped Post World War II suburban expansion. In our suburbs zoning dictates mutually exclusive uses in each district so that Industrial use is exclusive of commercial, which is exclusive of residential. In the suburbs separation of use combined with the platting of superblocks to replace the traditional grid network gives us a lifestyle that produces 10 auto trips per unit per day, because you need one car per driver to get around where much of America lives.

CIAM's view also formed the intellectual underpinning for large-scale high-rise public housing projects. Today we recognize that safe, sound and sanitary housing is not just indoor plumbing and more bedrooms, and that affordable housing is not just rent but includes utility and transportation costs and the right to live in a safe, mixed income, stably integrated neighborhood. Our sustainable city should stand upon the leg of social equity and include ethnic and income diversity. Neighborhoods should be sited at efficient locations with broad transportation choices. What will they look like? Most new urbanists think they will be similar to the diverse neighborhoods built at the turn of the last century. Other visionaries, such as Moshe Safdie, think it possible to integrate the variety and diversity of scattered private homes with the economics and density of a modern apartment building. Modular, interlocking concrete forms in Safdie's Expo '67 defined the space. The project was designed to create affordable housing with close but private quarters, each equipped with a garden. In a different vein, in outlying Grayslake, Illinois, cluster development that incorporates open space, wetlands, and a working organic farm enables residents to live (somewhat) sustainably in the country. Our future must recognize that we don't want everyone to live in Manhattan or Brooklyn, and we must provide for diverse tastes and lifestyles.

Will everything look futuristic, like the sets of Blade Runner or Star Wars? Historic Buildings not only have a special charm but they represent a great deal of embodied energy that is wasted if they are demolished. The government and marketplace will probably continue to promote historic rehab, including adaptive reuse where new uses are found for old buildings through rehab that installs modern utilities and fixtures while preserving the outer shell's look and feel. In Chicago the Sears Powerhouse was converted to a charter school and in Philadelphia Urban Outfitters took the old Navy Yard and transformed it into a new corporate headquarters. In all five of the former Navy Yard buildings, employees work in light-filled interiors with open layouts. Most of the furnishings are custom-made and contain recycled material (tabletops crafted from salvaged wood, for instance). Amenities such as a gym, yoga studio, dog park, and farmers' market further add to the lively and informal atmosphere.

All of these gestures to what the CEO calls "a quality of life thing" help Urban Outfitters boost employee satisfaction. Since moving into the new headquarters, employee turnover has dropped to 11 percent, and fewer sick days are being used. "They feel more linked to the community and culture of the company." The campus has improved his company's ability to attract new talent. The informal atmosphere is alluring to Millennial-aged employees, who tend to value open, flexible work arrangements more than previous generations of workers. "The campus has improved creative collaboration, which ultimately impacts our bottom line."

11.2.12 Work and Commuting

In the past we had to live near the places where we built things and conducted our business. The factories of the industrial revolution demanded labor, and packed the exploited workforce in nearby tenement housing. Today intelligent machines perform most of the work in manufacturing our goods and moving them from place to place. In the Information Age most tasks can be performed anywhere within reach of the World Wide Web. In Understanding Media Marshall McLuhan showed how "improved roads and transport have reversed the ancient pattern and made cities the centers of work and the country the place of leisure and of recreation.

" The new reality once again reverses roles by locating the factories on vast campuses away from the people and, the city becomes a place to meet, be entertained and educated. Sustainable Cities of the future will probably still function as the center for service industries such as health and beauty care, hospitality, tourism, travel, and government, and other service industries, such as insurance, advertising and marketing, and financial services, are amenable to telework. Sure, we can eat our frozen dinners and get TV or on line entertainment at home, but it's still enjoyable to go out to eat and catch a live show, concert, sporting event or movie. We get a better view of the players on television, but the excitement of thousands of fans under one roof is palpable. Many of us in the **postindustrial Information Age** will not have to live near our factories, power plants or transportation centers, because we just have to connect to the World Wide Web. In the Information Age many of us might never have to attend physical meetings, but those of us who do might find ourselves going to the office only a few times a month. But it is important for those who tout cities as more sustainable places to live (i.e. Cities pollute less per capita[28]) to understand that rural areas can be just as benign as cities if one has the will and controls resource use with the appropriate life style. Communal farms, for example, generally have small ecological footprints, producing more resources than they consume.

Figure 11.7: Telecommuting *Source: Gilangreffi (Own work) [CC0[29]] via Wikimedia Commons[30]*

---

[29]http://creativecommons.org/publicdomain/zero/1.0/deed.en
[30]http://commons.wikimedia.org/wiki/File%3ATelecommuting_di_kafe.jpg

11.2.13 Power

Today huge plants generate electricity from coal (44.9%), natural gas (23.8%), atomic energy (19.6%), hydroelectric (6.2%), and other renewable (e.g. wind, solar) (4%) sources.

Power affects urban form in that urban centers must be connected to the grid, and the ubiquitous power line tethers us to the power plant. Sustainable cities will probably not lose the grid, but should accommodate those who want to produce their own power by running the meter backwards. Until and unless atomic fusion supplies cheap, safe, reliable power, renewables will compete with fossil fuels. Even as we hit peak oil, coal will be plentiful for the foreseeable future. Coal will continue to be cheap because its price will probably not reflect all the costs of smog, acid rain, and its subsequent effects on health and the environment [31] let alone recognize that the reserves are being depleted. As the technology evolves and as government policy requires utilities to buy power from small decentralized sources we will all get used to wind mills and photovoltaic arrays. Geothermal heat pumps will heat and cool space more efficiently. Zoning and building codes will have to be revised to deal with solar access rights, noise from windmills and odors from biomass and biofuels.

Figure 11.8: Windmills *Source: James McCauley from Enon, OH, United States of America (Flickr) [CC-BY-2.0[32]], via Wikimedia Commons[33]*

Figure 11.9: Local wind generator, Spain, 2010 *Source: By Patrick Charpiat (Own work) [CC-BY-SA-3.0[34]] via Wikimedia Commons[35]*

Technology will also enable us to operate more efficiently. One of the problems with conventional power generation is that the plants must be (over)sized to accommodate peak loads. In the future the "Smart Grid" should smooth peak loads by instructing consumer appliances to perform tasks, such as laundry and dishwashing, in low demand periods (middle of the night), and will offer lower rates as an incentive.

Figure 11.10: Microgrids A local microgrid in Sendai, Japan *Source: See page for author [Public domain], via Wikimedia Commons*[36]

11.2.14 Commerce

Our parents and grandparents have seen dramatic change in the area of commerce. Until 1950 we walked to the neighborhood store and most of the goods we bought were produced locally. On special occasions you'd take the trolley downtown to the central business district (CBD) to visit the large department stores (e.g. Marshall Fields in Chicago, Macy's in New York). With the suburbanization following World War II CBD's were replaced by suburban malls. We drove to the malls. The CBD's died out. For the last thirty years big box chains have dominated retail, but most recently ecommerce entices consumers with better selection and prices (and sometimes no sales tax). Most of us find that we shop online more efficiently and those that need the personal attention that retail establishments currently offer might find that they will have to engage the

---

[34]http://creativecommons.org/licenses/by-sa/3.0
[35]http://commons.wikimedia.org/wiki/File%3AWindgen59.JPG
[36]http://commons.wikimedia.org/wiki/File%3AMicrogrid.jpg

services of a personal shopper (note the shift from good to service). Most of the goods we purchase, even food, have been produced somewhere else. World trade, as measured in US dollars at current prices, has grown astronomically, from $10.1 billion in 1900

, to $62 billion in 1950, to $15.2 trillion in 2010. US imports and exports have risen from $1.4 billion (exports) in 1900 to $9.6/10.3 billion in 1950 and to $1.97/1.28 trillion in 2010.

In our Sustainable City of the Future ecommerce will probably rule, which will mean a reduction in actual physical commercial floor area. When we feel we need to see something in person we will visit centralized showrooms, and pay for that *service*, but most purchases will be made on line and the product delivered either by company delivery vehicles (e.g. Peapod) or through common carriers (e.g. UPS, Fedex). New uses will be found for dead malls.

Neighborhood stores will fare better in walkable neighborhoods, especially those that offer services in place of or in addition to goods.

It is unreasonable for us to expect to obtain all of our goods locally, but regional specialization in the production of goods will reflect climate, access to raw materials and markets, and locally developed expertise rather than cheap labor and the ability to avoid environmental and workplace safety regulations. Modern robots do not have to follow repetitive assembly line logic of repeated application of the same exact set of instructions. They can be programmed to intelligently consider each individual product and thus can produce a wider variety of products, and many products will be special ordered to fit individual tastes. Once we even out the playing field (of necessary government regulation to deal with the externalities of production) the cost of shipping should work towards more local production. Goods will be made "just in time"

thus reducing inventories and overproduction that is sent to landfills. Efficiency will be a big part of the Sustainable City.

Planned obsolescence and its impact upon material culture is more problematic. Fashion defies logic but speaks to the most basic instincts of human behavior. How do we avoid the need for more closet space, let alone offsite storage? New materials will enable us to change the look and feel of clothing. Advances in crystal technology, for example, will allow us to change its color and/or pattern.

Interlocking parts using material similar to Velcro could let us change lapels, sleeves and other components of garments, much as we now add or subtract liners for warmth. More complicated goods will be designed for disassembly and recycling,

or replacement of key parts while keeping most of the old components. Retrofit can add life to old buildings and machines, if we learn to view old and retro as cool and in.

A good example of how we can move towards sustainability is provided by Interface, which repositioned their carpeting business from the sale of goods to the leasing of floor covering services. Under the old paradigm the consumer purchased a new carpet a few years after the old one began to show wear. The selection was based upon the perception that the carpet would last (e.g. because it felt thicker), but the reality was that the carpet manufacturer made out better when new carpets had to be repurchased more frequently. Under the new leasing paradigm the manufacturer owns the carpet and therefore it is in their best interest to have it last longer. Interface's Solenium lasts four times longer and uses 40% less material than ordinary carpets, an 86% reduction in materials intensity. When marketed as floor covering services under its Evergreen Lease, modular floor tiles are replaced as soon as they show any wear and, since 80% of wear takes place on 20% of the area, this reduces material intensity by another 80%. In other words, **3%** of the materials are used under the new paradigm (yes, a **97%** reduction) than the old one. And the worn out panels are recycled, and no chlorine or other toxic materials are used in its manufacture.[37]

11.2.15 Education

Our children will find their place in tomorrow's workplace based upon their brains, not brawn. Education is the most important component in preparing for tomorrow's workplace. Classrooms today link via television and the internet to amazing resources. More importantly, artificial intelligence has the capacity to treat each student as an individual and to tailor instruction to meet his or her individual abilities and needs, in contrast to the classroom that moves, at best, at the speed of the average student.

Figure 11.11: E-Learning A ubiquitous-learning(u-learning) classroom where students use electronic textbooks in the form of tablet PCs. *Source: By B.C. (Own work) [CC-BY-3.0[38]] via Wikimedia Commons[39]*

The sustainable school should still contain classrooms, but it will probably be supplemented by individualized computer learning labs. Each student would have their own personal computer (see Cyborgean Man below) that would link them to the internet. Classrooms would have multi-media capabilities that would link to other classrooms around the world. Webinars would make expert instruction available to all. As noted earlier, the biophilia of green classrooms would improve learning and test scores.

11.2.16 Cyborgean Man & Big Brother

In his book "Understanding Media – The Extensions of Man" Marshall McLuhan explains how once man creates an extension of himself, let's say writing, he both gains (the ability to remember more in his records) and loses (not being able to remember as much without these written records) abilities.

Horse drawn carriages and automobiles enable man to travel faster and further even as his body gains weight and loses muscle tone. Tents, tepees and igloos enable man to migrate from the primordial forest[40] to inhospitable climates, but man, like the tortoise, must lug this shell of material civilization around with him.

---

[38]http://creativecommons.org/licenses/by/3.0
[39]http://commons.wikimedia.org/wiki/File%3AElearnroom.jpg

Miniaturization in the Computer Age now promises to let us reinternalize some of the external abilities we've created. Over ten years ago Thad Starner, a research assistant at MITs media lab, garnered a lot of publicity by calling himself a cyborg because he incorporated his computer monitor into his glasses, and let his keyboard and computer hang as appendages by his side.

Today half the civilized world has smartphones that link us via the Facebook, the World Wide Web, texts and tweets. In our sustainable city we could all be wired, possibly though implants directly into out brainstem. Artificial intelligence could provide a virtual butler that would be available to schedule and keep track of our appointments, order our groceries and other items, and help us with things we can't even imagine today. Advertising would be directed at us individually, as in Philip Dick's Minority Report

, as advertisers use software like doubleclick

and links to national databases (see Big Brother below) to track who we are and our buying preferences. This should be good for sustainability, as there will be no need to hoard things for possible future use, and to discard them when we no longer need them. Government would find it easier to poll citizen's preferences and opinions.

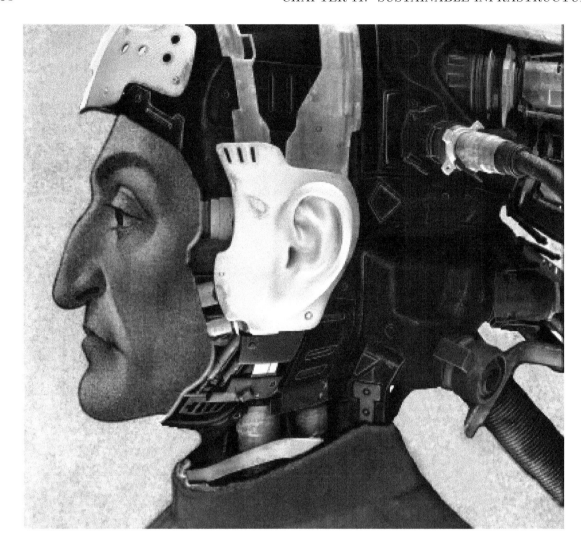

Figure 11.12: Cyborgean Man *Source: PIX-JOCKEY (Roberto Rizzato)* http://www.flickr.com/photos/rizzato/2342959844/[41]

In George Orwell's <u>1984</u> everyone is constantly reminded, "Big Brother is watching you."

In our sustainable city everyone will be watching everyone else. Video surveillance webcams might be everywhere, and everyone would have access to them. Everyone could have a reality show in which those wanting to follow you would merely tune into the appropriate URL and be able to choose the cameras and microphones that are in range. Some people would not even turn off the feeds, ever. Artificial intelligence (or actual humans for the more popular content) could provide edited condensed feeds. Crime would go down in those areas with eyes and ears, but crime will evolve and persist. It will be easy to research everyone you meet and to stay connected. Since this will be by and large electronic it will promote a sustainable lifestyle by not consuming additional resources.

---

[41]http://www.flickr.com/photos/rizzato/2342959844/

11.2.17 Review Questions

Question 11.2.1

Select an aspect of your day-to-day existence that has environmental consequences. Describe the environmental consequences, and briefly discuss more sustainable alternatives.

Question 11.2.2

What does a complete street look like? How does it differ from the street outside of your home?

Question 11.2.3

Describe a sustainable neighborhood that you're familiar with and explain what makes it sustainable.

Question 11.2.4

If sustainability is so beneficial why isn't everything sustainable? Name one market barrier to sustainability and explain what can be done to overcome it.

11.3 Sustainability and Buildings[42]

11.3.1 Learning Objectives

After reading this module, students should be able to

- understand the various ways buildings affect the environment
- describe the characteristics of sustainable buildings

11.3.2 Introduction

Buildings present a challenge and an opportunity for sustainable development. According to the most recent available Annual Energy Outlook from the U.S. Environmental Information Administration, buildings account for about 39% of the carbon dioxide emissions, 40% of primary energy use, and 72% of the electricity consumption in the U.S. Additional information from the U.S. Geological Survey indicates that 14% of the potable water consumption occurs in buildings.

Globally, buildings are the largest contributors to carbon dioxide emissions, above transportation and then industry. The construction of buildings requires many materials that are mined, grown, or produced and then transported to the building site. Buildings require infrastructure including roads, utility lines, water and sewer systems. People need to be able to get to and from buildings to work, live, or take advantage of the services provided within them. They need to provide a safe and comfortable environment for the people that inhabit them.

Consumption
Environmental Effects
Ultimate Effects

Siting Energy Waste Harm to human health

Design Water Air pollution Environmental degradation

---

[42]This content is available online at <http://legacy.cnx.org/content/m44261/1.1/>.

Construction Materials GHG emissions Loss of resources

Operation Natural resources Water pollution

Maintenance   Indoor pollution

Renovation   Heat islands

Deconstruction   Stormwater runoff

Noise

Consumption
Environmental Effects
Ultimate Effects

Siting Energy Waste Harm to human health

Design Water Air pollution Environmental degradation

Construction Materials GHG emissions Loss of resources

Operation Natural resources Water pollution

Maintenance   Indoor pollution

Renovation   Heat islands

Deconstruction   Stormwater runoff

Noise

Consumption
Environmental Effects
Ultimate Effects

Siting Energy Waste Harm to human health

Design Water Air pollution Environmental degradation

Construction Materials GHG emissions Loss of resources

Operation Natural resources Water pollution

Maintenance   Indoor pollution

Renovation   Heat islands

Deconstruction   Stormwater runoff

Noise

Aspects of Built Environment	Consumption	Environmental Effects	Ultimate Effects
Siting	Energy	Waste	Harm to human health
Design	Water	Air pollution	Environmental degradation
Construction	Materials	GHG emissions	Loss of resources
Operation	Natural resources	Water pollution	
Maintenance		Indoor pollution	
Renovation		Heat islands	
Deconstruction		Stormwater runoff	
		Noise	

Table 11.1: **Impacts of the Built Environment** *Source: U.S. Environmental Protection Agency*
http://www.epa.gov/greenbuilding/pubs/about.htm [43]

It is possible to design and construct fully functional buildings that have far fewer negative environmental impacts than current norms allow. Beyond benefitting the environment, green buildings provide economic benefits including reduced operating costs, expanded markets for green products and services, improved building occupant productivity, and optimized life-cycle performance. Green buildings also offer social benefits that range from protecting occupant comfort and health, to better aesthetic qualities, less strain on local infrastructure, and overall improvement in quality of life.

In 1994, a group of experts was brought together by the National Renewable Energy Laboratory (NREL) to develop a pathway and specific principles for sustainable development. According to these principles, building should be:

- **Ecologically Responsive**: The design of human habitat shall recognize that all resources are limited, and will respond to the patterns of natural ecology. Land plans and building designs will include only those with the least disruptive impact upon the natural ecology of the earth. Density must be most intense near neighborhood centers where facilities are most accessible.
- **Healthy, Sensible Buildings:** The design of human habitat must create a living environment that will be healthy for all its occupants. Buildings should be of appropriate human scale in a non-sterile, aesthetically pleasing environment. Building design must respond to toxicity of materials, care with EMF, lighting efficiency and quality, comfort requirements and resource efficiency. Buildings should be organic, integrate art, natural materials, sunlight, green plants, energy efficiency, low noise levels and water. They should not cost more than current conventional buildings.
- **Socially Just:** Habitats shall be equally accessible across economic classes.
- **Culturally Creative:** Habitats will allow ethnic groups to maintain individual cultural identities and neighborhoods while integrating into the larger community. All population groups shall have access to art, theater and music.
- **Beautiful:** Beauty in a habitat environment is necessary for the soul development of human beings. It is yeast for the ferment of individual creativity. Intimacy with the beauty and numinous mystery of nature must be available to enliven our sense of the sacred.
- **Physically and Economically Accessible:** All sites within the habitat shall be accessible and rich in resources to those living within walkable (or wheelchair-able) distance.
- **Evolutionary:** Habitats' design shall include continuous re-evaluation of premises and values, shall be demographically responsive and flexible to change over time to support future user needs. Initial designs should reflect our society's heterogeneity and have a feedback system.

---

[43]http://www.epa.gov/greenbuilding/pubs/about.htm

What is meant by a sustainable or green building? The U.S. EPA defines green building as "the practice of creating structures and using processes that are environmentally responsible and resource-efficient throughout a building's life-cycle from siting to design, construction, operation, maintenance, renovation and deconstruction. This practice expands and complements the classical building design concerns of economy, utility, durability, and comfort." (U.S. Environmental Protection Agency, 2010 (p. 550))

The benefits of sustainable buildings have already been documented. These buildings can reduce energy use by 24-50%, carbon dioxide emissions by 33-39%, water use by 40%, and solid waste by 70% (Turner & Frankel, 2008 (p. 550); Kats, Alevantis, Berman, Mills, & Perlman, 2003 (p. 550); Fowler & Rauch, 2008 (p. 549)). Green building occupants are healthier and more productive than their counterparts in other buildings, and this is important because in the U.S, people spend an average of 90% or more of their time indoors (U.S. Environmental Protection Agency, 1987 (p. 550)). Green buildings tend to have improved indoor air quality and lighting.

There are also numerous perceived business benefits to green buildings, including decreased operating costs and increased building value, return on investment, occupancy ratio, and rent ratio.

11.3.3 Materials and Methods of Construction

It is frequently stated that the most sustainable building is the one that is not built. This does not mean that we should not have buildings, but rather that we should make the most of our existing buildings. Those buildings already have the infrastructure and have utilized many materials for their construction.

A great deal of energy goes into making building materials. By volume, the major materials used within the U.S. construction industry are crushed rock, gravel, sand, cement, cement concrete, asphalt concrete, timber products, clay brick, concrete block, drywall, roofing materials, steel, aluminum, copper and other metals, plastics, paper, paints, glues, and other chemical products. The building industry has been the largest consumer of materials in the US for nearly 100 years (Horvath, 2004 (p. 549)).

The manufacturing of cement, for instance, is an enormous producer of greenhouse gas emissions. Cement is made of about 85% lime by mass, which is mixed with other ingredients such as shale, clay, and slate. It is formed into an inorganic adhesive by heating the ingredients to a temperature of 1450 °C (2640 °F), and then grinding the product into a powder. Cement comprises about 15% of concrete, which is made by mixing cement with sand, small rocks, and water. Because it requires so much energy, the manufacture of cement is estimated to account for as much as 5% of global anthropogenic greenhouse gas emissions (Humphreys & Mahasenan, 2002 (p. 550)).

Construction of buildings is also related to deforestation. Our consumption of wood to build buildings and furniture over the centuries has resulted in the clearing of many old-world forests and tropical forests. Trees are harvested not only for fuel but also for construction material and to clear land for construction.

The demolition of old buildings to make way for new and construction projects themselves generate huge amounts of waste. Careful **deconstruction** of buildings allows for reuse of materials in future construction projects or for recycling of materials into new building (and other) products. Deconstruction creates economic advantages by lower building removal costs due to value of materials and avoided disposal costs, reduces impact to site on soil and vegetation, conserves landfill space, and creates jobs due to the labor-intensity of the process.

A 1998 EPA study (p. 550) of building-related construction and demolition (C&D) debris generation in the U.S. found that an estimated 136 million tons of building-related C&D debris were generated in 1996, the equivalent to 2.8 pounds per person per day. 43% of the waste (58 million tons per year) was generated from residential sources and 57% (78 million tons per year) was from nonresidential sources. Building demolitions accounted for 48% of the waste stream, or 65 million tons per year; renovations accounted for 44%, or 60 million tons per year; and 8 percent, or 11 million tons per year, was generated at construction sites.

Even when deconstruction is not possible, the waste can be recycled by sorting the materials after they are collected and taken to a waste transfer station. Since new construction and renovation requires the input of many materials, this is an opportunity to utilize products that enhance the sustainability of the building. These products may be made of recycled content, sustainably grown and harvested wood and pulp materials, products that have **low emissions**, and products that are sourced locally. These products enhance the sustainability of the building by supporting local economies and reducing the fuel needed to transport them long distances.

11.3.4 Energy-saving Building Features

Energy efficient measures have been around a long time and are known to reduce the use of energy in residential and commercial properties. Improvements have been made in all of these areas and are great opportunities for further innovation. Green buildings incorporate these features to reduce the demand for heating and cooling.

11.3.5

11.3.5.1 Insulation

The building should be well insulated and sealed so that the conditioned air doesn't escape to the outside. Insulation can be installed in floors, walls, attics and/or roofs. It helps to have more even temperature distribution and increased comfort as well.

11.3.5.2 High-performance Windows

Several factors are important to the performance of a window (see Figure **A High-performance Window** (Figure 11.13)):

- Thermal windows are at least double-paned and vacuum-filled with inert gas. This gas provides insulation
- Improved framing materials, weather stripping and warm edge spacers reduce heat gain and loss
- Low-E coating block solar heat gain in the summer and reflect radiant heat indoors during the winter

11.3.5.3 Sealing of Holes and Cracks

Sealing holes and cracks in a building's **envelope** as well as the heating and cooling duct systems can reduce drafts, moisture, dust, pollen, and noise. In addition, it improves comfort and indoor air quality at the same time it saves energy and reduces utility and maintenance costs.

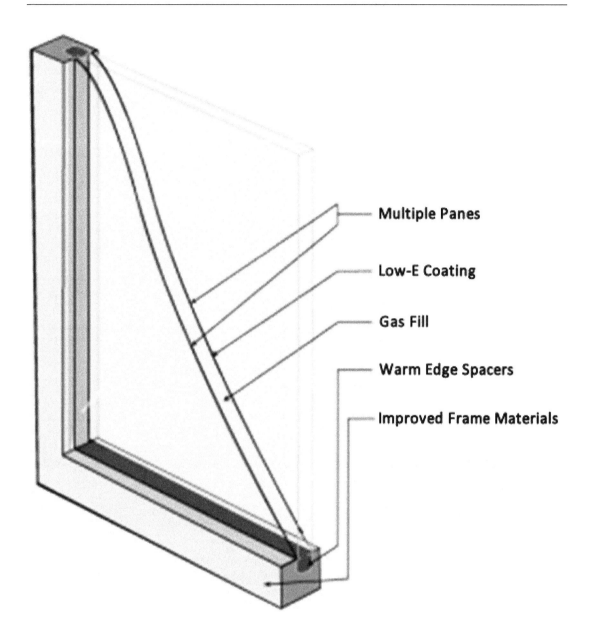

Figure 11.13: **A** **High-performance** **Window** *Source:*
http://www.energystar.gov/ia/new_homes/features/Windows_062906.pdf [44]

---

[44]http://www.energystar.gov/ia/new_homes/features/Windows_062906.pdf

11.3.5.4 Heating Ventilation and Air-conditioning (HVAC)

A large part of the energy consumption and thus environmental impact of a building is the building heating, ventilation and air-conditioning (HVAC) systems that are used to provide comfortable temperature, humidity and air supply levels. Buildings must be designed to meet local energy code requirements, but these are often not as aggressive targets as they could be to demand more energy efficiency. In the U.S. ENERGY Star provides guidance and benchmarking to help set more aggressive goals.

There are many ways HVAC systems can be designed to be more efficient. Variable air volume (VAV) systems increase air flow to meet the increase or decrease in heat gains or losses within the area served. Having fans power down when not needed saves energy, as does reducing the amount of air that needs to be conditioned and also reduces the need for reheat systems. These systems are used to warm up an area if the cooled air supply is making an area too cold. VAV systems can generally handle this by reducing air supply. All of this does need to be balanced by making sure there is enough fresh air supply to meet the needs of the number of occupants in a building. Otherwise, it will feel stuffy due to lack of air flow and oxygen.

Also using automated controls, whether it is a programmable thermostat in your home or a building automation system (BAS) that uses computers to control HVAC settings based on schedules and occupancy, can significantly reduce energy consumption.

The equipment itself can be made more energy efficient. For instance new home furnaces range in efficiency from 68-97%. Ideally, the most energy efficient furnace would be installed in a new home (U.S. Department of Energy, 2011 (p. 550)).

11.3.5.5 Passive Solar Design

This type of architectural design does not require mechanical heating and cooling of a building. Instead it uses heating and cooling strategies that have been used historically such as natural ventilation, solar heat gain, solar shading and efficient insulation. Figure **Passive Solar Design** (Figure 11.14) shows some of these elements. In the winter solar radiation is trapped by the greenhouse effect of south facing windows (north in the southern hemisphere) exposed to full sun. Heat is trapped, absorbed and stored by materials with high **thermal mass** (usually bricks or concrete) inside the house. It is released at night when needed to warm up the building as it loses heat to the cooler outdoors. Shading provided by trees or shades keeps the sun out in the hot months.

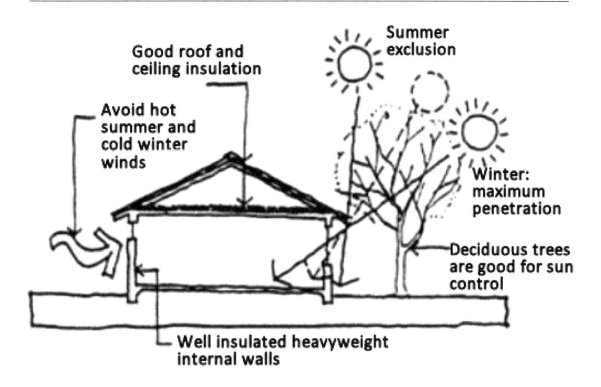

Figure 11.14: Passive Solar Design *Source: http://www.yourhome.gov.au/technical/fs45.html#what*
[45]

11.3.5.6 Lighting

Well-designed lighting can minimize the use of energy. This includes enhancing day lighting (natural light), through windows, skylights, etc. Using energy efficient lighting such as compact fluorescent light bulbs and LEDs (light-emitting diodes) can save energy as well. Using occupancy sensors also means that lights will only be on when someone is in a room. See Module Sustainable Energy Practices: Climate Action Planning (Section 11.4) for more energy-saving technologies that can be incorporated into buildings.

11.3.5.7 Water

Water usage can be minimized by using low-flow fixtures in restrooms, bathrooms, and kitchens. Dual-flush toilets allow for the user to have the option of select less water (e.g. for liquid waste) and more water (e.g. for solid waste) when flushing (See Figure **Dual Flush Toilet** (Figure 11.15)). These have long been in use in Europe, the Middle East and other places where water conservation is paramount. Fresh water consumption can be reduced further through the use of **greywater** systems. These systems recycle water generated from activities such as hand washing, laundry, bathing, and dishwashing for irrigation of grounds and even for flushing toilets.

---

[45]http://www.yourhome.gov.au/technical/fs45.html#what

Figure 11.15: Dual-flush Toilet This toilet has two flush controls on the water tank. Pushing only the circular button releases half as much (0.8 gallons, 3 liters) water as pushing the outer button. *Source: By Eugenio Hansen, OFS (Own work) [CC-BY-SA-3.0[46]], via Wikimedia Commons[47]*

11.3.5.8 Integrated Design

Integrated design is a design process for a building that looks at the whole building, rather than its individual parts, for opportunities to reduce environmental impact. Incremental measures would include those approaches described above. To accomplish integrated design of a building, all parties involved in the design–architects, engineers, the client and other stakeholders–must work together. This collaborative approach results in a more harmonious coordination of the different components of a building such as the site, structure, systems, and ultimate use.

11.3.6 Standards of Certification

Most countries establish certain standards to assure consistency, quality and safety in the design and construction of buildings. Green building standards provide guidelines to architects, engineers, building operators and owners that enhance building sustainability. Various green building standards have originated in different countries around the world, with differing goals, review processes and rating. In this section we will discuss a few examples.

A good certification system should be developed with expert feedback. In addition, it should be transparent, measurable, relevant and comparable.

- Expert-based: Was input acquired from experts and professionals in the fields of design, construction, building operation and sustainability?
- Transparent: Is information readily available to the public about how buildings are rated?
- Measurable: Does the rating system use measurable characteristics to demonstrate the extent of sustainable design incorporated into the building? Does the system use life-cycle analysis to evaluate?
- Relevance: Does the rating system provide a "whole building evaluation" rather than an evaluation of an individual design feature?
- Comparable: Is the rating system able to compare building types, location, years, or different sustainable design features?

Year established
Country of origin
Trans- parent
Expert-based
Measurable/ Uses LCA
Relevance
Comparable

BREEAM [48] 1990 UK $\sqrt{}$* - $\sqrt{}$ $\sqrt{}$ $\sqrt{}$

Green Globes [49] 1996 Canada √ √ √/√ √ √

LEED [50] 2000 US √ √ √/√ V 3.0 √ √

CASBEE [51] 2001 Japan √ √ √/√ √ √

ENERGY STAR [52] 1999 US √ √[#] √ Only energy √

| *Only assessment prediction check lists available publicly
[#]Benchmarking tool developed by US EPA

Year established
Country of origin
Trans- parent
Expert-based
Measurable/ Uses LCA
Relevance
Comparable

BREEAM [48] 1990 UK √* - √ √ √

Green Globes [49] 1996 Canada √ √ √/√ √ √

LEED [50] 2000 US √ √ √/√ V 3.0 √ √

CASBEE [51] 2001 Japan √ √ √/√ √ √

ENERGY STAR [52] 1999 US √ √# √ Only energy √

| *Only assessment prediction check lists available publicly
#Benchmarking tool developed by US EPA

	Year established	Country of origin	Trans-parent	Expert-based	Measurable/ Uses LCA	Relevance	Comparable
BREEAM[53]	1990	UK	√*	-	√	√	√
Green Globes[54]	1996	Canada	√	√	√/√	√	√
LEED[55]	2000	US	√	√	√/√ V 3.0	√	√
CASBEE[56]	2001	Japan	√	√	√/√	√	√
ENERGY STAR[57]	1999	US	√	√#	√	Only energy	√

| *Only assessment prediction check lists available publicly
#Benchmarking tool developed by US EPA

System	Year established	Country of origin	Trans- parent	Expert-based	Measurable
BREEAM [48]	1990	UK	$\sqrt{}$*	-	$\sqrt{}$
Green Globes [49]	1996	Canada	$\sqrt{}$	$\sqrt{}$	$\sqrt{}$/$\sqrt{}$
LEED [50]	2000	US	$\sqrt{}$	$\sqrt{}$	$\sqrt{}$/$\sqrt{}$ V 3.0
CASBEE [51]	2001	Japan	$\sqrt{}$	$\sqrt{}$	$\sqrt{}$/$\sqrt{}$
ENERGY STAR [52]	1999	US	$\sqrt{}$	$\sqrt{}$#	$\sqrt{}$
*Only assessment prediction check lists available publicly#Benchmarking tool developed

Table 11.2: **Comparison of Certification Systems** *Source: Klein-Banai, C.*[53]

11.3.7 Conclusion

The built environment is the largest manifestation of human life on the planet. Buildings have been essential for the survival of the human race, protecting us from the elements and forces of nature. However, they also consume a lot of material, energy and water, and they occupy land that might otherwise be undeveloped or used for agriculture. There are many ways to reduce that impact by building to a higher standard of conservation and reuse. There are a number of systems that can help architects, engineers, and planners to achieve those standards, and they should be selected with a full awareness of their limitations.

11.3.8 References

Fowler, K.M. & Rauch, E.M. (2008). *Assessing green building performance. A post occupancy evaluation of 12 GSA buildings.* (U.S. General Services Administration). PNNL-17393 Pacific Northwest National Laboratory Richland, Washington. Retrieved from http://www.gsa.gov/graphics/pbs/GSA_Assessing_Green_Full_Report.pdf[54]

---

[53] http://cnx.org/member_profile/cindykb
[49] http://www.breeam.org/page.jsp?id=66
[50] http://www.greenglobes.com/about.asp
[51] http://www.usgbc.org/
[52] http://www.ibec.or.jp/CASBEE/english/overviewE.htm
[53] http://www.energystar.gov/index.cfm?c=cbd_guidebook.cbd_guidebook
[54] http://www.gsa.gov/graphics/pbs/GSA_Assessing_Green_Full_Report.pdf

Horvath, A. (2004). Construction materials and the environment. *Annual Review of Energy and the Environment, 29* , 181-204.

Humphreys, K. & Mahasenan, M. (2002). Toward a Sustainable Cement Industry. Substudy 8, Climate Change. World Business Council for Sustainable Development. Retrieved from http://www.wbcsd.org/web/publications/batelle-full.pdf[55]

Kats, G., Alevantis, L., Berman, A., Mills, E. & Perlman, J. (2003). The costs and financial benefits of green building: A report to California's sustainable building task force. Retrieved from http://www.usgbc.org/Docs/News/News477.pdf[56]

Turner, C. & Frankel, M. (2008). *Energy performance of LEED for New Construction Buildings, Final Report.* Retrieved from http://newbuildings.org/sites/default/files/Energy_Performance_of_LEED-NC_Buildings-Final_3-4-08b.pdf[57]

U.S. Department of Energy. (2011). *Energy savers: Furnaces and boilers.* Retrieved from http://www.energysavers.gov/your_home/space_heating_cooling/index.cfm/mytopic=12530[58]

U.S. Environmental Protection Agency. (1987). *The total exposure assessment methodology (TEAM) study* (EPA 600/S6-87/002). Retrieved from http://exposurescience.org/pub/reports/TEAM_Study_book_1987.pdf[59]

U.S. Environmental Protection Agency. (1998). *Characterization of building-related construction and demolition debris in the United States.* (Report No. EPA530-R-98-010). Retrieved from http://www.epa.gov/wastes/hazard/generation/sqg/cd-rpt.pdf[60]

U.S. Environmental Protection Agency. (2010). Green Building Basic Information. Retrieved from http://www.epa.gov/greenbuilding/pubs/about.htm[61] .

11.3.9 Review Questions

Question 11.3.1
What are the positive and negative impacts that buildings have on the environment and society?

Question 11.3.2
How can those impacts be reduced?

Question 11.3.3
What would be the advantages and disadvantages of demolishing an old building and replacing it with a new, highly "sustainable" building vs. renovating an old building to new standards?

---

[55] http://www.wbcsd.org/web/publications/batelle-full.pdf
[56] http://www.usgbc.org/Docs/News/News477.pdf
[57] http://newbuildings.org/sites/default/files/Energy_Performance_of_LEED-NC_Buildings-Final_3-4-08b.pdf
[58] http://www.energysavers.gov/your_home/space_heating_cooling/index.cfm/mytopic=12530
[59] http://exposurescience.org/pub/reports/TEAM_Study_book_1987.pdf
[60] http://www.epa.gov/wastes/hazard/generation/sqg/cd-rpt.pdf
[61] http://www.epa.gov/greenbuilding/pubs/about.htm

11.4 Sustainable Energy Practices: Climate Action Planning[62]

11.4.1 Learning Objectives

After reading this module, students should be able to

- understand the considerations needed to make a move to a sustainable energy economy
- describe a path to get to a sustainable energy economy
- connect sustainable energy policies to climate action planning

11.4.2 Introduction

Traditionally, the United States has relied on fossil fuels with minimal use of alternatives to provide power. The resources appeared to be unlimited and they were found within our borders. As our population has grown and our reliance on power increased, our resources are decreasing. As discussed in **Module** Environmental Challenges in Energy, Carbon Dioxide, Air and Water (Section 8.2), this is particularly true of petroleum oil, which primarily powers transportation. Our electrical grid and transportation infrastructure of roads and highways support these fossil fuel dependent technologies. Fossil fuels store energy well, are available upon demand (not weather dependent), and are inexpensive. However, as we saw in **Module** Environmental Challenges in Energy, Carbon Dioxide, Air and Water (Section 8.2) there are many environmental, social, and even economic impacts of using these nonrenewable fuel sources that are not accounted for in the traditional methods of cost accounting. Further, the oil industry has been provided with many subsidies or tax incentives not available to other energy industries.

How do we move to a more sustainable energy economy? We need to pay more attention to the environment, humans, biodiversity, and respecting our ecosystems. It means finding ways to share our resources equitably both now and in the future so all people can have an equal opportunity to derive benefits from electricity, motorized transportation systems, industry, and conditioned indoor environments. At the same time, we must preserve human health and protect the natural world.

Energy use is one big piece of the sustainability puzzle, but it is not the only one. Changing the way we use energy is not easy because of infrastructure, the vision of the American Dream (own a house with a big yard, a big car, independence), changing government policy, lack of economic incentives, etc. Goals need to be set, plans made, and policy set to change the way we use energy. This chapter will discuss some of the commonly held views of where we can start and how we can change.

11.4.3 Climate Action Planning as a Model

Since one of the major sustainability issues is that of climate change and the major cause of climate change is energy use, climate action planning is a valuable framework for examining sustainable energy practices. Greenhouse gas emissions result primarily from our building and transportation energy uses, and they are a measure of the amount of fossil fuels used to provide that energy. They do not directly represent other environmental emissions, although they mostly parallel other air pollutants. Greenhouse gas emissions do not express other ecosystem effects such as land use and water, but this planning allows for economical solutions. A climate action plan provides a roadmap for achieving greenhouse gas reduction targets within a specific timeline and uses a number of strategies.

11.4.3.1 Who is Doing Climate Action Planning?

In absence of federal regulation, cities, states, government institutions, and colleges and universities, have all taken climate action initiatives. In Massachusetts[63] entities that generate more than 5,000 metric tons per year of Carbon Dioxide Equivalent (CO_2e) began in 2010 with 2009 emissions. The U.S. Environmental

---

[62]This content is available online at <http://legacy.cnx.org/content/m41741/1.2/>.
[63]http://www.mass.gov/dep/air/climate/ghgrinfo.htm

Protection Agency (EPA)[64] requires facilities that emit more than 25,000 metric tons CO_2e per year to start reporting in 2011 for 2010. Many cities have developed Climate Action Plans that set greenhouse gas reduction goals and lay out pathways to achieve them. Chicago launched its plan[65] in 2008 and reports annually on its progress. President Obama signed White House Executive Order 13514[66] , in October 2009 requiring all federal agencies to appoint a sustainability director, take inventory of greenhouse gas emissions, and work to meet sustainability targets. Over 670 American colleges and universities have signed the American College and University Presidents' Climate Commitment (ACUPCC)[67] that requires them to develop climate action plans. Private industries also develop climate action plans.

The National Wildlife Federation[68] suggests that there are six steps to reduce carbon emissions at universities – this could be similar for any other entity:

1. Commitment to emissions reduction
2. Institutional structures and support
3. Emissions inventory
4. Developing the plan
5. Launching the plan
6. Climate action planning over the long haul

Based on the climate change scenarios calculated by the Intergovernmental Panel on Climate Change[69] , it is recommended to reduce greenhouse gas emissions to 80 percent below the 1990 levels, whether or not there is continued growth. This is an absolute reduction to prevent greenhouse gases from reaching levels that will have severe effects. A climate action plan is made of a number of strategies to achieve that goal. To examine the impact of each strategy the **wedge approach** is used. Developed by two professors at Princeton, Socolow and Pacala, the approach proposes that in order to reach those levels, emissions must be decreased globally by seven gigatons of carbon (not carbon dioxide) compared to "business as usual" (BAU) scenarios which would increase emissions over time due to growth and increased demand for energy (**Figure** The Wedge Approach (a) (Figure 11.16(a)). These professors identified 15 proposed actions that could each reduce emissions by 1 gigaton, and if we could enact seven of them we would achieve the goal (**Figure** The Wedge Approach (b) (Figure 11.16(b)). Each of those technologies is represented by a "wedge" of the triangle, hence the designation of the "wedge approach."

---

[64]http://www.epa.gov/climatechange/emissions/ghgrulemaking.html
[65]http://www.chicagoclimateaction.org/
[66]http://www.whitehouse.gov/assets/documents/2009fedleader_eo_rel.pdf
[67]http://www.presidentsclimatecommitment.org/
[68]http://www.campusecology.org/
[69]http://www.ipcc.ch/

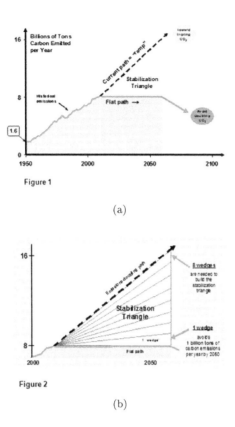

Figure 1

(a)

Figure 2

(b)

Figure 11.16: The Wedge Approach The upper figure (a) represents the current path of increasing carbon emissions and the lower figure (b) represents the effects of many different strategies used to reduce the emissions (a wedge of the triangle). *Source: The Carbon Mitigation Initiative, Princeton University*[70]

11.4.4 Sustainable Solutions

All of the proposed solutions in Sokolov and Pacala's proposal are existing technologies. However, for a solution to be sustainable it must be economically viable. Another aspect of developing a plan is the cost of the solutions. **Figure** Global GHG Abatement Cost Curve Beyond Business-As-Usual – 2030 (p. 553) shows the amount of greenhouse gas emissions that can be abated beyond "business as usual" in 2030, along with the costs of different abatement strategies. Those technologies that fall below the 0 line will actually have a negative cost or positive economic benefit. Those technologies that rise above the 0 line will have positive cost associated with them which could be offset by the technologies that fall below the line.

[70]http://cmi.princeton.edu/wedges/intro.php

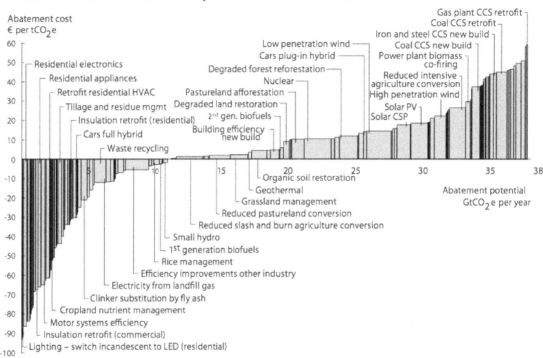

Figure 11.17:   Global GHG Abatement Cost Curve Beyond Business-As-Usual – 2030
Source: McKinsey & Company, Pathways to a Low-Carbon Economy. Version 2 of the Global Greenhouse Gas Abatement Cost Curve, 2009[71]

The types of technologies that fall below the line are primarily energy conservation and efficiency technologies. Energy conservation is the act of reducing energy use to avoid waste, save money, and reduce the environmental impact. In the framework of sustainable energy planning it allows the more expensive alternatives, such as renewables, to become more advanced and cost-effective, while we conserve as much as possible. Conservation has a behavioral aspect to it, such as turning off lights when not needed, lowering thermostats in the winter, or keeping the proper air pressure in a vehicle's tires. There is a very low cost to conservation but it entails behavioral change. There are technologies such as motion detectors that can control lights or programmable thermostats that adjust temperature that can help overcome the behavioral barrier. Energy efficiency[72] can be seen as a subset of conservation as it is really about using technological advancements to make more efficient energy-consuming equipment.

In the United States we use twice as much energy per dollar of GDP as most other industrialized nations (see **Figure** Energy Demand and GDP Per Capita (1980-2004) (p. 554)). There are many reasons for this. One reason is that we use less efficient vehicles and use proportionally more energy to heat and cool buildings, behaviors that could be modified to be more efficient.

---

[71]https://solutions.mckinsey.com/ClimateDesk/default.aspx
[72]http://www.eia.gov/tools/glossary/index.cfm?id=E

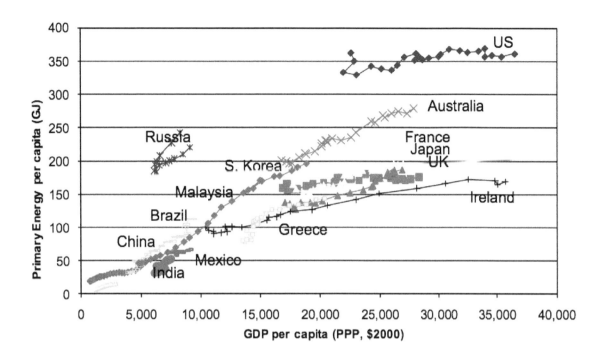

Source: UN and DOE EIA, Russia data 1992-2004 only

Figure 11.18: **Energy Demand and GDP Per Capita (1980-2004)** Each line represents a different country and the points are for the years 1980-2004, which the exception of Russian which is 1992-2004. *Source: U.S. Department of Energy, Sustainability and Maintaining US Competitiveness (June 2010), p. 4*[73]

---

[73]http://science.energy.gov/∼/media/s-4/pdf/100625.pdf

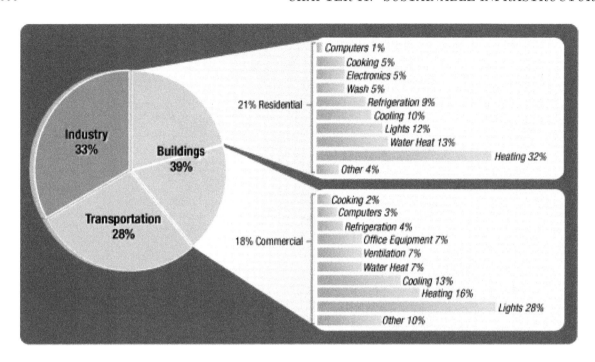

Figure 11.19:   U.S. Energy Consumption by Source Figure shows United States energy consumption by source, with breakdown for buildings. *Source: U.S. Department of Energy, Berkeley Lab*[74]

Another reason that the United States uses so much more energy than other industrialized countries has to do with heating, cooling, and illuminating buildings. Buildings account for about 40 percent of total energy consumption in the United States (costing $350 billion per year) and greenhouse gas emissions (see **Figure** U.S. Energy Consumption by Source (Figure 11.19)). Energy use in buildings is primarily for heating, cooling, and illumination, with significant differences between commercial and residential buildings. The rest of the energy use is for equipment such as office equipment, electronics, refrigeration, cooking, and washing. There are many ways to save energy in existing buildings and most of them have a good financial benefit of saving money on the energy costs, i.e. they have a short term financial payback, or return on investment (ROI).

11.4.4.1 Start with the Lights

The most prevalent message in energy efficiency is "change the light bulbs." Replacing traditional incandescent light bulbs with compact fluorescent light bulbs can save energy. The light bulb had not evolved much since Thomas Edison perfected it in 1879. Over the last few years there have been major initiatives across the United States to replace inefficient incandescent light bulbs with compact fluorescent light bulbs (CFLs) that can reduce energy use by 75 percent. The light bulbs also last 10 times as long, reducing waste and maintenance costs. In commercial buildings more efficient fluorescent light bulbs (T-8s) and ballasts[75] are replacing the older T-12s. In 2002, the U.S. Department of Energy required that T-12 ballasts no longer be manufactured, ending a five year phase out of this technology.

---

[74]http://newscenter.lbl.gov/feature-stories/2009/06/02/working-toward-the-very-low-energy-consumption-building-of-the-future/

[75]http://www.energystar.gov/index.cfm?c=cfls.pr_cfls_glossary

Figure 11.20: Compact Fluorescent Light Bulb Over its lifetime, each standard (13 watt) CFL will reduce electricity bills by about $30 and emissions from 200 lbs of coal over its lifetime. *Source: Kevin Rector*[76]

Already newer, more efficient technologies are hitting the market – light-emitting diodes (LEDs)[77] – which use less than 25 percent of the energy of an incandescent light and last at least 15 times longer, if it has the ENERGY STAR rating. ENERGY STAR[78] is the government-backed symbol for energy efficiency recognition. LEDs are small light sources that become illuminated by the movement of electrons through a semiconductor material (**Figure** Solid State Lighting (SSL) (Figure 11.21)). The technology is still evolving and not all LED lights are created equally. LEDs are more expensive and will have a longer pay back time, but they also last longer.

[76]http://commons.wikimedia.org/wiki/File:CompactFluorescentLightBulb.jpg
[77]http://www.energystar.gov/index.cfm?c=lighting.pr_what_are
[78]http://www.energystar.gov/index.cfm?c=products.pr_how_earn

Figure 11.21: Solid State Lighting (SSL) Solid state lighting (SSL) is comprised of many small LEDs. Since they release very little energy as heat, they are cool to the touch and highly efficient. *Source: Ocrho*[79]

If CFLs were used in all homes, the most advanced linear fluorescent lights in office buildings, commercial outlets and factories, and LEDs in traffic lights would reduce the percentage of electricity used for lighting in the world from 19 percent to sever percent. That's equivalent to 705 coal-fired power plants.

11.4.4.2 Buy More Efficient Equipment and Appliances

ENERGY STAR also ranks equipment for efficiency from refrigerators to air conditioners to computers and televisions. Policies and financial incentives encourage people to buy more energy efficient products which tend to be more expensive. However, by saving on energy costs consumers can recuperate the investment. Refrigeration makes up 9 percent of household energy use. Refrigerators have gotten more efficient from 3.84 cubic feet per kilowatt hour per day in 1972 to 11.22 cubic feet per kilowatt hour by 1996 (**Figure** Average Efficiency of New Refrigerators in the United States (1972-1997) (Figure 11.22)). The efficiency of an average new refrigerator has increased dramatically. New technology, increasing price of electricity, and anticipated energy efficiency standards contributed to increased efficiency in new refrigerators. The National Appliance Energy Conservation Act of 1987[80] set minimum efficiency standards for 13 product

---

[79]http://en.wikipedia.org/wiki/File:E27_with_38_LCD.JPG
[80]http://www1.eere.energy.gov/buildings/appliance_standards/history.html

types, including refrigerators. After 1993, no refrigerator could be sold that did not meet the standards. Standards were updated again in 2002. However, 3 percent more households had two or more refrigerators in 2001 compared to 1980, partially reducing the effect of increased efficiency, especially since the second refrigerator tends to be less efficient.

Today, consideration should be given to electronics in purchasing. Laptops, for instance use considerably less electricity than desktops and flat screens less than the old cathode ray tube (CRT) monitors. New HD televisions use more energy than older analog TVs. Also, there are many appliances that even if turned off, draw power from the grid. This is sometimes called **phantom load** or **vampire power**. Although it is a small amount, it can comprise up to 10 percent of home electricity use. Chargers for cell phones, digital cameras, computers, and power tools are very common sources of phantom load. Also, TVs, computer monitors, and DVD players have current whenever they are plugged in. Using a "smart" power strip can eliminate the need to manually up-plug. Plugging everything in to a strip that is control by one master device or activated by a motion detector provides the technology to replace the behavior of manually turning off and unplugging all the devices when they are not in use.

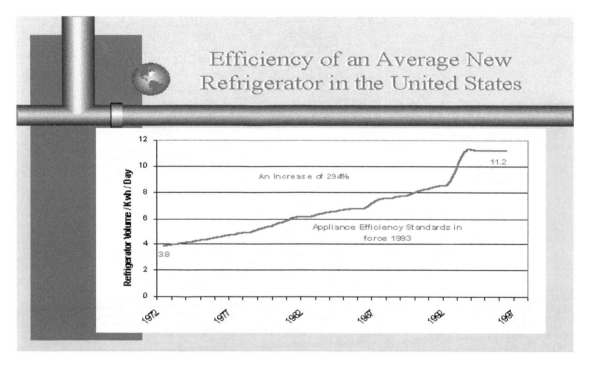

Figure 11.22: Average Efficiency of New Refrigerators in the United States (1972-1997)
Graph shows the efficiency of an average new refrigerator in the United States from 1972 to 1997. *Source: U.S. Energy Information Administration*[81]

11.4.4.3 Tighten Up the Building Envelope

The building envelope (e.g. walls, windows, foundations, doors, and roofs) greatly affects how efficient a building will be in maintaining comfortable interior temperatures. Insulation in walls and seals around windows and doors are prime factors. **Low-emittance** coatings (microscopically thin, virtually invisible, metal or metallic oxide layers deposited on a window or skylight glazing surface primarily to reduce the

---

[81]http://www.eia.doe.gov/emeu/25opec/sld026.htm

U-factor by suppressing radioactive heat flow), gas-fills, and insulating spacers and frames can significantly reduce winter heat loss and summer heat gain through windows.

Double-pane, insulated glass windows significantly reduce the load on the heating and cooling systems and drafts, which in turn, reduces energy demand. These projects are most financially beneficial when leveraged as part of other renovation projects. Existing windows can also be "fixed" with weather-stripping and caulking to seal them from air leakages. Good storm windows over single-pane glass windows can also provide similar insulation to double-pane without the need for the larger financial investment and the creation of waste that replacement entails.

Insulation in the attic or roof of a building and at the "seam" of the building between the basement and first floor, as well as the walls can be installed or increased to retain the heated or cooled air for building or home. Related to insulation is sealing of opening to prevent air from leaking out (see **Figure** Diagram of a Leaky Home (Figure 11.23)).

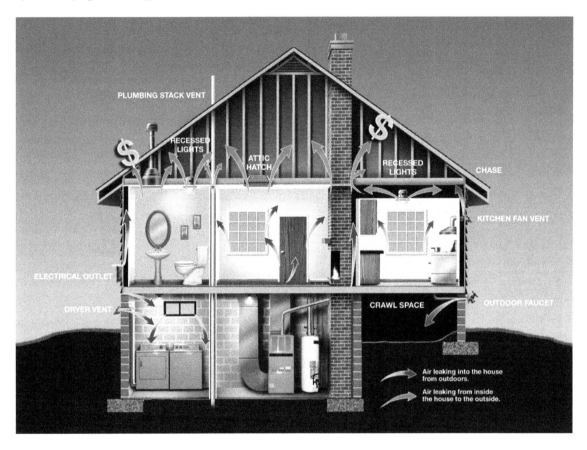

Figure 11.23: **Diagram of a Leaky Home** Diagram shows the various points in a home where energy may leak. Source: ENERGY STAR[82]

11.4.4.4 Maintain or Upgrade Heating, Ventilation and Air-Conditioning Systems

Heating, ventilation, and air-conditioning systems in commercial and industrial buildings need to be properly monitored and maintained for the most efficient function. This is often not done well after a system

---

[82]http://www.energystar.gov/ia/new_homes/behind_the_walls/DollarHouse.jpg

is installed because not enough resources are dedicated to maintenance of systems. Processes related to building commissioning make sure that buildings are ready for service after equipment installation and testing, problems are identified and corrected, and the maintenance staff is extensively trained. If this was not done or the effect has worn out, buildings may undergo recommissioning[83], or if it was never commissioned, retrocommissioning[84] can be performed.

If equipment such as motors, fans, boilers, and chillers are too old to fix or inefficient, they can be replaced or retrofitted with more energy efficient equipment. **Building automation systems** (BAS) use electronic technology to control and monitor building systems. They can schedule temperature settings and ventilation needs based on actual or scheduled occupancy so energy can be saved when space is unoccupied. In homes, this is typically done with a programmable thermostat that can set the temperature points to conserve energy during the day when a home is unoccupied and then go back to occupancy settings when the family returns.

Energy consulting companies can provide many services and innovative solutions for building owners that will reduce energy costs. This is a growing job sector within the United States economy as businesses try to capitalize on the savings that energy projects like those described above can provide.

11.4.4.5 Combining Heat and Power

One area of huge potential for energy efficiency is from capturing waste heat from electricity generation and many industries through a process called cogeneration or combined heat and power (CHP), which is discussed in greater detail in the **Module** Combined Heat and Power (Section 8.5.2). Cogeneration is the simultaneous production of heat and electrical power in a single thermodynamic process. Instead of discarding the heat produced by the electrical power production or industrial process, it is captured and used to provide space heating and hot water heating, humidification, cooling (via absorption chillers), as well as other uses, thus eliminating the added expense of burning fuels for the sole purpose of space heating (see **Figure** Comparison of Energy Efficiency of Standard Power Plant and Combined Heat and Power Plant (Figure 11.24)). The U.S. Department of Energy calculated that CHP generation from industrial processes alone is equal to the output of 40 percent of coal-fired generating plants that produced electricity in 2007.

---

[83] http://cx.lbl.gov/definition.html
[84] http://cx.lbl.gov/definition.html

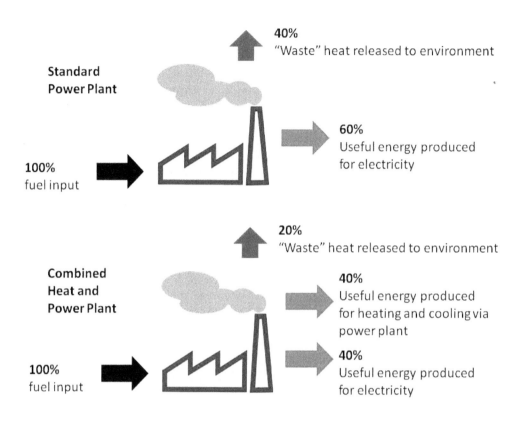

Figure 11.24:   Comparison of Energy Efficiency of Standard Power Plant and Combined Heat and Power Plant Diagram compares the energy efficiency of a standard power plant with a combined heat and power plant. *Source: Cindy Klein-Banai*[85]

11.4.5 Design New Buildings to Reduce Energy Use

The construction of new buildings consumes a lot of energy from the production of the raw materials, the transportation to the building site, the construction process, and ultimately the energy used to operate the building. In the last decade in the United States, there has been a growing recognition that much could be done to reduce the environmental impact of new construction. Therefore, building energy codes increasingly demand higher energy efficiency and green building certification and recognition systems have been developed, such as Green Globes[86] and Leadership in Energy and Environmental Design (LEED)[87] , to promote design for the environment. Aspects of construction that can enhance energy efficiency include site selection, energy and water efficiency, materials used, proximity to public transit and provision of biking amenities, and renewable energy. In addition, using a process of integrated design where the structure of the building itself provides the energy needed to heat, cool or illuminate the building, energy savings can be achieved more readily.

---

[85]http://cnx.org/member_profile/cindykb
[86]http://www.greenglobes.com/
[87]http://www.usgbc.org/

Figure 11.25: Lincoln Hall, LEED Gold Certified, University of Illinois at Chicago Lincoln Hall, LEED Gold certified building on the University of Illinois at Chicago campus. Features include geothermal heating and cooling, solar photovoltaic rooftop system, low-emittance, high-U windows, daylighting, native planting, bioswales for stormwater management, and use of recycled materials. *Source: UIC Office of Sustainability*[88]

11.4.6 Implementing Renewable Energy Technologies

When buildings have been retrofitted to be more energy efficient and combined heat and power systems are used more broadly, we will have reduced energy demand significantly and cost effectively, while creating more jobs domestically. We can then look at the mass deployment of renewable energy technologies. Over time these technologies will mature and become more affordable. This process can be enhanced through policy implementation that incentivizes renewable energy development.

The electric grid will need to be expanded. This will allow for more interstate transmission of renewable electricity from the areas where the resources are good such as the southwest, for solar, and the central and plains states, for wind, to the areas where the population centers are such as the east and west coasts. If these grids are smart and allow for real-time energy pricing then demand will be leveled out. This unified national smart grid would include more efficient, higher-voltage long-distance transmission lines; "smart" distribution networks that use the internet to connect smart meters in homes and along the grid; energy storage units (i.e. batteries) throughout the network; and two-way communication between the equipment that consumes electricity and the equipment that produces it.

---

[88]http://www.uic.edu/sustainability/

We can envision a future where most cars on the road are electric. At night, consumption across the grid is lower because lights are off, buildings are closed, and less manufacturing occurs. Owners of electric cars will plug their cars into the grid at night and recharge them after being driven during the day. Since, demand for electricity is lower, prices for this utility will be lower. With smart meters, residents will be charged for the actual cost of electricity at time of use rather than an average price. They will be incentivized to set washing machines and dishwashers to run at night when electricity demand is lowest. All of this evens out the demand on the grid, which means that power plants do not need to operate at peak capacity and reduces the need for new plants.

11.4.7 Energy Savings in Transportation

Transportation comprises nearly a third of energy demand in the United States so energy savings achieved here will translate to overall energy savings.To reduce energy consumption by vehicles we need to encourage vehicle efficiency and conservation. This is accomplished through the Corporate Average Fuel Economy (CAFÉ)[89] standards. Congress first enacted these standards in 1975 due to the rising cost of gas that resulted from the country's dependence on increasing levels of petroleum imports. The National Highway Traffic Safety Administration[90] sets fuel economy standards for cars and light trucks sold in the United States while the EPA calculates the average fuel economy for each manufacturer. In addition to CAFÉ standards, in 1975 the speed limit on United States highways was reduced to 55 mph to limit gas consumption. **Figure** Carbon Dioxide Emissions and Fuel Economy by Model Year (Figure 11.26) shows that model year 2009 had the lowest CO_2 emission rate (397 g/mi) and highest fuel economy (22.4 mpg) since tracking began in 1975.

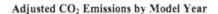

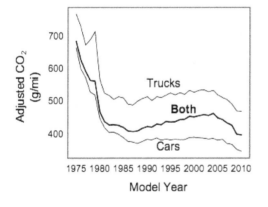 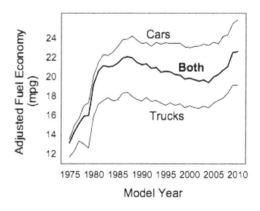

Figure 11.26:   Carbon Dioxide Emissions and Fuel Economy by Model Year Two graphs show carbon dioxide emissions and fuel economy by model year from 1975-2010. *Source: U.S. EPA, Light-Duty Automotive Technology, Carbon Dioxide Emissions, and Fuel Economy Trends: 1975 through 2010 (Nov. 2010), p. iv*[91]

Other ways to increase efficiency can be found through innovative alternative vehicle technologies, improved internal combustion engines, exhaust gas recycling, variable valve timing, vehicle downsizing, **lightweighting**, and behavior. Government policies need to make the cost of driving evident through full amortization, fuel/road tax, and insurance costs.

---

[89]http://www.nhtsa.gov/fuel-economy
[90]http://www.nhtsa.gov/
[91]http://www.epa.gov/otaq/cert/mpg/fetrends/420r10023.pdf

Another tactic to reduce fuel consumption is increasing the use of transportation alternatives. The use of **active transportation** will cause a change from environmentally harmful, passive travel to clean, active travel by bicycle, foot, and public transit. Convenient and safe public transit is not available in all communities, as it requires a certain population density to be viable. Moreover, since Americans often associate the car they drive with their material success and our communities are spread out, many people do not view public transportation favorably. Most metropolitan areas have some kind of transit system to provide transportation to those who cannot afford cars or cannot drive and/or to relieve traffic congestion. Historically, the United States has not invested equally in road and public transportation infrastructure meaning that often it is slower and more complicated to travel by transit. However, transit use is generally more economical than owning and driving a car. The American Public Transportation Association[92] has calculated the savings based on a two person-two car household going to one-car. They found that riding public transportation saves individuals, on average $9,656 annually, and up to $805 per month based on the January 5, 2011 average national gas price ($3.08 per gallon-reported by AAA) and the national unreserved monthly parking rate. Savings for specific cities are shown here[93].

Bicycling and walking are two forms of alternate transit that have no environmental impact on energy demand. Many local governments are devoting resources to adding bike routes and parking facilities to encourage bicycling as a mode of transportation. Sidewalks and safe cross-walks are prerequisites for safe walking.

There are some options for those who must drive to reduce their energy use. **Carpooling** and **car sharing** are also options that lower the number of cars on the road, while providing opportunities to travel by car when needed. Improved social network-based car-pooling programs can help to match riders with drivers in a dynamic way. Car sharing is a decentralized, hourly car rental system that allows people who do not own cars, but occasionally need one, to access a vehicle in proximity to their workplace or home.

11.4.8 Summary

There is no one silver bullet when it comes to solving the "energy problem" or planning for climate action. There are many viable solutions and the problem is so large that multiple pathways must be forged. The primary challenge is to use energy more efficiently so little goes to waste. From small actions like changing a light bulb, to large projects like CHP, the potential is great and the financial payback rewarding. Increased vehicle efficiency and active transportation are also strategies for reducing energy use. Both within the building sector and the transportation sector we have the greatest challenges to and potential for changing how we use energy today. We have already started to make that transition from more stringent CAFÉ standards to more green buildings. The challenge is to upscale all the strategies to make a significant impact.

11.4.9 Review Questions

Question 11.4.1
What does the chart in Figure Energy Demand and GDP Per Capita (1980-2004) (p. 554) tell us about developing countries such as China, India and Brazil's energy use? a) In comparison to developed countries. b) Over time.

Question 11.4.2
Briefly describe a path to reducing our dependency on fossil fuels for transportation energy consumption.

Question 11.4.3
Why is energy efficiency considered a sustainable energy choice?

---

[92] http://www.apta.com/Pages/default.aspx
[93] http://apta.com/mediacenter/pressreleases/2011/Pages/110601_TransitSavingsReport.aspx

11.4.10 References

Brown, L.R. (2008). *Plan B 3.0: Mobilizing to save civilization*. New York: Earth Policy Institute.

City of Chicago. (2011). *Chicago Climate Action Plan*. Retrieved September 12, 2011 from http://www.chicagoclimateaction.org/filebin/pdf/finalreport/CCAPREPORTFINALv2.pdf[94]

Eagan, D.J., Calhoun, T., Schott, J. & Dayananda, P. (2008). *Guide to climate action planning: Pathways to a low-carbon campus*. National Wildlife Federation: Campus Ecology. Retrieved September 12, 2011 from http://www.nwf.org/Global-Warming/Campus-Solutions/Resources/Reports/Guide-to-Climate-Action-Planning.aspx[95]

Gore, A. (2009). *Our choice: A plan to solve the climate crisis*. New York: Melcher Media.

Pacala, S. & Socolow, R. (2004). Stabilization wedges: Solving the climate problem for the next 50 years with current technologies. *Science, 305*, 968-972.

University of Illinois at Chicago. (2009). *UIC Climate Action Plan*. Retrieved September 12, 2011 from http://www.uic.edu/sustainability/climateactionplan/[96] .

11.5 Sustainable Transportation: Accessibility, Mobility, and Derived Demand[97]

11.5.1 Learning Objectives

After reading this module, students should be able to

- explain why the automobile-based system of transportation is unsustainable in terms of inputs, outputs, and social impacts
- explain why transportation is a derived demand and how making transportation sustainable depends on land use as well as vehicles and infrastructure
- differentiate between accessibility and mobility by comparing how they are currently treated by our transportation system
- analyze how a more sustainable system might address accessibility and mobility

11.5.2 What is Sustainable Transportation?

Transportation is a tricky thing to analyze in the context of sustainability. It consists in part of the built environment: the physical infrastructure of roads, runways, airports, bridges, and rail lines that makes it possible for us to get around. It also consists in part of individual choices: what mode we use to get around (car, bus, bike, plane, etc.), what time of day we travel, how many people we travel with, etc. Finally, it also is made up of institutions: federal and state agencies, oil companies, automobile manufacturers, and transit authorities, all of whom have their own goals and their own ways of shaping the choices we make.

Most importantly, transportation is complicated because it's what is called a **derived demand**. With the exception of joyriding or taking a walk or bicycle ride for exercise, very rarely are we traveling just for the sake of moving. We're almost always going from Point A to Point B. What those points are—home, work, school, shopping—and where they're located—downtown, in a shopping mall, near a freeway exit—influence how fast we need to travel, how much we can spend, what mode we're likely to take, etc. The *demand* for transportation is *derived* from other, non-transportation activities. So in order to understand transportation sustainability, we have to understand the spatial relationship between where we are, where we want to go, and the infrastructure and vehicles that can help get us there.

---

[94]http://www.chicagoclimateaction.org/filebin/pdf/finalreport/CCAPREPORTFINALv2.pdf
[95]http://www.nwf.org/Global-Warming/Campus-Solutions/Resources/Reports/Guide-to-Climate-Action-Planning.aspx
[96]http://www.uic.edu/sustainability/climateactionplan/
[97]This content is available online at <http://legacy.cnx.org/content/m42717/1.2/>.

Is our current transportation system in the U.S. sustainable? In other words, can we keep doing what we're doing indefinitely? The answer is clearly no, according to professional planners and academics alike. There are three main limitations: energy input, emissions, and social impacts (Black, 2010 (p. 575)).

11.5.2.1 Energy Inputs

The first reason that our current transportation system is unsustainable is that the natural resources that power it are finite. The theory of peak oil developed by geologist M. King Hubbert suggests that because the amount of oil in the ground is limited, at some point in time there will be a maximum amount of oil being produced (Deffeyes, 2002 (p. 575)). After we reach that peak, there will still be oil to drill, but the cost will gradually rise as it becomes a more and more valuable commodity. The most reliable estimates of the date of peak oil range from 2005 to 2015, meaning that we've probably already passed the point of no return. New technologies do make it possible to increase the amount of oil we can extract, and new reserves, such as the oil shale of Pennsylvania and the Rocky Mountains, can supply us for some years to come (leaving aside the potential for environmental and social damage from fully developing these sites). However, this does not mean we can indefinitely continue to drive gasoline-powered vehicles as much as we currently do.

Scientists are working on the development of alternative fuels such as biofuels or hydrogen, but these have their own limitations. For example, a significant amount of land area is required to produce crops for biofuels; if we converted every single acre of corn grown in the U.S. to ethanol, it would provide 10% of our transportation energy needs. Furthermore, growing crops for fuel rather than food has already sparked price increases and protests in less-developed countries around the world (IMF, 2010 (p. 575)). Is it fair to ask someone living on less then two dollars a day to pay half again as much for their food so we can drive wherever and whenever we want?

11.5.2.2 Emissions or Outputs

The engine of the typical automobile or truck emits all sorts of noxious outputs. Some of them, including sulfur dioxides, carbon monoxide, and particulate matter, are directly harmful to humans; they irritate our lungs and make it hard for us to breathe. (Plants are damaged in much the same way). These emissions come from either impure fuel or incomplete burning of fuel within an engine. Other noxious outputs cause harm indirectly. Nitrous oxides (the stuff that makes smog look brown) from exhaust, for example, interact with oxygen in the presence of sunlight (which is why smog is worse in Los Angeles and Houston), and ozone also damages our lungs.

Carbon dioxide, another emission that causes harm indirectly, is the most prevalent greenhouse gas (GHG), and transportation accounts for 23% of the CO_2 generated in the U.S. This is more than residential, commercial, or industrial users, behind only electrical power generation (DOE, 2009 (p. 575)). Of course, as was explained above, transportation is a derived demand, so to say that transportation itself is generating carbon emissions is somewhat misleading. The distance between activities, the modes we choose to get between them, and the amount of stuff we consume and where it is manufactured, all contribute to that derived demand and must be addressed in order to reduce GHG emissions from transportation.

11.5.2.3 Social Impacts

If the definition of sustainability includes meeting the needs of the present population as well as the future, our current transportation system is a failure. Within most of the U.S., lack of access to a personal automobile means greatly reduced travel or none at all. For people who are too young, too old, or physically unable to drive, this means asking others for rides, relying heavily on under-funded public transit systems, or simply not traveling. Consider, for example, how children in the U.S. travel to and from school. In 1970, about 50% of school-aged children walked or biked to school, but by 2001, that number had dropped to 15% (Appleyard, 2005 (p. 575)). At the same time that childhood obesity and diabetes are rising, children are getting less and less exercise, even something as simple as walking to school. Furthermore, parents dropping off their children at school can increase traffic levels by 20 to 25%, not just at the school itself, but also throughout the town in question (Appleyard, 2005 (p. 575)). At the other end of the age spectrum, elderly people may be functionally trapped in their homes if they are unable to drive and lack another means of getting to shopping, health care, social activities, etc. Finally, Hurricane Katrina made it clear that access to a car can actually be a matter of life or death: the evacuation of New Orleans worked very well for people with cars, but hundreds died because they didn't have the ability to drive away.

Another serious social impact of our transportation system is traffic accidents. Road accidents and fatalities are accepted as a part of life, even though 42,000 people die every year on the road in the U.S. This means that cars are responsible for more deaths than either guns, drugs, or alcohol (Xu et al., 2010 (p. 576)). On the bright side, there has been a steady reduction in road fatalities over the last few decades, thanks to a combination of more safety features in vehicles and stricter enforcement and penalties for drunk or distracted drivers. Nevertheless, in many other countries around the world, traffic accidents are in the top ten or even top five causes of death, leading the World Health Organization to consider traffic accidents a public health problem.

An additional problem with our current unsustainable transportation system is that much of the rest of the world is trying to emulate it. The U.S. market for cars is saturated, meaning that basically everyone who can afford or is likely to own a car already has one. This is why automobile manufacturers vie so fiercely with their advertising, because they know they are competing with each other for pieces of a pie that's not getting any bigger. In other countries such as China and India, though, there are literally billions of people who do not own cars. Now that smaller, cheaper vehicles like the Tata are entering these markets, rates of car ownership are rising dramatically. While the same problems with resources, emissions, and social impacts are starting to occur in the developing world, there are also unique problems. These include a lack of infrastructure, which leads to monumental traffic jams; a need for sharing the road with pedestrians and animals; and insufficient regulation to keep lead and other harmful additives out of gasoline and thus the air.

11.5.3 What Would Make Transportation Sustainable?

The circular answer to the question is to meet our current transportation needs without preventing future generations from meeting theirs. We can start by using fewer resources or using the ones we have more efficiently. One way to do this is by increasing the efficiency of new vehicles as they are manufactured. Since 1981, automotive engineers have figured out how to increase horsepower in the average American light-duty vehicle (cars and SUVs) by 60%, but they haven't managed to improve miles per gallon at all (see Figure World Oil Production - History and Projections (p. 568)). As gas prices continue to rise on the downside of the oil peak, consumers are already demanding more fuel-efficient cars, and federal legislation is moving in this direction to raise the Corporate Average Fuel Economy (CAFE) standards.

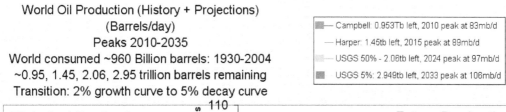

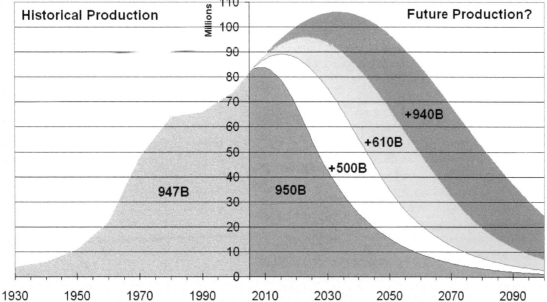

Figure 11.27: World Oil Production - History and Projections Historical production of oil (grey) and forecasts of future production (colors). According to the "peak oil" hypothesis, world oil production will peak and then decline. Estimates of future production vary widely as there is disagreement about the magnitude of undiscovered reserves. If most of the extractable oil has been discovered, we may have already reached peak oil (orange curve). If significant undiscovered reserves remain, peak oil may not arrive until 2030 or 2040. *Source: Released to public domain by Tom Ruen, via Wikimedia Commons*[98]

However, simply producing more fuel-efficient vehicles is not sufficient when we consider the **embodied energy** of the car itself. It takes a lot of energy to make a car, especially in the modern "global assembly line," where parts come from multiple countries for final assembly, and that energy becomes "embodied" in the metal, plastic, and electronics of the car. A study in Europe found that unless a car is over 20 years old, it does not make sense to trade it in for a more efficient one because of this embodied energy (Usón et al., 2011 (p. 576)). Most Americans trade in their cars after about a third of that time. A related concept is true for electric cars. In their daily usage, they generate zero carbon emissions, but we should also consider the source of power used to recharge the vehicle. In most parts of the U.S., this is coal, and therefore the emissions savings are only about 30% over a traditional vehicle (Marsh, 2011 (p. 575)).

If transportation is a derived demand, another way to meet our current transportation needs is by changing the demand. There are two related aspects to this. First, there is a clear causal link between having more transportation infrastructure and more miles traveled on that infrastructure, and greater economic growth. This is true between regions of the world, between individual countries, and between people and regions within countries. This causal connection has been used as a reason to finance transportation projects

---

[98]http://commons.wikimedia.org/wiki/File:Ultimatereserveoilprojections.gif

in hundreds of different contexts, perhaps most recently in the American Reinvestment and Recovery Act that distributed federal funds to states and localities to build infrastructure in the hopes that it would create jobs. Policymakers, businesspeople, and citizens therefore all assume that we need more transportation to increase economic growth.

However, it is also true that more transportation does not *automatically* mean more economic growth: witness the state of West Virginia, with decades' worth of high-quality road infrastructure bestowed upon it by its former Senator Robert Byrd, but still at the bottom of economic rankings of states. Furthermore, at some point a country or region gains no significant improvements from additional infrastructure; they have to focus on making better use of what they already have instead. We therefore need to *decouple* economic growth from transportation growth (Banister and Berechman, 2001 (p. 575)). We can substitute telecommunication for travel, work at home, or shop online instead of traveling to a store (although the goods still have to travel to our homes, this is more efficient than each of us getting in our own cars). We can produce the goods we use locally instead of shipping them halfway around the world, creating jobs at home as well as reducing resource use and emissions. All of these options for decoupling are ways to reduce the demand for transportation without also reducing the benefits from the activities that create that demand.

The other way to think about changing the derived demand of transportation is via the concepts of **accessibility** and **mobility**. Mobility is simply the ability to move or to get around. We can think of certain places as having high accessibility: at a major intersection or freeway exit, a train station, etc. Company headquarters, shopping malls, smaller businesses alike decide where to locate based on this principle, from the gas stations next to a freeway exit to the coffee shop next to a commuter rail station. At points of high accessibility, land tends to cost more because it's easier for people to get there and therefore more businesses or offices want to be there. This also means land uses are usually denser: buildings have more stories, people park in multi-level garages instead of surface lots, etc.

We can also define accessibility as our own ability to get to the places we want: where we shop, work, worship, visit friends or family, see a movie, or take classes. In either case, accessibility is partially based on what the landscape looks like—width of the roads, availability of parking, height of buildings, etc.—and partially on the mode of transportation that people have access to. If a person lives on a busy four-lane road without sidewalks and owns a car, most places are accessible to him. Another person who lives on that same road and doesn't have a car or can't drive might be literally trapped at home. If her office is downtown and she lives near a commuter rail line, she can access her workplace by train. If her office is at a major freeway intersection with no or little transit service, she has to drive or be driven.

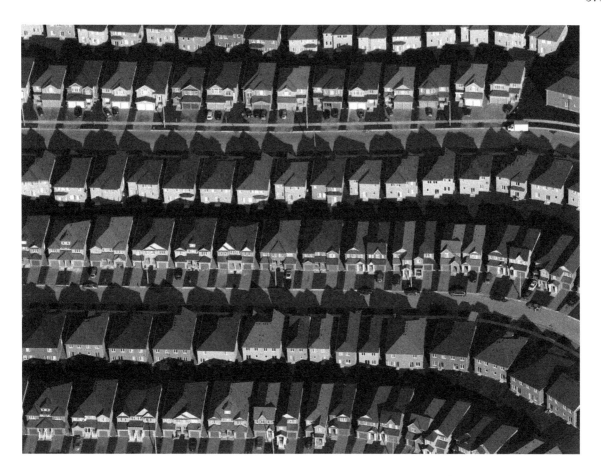

Figure 11.28: Subdivision A modern subdivision near Markham, Ontario. The suburb is residential only, and cars are the only visible means of transport; accessibility for those without personal vehicles is low. Photo by IDuke, November 2005. *Source: IDuke (English Wikipedia) [CC-BY-SA-2.5[99]], via Wikimedia Commons[100]*

Unfortunately, in the U.S. we have conflated accessibility with mobility. To get from work to the doctor's office to shopping to home, we might have to make trips of several miles between each location. If those trips are by bus, we might be waiting for several minutes at each stop or making many transfers to get where we want to go, assuming all locations are accessible by transit. If those trips are by car, we are using the vehicle for multiple short trips, which contributes more to air pollution than a single trip of the same length. Because of our land use regulations, which often segregate residential, retail, office, and healthcare uses to completely different parts of a city, we have no choice but to be highly mobile if we want to access these destinations. John Urry has termed this *automobility*, the social and economic system that has made living without a car almost impossible in countries like the US and the UK (2004 (p. 576)).

So how could we increase accessibility without increasing mobility? We could make it possible for mixed uses to exist on the same street or in the same building, rather than clustering all similar land uses in one place. For example, before a new grocery store opened in the student neighborhood adjacent to the University of Illinois campus in Champaign, people living there had to either take the bus, drive, or get a friend to drive them to a more distant grocery store. Residents of Campustown had their accessibility to fresh produce and

---

[99]http://www.creativecommons.org/licenses/by-sa/2.5
[100]http://commons.wikimedia.org/wiki/File:Markham-suburbs.id.jpg.jpg

other products increase when the new grocery store opened, although their mobility may have actually gone down. In a larger-scale example, the Los Angeles Metropolitan Transit Authority (MTA) was sued in the 1990s for discriminating against minorities by pouring far more resources into commuter rail than into buses. Commuter rail was used mainly by white suburbanites who already had high levels of accessibility, while the bus system was the only means of mobility for many African-American and Hispanic city residents, who had correspondingly less accessibility to jobs, shopping, and personal trips. The courts ruled that the transit authority was guilty of racial discrimination because they were providing more accessibility for people who already had it at the expense of those who lacked it. The MTA was ordered to provide more, cleaner buses, increase service to major job centers, and improve safety and security. More sustainable transportation means ensuring equitable accessibility — not mobility — for everyone now and in the future.

11.5.4 Making Transportation Sustainable

How do we go about making transportation more sustainable? There are three main approaches: inventing new technologies, charging people the full costs of travel, and planning better so we increase accessibility but not mobility.

11.5.4.1 New Technology

This is the hardest category to rely on for a solution, because we simply can't predict what might be invented in the next five to fifty years that could transform how we travel. The jet engine totally changed air travel, making larger planes possible and increasing the distance those planes could reach without refueling, leading to the replacement of train and ship travel over long distances. However, the jet engine has not really changed since the 1960s. Is there some new technology that could provide more propulsion with fewer inputs and emissions? It's possible. But at the same time, it would be unreasonable to count on future inventions magically removing our sustainability problems rather than working with what we already have.

Technology is more than just machines and computers, of course; it also depends on how people use it. When the automobile was first invented, it was seen as a vehicle for leisure trips into the country, not a way to get around every day. As people reshaped the landscape to accommodate cars with wider, paved roads and large parking lots, more people made use of the car to go to work or shopping, and it became integrated into daily life. The unintended consequences of technology are therefore another reason to be wary about relying on new technology to sustain our current system.

11.5.4.2 Charge Full Costs

The economist Anthony Downs has written that traffic jams during rush hour are a good thing, because they indicate that infrastructure is useful and a lot of people are using it (Downs, 1992 (p. 575)). He also notes that building more lanes on a highway is not a solution to congestion, because people who were staying away from the road during rush hour (by traveling at different times, along different routes, or by a different mode) will now start to use the wider road, and it will become just as congested as it was before it was widened. His point is that the road itself is a resource, and when people are using it for free, they will overuse it. If instead, variable tolls were charged depending on how crowded the road was—in other words, how much empty pavement is available—people would choose to either pay the toll (which could then be invested in alternative routes or modes) or stay off the road during congested times. The point is that every car on the road is taking up space that they aren't paying for and therefore slowing down the other people around them; charging a small amount for that space is one way of recovering costs.

Figure 11.29: Freeway Traffic Typical congested traffic on an urban freeway – I-80 in Berkeley, California. Residents of U.S. cities typically require automobiles to experience mobility. Note the externalities that the drivers are imposing on others such as air pollution and congestion. The left lane is for car-pooling – as marked by the white diamond – an attempt to address the congestion externality. *Source: By User Minesweeper on en.wikipedia (Minesweeper) CC-BY-SA-3.0[101], via Wikimedia Commons[102]*

Traffic congestion is an example of what economists call **externalities**, the costs of an activity that aren't paid by the person doing the activity. Suburbanites who drive into the city every day don't breathe the polluted air produced by their cars; urban residents suffer that externality. People around the country who use gasoline derived from oil wells in the Gulf of Mexico didn't experience oil washing up on their beaches after the BP disaster in 2010. By charging the full cost of travel via taxes on gas or insurance, we could, for example, pay for children's hospitalization for asthma caused by the cars speeding past their neighborhoods. Or we could purchase and preserve wetland areas that can absorb the floodwaters that run off of paved streets and parking lots, keeping people's basements and yards drier. Not only would this help to deal with some of the externalities that currently exist, but the higher cost of gas would probably lead us to focus on accessibility rather than mobility, reducing overall demand.

---

[101] http://creativecommons.org/licenses/by-sa/3.0/
[102] http://commons.wikimedia.org/wiki/File%3AI-80_Eastshore_Fwy.jpg

11.5.4.3 Planning Better for Accessibility

The other way we can produce more sustainable transportation is to plan for accessibility, not mobility. Many transportation planners say that we've been using the *predict and provide* model for too long. This means we assume nothing will change in terms of the way we travel, so we simply predict how much more traffic there is going to be in the future and provide roads accordingly. Instead, we should take a *deliberate and decide* approach, bringing in more people into the planning process and offering different options besides more of the same. Some of the decisions we can make to try and change travel patterns include installing bike lanes instead of more parking, locating retail development next to housing so people can walk for a cup of coffee or a few groceries, or investing in transit instead of highways.

Figure 11.30: Traditional Plaza A traditional city center in Piran, Slovenia. The region around the square is mixed use, with buidlings serving both residential and commercial functions. The square is highly accessible to residents. *Source: Plamen Agov studiolemontree.com*[103].

For example, the school district in Champaign, Illinois, is considering closing the existing high school next to downtown, to which many students walk or take public transit, and replacing it with a much larger facility on the edge of town, to which everyone would have to drive or be driven. The new site would require more mobility on the part of nearly everyone, while many students and teachers would see their

---

[103]http://studiolemontree.com/

accessibility decrease. As gas prices continue to rise, it will cost the school district and parents more and more to transport students to and from school, and students will be more likely to drive themselves if they have access to a car and a driver's license. Putting the new school in a more accessible location or expanding the existing one would keep the school transportation system from becoming less sustainable.

You may have noticed that these proposed changes to increase transportation sustainability aren't really things that one person can do. We can certainly make individual choices to drive less and walk or bike more, to buy a more fuel-efficient car, or to use telecommunications instead of transportation. In order to make significant changes that can reduce overall energy usage and emissions production, however, the system itself has to change. This means getting involved in how transportation policy is made, maybe by attending public meetings or writing to city or state officials about a specific project. It means contacting your Congressional representatives to demand that transportation budgets include more money for sustainable transportation modes and infrastructure. It means advocating for those who are disadvantaged under the current system. In means remembering that transportation is connected to other activities, and that focusing on how the demand for transportation is derived is the key to making and keeping it sustainable.

11.5.5 Review Questions

Question 11.5.1
Explain the concept of a derived demand and how it accounts for the connections between transportation and land use planning.

Question 11.5.2
What is the concept of embodied energy? Why does it suggest that switching to electric cars is not a surefire way to make transportation more sustainable?

Question 11.5.3
Give an example in your daily life that could be used to explain the difference between accessibility and mobility.

11.5.6 References

Appleyard, B. S. 2005. Livable Streets for School Children: How Safe Routes to School programs can improve street and community livability for children. National Centre for Bicycling and Walking Forum, available online: http://www.bikewalk.org/pdfs/forumarch0305.pdf[104]

Banister, D. and Berechman, Y. 2001. Transport investment and the promotion of economic growth. *Journal of Transport Geography* 9:3, 209-218.

Black, W. 2010. Sustainable Transportation: Problems and Solutions. New York: Guilford Press.

Deffeyes, K. 2002. Hubbert's Peak: The Impending World Oil Shortage. Princeton, NJ: Princeton University Press.

DOE (Department of Energy). 2009. Emissions of greenhouse gases report. DOE/EIA-0573, available online: http://www.eia.doe.gov/oiaf/1605/ggrpt/carbon.html[105]

Downs, A. 1992. Stuck in Traffic: Coping With Peak-Hour Traffic Congestion. Washington, DC: Brookings Institution Press.

IMF (International Monetary Fund). 2010. Impact of high food and fuel prices on developing countries. Available online: http://www.imf.org/external/np/exr/faq/ffpfaqs.htm[106]

Maring, G. 2007. Surface transportation funding issues and options. Presentation to the National Surface Transportation Infrastructure Financing Commission. Available online: http://financecommission.dot.gov/Documents/Surface%20Transportation%20Funding%20Issues%20and%20Options_Gary%

---

[104]http://www.bikewalk.org/pdfs/forumarch0305.pdf
[105]http://www.eia.doe.gov/oiaf/1605/ggrpt/carbon.html
[106]http://www.imf.org/external/np/exr/faq/ffpfaqs.htm
[107]http://financecommission.dot.gov/Documents/Surface%20Transportation%20Funding%20Issues%20and%20Options_Gary%20Maring.ppt

Marsh, B. 2011. Kilowatts vs. Gallons. *New York Times*, May 28. Available online: http://www.nytimes.com/interactive/2011/05/29/weekinreview/volt-graphic.html?ref=weekinreview[108]

UPI (United Press International). 2011. Global biofuel land area estimated. Available online: http://www.upi.com/Science_News/2011/01/10/Global-biofuel-land-area-estimated/UPI-97301294707088/[109]

Urry, J,. 2004. The 'System' of Automobility. *Theory Culture and Society* 21:4-5, 25-39.

Usón, A.A., Capilla, A.V., Bribián, I.Z., Scarpellini, S. and Sastresa, E.L. 2011. Energy efficiency in transport and mobility for an eco-efficiency viewpoint. *Energy* 36:4, 1916-23.

Xu, J., Kochanek, K., Murphy, S., and Tejada-Vera, B. 2010. Deaths: Final Data for 2007. National Vital Statistics Reports, 58:19, available online: http://www.cdc.gov/NCHS/data/nvsr/nvsr58/nvsr58_19.pdf[110]

11.6 Sustainable Stormwater Management[111]

11.6.1 Learning Objectives

After reading this module, students should be able to

- describe how stormwater runoff affects water quality in urban watersheds
- explain how stormwater is currently managed in the United States
- analyze some of the conventional and innovative techniques that have been developed to address the water pollution and flood risks associated with urban stormwater runoff

11.6.2 Introduction

This module reviews some of the complex issues of urban stormwater management. It first examines the hydrological issues affecting the discharge of stormwater runoff to our urban rivers and streams, and then provides an overview of how urban stormwater is managed under the Clean Water Act. After describing the conventional approaches to urban stormwater management, the final section provides an overview of various "sustainable" strategies, especially the use of "green infrastructure," that can be considered to reduce the water pollution and flooding risks generated by urban stormwater runoff.

11.6.3 The Hydrological Context of Urban Stormwater

Stormwater runoff (or overland flow) is the portion of precipitation reaching the ground that does not infiltrate into soils, is not taken up and transpired by plants, nor is it evaporated into the atmosphere. It is an especially important component of the hydrological cycle in urban areas, since it can cause both pollution and flooding risks to nearby waterways and their adjacent communities. It should also be noted that many of the current models of global climate change predict changes in the hydrological cycle in the future. They predict many more severe storms likely in parts of the Midwest as a result of the moisture and energy in the atmosphere increasing over the next century because of increasingly higher concentrations of greenhouse gases. Higher frequencies of more severe storms are likely to further increase the pollution and flooding risks posed by stormwater runoff, especially in urban areas (USGCRP, 2009 (p. 588)).

Current strategies to manage these risks employ the concept of a **watershed** – the variations in natural topography that cause both surface water and surficial ground water to flow downhill towards lower-lying areas or points of discharge, usually to a stream or river. Watershed boundaries are defined topographically by mapping variations in land elevations around waterways that create hydrologic divides between adjacent

---

[108]http://www.nytimes.com/interactive/2011/05/29/weekinreview/volt-graphic.html?ref=weekinreview
[109]http://www.upi.com/Science_News/2011/01/10/Global-biofuel-land-area-estimated/UPI-97301294707088/
[110]http://www.cdc.gov/NCHS/data/nvsr/nvsr58/nvsr58_19.pdf
[111]This content is available online at <http://legacy.cnx.org/content/m42716/1.2/>.

watersheds and between sub-watersheds. The amount of stormwater that ends up as runoff within a watershed not only depends on the intensity and amount of precipitation reaching the ground in the form of rain or snow, but also on the characteristics of the watershed itself. State and federal environmental protection agencies have developed a number of sophisticated hydrological simulation models that enable the amount and characteristics of stormwater runoff (in terms of its volume and the pollutant load that would be carried by the stormwater to rivers and streams within the watershed) to be forecasted. They forecast this based on historical estimates of the amount of precipitation entering the watershed, the characteristics of a watershed's terrain and soils, the amount and location of impermeable surfaces associated with the development of the watershed, and the extent and types of ground cover within the watershed's drainage area (NRC 2008, Appendix D (p. 587)). A change in any of these factors will affect the amount and extent of flooding and water pollution attributable to the discharge of stormwater runoff into a river or stream.

Since the pattern of precipitation varies seasonally the water pollution and flooding risks posed by stormwater runoff also tend to vary seasonally. Generally, larger flood and pollution risks will occur in the spring, when rapid snowmelt can generate a lot of runoff volume (especially if the ground is still frozen), which can carry pollutants that have accumulated within the snow cover over the winter months to nearby streams and rivers. There can also be storm-related flood and pollution "spikes" when heavy rain strikes the ground at a faster rate than it can be infiltrated into the soils, or when it is prevented from infiltrating into the soils by roofs, paving, or other impermeable surfaces. This initially high volume of stormwater runoff can carry greater amounts of contaminants – a process often described as the **"first flush" phenomenon**. Usually, the first half-inch of stormwater will be carrying the highest pollution load, so its capture and management becomes a priority for water quality protection.

How some of these features, especially the amount of impervious surface associated with different densities of development, affect the generation of urban runoff are illustrated in Figure **Degrees of Imperviousness and its Effects on Stormwater Runoff** (Figure 11.31). Research by the Center for Watershed Protection has found that stream quality becomes impaired when 10% of the stream's watershed is impervious and that an urban stream's ecology is severely impacted when more than 25% of its watershed is impervious.

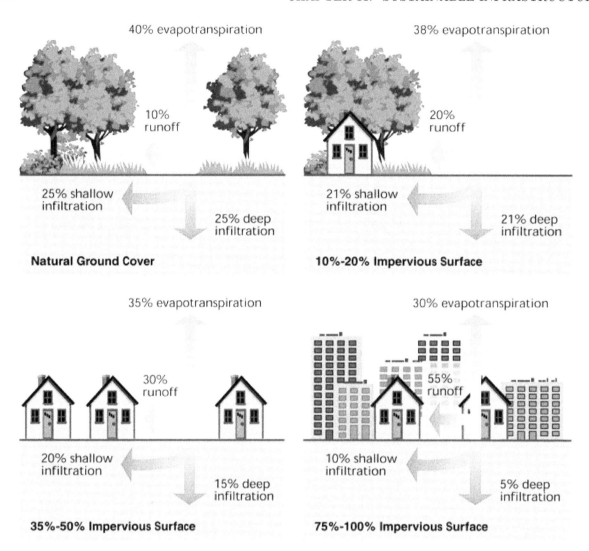

Figure 11.31: Degrees of Imperviousness and its Effects on Stormwater Runoff These four
images show increasing amount of stormwater runoff as the area becomes developed with more impervious
surfaces. *Source: In Stream Corridor Restoration: Principles, Processes, and Practices (10/98) By the
Federal Interagency Stream Restoration Working Group (FISRWG) (15 Federal agencies of the U.S.)*[112]

When flowing downhill within a watershed, stormwater runoff can pick up pollutants from various anthropogenic sources and activities. It can also collect pollutants from the atmospheric deposition of particulates
and air pollutants carried to the earth's surface by precipitation, by windblown dust, or by simply settling
out of the atmosphere. Urban runoff can also dissolve or transport chemicals that may be found naturally in
soil or nutrients which may have been deliberately added to lawns. Common urban pollutants can include
such things as pesticides and fertilizers applied to residential lawns, parks and golf courses, enteric microbes
from animal waste, industrial chemicals that may have been accidentally spilled on the ground or improperly
stored, or oils and greases leaking from cars parked in lots or on driveways.

As stormwater runoff flows towards lower-lying areas of the watershed, it carries these contaminants

---

[112]http://www.nrcs.usda.gov/Internet/FSE_MEDIA/nrcs143_024824.jpg

with it and therefore contributes to the pollution of the stream, river or lake into which it is discharging. Once it reaches a river or stream, the concentrations of pollutants in the receiving waters are naturally reduced as the contaminants are carried downstream from their sources, largely through dilution but also by settlement, by uptake by posure to sunlight and oxygen, and by interactions with various chemical and physical proplants and animals (including bacteria and other microorganisms), through degradation by excesses occurring within the waterway and its streambed.

11.6.3.1 Regulating Urban Runoff

Water pollution risks within watersheds are managed under the federal Clean Water Act[113] , which requires state environmental protection agencies to regulate the discharge of pollutants into navigable waterways and waterbodies pursuant to federal guidelines (NRC, 2008 (p. 587)). The Clean Water Act employs maximum concentration standards for common pollutants that can impair the recreational or ecological functions of a river or stream. One class of polluters regulated under the Clean Water Act consists of those that are directly discharging pollutants into a waterway from an industry or sewage treatment plant through a pipe, ditch, outfall or culvert – these are called **point sources**.

Point sourcesare managed under the Clean Water Act by the requirement that each direct source have a renewable discharge permit, called a National Pollution Discharge Elimination System (NPDES) permit. NPDES permits set limits for the various pollutants being discharged by that source based on the **ambient water quality** of the waterway and its proposed use (e.g. its use as a public water supply source, or for fishing, or recreational use). The other regulated class of polluters managed under the Clean Water Act consists of those sources that introduce contaminants into a waterway through overland or subsurface flow – these are called **non-point sources**, and include most of the water pollution loads carried by urban stormwater runoff.

Since the 1970s, the principal approach used by state and federal environmental protection agencies to control water pollution is to try to simply reduce the quantity of pollutants being released into our rivers and streams (NRC, 2008 (p. 587)). NPDES permits control the direct discharge of contaminants into our waterways, while non-point sources are managed through Best Management Practices (BMPs) that are designed to limit the amount of pollutants released into a watershed, where they could later be carried by stormwater runoff or by groundwater flow to a receiving stream or river. Depending on the pollutant of concern, BMPs could be as simple as requiring pet owners to clean up after their pets or as complex as requiring that industries using toxic materials design, construct and manage loading and storage areas in order to keep spilled materials from being transported off-site by stormwater or groundwater flow. BMPs can even include encouraging some industries to change their production processes in order to reduce the total amount of toxic materials they use, a pollutant reduction strategy known as **pollution prevention** (since the fewer toxics used, the lower the risk that they will inadvertently be released into the environment).

The strategy of simply reducing the amount of pollutants entering the environment is complicated by the fact that many of the non-point pollutants are not amenable to management through local BMPs. For example, agricultural activities are expressly exempted from the Clean Water Act, even though stormwater runoff from farms and animal feedlots can carry agricultural chemicals, fertilizers and manure into adjacent waterways, along with topsoil from freshly-plowed fields. Pollutants could also be introduced into an urban watershed by the deposition of air pollutants. Airborn particulate matter, for example, can be transported very long distances by the wind, making most locally administered BMPs (except possibly instituting regular street-sweeping programs) ineffective in reducing the distribution and quantities of these types of urban stormwater pollutants.

In response to these challenges, the Clean Water Act was amended to require state environmental protection agencies to calculate pollution budgets for the impaired segments of their streams and rivers. The "impaired segments" were those reaches of a stream or river that did not meet the water quality standards for their intended uses. Models were used to calculate the "total maximum daily load" (TMDL) of pollutants entering the waterway through both point and non-point sources that would enable the stream segments

---

[113]http://www.epa.gov/agriculture/lcwa.html

to achieve their highest proposed use. The Clean Water Act's new TMDL program provides a more sophisticated framework for evaluating the impacts of non-point pollution on water quality. However, given the limitations of trying to put more and better BMPs into place, environmental protection agencies have begun to refocus some of their attention from reducing the total amount of pollutants being released within a watershed to also reducing the amount of stormwater runoff.

Environmental protection agencies have developed strategies for urban stormwater management that involve modifying a development site so that more precipitation would be retained on-site rather than flowing off of it into nearby waterways or waterbodies. These stormwater retention strategies initially stressed traditional engineering solutions, such as installing a stormwater collection system that temporarily stores the stormwater on-site in order to reduce the rate and amount of stormwater being released to a waterway. The strategies were later expanded to include various site modifications, such as constructing vegetated buffer strips or **swales** (ditches),in order to encourage more stormwater to infiltrate into the ground.

Reducing the volume of urban stormwater leaving a site as runoff also offers an additional hydrologic benefit in urban watersheds – reducing flood risks (NRC 2008 (p. 587)). Besides having the potential to carry pollutants, stormwater runoff discharge increases the amount of water entering into a lake, stream or river, increasing both the water volume and flow velocity of the waterway. A relatively large amount of stormwater runoff entering a waterway over a relatively short time can quickly raise a stream's water levels beyond its banks, causing flooding that could threaten adjacent development. Stormwater contribution to a river or stream can also increase the velocity of the stream's flow, causing increased channel and bank erosion, undercutting or damaging dikes, levees and other water control structures, and scouring the stream or river bed. Stream edge or streambed erosion can impair water quality by increasing the cloudiness (or turbidity) of the waterway, which can also damage aquatic and riparian habitats.

Stormwater-induced flood risks are managed by the National Flood Insurance Act[114] , where hydrologic models (adjusted by historical flood events) are used to forecast the potential flooding caused by a 100-year storm (a storm that has a one percent chance of occurring in any given year). The Act forces financial institutions to require homeowners within the designated 100-year floodplains to purchase flood insurance in order to get a mortgage, with the federal government subsidizing the insurance premiums if the community adopts a flood management program restricting development from extremely hazardous areas and instituting building code changes to lessen flood damage.

In assessing flood risks, it is important to realize that managing the volume and rate of urban stormwater being discharged from developed areas does not affect the total amount of stormwater that is being discharged to a river or stream within a watershed – they only affect the timing of when a storm's precipitation will be discharged to the waterway (NRC, 2008 (p. 587)). Both the conventional and the newer, more sustainable, ways of managing stormwater discussed below seek to delay the time it takes for stormwater runoff to reach a waterway in order to reduce the water levels and flow velocities of the receiving streams after a storm. Slowing the rate by which stormwater is being contributed to a stream spreads out the peak of the resultant flood levels over a longer time period, allowing many flood risks to be substantially reduced.

11.6.4 Conventional Stormwater Management

Urban stormwater is traditionally managed by the construction of engineered stormwater facilities, such as storm sewers and detention basins, as part of the land development process. These engineering processes are specifically designed to modify the natural **hydrology** of a site. For example, when land is being developed, the parcel is usually graded for development and stormwater infrastructure is installed to channel the stormwater from individual lots into a separate stormwater sewer system connected to a detention basin where it is retained until it can be discharged off-site. Site preparation also includes elevating building sites so that they are constructed on slightly elevated "pads" to encourage stormwater to flow away from building foundations and toward the streets. After reaching the street, stormwater is then directed to the stormwater sewers by curbs and gutters.

---

[114]http://www.fema.gov/library/viewRecord.do?id=2216

Conventional stormwater detention facilities were historically built to reduce off-site flood risks, and were not expressly designed to reduce off-site water pollution risks. Any stormwater detention that was provided was only temporary, often providing an insufficient retention time to allow the natural attenuation of any pollutants that were carried by the runoff into the detention basin – unlike the natural attenuation processes occurring in a river or riparian wetland (where ambient pollution levels are gradually reduced through dilution, oxidation, chemically binding to rocks and soils, being gobbled up by microorganisms, etc.). Stormwater is usually detained on-site after a storm only for a period of hours or, at most, days and then released to a waterway. Some of the particulate contaminants in the stored runoff might settle out if they are large or heavy enough to do so during that short time, some might infiltrate into the soils in the bottom of the detention basin, and some pollutants might be taken up by grass lining the basin, but many pollutants still end up being carried into the waterway along with the released stormwater.

Since the 1990s, environmental protection agencies have begun to consider the water pollution impacts of releases from stormwater detention facilities, after the Clean Water Act was amended to require states to treat stormwater discharges from detention basins as a type of direct source and to require that NPDES permits be phased in for discharges from Municipal Separate Stormwater Sewer Systems ("MS4") in cities and urban areas above certain population thresholds (NRC, 2008 (p. 587)). The NPDES permits issued under the U.S. Environmental Protection Agency's (U.S. EPA) MS4 program now require the water pollution loads from stormwater detention basin discharges to be assessed through the creation and adoption of local stormwater management plans and that the contaminants carried by the stormwater runoff to the basins for later re-release to a waterway be better managed and reduced through the adoption of local BMPs. MS4 permit regulations issued by state environmental protection agencies usually involve the issuance of a "general permit" by the agency, applying to all applicable Municipal Separate Stormwater Sewer Systems located within the state's designated urban areas.

11.6.4.1 Stormwater Sewer Systems Located within the State's Designated Urban Areas

A different set of stormwater management issues arise in older urban areas that are already developed. Most of the United States' older cities and suburbs, especially those established in the late-19th and early 20th centuries, do not have Municipal Separate Stormwater Sewer Systems. Instead, they have what are known as **combined sewer systems** – sewers that carry both the stormwater runoff from paved streets and the wastewater (sewage) from homes, stores and factories. These combined sewers transport the mixed wastewater and stormwater to municipal sewage treatment plants where the diluted sewage is treated and then discharged to a waterway under an NPDES permit (NRC, 2008 (p. 587)).

Water quality problems arise when rainstorms deposit more precipitation in the city than can be handled by the sewage treatment plant. As the diluted wastewater begins to fill up the combined sewer system at a faster rate than it can be treated, the sewage treatment plant operators are faced with a difficult choice – they can either allow the diluted sewage to continue to back up in the sewers, eventually flooding residents' basements (a politically unpopular as well as unhealthy option), or they can allow the diluted wastewater to bypass the sewage treatment plant and be discharged directly into the waterway, with the untreated wastewater's pollutant levels usually exceeding the limits set forth in the plant's NPDES permit. Most treatment plant operators choose the more politically acceptable option of releasing the wastewater in violation of their NPDES permit, creating water pollution incidents called **combined sewer overflows (CSOs)**.

11.6.4.2 Strategies to Manage CSOs

CSO problems are very difficult and expensive to resolve in older cities. One approach to managing stormwater off-site is to tear up the city's streets, digging up the old combined sewers and replacing them with separate stormwater and wastewater sewer systems. The high costs of retrofitting new separate sewer systems are often prohibitively expensive, especially in these times of stressed state and local budgets. Moreover, the extensive traffic disruptions involved in replacing most streets would not make this a politically popular choice.

A second approach to managing CSO issues off-site in developed areas is to keep the combined sewer system, but to construct a reservoir system large enough to store the diluted wastewater until it can be treated by the sewage treatment plant. This is the approach used by both the City of Milwaukee, Wisconsin[115] and by the Metropolitan Water Reclamation District of Greater Chicago in its Tunnel and Reservoir Plan[116] , or TARP. Although most of TARP has been built, all of the reservoirs have not yet been completed because of federal budgetary cutbacks. The tunnels themselves and one reservoir are currently able to temporarily store the combined sewage and the runoff from only the first 3/8-inch (.95 cm) of rain falling in the Metropolitan Water Reclamation District's service area. The extremely high expense of installing such a supplementary sewage and stormwater storage system would make it unaffordable to most cities unless very substantial federal and state grants are provided.

A third way to address CSO issues off-site is to use the streets themselves to temporarily store stormwater by installing low speed bump-like structures at intersections and by restricting the streets' sewer intakes to the combined sewer system (US EPA, 2000 (p. 587)). This urban retrofit strategy would allow stormwater to flow from lots into the streets, which would flood up to their gutter tops during heavy storms, functioning as stormwater reservoirs. The stored stormwater would then slowly be discharged to the combined sewers through the restricted grates over a period of hours after the storm, reducing the amount of diluted sewage flow to a quantity that could be adequately treated by sewage treatment plants. The flooding of streets, impairing automobile access, and the possibility of stormwater overflowing the curbs and damaging parked cars and adjacent property during very heavy rainstorms may not make this a politically popular option, though.

11.6.5 Managing Urban Stormwater More Sustainably

There is a fourth approach to dealing with CSO problems, which involves intercepting and delaying the discharge of precipitation from a parcel of land before it flows off-site to a separate or combined sewer system, or to an adjacent waterway. Encouraging on-site storage or infiltration reduces the stormwater contribution to a combined sewer's flow in developed areas, thereby reducing the amount of diluted wastewater being generated and enabling combined sewer systems to better handle their wastewater loads during rainstorms. These decentralized on-site approaches to managing stormwater could also be used to reduce the amount of conventional stormwater infrastructure needed in new developments using separate stormwater sewer systems. Because these on-site approaches are less resource-intensive and more cost-effective than conventional stormwater management approaches, they are also more sustainable investments.

On-site stormwater management techniques are also often known as "green infrastructure" (Jaffe et al., 2010 (p. 587)). Development projects using "green infrastructure" for urban stormwater management are commonly known as **"Low Impact Developments."** Low Impact Development projects using green infrastructure usually allow stormwater to be managed at lower costs than by using conventional detention practices (US EPA, 2007 (p. 587)).

There are essentially three strategies for on-site stormwater management: (1) techniques that encourage the infiltration of stormwater into soils to reduce its volume before it reaches a sewer system, or which employ more selective grading and the planting of vegetation to reduce its rate of flow from the site; (2) techniques that encourage the temporary storage of stormwater on-site, instead of transporting it off-site for centralized detention within a development project or a municipality; and (3) techniques, such as the construction of artificial wetlands, which also allow some degree of longer-term retention and treatment of the stormwater by natural processes before it is discharged. Infiltration techniques might also provide some water treatment capabilities due to the longer retention times of groundwater before discharge, but the degree of such treatment would largely depend on soil characteristics, the amount of overlying vegetation and the depth of the soil's unsaturated zone.

---

[115]http://v3.mmsd.com/DeepTunnel.aspx
[116]http://www.mwrd.org/irj/portal/anonymous/tarp

11.6.6 Increasing Stormwater Infiltration

Techniques to decrease the volume of stormwater runoff and to reduce the rates at which it is discharged include the use of permeable paving and the construction of "rain gardens" and vegetated swales (see Figure **Permeable Paving & Vegetated Swales** (Figure 11.32)). Permeable paving uses materials which are specially formulated to have air voids in their matrix, allowing water to flow into and through the paving materials after they are installed. It also includes the more common installation of precast porous pavers that are designed with holes through their surfaces, allowing stormwater to flow through their holes into the soils beneath them. Permeable paving needs to be periodically maintained because its pores can be clogged by fine grains of topsoil or with other small particles (such as soot from atmospheric deposition) carried along by the runoff. Maintenance includes periodically sweeping or vacuuming the paving to control the build-up of clogging particles.

Figure 11.32: Permeable Paving & Vegetated Swales Permeable paving drains into a vegetated swale as part of Elmhurst College's (in Illinois) parking lot's "green" stormwater management system. *Source: Jaffe, M., et al. (2010) (p. 587), Fig. 14, p. 117.*

"Rain gardens" can also be used to encourage stormwater to infiltrate into the soils, where it can be taken up by plants and transpired to the atmosphere, evaporated from the soils, or allowed to infiltrate deeper into the soils to become groundwater. Rain gardens are created in areas of low-lying terrain that are expressly designed for, or engineered with, well-drained soils and are usually planted with deep-rooted **native vegetation** that often can survive the drier soil conditions between rains. Rain gardens can be quite effective in intercepting and infiltrating stormwater being discharged from roofs, with roof downspouts directing the discharge of stormwater into a rain garden instead of allowing it to flow across the lot and into the street sewer system. Some native vegetation, however, may have special maintenance requirements, such as the periodic burning needed to manage some prairie plants.

Vegetated ditches or swales can also be used to transport stormwater runoff to a conventional stormwater management system, with the vegetation planted in the ditch slowing the rate of stormwater flow while also allowing a portion of the runoff to be infiltrated into the soils or taken up by plants. In many cases, vegetated swales and rain gardens can provide less-expensive alternatives to the installation of separate stormwater sewer system, since it reduces the need for the construction of street gutters, grates, street catchment basins and sewer pipes (US EPA, 2007 (p. 587)). Interception of the stormwater by infiltration and plant uptake in a rain garden or vegetated swale may also reduce the amount, capacity and size of the sewers that would have to be built to manage a predicted volume of stormwater, if these green infrastructure techniques are used to supplement a conventional stormwater collection system.

11.6.7 Increasing Interim On-site Storage

Sustainable management techniques that can temporarily store stormwater on-site until it can be released off-site to a sewer system or to conventional stormwater detention facilities include the use of "green roofs" and **rain barrels** connected to roof downspouts. Rain barrels allow precipitation to be collected and stored, and then used for non-potable purposes (lawn irrigation, for instance) allowing the captured stormwater to substitute for more expensive, treated water (see Figure **A Rain Barrel Collection System** (Figure 11.33)).

Figure 11.33: A Rain Barrel Collection System This "green" building (Ryerson Woods Welcome Center, Lake County (Illinois) Forest Preserve District)uses both a rain barrel to collect stormwater draining from the roof, and a rain garden to help infiltrate precipitation. *Source: Jaffe, M., et al. (2010)* (p. 587), *Fig. 12, p. 116.*

A **green roof** is a flat roof surface that uses amended soil materials installed above a layer of waterproof roofing materials to allow shallow-rooted plants to be planted. While still being an impermeable feature of a development site (because of its waterproof layer), a green roof can temporarily store rainwater before it is discharged to the ground by the roof gutters and downspouts (see Figure **A Green Roof** (Figure 11.34)). Just as a rain barrel can store (and re-use) a portion of the stormwater precipitation being discharged from impervious roofs, the soils of a green roof can capture and temporarily store stormwater precipitation as the pores between the soil particles fill up with rainwater. Green roofs can even partially reduce the runoff's pollution load through plant uptake and by other biological and physical processes within the roofs' soil materials while they are saturated. Because of the need to both water-proof the roof while installing a biological system on top of it, green roofs tend to cost more than conventional roofs, even ignoring the additional structural engineering that might be necessary to accommodate the weight of the green roof's soil and plantings.

Figure 11.34: A Green Roof The green roof on this police station in Village of Villa Park, Illinois has shallow-rooted plants placed in a thin layer of growing medium installed on top of a waterproof roof membrane. *Source: Jaffe, M. et al. (2010) (p. 587), Fig. 13, p. 116.*

The stormwater management benefits of rain barrels and green roofs depend on their storage capacity relative to the amount of impervious surface area of the roof with which they are associated. Rain barrels might be able to capture only a fraction of an inch of the stormwater falling on a roof and being discharged from a downspout, while several inches of amended soils on a rooftop might be able to store substantially more precipitation before it evaporates, is taken up by the roof's plants, or is discharged from the green roof via its gutters and downspouts. In both cases, however, the interception and temporary retention of stormwater by these green technologies may allow conventional stormwater management systems to function more efficiently by reducing the amount of stormwater being discharged into the systems. They would also certainly reduce some of the "**peakiness**" of stream flooding by being able to temporarily store and then release stormwater from impermeable roof surfaces later after a storm event.

11.6.8 Treating Urban Stormwater

Some sustainable stormwater management approaches have the potential to actually treat the water to remove pollutants as well as control its volume and rate of discharge. These strategies include constructing wetlands and planting trees. Wetlands have proven to be very effective in both temporarily storing stormwater runoff and reducing flooding risks, while also reducing the pollutant load carried to the wetland (because of its high biological activity that can capture and degrade the contaminants). As a result, the federal government has adopted a "no net loss" policy with respect to protecting existing wetlands. Section 404 of the federal Clean Water Act requires that the U.S. Army Corps of Engineers (under U.S. EPA oversight) review any proposals to fill or damage any wetlands that are directly hydrologically associated with navigable waterways. Any actions affecting existing wetlands will need a Corps 404 permit in addition to any local or state approvals.

Besides preserving existing wetlands, new wetlands can also be designed, created and maintained as part of a "green" stormwater management strategy (NRC, 2008 (p. 587)). The constructed wetland can be designed and used to intercept, temporarily store and treat stormwater runoff before it is released to a stream or river. Water control structures are also usually installed to ensure that the constructed wetlands remain flooded for long enough periods of time to support wetland vegetation. If appropriate plants are selected, they can also provide important habitats. Wetland maintenance involves the control of invasive plant species (e.g. Purple Loosestrife) and the management of any sediment that can be carried by stormwater runoff into the wetland, since the sedimentation of wetlands can fill them in, impairing their ecological and treatment functions.

The planting of trees is an especially valuable strategy to manage urban stormwater, especially when the trees become mature. Tree canopies break rain velocity, reducing runoff flow rates, while tree roots can stabilize soils against being eroded by urban runoff. Tree canopies reduce temperatures, mitigating urban heat island effects, by providing shade and through their transpiration processes. Their leaves and roots can also capture some stormwater contaminants and provide carbon sequestration to reduce climate change impacts. Moreover, trees provide a valuable soil amendment as their fallen leaves decay into mulch, improving the infiltration rate and biological activity of surrounding soils, while larger broken branches falling into urban streams can slow stream velocities and provide improved riparian and aquatic habitat. The shading of streams by riparian trees is particularly important in ensuring that a stream's ecological functions remain resilient in the face of rising temperatures caused by global climate change.

11.6.9 Conclusions

All of the green infrastructure and Low Impact Development techniques that provide interim on-site stormwater storage to reduce flood risks can also provide some pollution removal capabilities, as well. The American Society of Civil Engineers and U.S. EPA maintain an International Stormwater BMP Database[117] of development projects using green infrastructure. This on-line resource reviews the effectiveness of various stormwater management practices and makes these sustainable techniques more accessible to local officials and municipal public works departments charged with managing stormwater runoff in their communities.

There is increasing public interest in using sustainable stormwater management techniques to replace or supplement conventional stormwater facilities. The U.S. federal government, for example, is now requiring that green infrastructure be used in all federal projects above a certain size to manage urban stormwater runoff. Local officials are also showing a greater interest in these sustainable approaches, since they are often less expensive to install and maintain over their life-spans than conventional stormwater sewer systems and

---

[117]http://www.bmpdatabase.org/

detention facilities. Finally, state governments are beginning to set aside money in their revolving loan funds for public infrastructure that is earmarked for green infrastructure projects. It is likely that this interest in sustainable urban stormwater management will continue to grow.

11.6.10 Review Questions

Question 11.6.1
Which of the sustainable urban stormwater management practices can best be used in existing neighborhoods, and which are best suited for new development?

Question 11.6.2
The performance of many of the green infrastructure practices often depends on how well they are maintained over their life-spans. What are some effective strategies that local officials can consider in order to ensure that the green infrastructure being used to manage urban stormwater in their communities is adequately maintained and continues to perform as designed?

11.6.11 Resources

For more information about the:

- Clean Water Act, visit http://www.epa.gov/agriculture/lcwa.html[118] .
- International Stormwater BMP Database, visit http://www.bmpdatabase.org[119] .
- Metropolitan Water Reclamation District of Greater Chicago, visit http://www.mwrd.org/irj/portal/anonymous/tarp[120] .
- Milwaukee Metropolitan Sewerage District, visit http://v3.mmsd.com/DeepTunnel.aspx[121] .
- National Flood Insurance Act, visit http://www.fema.gov/library/viewRecord.do?id=2216[122] .

11.6.12 References

Gulliver, G.S. & Anderson, J.L. (eds.). (2008). Assessment of Stormwater Best Management Practices. *Stormwater Management Practice Assessment Study*. Minneapolis: University of Minnesota.

Jaffe, M., Zellner, M., Minor, E., Gonzalez-Meler, M., Cotner, L., Massey, D., Ahmed, H., Elbert M., Wise, S., Sprague, H., & Miller, B. (2010). *Using Green Infrastructure to Manage Urban Stormwater Quality: A Review of Selected Practices and State Programs*. Springfield, IL: Illinois Environmental Protection Agency. Retrieved June 23, 2011 from http://www.epa.state.il.us/green-infrastructure/docs/public-act-recommendations.pdf[123]

National Research Council. (2008). *Urban Stormwater Management in the United States*. Washington, DC: National Academies Press. Retrieved June 23, 2011 from http://www.epa.gov/npdes/pubs/nrc_stormwaterreport.pdf[124]

U.S. Environmental Protection Agency. (2000, October). *Street Storage for Combined Sewer Surcharge Control: Skokie and Wilmette, Illinois (Factsheet)*. (EPA Publication No. EPA-841-B-00-005C). Washington, D.C. Retrieved May 17, 2011 from http://www.lowimpactdevelopment.org/pubs/Street_Storage_Factsheet.pdf[125]

[118]http://www.epa.gov/agriculture/lcwa.html
[119]http://www.bmpdatabase.org/
[120]http://www.mwrd.org/irj/portal/anonymous/tarp
[121]http://v3.mmsd.com/DeepTunnel.aspx
[122]http://www.fema.gov/library/viewRecord.do?id=2216
[123]http://www.epa.state.il.us/green-infrastructure/docs/public-act-recommendations.pdf
[124]http://www.epa.gov/npdes/pubs/nrc_stormwaterreport.pdf
[125]http://www.lowimpactdevelopment.org/pubs/Street_Storage_Factsheet.pdf

U.S. Environmental Protection Agency. (2007, December). *Reducing Stormwater Costs through Low Impact Development (LID) Strategies and Practices.* (EPA Publication No. EPA 841-F-07-006). Washington. D.C. Retrieved June 23, 2011 from http://www.epa.gov/owow/NPS/lid/costs07/documents/reducingstormwatercosts.pdf[126]

U.S. Global Climate Change Research Program (USGCCRP). 2009. *Global Climate Change Impacts in the United States.* Cambridge: Cambridge University Press. Retrieved May 18, 2011 from http://downloads.globalchange.gov/usimpacts/pdfs/climate-impacts-report.pdf[127]

11.7 Case Study: A Net-Zero Energy Home in Urbana, Illinois[128]

How much fossil fuel does it take to operate a comfortable home for a couple of retired American baby-boomers?

None.

That's according to Ty and Deb Newell of Urbana, Illinois. Moreover, they hope the example of their home, the Equinox House[129] , will awaken others to the opportunity of constructing a net-zero energy house in the Midwest using technology available today.

---

[126]http://www.epa.gov/owow/NPS/lid/costs07/documents/reducingstormwatercosts.pdf
[127]http://downloads.globalchange.gov/usimpacts/pdfs/climate-impacts-report.pdf
[128]This content is available online at <http://legacy.cnx.org/content/m44455/1.2/>.
[129]http://newellinstruments.com/equinox/

Figure 11.35: The Equinox House The picture of the house on a sunny November day shows the passive solar entering the clerestory windows. *Source: ©2012 Equinox Built Environment Engineering; a division of Newell Instruments Inc.*[130]

The Newells celebrated the first anniversary of life in the Equinox House in late 2011, so they now possess more than a year's worth of data about how much electricity they used on day-to-day basis, as well as how much electricity their solar panels produced.

According to Ty Newell, who is professor emeritus of mechanical engineering at the University of Illinois at Urbana-Champaign, the Equinox House required about 12,000 kilowatt-hours of electricity to operate from December 2010 through November 2011. That total includes electricity for heating and air conditioning, hot water heat, clothes washing and drying, and all other appliances. No natural gas is used in the house.

Newell noted that energy use in the Equinox House for the first year was approximately 20 percent greater than it will be in 2012 and subsequent years. That's because he was using the least efficient of three different heating systems that will be tested in the home.

During the first year, the solar panels that power the Equinox House produced approximately 11,000 kilowatt-hours of electricity. This would have made the Newells purchasers of 1,000 kilowatt-hours, in net terms, had it not been for the fact that the solar panels were on line for some time before they moved into the house.

[130]http://buildequinox.com/projects/equinox-house/equinox-blog/nov-8-2010-more-kitchen-solar-update-10000-kw-hr/

Thanks to the more efficient heating system now in place, the Equinox House will produce surplus electricity in 2012 and in the future. That's by design. The surplus will be used to power their all-electric Ford Focus for the 8,000 miles of in-town driving they do annually.

In conjunction with its solar panels, the Equinox House achieves net-zero energy use because it requires far less energy than even a well-built conventional home—about one-fifth as much. It does so through the use of design and technology that did not add a significant burden to the cost of construction.

The walls and roof of the Equinox House are constructed with twelve-inch thick structural insulated panels, which are four to five times more effective at preventing thermal transfer than the walls of a typical house. Great care has also been taken to minimize any leakage of air through envelope of the house.

The Equinox House uses high performance, triple-pane windows, which also help to prevent thermal transfer. Beyond that, the windows are oriented to allow direct sunlight into living space for the heat it provides during the cooler half of the year—beginning on the Fall equinox—and to exclude direct sunlight during the warmer half of the year—beginning on the Spring equinox—when it would increase the load on the cooling system.

Ultimately, the demands of the Equinox House for heating, cooling, ventilation, and humidity control will all be met by a single, heat-pump based system, developed by Ty Newell and his son Ben through their company, Newell Instruments. Aside from the fact that it maintains a comfortable temperature and level of humidity in the house, this system also delivers a constant flow of fresh air from the outside, and it does that without the loss of conditioned air that occurs in a drafty house.

Of course the Equinox House will be outfitted in other ways that emphasize conservation, including LED lighting, low-flow plumbing fixtures, etc. It even features a system for collecting rainwater that is designed to meet 80 percent of the annual water needs for a family of four.

When he talks about the Equinox House, Ty Newell emphasizes how well it works from an economic perspective, since the couple's average daily cost for energy is a mere $3.00. That's based on a twenty-year life for the solar array, which cost a net of $20,000 installed.

In addition, Newell enjoys the fact that a significant part of their up-front expenditure supported job creation, the labor that went into the manufacture and installation of their solar panels. That's in contrast to money they might have otherwise spent on fossil fuel.

You might think that the Newells must be sacrificing comfort for the sake of energy savings, but that's not the case. Their house boasts 2,100 square feet of living space and all of the amenities you would expect in a contemporary suburban residence.

On top of that, they enjoy much better indoor air quality than people who live in conventional homes, thanks to a constant flow of conditioned fresh air from the outside.

You can find photos and further information about the Equinox House and net-zero living at http://newellinstruments.com/equinox

Glossary

" **"first flush" phenomenon**

The higher pollutant concentrations found at the beginning of a storm or spring snowmelt.

"peaky" waterways

The "peakiness" of a waterway describes the more rapid increase and decline in stream flow and the higher stream levels after a storm in urbanized watersheds compared to the more gradual rise and decline in stream volumes and lower water levels in less-developed drainage basins after the same storm event, largely because of the greater amounts of impervious surfaces and runoff generated within urban areas.

A **Absorption Chiller**

Utilizes heat instead of mechanical energy to provide cooling. A thermal compressor (fueled by the waste heat from the CHP system) is used in place of an electrically powered mechanical compressor in the refrigeration process.

accessibility

In transportation, a measure of the ease with which people are able to get places they want or need to go.

acid mine drainage

Surface water or groundwater that is highly acidic due to oxidation of sulfide minerals at a mineral mine.

Active Transportation

Means of transportation that involve more physical activity, typically considered walking, biking, and use of public transit (bus and rail).

adaptation

Focuses on the need for strategies to deal with the climate change that is unavoidable because of increased carbon already in the atmosphere.

additionality

The extent to which a new action (policy, project etc.) adds to the benefits or costs associated with existing conditions.

aerobic

Living systems or processes that require, or are not destroyed by, the presence of oxygen.

albedo

A measure of how reflective a surface is. A perfectly black surface has an albedo of 0, while a perfectly white surface has an albedo of 1.

allocation

For a chain which produces multiple products or services, the partitioning of inventory quantities among these co-products or co-services.

ambient standard

A minimum level of overall environmental quality that must be reached.

ambient temperature

The temperature of the surrounding environment.

ambient water quality

The concentration of pollutants found within waterbodies and waterways.

ammonification

The release of ammonia by decomposerswhen they break down the complex nitrogen compounds in organic material

anaerobic

A living system or process that occurs in, or is not destroyed by, the absence of oxygen.

anthropocene

A term bestowed by Noble Laureate Paul Crutzen to describe the last 200-year period of human industrialization. The prefix "anthro" points to the decisive impact of human population growth and technological development on the planetary biosphere since 1800, as its principal agents of change superceding all other factors.

anthropogenic

Caused or produced by humans.

anthropogenic CO2 emissions

Human release of CO_2 into the atmosphere by burning fossil fuels and changing land use.

Anthropogenic

Relating to or resulting from the influence that humans have on the natural world.

aqueduct

An aqueduct is a water supply or navigable channel constructed to convey water. In modern engineering, the term is used for any system of pipes, ditches, canals, tunnels, and other structures used for this purpose.

aquifer

Rock or sediment that is capable of supplying groundwater from a well at a useful rate.

aquitard

Earth material with low hydraulic conductivity.

arsenic

A type of water pollutant that can be fatal in large doses and can cause health problems in small doses over a long time.

artesian well

Water well drilled into a confined aquifer where the water level in the well moves above the local water table.

assimilation

Acquisition and incorporation of nutrients or resources by plants e.g. nitrogen or carbon.

avoided cost

A type of direct method that equates the value of an environmental improvement with a cost that can then be avoided.

Avoided Cost of Power

The marginal cost for a utility to produce one more unit of power.

axial precession

The movement in the axis of rotation, which change in the direction of Earth's axis of rotation relative to the stars.

axial tilt

The angle between a planet's axis of rotation and the line perpendicular to the plane in which it orbits. The Earth's current axial tilt is 23.5 degrees.

B benefit transfer

A method for estimating the value of a natural amenity by applying estimates from a complex study of a slightly different (but similar) amenity to the case at hand.

Betz's Law

The theoretical highest possible efficiency for wind turbines, 59 percent, derived in 1919 by German physicist, Albert Betz. Click here[131] for more information.

bioaccumulation

The increase in concentration of a substance in an organism over time.

bioassay

An assay for determining the potency (or concentration) of a substance that causes a biological change in experimental animals.

biocatalysis

Catalysis conducted by enzymes – catalysis within the body, for example.

biochemical oxygen demand

The amount of oxygen used by aerobic (in presence of oxygen) bacterial decomposition of organic matter.

biocomplexity

[131] http://en.wikipedia.org/wiki/Betz'_law

A defining characteristic of living things and their relationships to each other. The biocomplexity concept emphasizes the multiple dependent connections within ecosystems, and between ecosystems and human societies.

biodiesel

A fuel usually made from soybean, canola, or other vegetable oils; animal fats; and recycled grease and oils. It can serve as a substitute for conventional diesel or distillate fuel.

biodiversity and extinction

Thriving ecosystems are characterized by diverse plant and animal populations; there is, therefore, a strong correlation between current ecosystem decline globally, and the rate of extinction of species, which is in the order of a thousand times that of background rates. This has prompted scientists to label the current period the Sixth Mass Extinction in the long history of the biosphere, and the first since the end of the dinosaurs.

biodiversity

The number of different species within an ecosystem (or globally). Biodiversity is also considered a metric of ecosystem health.

biofuels

Liquid fuels and blending components produced from biomass materials, used primarily in combination with transportation fuels, such as gasoline.

biogeochemical cycles

A concept describing how chemical elements (e.g., nitrogen, carbon) or molecules (e.g. water) are transformed and stored by both physical and biological components of the Earth system.

bioleaching of minerals

Microbial dissolution of metals.

biological components of the earth system

All living organisms, including plants, animals and microbes.

biological nitrogen fixation

Where microbes convert N_2 gas in the atmosphere into ammonium that can be absorbed by plants.

biological processes

Processes of ore formation that involve the action of living organisms. Examples include the formation of pearls in oysters, as well as phosphorous ore in the feces of birds and the bones and teeth of fish.

biological treatment

A treatment technology that uses bacteria to consume organic fraction of municipal solid waste/wastewater.

biomass

Organic, non-fossil material of biological origin that is renewable because it can be quickly re-grown, taking up the carbon that is released when it is burned.

biomimicry

Biomimicry or biomimetics is the examination of nature, its models, systems, processes, and elements to emulate or take inspiration from in order to solve human problems. The terms biomimicry and biomimetics come from the Greek words bios, meaning life, and mimesis, meaning to imitate. Examples include adhesive glue from mussels, solar cells made like leaves, fabric that emulates shark skin, harvesting water from fog like a beetle, etc.

biooxidation of minerals

Microbial enrichment of metals in a solid phase.

bioremediation

Method of groundwater remediation involving the addition oxygen or nutrients. to stimulate growth of microorganisms, which decompose an organic pollutant.

biosorption of minerals

Attachment of metals to cells.

black smoker

Discharge of mineral-rich waters up to $350\,°C$ from cracks in oceanic crust; these waters precipitate a variety of metallic sulfide ore minerals that make the water appear black.

bottled water

Drinking water packaged in plastic bottles or glass bottles, bottled water is not a sustainable solution to the water crisis because of the nonrenewable energy and material resources involved in manufacturing and transporting it.

Building Automation System (BAS)

Controls and monitors a buildings mechanical and lighting systems through a computerized, intelligent network [http://en.wikipedia.org/wiki/Computer_networking[132]] of electronic devices.

C Car Sharing

A program that allows for more than one person to have use of a car. Generally, it works like a short-term (hourly) car rental service. Cars are located near residences and work places to facilitate the access to the vehicles and to reduce the need for individual car ownership.

carbon neutrality

To be carbon neutral, the carbon emissions of a consumable product or human activity must either not involve the consumption of carbon-based energy (a difficult thing to achieve under our present regime), or offset that consumption through the drawdown of an equivalent amount of atmospheric carbon during its lifecycle.

carbon sequestration

The storage of carbon dioxide underground in geologic formations consisting of depleted oil and gas wells, unmineable coal beds, and deep saline aquifers.

carcinogenicity

Defines the ability or tendency to produce cancer.

Carpooling

When two or more people travel to and from proximal departure and arrival destinations in the same vehicle.

Carrying Capacity

The maximum population that a given environment can sustain.

chronic reference dose (RfD)

An estimate (with uncertainty spanning perhaps an order of magnitude) of a daily oral exposure for a chronic duration (up to a lifetime) to the human population (including sensitive subgroups) that is likely to be without an appreciable risk of deleterious effects during a lifetime. It can be derived from a NOAEL, LOAEL, or benchmark dose, with uncertainty factors generally applied to reflect limitations of the data used. Generally used in EPA's noncancer health assessments.

climate

The average of the weather.

closed loops

The sustainable reform of industrial production and waste management emphasizes the recycling of materials back into the environment or into the industrial cycle, that is, to eliminate the concept of waste entirely.

coase theorem

The idea that with property rights and frictionless negotiation, private agents will bargain to reach efficient outcomes even in the face of externalities.

Combined Heat and Power (CHP)

An integrated system, located at or near the building or facility, that generates utility grade electricity which satisfies at least a portion of the electrical load of the facility and captures/ recycles the waste heat from the electric generating equipment to provide useful thermal energy to the facility.

combined sewer overflows (CSOs)

The overflow and discharge of excess wastewater to surface waters during storms, when diluted wastewater flows exceed the capacity of a combined sewer systems or sewage treatment plant.

---

[132]http://en.wikipedia.org/wiki/Computer_networking

combined sewer systems

A single set of underground pipes used to collect both sewage and. storm water runoff from streets for wastewater treatment.

combined sewer systems

Sewer systems that are designed to collect stormwater runoff and domestic and industrial wastewater within the same sewer pipes.

command and control

Regulations that set strict, specific guidelines to govern the behavior of polluters and resource users.

common but differentiated responsibilities

An ethical framework, promoted particularly by developing nations, that recognizes mitigation of global warming as a shared responsibility, but at the same time argues that the wealthy, industrialized countries of the West that have been the historical beneficiaries of carbon-based development should accept a greater burden for both reducing global carbon emissions, and providing developing nations with the technology and economic means to modernize in sustainable ways.

common pool resource

A resource that is open to all users, but which is highly rival in use.

community-supported agriculture

A collaborative system where local food producers and consumers share in the costs and harvests associated with farming.

compost

The stable, decomposed organic material resulting from the composting process.

condensation

Change in the physical state of water where it goes from gas to liquid.

cone of depression

A localized drop in the water table around a pumping well.

confined (or concentrated) animal feeding operation (CAFO)

The practice of raising livestock in high-density settings to maximize production speed; some of the largest CAFOs have more than 100,000 cattle, 10,000 hogs, or 1,000,000 chickens at a single facility; sometimes called factory farming.

confined aquifer

An aquifer that is bounded by aquitards below and above.

conjoint analysis

A stated preference valuation tool that allows an analyst to estimate the marginal values of multiple attributes of an environmental good.

Connectivity

An important feature of complex systems. Connections exist between even apparently remote and disparate things. For example, drought in Australia might impact the price of bread in Egypt, which in turn has repercussions for U.S. foreign policy.

constructed wetland

Marsh built to treat contaminated water.

consumptive water use

A societal use of water that is a type of offstream use where water does not return to the river or groundwater system immediately after use.

contaminant plume

A large body of flowing polluted groundwater.

contingent valuation

A stated preference valuation tool that describes a single environmental good and elicits survey responses from which the analyst can estimate people's value for that good.

Conventional CHP (Topping Cycle CHP)

Utilizes a single dedicated fuel source to sequentially produce useful electric and thermal power.

Cornucopian

The view that economic growth and technological innovation will continue to improve the conditions of humanity as they have done for the past 500 years, and that no environmental constraints are important or permanent.

corrosivity

The ability to corrode metal. Corrosive wastes are wastes that are acidic and capable of corroding metal such as tanks, containers, drums, and barrels.

cost effectiveness

The extent to which an outcome is achieved at the lowest cost possible.

cost-benefit analysis

Evaluation of how the overall benefits of a project compare to its costs.

cost-effective

As inexpensive as possible; cost minimizing.

counterfactual

The scenario against which a different scenario should be compared; in policy analysis, the way the world would have been in the absence of the policy.

Cradle-to-Grave

From creation to disposal; throughout the life cycle.

cretaceous period

The period between 65 and 145 million years ago, which was the final period of Earth's history that included dinosaurs.

Cultural Ecosystem Services

The aesthetic and spiritual values we place on nature as well as the educational and recreational activities dependent on ecosystems.

cultural eutrophication

Rapid aquatic plant growth, particularly algae, in a surface water body.

D dam

A barrier built across a river to obstruct the flow of water.

deadweight loss

The extent to which net benefits are lower than they could be.

decomposers

Bacteria and fungi that break down rotting organic material, releasing component elements in the process.

deconstruction

The selective dismantling or removal of materials from buildings prior to or instead of conventional demolition.

denaturation

A process in which proteins or nucleic acids lose their tertiary structure and secondary structure by application of heat.

denitrifying bacteria

Microbes that convert nitrates to nitrous oxide or N_2 gases that are released back to the atmosphere.

derived demand

Demand for a good or service that comes not from a desire for the good or service itself, but from other activities that it enables or desires it fulfills.

desalination

Removing dissolved salt from seawater or saline groundwater.

Desiccant Dehumidification

Process that removes moisture (latent load) from a building air stream by passing the air over a desiccant wheel (normally a silica gel). The recovered heat from a CHP system is utilized to regenerate the desiccant by driving the moisture off the desiccant wheel to the outside.

deterministic risk assessment

Risk evaluation involving the calculation and expression of risks as single numerical values or "single point" estimates of risk, with uncertainty and variability discussed qualitatively.

diachronic/synchronic

A diachronic view of a system examines it evolution over time, while a synchronic view is concerned with its characteristics at a single point in time.

diesel

Any liquid fuel used in diesel engines.

digestion

The biochemical decomposition of organic matter of MSW, resulting in its partial gasification, liquefaction, and mineralization.

direct methods

Valuation tools that use data on actual market transactions to estimate the value of a change in the environment.

discharge area

Location on Earth where groundwater leaves the groundwater flow system.

discounting

The process of converting future values (costs or benefits) into an equivalent amount of money received today; controls for human time preference.

drainage basin

Geographic area drained by a river and its tributaries.

E e-commerce

Electronic commerce, commonly known as e-commerce, eCommerce or e-comm, refers to the entire online process of developing, marketing, selling, delivering, servicing and paying for products and services.

eccentricity

A measure of how much an ellipse departs from circularity.

eco-efficiency

An approach that seeks to minimize environmental impacts by maximizing material and energy efficiencies of production.

eco-efficiency

An evolutionary business model in which more goods and services are created with less use of resources, and fewer emissions of waste and pollution.

Ecological Footprint (EF)

Represents the area of land on earth that provides for resources consumed and assimilates the waste produced by a given entity.

ecological footprint

Ecological footprint is a measure of human demand on the Earth's ecosystems. It is a standardized measure of demand for natural capital that may be contrasted with the planet's ecological capacity to regenerate. It represents the amount of biologically productive land and sea area necessary to supply the resources a human population consumes, and to mitigate associated waste. Using this assessment, it is possible to estimate how much of the Earth (or how many planet Earths) it would take to support humanity if everybody followed a given lifestyle.

ecological services

Ecosystem functions that are essential to sustaining human health and well-being. Examples include provisioning services such as food, fiber and water; regulating services such as climate, flood, and disease control; cultural services such as spiritual and recreational benefits, and supporting services such as nutrient cycling. Also called ecosystem services.

economic input output life cycle assessment (EIO-LCA)

An aggregated approach to LCA in which the environmental impacts of a product or service are determined through an analysis of the complete economy.

economic potential

The technical potential that can be produced below a given cost threshold, typically the cost of a specified, locally relevant alternative.

Ecosystem

A dynamic complex of plant, animal, and microorganism communities and the nonliving environment interacting as a functional unit.

Ecosystem

All living organisms and non-living things that exist and interact in a certain area at the same time.

ecosystem function

Processes such as decomposition, production, nutrient cycling, and fluxes of nutrients and energy that allow an ecosystem to maintain its integrity as a habitat.

Ecosystem Goods and Services

An essential service an ecosystem provides that supports life and makes economic activity possible. For example, ecosystems clean air and water naturally, recycle nutrients and waste generated by human economic activity.

ecosystem services

Resources and processes through which the environment gives benefits to humanity.

ecosystem services

The benefits humans receive from ecosystems

Ecosystem Services

The benefits people obtain from ecosystems.

ecosystems

Dynamic systems of human, plant, animal, and microorganism communities and the nonliving environment that interact as a functional unit

efficiency

The fraction of energy at the input that is delivered to the output of a device. Electric motors can convert incoming electricity to rotary motion at more than 90 percent efficiency, while gasoline engines convert only about 25 percent of the chemical energy of the fuel to motion of the wheels.

efficient

Having the feature that net benefits are maximized.

electricity grid

The network of wires and transformers that delivers electric power from generation stations such as those powered by coal, natural gas, hydroelectricity, sunlight or wind to end uses such as lighting, transportation, refrigeration, computation or communication. The electricity grid is conventionally divided into higher voltage transmission lines for long distances, lower voltage distribution lines for short distances and transformers in substations for converting the voltage between the two categories.

embodied energy

The sum of all energy used to produce a good, including all of the materials, processes, and transportation involved.

emergy (EMbodied energy)

The unit of energy into which any resource, product, or process can be converted to simplify comparisons between diverse items.

emergy performance index (EMPI)

Value produced by converting all materials and processes to amounts of energy in order to evaluate renewability and sustainability.

Emergy

The amount of energy of one kind (solar) that has been used directly or indirectly (through a transformation process) to make a service or a product as one type and it is expressed in units of (solar) emjoule.

Emjoule

The unit of emergy or emergy joule. Using emergy, sunlight, fuel, electricity, and human service can be put on a common basis by expressing each of them in the emjoules of solar energy that is required to produce them. If solar emergy is the baseline, then the results are solar emjoules (abbreviated seJ). Sometimes other baselines such as coal emjoules or electrical emjoules have been used but in most cases emergy data are given in solar emjoules.

end-of-life costs

Those costs that arise through activities associated with the disposition of a product at the end of its useful life. These include costs associated with disposal, recycling, reuse, and remanufacturing.

energy carrier

A medium, such as electricity, gasoline or hydrogen, that can move energy from one place to another, usually from the point of production (e.g. an electrical generator or petroleum refinery) to the point of use (e.g. an electric light or motor or a gasoline engine).

energy density

The amount of energy contained in a given volume (say a gas tank). The higher the energy density of a fuel, the farther the car will go on a tank of the fuel.

Energy Density

The energy contained in a volume or mass divided by the volume or mass it occupies. High energy density materials pack a large energy into a small space or mass; low energy density materials require more space or mass to store the same amount of energy. The electrical energy of batteries is at the low end of the energy density scale, the chemical energy of gasoline is at the high end, approximately a factor of 30-50 larger than batteries.

enrichment factor

Ratio of the metal concentration needed for an economic ore deposit over the average abundance of that metal in Earth's crust.

Entropy

The degree of disorder in a substance, system or process as in the second law of thermodynamics that states that the make-up of energy tends to change from a more-ordered state to a less-ordered state, whereby increasing entropy.

envelope

The physical barrier between the interior and exterior of a building including the walls, roof, foundation, and windows.

environmental performance indicators (EPI)

Any of the ways in which environmental outcomes and/or impacts can be assessed.

environmental sustainability index (ESI)

A composite value produced by including ecological, social, economic, and policy data.

epidemiology

The study of the distribution and determinants of health-related states or events in specified populations.

eutectics

A combination of two or more compounds of either organic, inorganic or both which may have a different melting point to their individual and separate compounds.

eutrophication

Accelerated plant growth and decay caused by nitrogen pollution.

evaporation

The process whereby water is converted from a liquid into a vapor, as a result of absorbing energy (usually from solar radiation).

evaporation

Where water changes from liquid to gas at ambient temperatures.

evapotranspiration

Evaporation from vegetated land that includes water transpired by plants as well as evaporation from open water and soils.

excessive plant nutrient

A type of water pollutant involving a limiting plant nutrient that usually is present in water at low concentrations and therefore restricts the total amount of plant growth, examples include nitrogen and phosphorous.

Exergy

The maximum work that can be extracted from a system as it moves to thermodynamic equilibrium with a reference state.

extended product/producer responsibility

The creation of financial incentives, and legal disincentives, to encourage manufacturers to make more environmentally friendly products that incorporate end-of-life costs into product design and business plans.

externality

Cost of an activity not paid by the person doing the activity.

externality tax

A tax on something that causes negative externalities.

externalization

The process by which costs inherent to the production of goods—particularly environmental costs—are not included in the actual price paid.

extinction

The death of all individuals within a species. A species may be functionally extinct when a low number of surviving individuals are unable to reproduce.

extirpation

Local extinction of a species; elimination or removal of a species from the area of observation.

F   fermentation

The conversion of sugars into alcohols or hydrocarbons by microbes.

finned Tube

Tube with an extending part on a surface to facilitate cooling.

Fischer-Tropsch synthesis

The inorganic catalytic reaction between CO and H_2 (synthesis gas), which produces diesel and jet fuel.

fluxes

Transformations or flow of materials from one pool to another in a biogeochemical cycle.

food miles

The distance food travels from producer to consumer.

food security

The measure of the availability and access to sufficient, safe, and nutritious food.

fossil fuels

Oil, gas and coal produced by chemical transformation of land plants (coal) and marine animals (oil and gas) trapped in the earth's crust under high pressure and temperature and without access to oxygen. The formation of fossil fuels can take.

free rider

A person who does not contribute to a public good in hopes that they can benefit from provision by other people.

Fuel Cell

An exothermic electrochemical reaction that combines hydrogen and oxygen ions through an electrolyte material to generate electricity (DC) and heat.

functional unit

The basis for comparing two or more products, processes, or services that assures equality of the function delivered.

G   gas phase

One of the three classical states of matter.

Gas Turbine

An internal-combustion engine consisting essentially of an air compressor, combustion chamber, and turbine wheel that is turned by the expanding products of combustion.

gasification

The conversion of biomass at very high temperature ($1000 - 1200\,°C$) in an oxygen atmosphere that results in a "synthesis gas" intermediate – a mixture of carbon monoxide (CO) and hydrogen (H_2).

gasoline

A toxic translucent, petroleum-derived liquid that is primarily used as a fuel in internal combustion engines. The term "gasoline" is often shortened in colloquial usage to gas. Under normal ambient conditions its material state is liquid, unlike liquefied petroleum gas or "natural gas."

genetic effects

Effects from some agent, like radiation that are seen in the offspring of the individual who received the agent. The agent must be encountered pre-conception.

genetic engineering of microbes (mineral application)

Creating microorganisms specialized in extracting metal from ore.

geographical potential

The energy flux for a particular renewable energy theoretically extractable from geographical areas that are considered suitable and available.

geothermal energy

Energy from the earth.

geothermal energy

Hot water or steam extracted from geothermal reservoirs in the earth's crust. Water or steam extracted from geothermal reservoirs can be used for geothermal heat pumps, water heating, or electricity generation. Geothermal heat or cooling may also come from ground source heat exchange taking advantage of the constant temperature in the ground below the surface.

geothermal plant

A power plant in which the prime mover is a steam turbine. The turbine is driven either by steam produced from hot water or by natural steam that heat source is found in rock.

ghost acres

The acres of land needed to indirectly support human needs, or land that is unavailable because of habitat degradation.

glacial period

A long period of time in which ice -sheets and glaciers are advanced in their extent.

Global Warming Potential (GWP)

Each gas, based on its atmospheric chemistry, captures different amounts of reflected heat thus contributing differently to the greenhouse effect contributing to its GWP. Carbon dioxide, the least capture efficient of these gases, acts as the reference gas with a global warming potential of 1.

graphite matrix

Composite material with graphite being a metal (see metal matrices).

great ocean conveyor belt (or Termohaline Current)

The current spanning the Pacific, Antarctic, Indian and Atlantic Oceans that carries warm surface water to the cold deep ocean and takes 400-1000 years to complete one cycle.

green roof

Vegetation and planting media installed on a rooftop in order to store and delay stormwater runoff from the roof's surface.

greenhouse effect

The process by which the atmosphere acts to trap heat, warming the climate.

greenhouse gases

Gases in Earth's atmosphere that absorb long-wave radiation and retain heat.

greenhouse gases

Those gases in the atmosphere that warm the climate, most importantly, water vapor, carbon dioxide, methane, and ozone.

greenwashing

Claims made by businesses about the superior contributions of their products and services to sustainability without substantive backing or via a very subjective analysis.

greywater

The water generated from activities such as handwashing, laundry, bathing, and dishwashing that can be recycled on-site to be used for irrigation of grounds and even for flushing toilets.

Gross Domestic Product

The sum of gross value added by all resident producers in the economy plus any product taxes and minus any subsidies not included in the value of the products. It is calculated without making deductions for depreciation of fabricated assets or for depletion and degradation of natural resources.

groundwater discharge

Flow of water from below-ground into rivers, lakes, or the ocean.

groundwater mining

A depletion in groundwater resources caused by a large number of water wells that pumped water for a long time.

groundwater

Water located in small spaces between mineral grains and fractures in subsurface rock or sediment.

H hard water

Water with abundant calcium and magnesium, which reduces its ability to develop soapsuds and enhances scale; hard water does not have negative health effects in people.

Heap leaching

Method of gold mining where cyanide-rich water percolates through finely ground gold ore and dissolves the gold over a period of months; eventually the water is collected and treated to remove the gold.

heat

A type of water pollutant that causes a drop in the dissolved oxygen content, which can stress fish.

heat of fusion

The amount of heat required to convert a unit mass of a solid at its melting point into a liquid without an increase in temperature.

heat pump

A device that allows heat to be removed at a lower temperature and supplied at a higher temperature, for example an air conditioner.

heat, ventilation and air conditioning systems (HVAC)

Systems such as furnaces and air conditioners that are commonly used in homes and commercial buildings.

heavy metal

A type of water pollutant involving elements such as lead, mercury, arsenic, cadmium, and chromium, which can accumulate through the food chain.

hedonic price analysis

A revealed preference tool that uses data on house prices and characteristics to estimate the value of features of the environment that vary among houses.

hedonic wage analysis

A revealed preference tool that uses data on wages and risk of death by job type estimate willingness to pay to reduce the risk of death.

high level radioactive waste (HLW)

The radioactive waste material that results from the reprocessing of spent nuclear fuel, including liquid waste produced directly from reprocessing and any solid waste derived from the liquid that contains a combination of transuranic and fission product nuclides in quantities that require permanent isolation.

Hushing

Method of placer mining developed by the ancient Romans where a torrent of water is sent through a landscape via an aqueduct.

Hybrid Vehicle

A car that contains two drive systems, one based on the internal combustion engine and one on the electric motor. Conventional hybrids, such as the Toyota Prius, use the electric motor only when high power is needed: starting from a stop, passing, and going uphill. The electricity to run the motor is generated on board by an alternator powered by the internal combustion engine and by regenerative breaking. Plug-in hybrids such as the Chevy Volt, in contrast, use the electric motor as the main drive for the car, relying on the gasoline engine only when the battery is low or empty.

hydrated salt

A solid compound containing water molecules combined in a definite ratio as an integral part of a crystal.

Hydraulic mining

Method of placer mining where high pressure hoses cut into natural landscapes.

hydrological cycle

The continuous movement of water on, above and below the surface of the earth. This cycle is dominated by the global equilibrium in evaporation and condensation.

hydrology

The scientific examination of the occurrence, distribution, movement and properties of water within the natural environment.

hydrothermal

Ore forming process involving hot salty water that dissolves metallic elements from a large area and then precipitates ore minerals in a smaller area, commonly along rock fractures and faults.

hydrotreating

Reaction in the presence of hydrogen.

hypoxia

Very low oxygen water due to prolific growth of algae, algal death, and then decomposition, also called dead zone.

I ice sheets

Glaciers big enough to cover a continent. Currently, ice sheets are found in Antarctica and Greenland, but during glacial periods, ice sheets have covered other land masses, including North America.

igneous crystallization

Ore forming process where molten rock cools to form igneous rock.

igneous rock

Forms by cooling and solidification of hot molten rock.

ignitability

Ability to create fire under certain conditions. Ignitable wastes can create fires under these certain conditions.

impacts

Long-term and more widespread results of an activity.

incineration

A thermal process of combusting MSW.

Indicator

A variable equal to an operational representation of an attribute of a system.

Indicator-Based Systems

Systems that use quantitative measures of economic progress, social welfare, or environmental activity that can be interpreted to explain the state of that system. Examples of these are gross domestic product, greenhouse gas emissions, and the unemployment rate.

Induction Generator

Converts the mechanical shaft power from the CHP prime mover to utility grade Alternating Current Power. An induction generator can only operate when connected to an external reactive power source (normally provided by the utility grid).

industrial ecology

An applied science that is concerned with material and energy flows through industrial systems.

industrial revolution

The transition from simple tools and animal power for producing products to complex machinery powered by the combustion of fuels. The Industrial Revolution began in England in the mid-18th Century initially centered around the development of the steam engine powered by coal.

infiltration

Flow of water from the land surface into soils and rocks.

infrared spectrum

The light radiation just below the range of wavelengths visible to the human eye. Also referred to as thermal radiation.

infrastructure compatible

Compatible with existing oil pipelines, storage tanks, petroleum refineries, and internal combustion engines.

inorganic catalysis

Solid, inorganic materials such as platinum nanoparticles deposited onto activated carbon, which accelerate the rate of chemical reactions without being consumed in the process.

inputs

The specific resources or services used by an activity.

insolation

The measure of the amount of solar radiation falling on a surface.

instream water use

A societal use of water that does not remove it from its source.

instrumentalist

An attitude to environmental resources characteristic of the last 500-year period of global human economic development, whereby ecosystem provisions—water, minerals, oil and gas, etc.—are perceived only in terms of their use value to human beings, rather than as integral elements of a wider natural system.

integrated waste management

A practice of using several alternative waste management techniques to manage and dispose of MSW.

interdisciplinarity

A trend in higher education research and teaching of the last thirty years that emphasizes the bridging of traditional disciplines, and that is an essential framework for sustainability studies.

interglacial period

The warm periods of the Quaternary in which glaciers and ice-sheets retreat.

These occur between the longer glacial periods.

internal combustion engine

The combustion of fuel inside or "internal" to the cylinder and moving piston which produces motion; gasoline engines are a common example. In contrast, steam engines are external combustion engines where combustion and steam generation are outside the cylinder containing the moving piston. The internal combustion engine is lighter and more portable than the steam engine, enabling modern transportation in cars, diesel powered trains, ships and airplanes.

Internal Combustion Engine

The engine that converts the chemical energy of gasoline into the mechanical energy of motion, by exploding small amounts of fuel in the confined space of fixed cylinder containing a moving piston. A precise amount of fuel must be metered in, and a spark created at a precise moment in the piston's journey to produce the maximum explosive force to drive the piston. The internal combustion engine is an engineering marvel (the word engineering celebrates it) perfected over more than a century. In contrast, the electric motor is much simpler, more efficient and less expensive for the same power output.

Inverter

Converts Direct Current electric power into utility grade Alternating Current electric power. Normally used with fuel cell systems.

isotopes

Atoms that have same number of protons but different numbers of neutrons. This means that they are the same element (e.g. oxygen), have the same chemical properties, but different masses.

J Jevons paradox

The principle that as technological progress increases the efficiency of resource utilization, consumption of that resource will increase.

K kWh and MWh

Units of energy used in power engineering. kWh is one kilowatt of power delivered for one hour, MWh is one megawatt of power delivered for one hour.

L land use change

Human change in the use of land, e.g. deforestation or urbanization.

landfills

Designed, controlled and managed disposal sites for MSW spread in layers, compacted to the smallest practical volume, and covered by material applied at the end of each operating day.

last glacial maximum

The time at which ice sheets were at their greatest extent during the latest glacial period.

latent heat

The heat which flows to or from a material without a change to temperature.

leachate

Wastewater that collects contaminants as it trickles through MSW disposed in a landfill.

leaching

Loss of nitrates from soil in drainage water

leaching

Using chemicals to dissolve metal from a large volume of crushed rock.

Li-ion battery

A type of rechargeable battery in which lithium ions move from the negative electrode to the positive electrode during discharge and from the positive electrode to negative electrode during charge.

liability

A legal construct meaning that an agent is held responsible by the courts to pay when that agent does something that imposes costs on other people in society.

life cycle assessment (LCA)

A method for quantifying the materials and energy needed to make or deliver a product or service that assesses the wastes produced and potential environmental impacts across all or a part of the product chain.

life cycle impact assessment (LCIA)

The stage of an LCA in which the environmental impacts associated with the manufacture and delivery use and disposal of a product are calculated.

life cycle inventory (LCI)

The stage of an LCA in which information on the use of energy and various materials used to make a product or service at each part of the manufacturing process is collected.

lifecycle

In terms of sustainability, the entire lifecycle of a product must be measured for its environmental impact, not simply its point of production, consumption, or disposal. A key aspect of general sustainability education is the understanding of where goods originate, the industrial processes required for their manufacture and transport, and their fate after use.

Lightweighting

Making a product out of materials that weigh less than were previously used

lignocellulose

The non-food portion of plants such as the stalks and leaves of corn plants (corn stover).

liquified petroleum gas

A flammable mixture of hydrocarbon gases used as a fuel in heating appliances and vehicles.

little ice age

A cool period in the NH, primarily in Europe from the sixteenth to the nineteenth century.

locavore

A person who consumes locally-produced food products.

low impact cluster development

Low impact cluster development is the grouping of buildings on a portion of the site and devoting the undeveloped land to open space, recreation or agriculture. Though cluster development lowers development cost through savings on roads and infrastructure (sewers, electric and water lines, etc.), it has issues such as conflicts with many older zoning ordinances, perceptions of personal space (lower individual lot size) and maintenance of common areas.

low impact development

An approach to land development (or re-development) that uses natural drainage and environmental processes to manage stormwater as close to its source as possible.

low-emissions

Materials that have little to no volatile organic compounds and other toxic chemicals that are released into the environment after installation.

Low-Emittance Coatings

Microscopically thin, virtually invisible, metal or metallic oxide layers deposited on a window or skylight glazing surface primarily to reduce the U-factor by suppressing radioactive heat flow.

low-level radioactive waste (LLW)

Radioactive waste material that is not high-level radioactive waste, spent nuclear fuel, or byproduct material (see HLW).

M marginal benefit

The additional benefit of doing one more unit of something.

marginal cost

The additional cost of doing one more unit of something.

market failure

A condition that causes a market not to yield the efficient outcome.

Maximum Sustainable Yield (MSY)

An outgrowth of carrying capacity and the goal is to reach the maximum amount of resource extraction while not depleting the resource from one harvest to the next.

McMansion

A slang term that describes a large, opulent house that may be generic in style and represents a good value for a homebuyer in terms of its size. This type of home is built to provide middle and/or upper middle class homeowners with the luxurious housing experience that was previously only available to high-net-worth individuals.

mechanical biological treatment (MBT)

The process that combines sorting with a form of biological treatment such as composting or anaerobic digestion.

medical waste

Any municipal solid waste generated in the diagnosis, treatment, or immunisation of human beings or animals.

medieval warm period

A warm period in the NH during the tenth and eleventh centuries.

mercury

A type of water pollutant that acts on the central nervous system and can cause loss of sight, feeling, and hearing as well as nervousness, shakiness, and death.

Mercury amalgamation

Method of gold panning where liquid mercury is added to gold pans because mercury can form an alloy with gold.

metabolism and footprint

Two metaphors, related to the human body, for conceptualizing the relationship between consumption and waste at the social level. Metabolism emphasizes a system of inputs and outputs dependent upon "energy" and measured according to the "health" of the whole, while footprint is a popular metric for quantifying the environmental impacts of goods, services, and lifestyles.

metal matrices

Composite material with at least two constituent parts, one being a metal.

metamorphic rock

Forms when a preexisting rock changes the shape or type of minerals due to intense heat and pressure deep within the Earth.

metamorphism

Process of ore formation that occurs deep in the earth under very high temperature and pressure and produces several building stones, including marble and slate, as well as some nonmetallic ore, including asbestos, talc, and graphite.

milankovitch cycles

Periodic variations in the Earth's orbit that influence its climate. These cycles are named after Milutin Milankovitch, a mathematician who quantified the theory.

mill tailings

Waste material from a conventional uranium recovery facility.

mineral conservation

Method of extending the mineral supply that includes improved efficiency, substitution, reduce, reuse, and recycle.

mineral

Naturally occurring inorganic solid with a defined chemical composition and crystal structure.

mineral recycling

Method of extending the mineral supply that involves processing used Minerals into new products to prevent waste of potentially useful materials.

mineral reserves

The known amount of ore in the world.

mineral resources

Total amount of a mineral used by society that is not necessarily profitable to Mine today but has some sort of economic potential.

mineral reuse

Method of extending the mineral supply that involves using a mineral multiple times.

mineral substitution

Method of extending the mineral supply; involves substituting a rare nonrenewable resource with either a more abundant nonrenewable resource or a renewable resource.

mitigation

Refers to the importance of reducing carbon emissions so as to prevent further, catastrophic changes in the climate system.

mobility

The ability to move or to get around.

monte-carlo method

A repeated random sampling from the distribution of values for each of the parameters in a generic (exposure or dose) equation to derive an estimate of the distribution of (doses or risks in) the population.

morbidity

The relative frequency of occurrence of a disease.

mortality

The number of deaths that occur at a specific time, in a specific group, or from a specific cause.

municipal solid waste (MSW)

Includes non-hazardous waste generated in households, commercial and business establishments, institutions, and non-hazardous industrial process wastes, agricultural wastes and sewage sludge. Specific definition is given in regulations.

N Narrative Assessments

Descriptive documentation of a program, plan, or project.

native vegetation

"Wild" plants that have naturally evolved and successfully adapted to a region's environmental conditions.

negative externality

A cost that is borne by someone who did not agree to the activity that caused the cost.

net benefits

The difference between total benefits and total costs.

net present value

The present discounted value of a stream of net benefits.

nitrification

Conversion of ammonia into nitrates by microbes.

nominal voltage

Voltage of a fully charged cell or battery when delivering maximum amount of energy that can be withdrawn from a battery at a specific discharge rate.

non-point source

The term "nonpoint source" is defined to mean any source of water pollution that does not meet the legal definition of "point source" in section 502(14) of the Clean Water Act (see "Point Source" definition below)

non-renewable fuels

Fuels that will be used up, irreplaceable.

non-use values

Values people have for nature that do not stem from direct interaction.

nonlinear

Changes in a system are nonlinear when they exhibit sudden changes in rate of increase or decline. The population of a particular tropical frog species, for example, may suddenly crash as a result of warming temperatures, rather than show gradual decline.

nonpoint source (of water pollution)

Large and diffuse location where a pollution source occurs.

Normalization

An acquired evolutionary trait characteristic of human beings, whereby even radical changes are quickly adapted to and represented as normal.

normative analysis

A study of how things should be.

northwest passage

A sea route for commerce through the Arctic Ocean north of Canada.

O obliquity

See Axial Tilt.

offstream water use

A societal use of water that removes it from its source.

oil shocks

Two events of the 1970s triggered by OPEC's oil embargo and price increases that caused shortages of gasoline and eventually a ten fold increase in the price oil by 1981.

oil spill

A type of organic water pollutant involving the release of liquid petroleum into the environment due to human activity.

once through

A single pass of nuclear fuel through a reactor followed by long-term geologic storage.

open-pit mine

Type of surface mineral mine which commonly involve large holes that extract relatively low-grade metallic ore.

opportunity cost

The cost of foregoing the next best choice when making a decision.

ore deposit

Location with abundant ore.

ore

Rock with an enrichment of minerals that can be mined for profit.

Organic Rankine Cycle (ORC)

Uses an organic, high molecular mass fluid with a liquid-vapor phase change or boiling point occurring at a lower temperature than the water-steam phase change. The fluid allows rankine cycle heat recovery from lower temperature sources where the heat is converted into useful work, which can then be converted into electricity.

outcomes

The short-term results of an activity.

outputs

The goods and services being created by an activity, and the manner and degree in which they are delivered.

overconsumption

A long-term result in which the increase in consumption is greater than the efficiency improvement

oxygen-demanding waste

A type of water pollutant involving abundant dead organic matter.

P Panning

Method of placer mining where water in a hand-held conical metal pan swirls around.

paraffin

A white, odorless, tasteless, waxy solid to store heat with a specific heat capacity of 2.14–2.9 J g^{-1} K^{-1} and a heat of fusion of 200–300 J g^{-1}.

pathogens

Disease-causing microorganisms, e.g., viruses, bacteria, parasitic worms, and protozoa, which cause a variety of intestinal diseases such as dysentery, typhoid fever, hepatitis, and cholera.

peak oil / Hubbert's peak

A single oil well follows a pattern of increasing production in initial years as its plentiful resources are tapped to declining production in mature years as its resources are depleted. These two trends are separated by a peak in production of the well. M. King Hubbert extrapolated this pattern from one well to many and in 1956 predicted that the United States' oil production would peak in the mid-1970s. Although widely criticized at the time, Hubbert's prediction proved true. This success led to widespread predictions for the peak of world oil production. The concept of peak oil is an inevitable consequence of using oil faster than it can be made. However, attempts to predict when the peak will occur are notoriously difficult.

peak oil

The peak in world oil production that must come about as oil consumption surpasses the discovery of new oil.

performance standard

A regulation specifying something about the outcome of private behaviors.

permafrost

Soil that has a temperature that has remained below freezing (0 °C or 32 °F) for at least two years.

permeability

Measure of the speed that groundwater can flow through rock or sediment.

persistent organic pollutant

A group of organic water pollutants that are long-lived in the environment, accumulate through the food chain, and can be toxic.

Phantom Load or Vampire Power

Refers to the electrical load of appliances and chargers when they are not in use but plugged in, as they still draw power but provide no service.

phase change material

A material that stores heat in the form of latent heat of fusion.

phase change materials

Materials that can absorb and deliver larger amount of heat than common building materials because they can change their state (solid or liquid).

photosynthesis

The process in which plants use energy from sunlight to combine CO_2 from the atmosphere with water to make sugars, and in turn build biomass.

photovoltaic cells

An electronic device consisting of layers of semiconductor materials that are produced to form adjacent layers of materials with different electronic characteristics and electrical contacts and being capable of converting incident light directly into electricity (direct current).

physical components of the earth system

Nonliving factors such as rocks, minerals, water, climate, air, and energy.

placer deposit

Ore forming process where dense gold particles and diamonds are concentrated by flowing water in rivers and at beaches.

placer mine

Type of surface mineral mine which extracts gold or diamonds from river and beach. sediment by scooping up the sediment and then separating the ore by density.

Point of Production

The first (or at least an early) step in the energy chain, where the energy that ultimately will perform a function at the point of use is put into its working form. For gasoline-driven cars, this is the refinery where gasoline is produced from crude oil, for battery-driven cars this is the power generation plant were electricity is produced. Gasoline is then delivered to the pump and finally to the car, where it is converted (the point of use) to mechanical motion by the engine. Similarly, electricity is delivered to the battery of an electric car by the grid, and converted by the electric motor of the car (the point of use) to mechanical motion.

Point of Use

The last step in the energy chain, where energy accomplishes its intended function. For vehicles, this is the conversion of chemical energy in gasoline cars or electric energy in battery cars to motion of the wheels that moves the car along the road.

point source (of water pollution)

Readily identifiable and relatively small location where a pollution source occurs.

point source

Defined by Section 502(14) of the Clean Water Act as any single identifiable and discrete source of pollution from which pollutants are discharged, such as from a pipe, ditch, channel, culvert, confined animal feeding operation, or discharged from a floating vessel.

pollution prevention

Reducing or eliminating waste at the source by modifying production processes, promoting the use of non-toxic or less-toxic substances, implementing conservation techniques, and re-using materials rather than putting them into the waste stream.

pollution prevention

The active process of identifying areas, processes, and activities which generate excessive waste for the purpose of substitution, alteration, or elimination of the process to prevent waste generation in the first place.

pools

Amounts of material in biogeochemical cycles that share some common characteristic and are relatively uniform in nature.

pore space

Small spaces between mineral grains in subsurface rock or sediment.

porosity

Percentage of pore space in rock or sediment.

positive analysis

A study of how things are.

positive externality

A benefit that accrues to someone who did not agree to the activity that caused the benefit.

positive feedback

A runaway process which amplifies the effect of an initial change.

post-traumatic stress disorder

PTSD - a psychological condition affecting people who have suffered severe emotional trauma as a result of an experience such as combat, crime, or natural disaster, and causing sleep disturbances, flashbacks, anxiety, tiredness, and depression.

postindustrial information age

Is a way of capturing the nature of western economies, in which most people are no longer engaged in the production of goods (which is highly automated) but rather deal with the publication, consumption, and manipulation of information, especially by computers and computer networks. A post-industrial society has five primary characteristics: the domination of service, rather than manufacturing, the pre-eminence of the professional and technical classes, the central place of theoretical knowledge as a source of innovations, the dominating influence of technology, and levels of urbanization higher than anywhere else in the world.

precautionary principle

The proposition that decision-making should be driven by a concern for the avoidance of bad outcomes. In environmental terms, this means coordinating economic development and the profit motive with the need to maintain resilient ecosystems.

precipitation

The conversion of atmospheric water from vapor into liquid (rain) or solid forms (snow, hail) that then fall to Earth's surface.

present discounted value

The value of something in present-day (rather than future) terms.

primary energy

The energy embodied in natural resources prior to undergoing any human-made conversions or transformations. Examples include the chemical energy in coal or the sunlight falling on a solar cell before it is converted to electricity, the nuclear energy in the fuel of a nuclear reactor, or the kinetic energy of wind before it turns the blades of a turbine.

primary producers

The primary entry point of carbon into the biosphere—in nearly all land and aquatic ecosystems plants perform this role by virtue of photosynthesis.

Prime Mover

The term utilized to denote the CHP system equipment that converts input fuel into mechanical shaft power (reciprocating engine, gas turbine, steam turbine, micro-turbine).

probabilistic risk assessment

Risk evaluation involving the calculation and expression of risks using multiple risk descriptors to provide the likelihood of various risk levels. Probabilistic risk results approximate a full range of possible outcomes and the likelihood of each, which often is presented as a frequency distribution graph, thus allowing uncertainty or variability to be expressed quantitatively.

product chain

Those stages in the conception, design, manufacture, marketing, use, and end-of-life that define the impacts of a product or service on society.

product stewardship

An approach to product development in which products are conceived, designed, manufactured, and marketed within a "systems thinking" context. It is a way of framing environmental problems that recognizes the three parts of the sustainability paradigm, and incorporates the concepts of sustainable manufacturing, marketing, utility-to-society, impacts of the use of the product, and end-of-life disposition of the product.

Provisioning Ecosystem Services

Aspects of the natural world used by us to meet our resource needs, e.g. food, water, timber, and fiber.

proxy data

Information about the climate that accumulates through natural phenomena.

public good

A good with two features: (i) it has a benefit that does not diminish with the number of people enjoying it, and (ii) no one can be excluded from consuming it.

pyrolysis

The conversion of biomass at moderately high temperature (500 – 800 °C) in an inert atmosphere that results in a "bio-oil" intermediate.

Q Quantitative Data

Information that can be quantified numerically such as tons of waste, gallons of gasoline, and gallons of wastewater.

quaternary period

The most recent geological period, spanning the time from 2.6 million years ago to today.

R radiative forcing

Change in net irradiance (an energy flux) measured at some boundary. For this text the boundary is typically at the surface of the earth or the top of atmosphere. A positive change indicates warming and a negative change indicates cooling.

radioactive half-lives

The amount of time necessary to decrease the radioactivity of radioactive material to one-half the original level.

radioactive waste

Any waste that emits energy as rays, waves, or streams of energetic particles.

rain barrel

A cistern, barrel or storage system that collects and stores the rainwater or snowmelt from roofs that would otherwise be diverted to storm drains and streams as stormwater runoff.

rainwater harvesting

Catching and storing rainwater for reuse before it reaches the ground.

reactivity

Materials susceptible to unstable conditions. Reactive wastes are unstable under normal conditions and can create explosions and or toxic fumes, gases, and vapors when mixed with water.

recharge area

Location on Earth where surface water infiltrates into the ground rather than runs off into rivers or evaporates.

Reciprocating Engine

A heat engine that uses one or more reciprocating pistons to convert pressure into mechanical rotating shaft power.

reclaimed mine

Mineral mine restored to a useful landscape.

recycling

Separation physical/mechanical process by which secondary raw materials (such as paper, metals, glass, and plastics.) are obtained from MSW.

Regulating Ecosystem Services

Processes in the Earth system that control key physical and biological elements of our environment, e.g. climate regulation, flood regulation, disease regulation, water purification.

remote responsibilities

An ethical extension of systems literacy and the principle of connectivity: we are linked to peoples and places remote from us through the web of global industrial production and commerce, and thus have responsibility toward them.

renewable fuels

Fuels that are never exhausted or can be replaced.

renewable generation variability

The variation of the output of a solar or wind plant depending on weather. Solar plants often produce only 15-20 percent of their maximum output (also called installed capacity) because the sun shines only during the day and passing clouds can obscure it; wind plants produce 20-40 percent of their maximum capacity because the wind speed varies with weather conditions, often becoming calm for days at a time.

reprocessing

Chemically processing spent nuclear fuel to recover the unused portion, which is then passed through the reactor again to produce more power. Reprocessing uses a greater fraction of the energy of the fuel but also increases the risk of illegal diversion of nuclear material for weapons proliferation.

reservoir

Large artificial lake used as a source of water.

resilience and vulnerability

Important terms of measurement for the impact of environmental change, particularly on human communities. The goal of sustainability analysis and policy, at all levels, is to enhance the resilience of communities to change, in other words, to mitigate their vulnerability.

Resilience

The ability of an ecological community to change in response to disturbance and the degree or time needed for that system that provides desirable to go back to its original state.

respiration

Metabolic process in all organisms that generates energy and synthesizes biomass while releasing CO_2 as a by-product.

reuse

Using a component of MSW in its original form more than once.

revealed preference

Valuation tools that use behaviors such as job choice, housing choice, and recreational site choice to reveal information about the values people have for features of the environment.

river discharge

Volume of water moving through a river channel over time.

rock

A solid coherent piece of planet Earth.

S saltwater intrusion

Saltwater that enters an aquifer due to overpumping of freshwater aquifers near ocean coastlines.

saturated zone

Subsurface area where groundwater completely fills pore spaces in rock or sediment.

scenario

A global development path based on specific assumptions for the economic, technological and social global ccontext, predicting energy demand, energy cost, and growth of energy technologies.

scoping

The stage of a LCA in which the rationale for carrying out the assessment is made explicit, where the boundaries of the system are defined, where the data quantity, quality, and sources are specified, and where any assumptions that underlie the LCA are stated.

sediment

A type of water pollutant that degrades drinking water and can kill underwater plants that need sunlight for photosynthesis.

sedimentary processes

Processes of ore formation that occur in rivers and concentrate sand and gravel (used in construction), as well as dense gold particles and diamonds that weathered away from bedrock.

sedimentary rock

Forms by hardening of layers of sediment (loose grains such as sand or mud) deposited at Earth's surface or by mineral precipitation, i.e., formation of minerals in water from dissolved mineral matter.

sensible heat

The heat energy stored in a substance as a result of an increase in its temperature.

sensitivity analysis

Evaluation of how sensitive the results of an analysis are to changes in assumptions used in the analysis.

septic tank system

An individual sewage treatment system for homes in rural and even some urban settings.

Sequestered

Removed from the atmosphere

sewage treatment plant

A facility that processes wastewater with the main goal of removing organic matter (oxygen-demanding waste) and killing bacteria.

slag

Glassy unwanted by-product of smelting ore.

sludge

Concentrated organic solid produced during primary and secondarytreatment of sewage treatment.

Sluice box

Method of placer mining where running water passes through a wooden box with riffles on the bottom.

smart grid

The addition of sensors to monitor power flow and two-way communication to transmit the power flow information to the utility and the customer in real time. The addition of sensors and communication to the grid enables several new operating modes: the customer decide in real time to curtail his electricity use during peak times when rates are high (known as demand-response), the utility can identify precisely the time and place of power flow failures due to weather or other events, and the grid can be equipped with automatic circuit breakers (known as fault current limiters) and other protection devices that respond immediately to power flow failures, limiting damage to the grid and the risk of triggering a cascade of failures.

smelting

Heating ore minerals with different chemicals to extract the metal.

snowball earth

A condition in which the entire planet is covered in ice, last thought to have happened 650 million years ago.

soil moisture

Water in the unsaturated zone.

solar energy

The sun's radiation that reaches the earth.

solar radiation

The energy emitted by the sun in the form of light.

solid waste

According to the Resource Conservation and Recovery Act (RCRA), solid waste is: garbage; refuse; sludge from a waste treatment plant, water supply treatment plant, or air pollution control facility; and other discarded materials, including solid, liquid, or contained gaseous material resulting from industrial, commercial, mining, and agricultural operations, and from community activities.

solvent

Capacity of a liquid such as water to dissolve soluble minerals.

somatic effects

Effects from some agent, like radiation that are seen in the individual who receives the agent.

spring

River that emerges from underground due to an abrupt intersection of the water table with the land surface.

stated preference

Valuation tools that use survey responses to hypothetical questions rather than data on actual choices.

Steam Turbine

Utilizes the Rankine Cycle to extract heat from steam and transform the heat into mechanical shaft power by expanding the steam from high pressure to low pressure through the turbine blades.

stormwater runoff

The overland flow of precipitation generated by that portion of rain and snowmelt that does not infiltrate into the ground, is not taken up by plants, and is not evaporated into the atmosphere.

strategic mineral

Mineral considered essential to a country for some military, industrial, or commercial purpose but the country must import the mineral to meet its needs.

streamflow

Flow of water in streams.

strip mine

Type of surface mineral mine which extracts horizontal layers of ore or rock.

strong sustainability

All forms of capital must be maintained intact independent of one another. The implicit assumption is that different forms of capital are mainly complementary; that is, all forms are generally necessary for any form to be of value. Produced capital used in harvesting and processing timber, for example, is of no value in the absence of stocks of timber to harvest. Only by maintaining both natural and produced capital stocks intact can non-declining income be assured.

superconducting cable

An underground cable made of superconductor, which loses all resistance to electric current at low temperature. Superconducting cables made of second-generation coated conductors based on the copper oxide family of superconductors discovered in 1986 are now entering the grid. Because superconductors conduct electricity without producing heat, they can carry up to five times more power than conventional copper cables in the same cross-sectional area.

superfund

A federal program created in 1980 and designed to identify and clean up the worst of the hazardous chemical waste sites in the U.S.

Supporting Ecosystem Services

The biogeochemical cycles, as well as biological and physical processes that drive ecosystem function, e.g. soil formation, nutrient cycling, and photosynthesis.

surface mine

Mineral mine that occurs at Earth's surface.

surface runoff

Flow of water over the land surface.

surface runoff

Unchannelized overland flow of water.

sustainable development

Development that meets the needs of the present without compromising the ability of future generations to meet their own needs.

swales

Graded and engineered landscape features designed as vegetated, shallow, open channels or ditches that are usually planted with flood tolerant and erosion resistant plants.

Synchronous Generator

Converts the mechanical shaft power from the CHP prime mover to utility grade Alternating Current Power. A synchronous generator is self-exciting (contains its own source of reactive power) and can operate independent of, or isolated from, the utility grid.

synthetic biology

The field of biology in which microbes are engineered to control metabolic pathways.

systems literacy

An educational philosophy that emphasizes a student's competence in a wide variety of disciplines, so that he or she might better understand the operations of those complex systems, both human and natural, that underpin sustainability.

systems thinking

In the context of sustainability, systems thinking is a way of conceiving human-created and natural systems as functional parts of a larger, integrated system.

T tailings

Fine-grained waste produced from processing ore.

technical potential

The geographical potential after the losses due to conversion of the primary energy flux to secondary energy carriers or forms, such as electricity.

technology standard

A regulation specifying what kind of technology agents must or must not use in their activities.

telework

Working from a remote location, usually a home office, by electronically linking to a company.

thermal mass

The ability of a material to absorb heat energy. High density materials like concrete, bricks and tiles need a lot of heat to change their temperature and thus have a high thermal mass. Lightweight materials such as wood have a low thermal mass.

tipping point

The critical moment of nonlinear change whereby a system changes suddenly from one state to another.

total dissolved solids

Total amount of dissolved material in water, typically reported in parts per million (ppm) units.

toxic chemical

A type of organic water pollutant involving chemicals with a severe human health risk.

toxicity

The degree to which a chemical substance (or physical agent) elicits a deleterious or adverse effect upon the biological system of an organism exposed to the substance over a designated time period.

tradable permits

A policy in which the total amount of an activity is limited, but agents can trade the rights to engage in that activity (permits).

transesterification

The base catalyzed reaction of plant oil with methanol with breaks the oil into long fatty acid chains, which can be used as a low quality diesel fuel.

transpiration

Loss of water by plants to the atmosphere.

transuranic radioactive waste (TRU)

TRU waste contains more than 100 nanocuries of alpha-emitting transuranic isotopes, with half-lives greater than twenty years, per gram of waste.

travel cost analysis

A revealed preference tool that estimates the values of natural resource amenities by analyzing data on recreational site characteristics and people's visitation patterns and travel costs.

triple bottom line

A reference to the value of a business going beyond dollar profitability to include social and environmental costs and benefits as well.

Triple Bottom Line

Accounting for ecological and social performance in addition to financial performance

U **U-factor**

The rate of heat loss is indicated in terms of the of a window assembly. The lower the U-factor, the greater a window's resistance to heat flow and the better its insulating properties.

unconfined aquifer

Aquifer with no aquitard above it.

underground fuel storage tank

A type of water pollutant if it leaks.

underground mine

Mineral mine that involves a network of tunnels to access and extract the ore.

unsaturated zone

Subsurface area where pore spaces contain only air and water films on mineral grains.

urban sprawl

Any environment characterized by (1) a population widely dispersed in low density residential development; (2) rigid separation of homes, shops, and workplaces; (3) a lack of distinct, thriving activity centers, such as strong downtowns or suburban town centers; and (4) a network of roads marked by large block size and poor access from one place to another) has been found to correlate with increased body mass index.

use values

Benefits associated with direct interaction with nature and the environment.

V valuation

The process of estimating a dollar value for an amenity or a disamenity.

value of a statistical life

A statistical concept that can be used as the value of reducing the number of deaths in a population by one.

visible spectrum

The light radiation that is in the range of wavelengths that is visible to the human eye.

volatile organic compounds

(VOC - an organic compound that evaporates at a relatively low temperature and contributes to air pollution, e.g. ethylene, propylene, benzene, or styrene).

W walkability

Walkability is a measure of how friendly an area is to walking. Walkability has many health, environmental, and economic benefits. Factors influencing walkability include the presence or absence and quality of footpaths, sidewalks or other pedestrian right-of-ways, traffic and road conditions, land use patterns, building accessibility, destination density and safety, among others. Walkability is an important concept in sustainable urban design.

Waste Heat to Power (Bottoming Cycle CHP)

Captures the waste heat generated by an industrial or commercial process, utilizing the waste heat as the free fuel source for generating electricity.

waste minimization

Measures or techniques that reduce the amount of wastes generated during industrial production processes; the term is also applied to recycling and other efforts to reduce the amount of waste going into the waste management system.

waste prevention

The design, manufacture, purchase or use of materials or products to reduce their amount or toxicity before they enter the municipal solid waste stream. Because it is intended to reduce pollution and conserve resources, waste prevention should not increase the net amount or toxicity of wastes generated throughout the life of a product.

waste to energy

Combustion of MSW to generate electrical energy or heat

water conservation

Using less water and using it more efficiently

water crisis

A global situation where people in many areas lack access to sufficient water or clean water or both.

water cycle

The continuous movement of water through water reservoirs located on, above, and below Earth's surface.

water pollution

Contamination of water by an excess amount of a substance that can cause harm to human beings and the ecosystem.

water reservoir (in water cycle)

General location on Earth where water is located including oceans, atmosphere, glaciers, groundwater, lakes, rivers, and biosphere.

water table

Interface between the unsaturated zone and saturated zone.

water table well

Water well drilled into an unconfined aquifer where the water level in the well coincides with the water table.

watershed

A geographic area that naturally drains to a specific waterway or waterbody.

watts per square meter (W/m2)

Energy (Joules) per second moving through a surface (square meter). A flux of energy through a surface area.

weak sustainability

All forms of capital are more or less substitutes for one another; no regard has to be given to the composition of the stock of capital. Weak sustainability allows for the depletion or degradation of natural resources, so long as such depletion is offset by increases in the stocks of other forms of capital (for example, by investing royalties from depleting mineral reserves in factories).

weather

A description of the short term state of the atmosphere.

weathering

Ore forming process where soil water in a tropical rain forest environment concentrates insoluble elements such as aluminum (bauxite) by dissolving away the soluble elements.

Wedge Approach

A way of expressing the concept that there is no one solution to the challenge of reducing greenhouse gas emissions. Each technology, action or change is represented by a triangular wedge in a chart of time vs. emissions.

welfare

Broadly defined, welfare is well-being.

well-mixed gas

A gas that can be found at the same concentration throughout the lower atmosphere regardless of location.

willingness to accept

The amount of money you would have to pay someone to compensate them for a deleterious change.

willingness to pay

The amount of money someone is willing to pay for something good.

Index of Keywords and Terms

Keywords are listed by the section with that keyword (page numbers are in parentheses). Keywords do not necessarily appear in the text of the page. They are merely associated with that section. *Ex.* apples, § 1.1 (1) **Terms** are referenced by the page they appear on. *Ex.* apples, 1

Attributions

Collection: *Sustainability: A Comprehensive Foundation*
Edited by: Tom Theis and Jonathan Tomkin, Editors
URL: http://legacy.cnx.org/content/col11325/1.43/
License: http://creativecommons.org/licenses/by/3.0/

Module: "Foreword"
By: U of I Open Source Textbook Initiative
URL: http://legacy.cnx.org/content/m43491/1.2/
Pages: 1-2
Copyright: U of I Open Source Textbook Initiative
License: http://creativecommons.org/licenses/by/3.0/

Module: "Preface"
By: Tom Theis, Jonathan Tomkin
URL: http://legacy.cnx.org/content/m41663/1.3/
Page: 3
Copyright: U of I Open Source Textbook Initiative
License: http://creativecommons.org/licenses/by/3.0/

Module: "An Introduction to Sustainability: Humanity and the Environment"
By: Tom Theis
URL: http://legacy.cnx.org/content/m41187/1.5/
Page: 5
Copyright: U of I Open Source Textbook Initiative
License: http://creativecommons.org/licenses/by/3.0/

Module: "What is Sustainability?"
By: Tom Theis
URL: http://legacy.cnx.org/content/m41188/1.7/
Pages: 5-7
Copyright: U of I Open Source Textbook Initiative
License: http://creativecommons.org/licenses/by/3.0/

Module: "The IPAT Equation"
By: Tom Theis
URL: http://legacy.cnx.org/content/m41190/1.5/
Pages: 8-9
Copyright: U of I Open Source Textbook Initiative
License: http://creativecommons.org/licenses/by/3.0/

Module: "Human Consumption Patterns and the "Rebound" Effect"
By: Tom Theis
URL: http://legacy.cnx.org/content/m41191/1.6/
Pages: 9-11
Copyright: U of I Open Source Textbook Initiative
License: http://creativecommons.org/licenses/by/3.0/

Module: "Challenges for Sustainability"
By: Tom Theis
URL: http://legacy.cnx.org/content/m41192/1.5/
Pages: 11-13
Copyright: U of I Open Source Textbook Initiative
License: http://creativecommons.org/licenses/by/3.0/

Module: "Chapter Review Questions"
By: Tom Theis
URL: http://legacy.cnx.org/content/m41193/1.5/
Page: 14
Copyright: U of I Open Source Textbook Initiative
License: http://creativecommons.org/licenses/by/3.0/

Module: "The Evolution of Environmental Policy in the United States – Chapter Introduction"
By: Tom Theis
URL: http://legacy.cnx.org/content/m42118/1.4/
Page: 15
Copyright: U of I Open Source Textbook Initiative
License: http://creativecommons.org/licenses/by/3.0/

Module: "The American Conservation Movement"
By: Tom Theis
URL: http://legacy.cnx.org/content/m42117/1.4/
Pages: 16-27
Copyright: U of I Open Source Textbook Initiative
License: http://creativecommons.org/licenses/by/3.0/

Module: "Environmental Risk Management"
By: Tom Theis
URL: http://legacy.cnx.org/content/m42115/1.4/
Pages: 27-35
Copyright: U of I Open Source Textbook Initiative
License: http://creativecommons.org/licenses/by/3.0/

Module: "Sustainability and Public Policy"
By: Tom Theis
URL: http://legacy.cnx.org/content/m42116/1.4/
Pages: 35-38
Copyright: U of I Open Source Textbook Initiative
License: http://creativecommons.org/licenses/by/3.0/

Module: "Public Health and Sustainability"
By: Cindy Klein-Banai
URL: http://legacy.cnx.org/content/m43321/1.2/
Pages: 39-48
Copyright: U of I Open Source Textbook Initiative
License: http://creativecommons.org/licenses/by/3.0/

Module: "Climate and Global Change – Chapter Introduction"
By: Jonathan Tomkin
URL: http://legacy.cnx.org/content/m41664/1.4/
Page: 49
Copyright: U of I Open Source Textbook Initiative
License: http://creativecommons.org/licenses/by/3.0/

Module: "Climate Processes; External and Internal Controls"
By: Jonathan Tomkin
URL: http://legacy.cnx.org/content/m38482/1.18/
Pages: 50-63
Copyright: U of I Open Source Textbook Initiative
License: http://creativecommons.org/licenses/by/3.0/

Module: "Milankovitch Cycles and the Climate of the Quaternary"
By: Jonathan Tomkin
URL: http://legacy.cnx.org/content/m38572/1.10/
Pages: 63-76
Copyright: U of I Open Source Textbook Initiative
License: http://creativecommons.org/licenses/by/3.0/

Module: "Modern Climate Change"
By: Eric Snodgrass
URL: http://legacy.cnx.org/content/m41579/1.6/
Pages: 76-97
Copyright: U of I Open Source Textbook Initiative
License: http://creativecommons.org/licenses/by/3.0/

Module: "Climate Projections"
By: Eric Snodgrass
URL: http://legacy.cnx.org/content/m41580/1.8/
Pages: 98-115
Copyright: U of I Open Source Textbook Initiative
License: http://creativecommons.org/licenses/by/3.0/

Module: "Biosphere – Chapter Introduction"
By: Andrew Leakey
URL: http://legacy.cnx.org/content/m41617/1.5/
Pages: 117-119
Copyright: U of I Open Source Textbook Initiative
License: http://creativecommons.org/licenses/by/3.0/

Module: "Biogeochemical Cycles and the Flow of Energy in the Earth System"
By: Andrew Leakey
URL: http://legacy.cnx.org/content/m41618/1.6/
Pages: 119-126
Copyright: U of I Open Source Textbook Initiative
License: http://creativecommons.org/licenses/by/3.0/

Module: "Biodiversity, Species Loss, and Ecosystem Function"
By: Jeffrey Brawn, Michael Ward, Angela Kent
URL: http://legacy.cnx.org/content/m41619/1.6/
Pages: 126-134
Copyright: U of I Open Source Textbook Initiative
License: http://creativecommons.org/licenses/by/3.0/

Module: "Soil and Sustainability"
By: David Grimley
URL: http://legacy.cnx.org/content/m41620/1.8/
Pages: 135-147
Copyright: U of I Open Source Textbook Initiative
License: http://creativecommons.org/licenses/by/4.0/

Module: "Physical Resources: Water, Pollution, and Minerals - Chapter Introduction"
By: Steve Altaner
URL: http://legacy.cnx.org/content/m41523/1.3/
Pages: 149-151
Copyright: U of I Open Source Textbook Initiative
License: http://creativecommons.org/licenses/by/3.0/

Module: "Water Cycle and Fresh Water Supply"
By: Steve Altaner
URL: http://legacy.cnx.org/content/m41397/1.5/
Pages: 151-179
Copyright: U of I Open Source Textbook Initiative
License: http://creativecommons.org/licenses/by/3.0/

Module: "Case Study: The Aral Sea - Going, Going, Gone"
By: Steve Altaner
URL: http://legacy.cnx.org/content/m41400/1.4/
Pages: 179-183
Copyright: U of I Open Source Textbook Initiative
License: http://creativecommons.org/licenses/by/3.0/

Module: "Water Pollution"
By: Steve Altaner
URL: http://legacy.cnx.org/content/m41441/1.8/
Pages: 184-209
Copyright: U of I Open Source Textbook Initiative
License: http://creativecommons.org/licenses/by/4.0/

Module: "Case Study: The Love Canal Disaster"
By: Steve Altaner
URL: http://legacy.cnx.org/content/m41444/1.5/
Pages: 209-212
Copyright: U of I Open Source Textbook Initiative
License: http://creativecommons.org/licenses/by/3.0/

Module: "Mineral Resources: Formation, Mining, Environmental Impact"
By: Steve Altaner
URL: http://legacy.cnx.org/content/m41470/1.5/
Pages: 212-227
Copyright: U of I Open Source Textbook Initiative
License: http://creativecommons.org/licenses/by/3.0/

Module: "Case Study: Gold: Worth its Weight?"
By: Steve Altaner
URL: http://legacy.cnx.org/content/m41467/1.5/
Pages: 227-231
Copyright: U of I Open Source Textbook Initiative
License: http://creativecommons.org/licenses/by/3.0/

Module: "Environmental and Resource Economics - Chapter Introduction"
By: Amy Ando
URL: http://legacy.cnx.org/content/m38598/1.7/
Pages: 233-234
Copyright: U of I Open Source Textbook Initiative
License: http://creativecommons.org/licenses/by/3.0/

Module: "Tragedy of the Commons"
By: Amy Ando
URL: http://legacy.cnx.org/content/m38612/1.6/
Pages: 234-242
Copyright: U of I Open Source Textbook Initiative
License: http://creativecommons.org/licenses/by/3.0/

Module: "Case Study: Marine Fisheries"
By: Amy Ando
URL: http://legacy.cnx.org/content/m38878/1.5/
Pages: 243-246
Copyright: U of I Open Source Textbook Initiative
License: http://creativecommons.org/licenses/by/3.0/

Module: "Environmental Valuation"
By: Amy Ando
URL: http://legacy.cnx.org/content/m38954/1.5/
Pages: 246-254
Copyright: U of I Open Source Textbook Initiative
License: http://creativecommons.org/licenses/by/3.0/

Module: "Evaluating Projects and Policies"
By: Amy Ando
URL: http://legacy.cnx.org/content/m38611/1.7/
Pages: 254-260
Copyright: U of I Open Source Textbook Initiative
License: http://creativecommons.org/licenses/by/3.0/

Module: "Solutions: Property Rights, Regulations, and Incentive Policies"
By: Amy Ando
URL: http://legacy.cnx.org/content/m38956/1.6/
Pages: 261-266
Copyright: U of I Open Source Textbook Initiative
License: http://creativecommons.org/licenses/by/4.0/

Module: "Modern Environmental Management – Chapter Introduction"
By: Tom Theis
URL: http://legacy.cnx.org/content/m41573/1.3/
Pages: 267-268
Copyright: U of I Open Source Textbook Initiative
License: http://creativecommons.org/licenses/by/3.0/

Module: "Systems of Waste Management"
By: Krishna Reddy
URL: http://legacy.cnx.org/content/m41572/1.5/
Pages: 268-278
Copyright: U of I Open Source Textbook Initiative
License: http://creativecommons.org/licenses/by/3.0/

Module: "Case Study: Electronic Waste and Extended Producer Responsibility"
By: Krishna Reddy
URL: http://legacy.cnx.org/content/m41571/1.3/
Pages: 279-281
Copyright: U of I Open Source Textbook Initiative
License: http://creativecommons.org/licenses/by/3.0/

Module: "Government and Laws on the Environment"
By: Amid Khodadoust
URL: http://legacy.cnx.org/content/m41570/1.3/
Pages: 281-290
Copyright: U of I Open Source Textbook Initiative
License: http://creativecommons.org/licenses/by/3.0/

Module: "Risk Assessment Methodology for Conventional and Alternative Sustainability Options"
By: Serap Erdal
URL: http://legacy.cnx.org/content/m41566/1.4/
Pages: 290-301
Copyright: U of I Open Source Textbook Initiative
License: http://creativecommons.org/licenses/by/3.0/

Module: "Sustainable Energy Systems - Chapter Introduction"
By: George Crabtree
URL: http://legacy.cnx.org/content/m41724/1.3/
Pages: 303-308
Copyright: U of I Open Source Textbook Initiative
License: http://creativecommons.org/licenses/by/3.0/

Module: "Environmental Challenges in Energy, Carbon Dioxide, Air, Water and Land Use"
By: Cindy Klein-Banai
URL: http://legacy.cnx.org/content/m41725/1.4/
Pages: 309-333
Copyright: U of I Open Source Textbook Initiative
License: http://creativecommons.org/licenses/by/3.0/

Module: "Case Study: Greenhouse Gases and Climate Change"
By: Cindy Klein-Banai
URL: http://legacy.cnx.org/content/m41726/1.3/
Pages: 333-338
Copyright: U of I Open Source Textbook Initiative
License: http://creativecommons.org/licenses/by/3.0/

Module: "Electricity"
By: George Crabtree
URL: http://legacy.cnx.org/content/m41728/1.3/
Pages: 338-347
Copyright: U of I Open Source Textbook Initiative
License: http://creativecommons.org/licenses/by/3.0/

Module: "Fossil Fuels (Coal and Gas)"
By: George Crabtree
URL: http://legacy.cnx.org/content/m41727/1.3/
Pages: 347-352
Copyright: U of I Open Source Textbook Initiative
License: http://creativecommons.org/licenses/by/3.0/

Module: "Nuclear Energy"
By: George Crabtree
URL: http://legacy.cnx.org/content/m41729/1.3/
Pages: 352-356
Copyright: U of I Open Source Textbook Initiative
License: http://creativecommons.org/licenses/by/3.0/

Module: "Renewable Energy: Solar, Wind, Hydro and Biomass"
By: George Crabtree
URL: http://legacy.cnx.org/content/m41731/1.3/
Pages: 356-367
Copyright: U of I Open Source Textbook Initiative
License: http://creativecommons.org/licenses/by/3.0/

Module: "Fossil Fuel (Oil)"
By: George Crabtree
URL: http://legacy.cnx.org/content/m41735/1.3/
Pages: 367-368
Copyright: U of I Open Source Textbook Initiative
License: http://creativecommons.org/licenses/by/3.0/

Module: "The Conversion of Biomass into Biofuels"
By: John Regalbuto
URL: http://legacy.cnx.org/content/m41736/1.3/
Pages: 368-377
Copyright: U of I Open Source Textbook Initiative
License: http://creativecommons.org/licenses/by/3.0/

Module: "Geothermal Heating and Cooling"
By: Sohail Murad
URL: http://legacy.cnx.org/content/m41737/1.4/
Pages: 377-385
Copyright: U of I Open Source Textbook Initiative
License: http://creativecommons.org/licenses/by/3.0/

Module: "Electric and Plug-in Hybrids"
By: George Crabtree
URL: http://legacy.cnx.org/content/m41738/1.2/
Pages: 385-390
Copyright: U of I Open Source Textbook Initiative
License: http://creativecommons.org/licenses/by/3.0/

Module: "Combined Heat and Power"
By: John Cuttica
URL: http://legacy.cnx.org/content/m41740/1.2/
Pages: 390-397
Copyright: U of I Open Source Textbook Initiative
License: http://creativecommons.org/licenses/by/3.0/

Module: "Applications of Phase Change Materials for Sustainable Energy"
By: Said Al-Hallaj, Riza Kizilel
URL: http://legacy.cnx.org/content/m41734/1.4/
Pages: 397-407
Copyright: U of I Open Source Textbook Initiative
License: http://creativecommons.org/licenses/by/3.0/

Module: "Problem-Solving, Metrics, and Tools for Sustainability - Chapter Introduction"
By: Tom Theis
URL: http://legacy.cnx.org/content/m38623/1.3/
Pages: 409-410
Copyright: U of I Open Source Textbook Initiative
License: http://creativecommons.org/licenses/by/3.0/

Module: "Life Cycle Assessment"
By: Tom Theis
URL: http://legacy.cnx.org/content/m38643/1.12/
Pages: 410-424
Copyright: U of I Open Source Textbook Initiative
License: http://creativecommons.org/licenses/by/3.0/

Module: "Sustainability Metrics and Rating Systems"
By: Cindy Klein-Banai
URL: http://legacy.cnx.org/content/m41616/1.7/
Pages: 424-435
Copyright: U of I Open Source Textbook Initiative
License: http://creativecommons.org/licenses/by/4.0/

Module: "Footprinting: Carbon, Ecological and Water"
By: Cindy Klein-Banai
URL: http://legacy.cnx.org/content/m41615/1.5/
Pages: 435-450
Copyright: U of I Open Source Textbook Initiative
License: http://creativecommons.org/licenses/by/3.0/

Module: "Case Study: Comparing Greenhouse Gas Emissions, Ecological Footprint and Sustainability Rating of a University"
By: Cindy Klein-Banai
URL: http://legacy.cnx.org/content/m41605/1.4/
Pages: 450-455
Copyright: U of I Open Source Textbook Initiative
License: http://creativecommons.org/licenses/by/3.0/

Module: "Food Miles"
By: Dennis Ruez
URL: http://legacy.cnx.org/content/m38680/1.4/
Pages: 455-462
Copyright: U of I Open Source Textbook Initiative
License: http://creativecommons.org/licenses/by/3.0/

Module: "Environmental Performance Indicators"
By: Dennis Ruez
URL: http://legacy.cnx.org/content/m38877/1.5/
Pages: 462-469
Copyright: U of I Open Source Textbook Initiative
License: http://creativecommons.org/licenses/by/3.0/

Module: "Case Study: UN Millennium Development Goals Indicator"
By: Dennis Ruez
URL: http://legacy.cnx.org/content/m41602/1.3/
Pages: 469-470
Copyright: U of I Open Source Textbook Initiative
License: http://creativecommons.org/licenses/by/3.0/

Module: "Sustainability and Business"
By: Tom Theis
URL: http://legacy.cnx.org/content/m42273/1.3/
Pages: 470-474
Copyright: U of I Open Source Textbook Initiative
License: http://creativecommons.org/licenses/by/3.0/

Module: "The Human Dimensions of Sustainability: History, Culture, Ethics"
By: Gillen Wood
URL: http://legacy.cnx.org/content/m39378/1.5/
Pages: 476-477
Copyright: U of I Open Source Textbook Initiative
License: http://creativecommons.org/licenses/by/3.0/

Module: "It's Not Easy Being Green: Anti-Environmental Discourse, Behavior, and Ideology"
By: Gillen Wood
URL: http://legacy.cnx.org/content/m41067/1.4/
Pages: 478-483
Copyright: U of I Open Source Textbook Initiative
License: http://creativecommons.org/licenses/by/3.0/

Module: "The Industrialization of Nature: A Modern History (1500 to the present)"
By: Gillen Wood
URL: http://legacy.cnx.org/content/m40821/1.5/
Pages: 483-490
Copyright: U of I Open Source Textbook Initiative
License: http://creativecommons.org/licenses/by/3.0/

Module: "Sustainability Studies: A Systems Literacy Approach"
By: Gillen Wood
URL: http://legacy.cnx.org/content/m41039/1.5/
Pages: 490-494
Copyright: U of I Open Source Textbook Initiative
License: http://creativecommons.org/licenses/by/3.0/

Module: "The Vulnerability of Industrialized Resource Systems: Two Case Studies"
By: Gillen Wood
URL: http://legacy.cnx.org/content/m41068/1.4/
Pages: 494-498
Copyright: U of I Open Source Textbook Initiative
License: http://creativecommons.org/licenses/by/3.0/

Module: "Case Study: Agriculture and the Global Bee Colony Collapse"
By: Gillen Wood
URL: http://legacy.cnx.org/content/m41055/1.5/
Pages: 498-501
Copyright: U of I Open Source Textbook Initiative
License: http://creativecommons.org/licenses/by/3.0/

Module: "Case Study: Energy and the BP Oil Disaster"
By: Gillen Wood
URL: http://legacy.cnx.org/content/m41066/1.5/
Pages: 501-503
Copyright: U of I Open Source Textbook Initiative
License: http://creativecommons.org/licenses/by/3.0/

Module: "Sustainability Ethics"
By: Gillen Wood
URL: http://legacy.cnx.org/content/m41069/1.6/
Pages: 503-509
Copyright: U of I Open Source Textbook Initiative
License: http://creativecommons.org/licenses/by/3.0/

Module: "Sustainable Infrastructure - Chapter Introduction"
By: Tom Theis
URL: http://legacy.cnx.org/content/m44985/1.1/
Pages: 511-512
Copyright: U of I Open Source Textbook Initiative
License: http://creativecommons.org/licenses/by/3.0/

Module: "The Sustainable City"
By: Eugene Goldfarb
URL: http://legacy.cnx.org/content/m44935/1.2/
Pages: 512-535
Copyright: U of I Open Source Textbook Initiative
License: http://creativecommons.org/licenses/by/3.0/

Module: "Sustainability and Buildings"
By: Cindy Klein-Banai
URL: http://legacy.cnx.org/content/m44261/1.1/
Pages: 535-550
Copyright: U of I Open Source Textbook Initiative
License: http://creativecommons.org/licenses/by/3.0/

Module: "Sustainable Energy Practices: Climate Action Planning"
By: Cindy Klein-Banai
URL: http://legacy.cnx.org/content/m41741/1.2/
Pages: 551-566
Copyright: U of I Open Source Textbook Initiative
License: http://creativecommons.org/licenses/by/3.0/

Module: "Sustainable Transportation: Accessibility, Mobility, and Derived Demand"
By: Julie Cidell
URL: http://legacy.cnx.org/content/m42717/1.2/
Pages: 566-576
Copyright: U of I Open Source Textbook Initiative
License: http://creativecommons.org/licenses/by/3.0/

Module: "Sustainable Stormwater Management"
By: Martin Jaffe
URL: http://legacy.cnx.org/content/m42716/1.2/
Pages: 576-588
Copyright: U of I Open Source Textbook Initiative
License: http://creativecommons.org/licenses/by/3.0/

Module: "Case Study: A Net-Zero Energy Home in Urbana, Illinois"
By: Rob Kanter
URL: http://legacy.cnx.org/content/m44455/1.2/
Pages: 588-590
Copyright: U of I Open Source Textbook Initiative
License: http://creativecommons.org/licenses/by/3.0/

Sustainability: A Comprehensive Foundation

With "Sustainability: A Comprehensive Foundation", first and second-year college students are introduced to this expanding new field, comprehensively exploring the essential concepts from every branch of knowldege – including engineering and the applied arts, natural and social sciences, and the humanities. As sustainability is a multi-disciplinary area of study, the text is the product of multiple authors drawn from the diverse faculty of the University of Illinois: each chapter is written by a recognized expert in the field. With "Sustainability: A Comprehensive Foundation", first and second-year college students are introduced to this expanding new field, comprehensively exploring the essential concepts from every branch of knowldege – including engineering and the applied arts, natural and social sciences, and the humanities. As sustainability is a multi-disciplinary area of study, the text is the product of multiple authors drawn from the diverse faculty of the University of Illinois: each chapter is written by a recognized expert in the field. In order to assist us in assessing the value of openly-available textbooks such as this one, we would appreciate notification from faculty who elect to make use of this text in their courses. Simply send us a note using the "E-mail the collection author" link found below. Thank you for helping us make future open texts possible.

About OpenStax-CNX

Rhaptos is a web-based collaborative publishing system for educational material.

CPSIA information can be obtained
at www.ICGtesting.com
Printed in the USA
LVHW051710090119
603305LV00006B/93/P